5 MAR 1959

D0410321

DEPARTMENT OF AGRICULTURE
DUBLIN
LIBRARY
43178

58.11.58(02)

Heterosis

HETEROSIS

A record of researches directed toward explaining
and utilizing the vigor of hybrids

Edited by

JOHN W. GOWEN

Professor of Genetics
Iowa State College

IOWA STATE COLLEGE PRESS

AMES · IOWA

Copyright 1952 by The Iowa State College Press
All rights reserved. Composed and printed in the
United States of America

Preface

Heterosis grew out of a desire on the part of Iowa State College to gather together research workers from marginal fields of science, each with something to contribute to a discussion of a central problem of major national interest. The problem of heterosis, as synonymous in large part with that of hybrid vigor, formed a natural theme for discussion. As the reader will note, many fields of science have contributed or stand to make significant contributions to the subject. Major steps in the advance have led to divergent views which may be rectified only through joint discussions followed by further research. The conference of students of this problem was held June 15 to July 20, 1950.

In furnishing the opportunity for these discussions by active research workers in the field, Iowa State College hoped: to facilitate summarization and clarification of the accumulated data on the subject, to encourage formulation and interpretation of the observations in the light of present day biological information, to stimulate further advances in the controlled successful utilization and understanding of the biological processes behind the phenomenon of heterosis, and to increase the service rendered by this discovery in expanding world food supply.

Iowa has a direct, vested interest in heterosis. Today the agricultural economy of the state is based upon hybrid corn. The scene portraying a hybridization block of corn, shown here, is familiar to all who travel within the state as well as to those in surrounding regions, for this method of corn breeding has been shown to be surprisingly adaptable and useful in producing more food per acre over wide areas of the world's agricultural lands.

Iowa's indebtedness to heterosis, generated through crossing selected and repeatedly tested inbred strains, is well known. Few outside the workers in the field realize the full magnitude of this debt.

With the progressive introduction of hybrid corn in 1936 there came a steady increase in corn yields over both the former yields and over the yields of other agricultural crops, as that of tame hay, which were not subject to this genetic method of yield improvement. It seems likely that in no other period of like years has there been such an increase in food produced over so many acres of land. The return from hybrid corn has been phenomenal, but it is now evidently approaching an asymptotic value. It behooves us to find out as much as possible about the techniques and methods which

v

made these advances possible. Even more we should determine what is going on within the breeding and physiological systems through which heterosis finds expression, if further increases in yields are to be obtained or better systems of breeding are to be developed.

Toward this end the conference topics were arranged under four major

Controlled heterosis in the making through pollinations and fertilizations of selectively purified genetic strains of corn (maize). (From G. F. Sprague.)

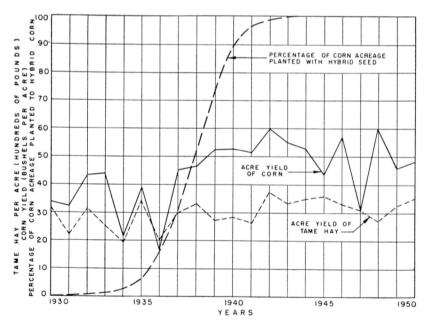

Trends in acre production of maize before and after heterosis was in use and tame hay over which there has been no such breeding control 1930–1950. (From G. F. Sprague.)

headings. The early history and development of the heterosis concepts and the cytological aspects of the problem occupied the first week. The contributions of physiology, evolution, and specific gene or cytoplasmic effects to the vigor observed in hybrids were dealt with the second week. The third week's meetings covered postulated gene interactions, as dominance, recombination, and other possible gene effects. During the fourth week breeding systems and methods of utilizing and evaluating heterosis effects were considered. In the final week the students considered the problems that lie ahead and recent methods of meeting them.

At each daily conference the speaker of the day presented a formal morning lecture covering his subject. In the afternoon, he led a conference session on the subject of the morning lecture. At this time, all present had an opportunity to participate.

Accompanying, and as a supplement to the Heterosis Conference, a Methods Workshop was held from July 3 to July 13. The Workshop was devoted to recent techniques for evaluating the kinds of data which occur frequently in animal breeding experiments. Workshop meetings were organized by Professor R. E. Comstock of North Carolina State College and Professor Jay L. Lush of Iowa State College.

The meetings were led by men from several institutions besides Iowa State College. Professors Oscar Kempthorne, Jay L. Lush, C. R. Henderson, G. E. Dickerson, L. N. Hazel, F. H. Hull, A. E. Bell, A. M. Dutton, J. Bruce Griffing, C. C. Cockerham, F. H. W. Morley, R. M. Koch, and A. L. Rae contributed much to this phase of the program. It is with regret that it is impossible to present the meat of the methods presented and developed in the Workshop and the afternoon discussions. To many, this material contributed much to the merit of the conference and the use to which the results were put later.

In the field of worth-while living, as well as to see heterosis in operation, conferees were guests, on various weekends, of three nearby companies putting heterosis to the practical test of commercial seed stock production in crops and live stock—the Ames Incross Company, the Farmers Hybrid Corn Company, and the Pioneer Hi-Bred Corn Company.

Finally, the organization of the conference was the product of the joint effort of the genetic group of Iowa State College. This group transcends all departmental lines having as the common interest what goes on in inheritance. They were Jay L. Lush, G. F. Sprague, Oscar Kempthorne, S. S. Chase, Janice Stadler, L. N. Hazel, A. W. Nordskog, Iver Johnson, W. A. Craft, J. Bruce Griffing, and John W. Gowen.

In last analysis it was the interest of the audience and their participations in the discussions that made the Conference worth while. The papers covering material presented by the leaders of these discussions follow.

Table of Contents

CONWAY ZIRKLE
University of Pennsylvania

Chapter 1

Early Ideas on Inbreeding and Crossbreeding

In tracing the historical background of a great scientific advance or dis-covery, the historian nearly always has the opportunity of showing that the scientists who receive the credit for the work are really late-comers to the field, and that all the basic principles and facts were known much earlier. Finding these earlier records is always something of a pleasure; comparable, perhaps, to the pleasure a systematist experiences in extending the range of some well known species.

The historian may be tempted, in consequence, to emphasize these earlier contributions a little too strongly and to re-assign the credits for the scientific advances which have been made. In the present state of the history of sci-ence, it requires only a little searching of the records to discover contributions which have been overlooked and which are very pertinent to the advance in question. This wealth of data, which accumulates almost automatically, seems to deserve emphasis. But great steps forward generally are made not by the discovery of new facts, important as they are, or by new ideas, brilliant as they may be, but by the organization of existing data in such a way that hitherto unperceived relationships are revealed, and by incor-porating the pertinent data into the general body of knowledge so that new, basic principles emerge.

For example, even so monumental a work as Darwin's *Origin of Species* contains few facts, observations or even ideas which had not been known for a long time. The work of many pre-Darwinians now appears important, especially after Darwin's synthesis had shown its significance. Of course, this does not belittle Darwin in the slightest. It only illustrates the way science grows.

The emergence of the scientific basis of heterosis or hybrid vigor is no exception. Practically all of its factual background was reported before Mendel's great contribution was discovered. Even workable methods for utilizing hybrid vigor in crop production were known, but it was not until the classic post-Mendelian investigations of Shull, East, and Jones were completed, that heterosis took its proper place in genetics. The following discussion of the importance of heterosis will be confined to its pre-Mendelian background.

Heterosis can be described as a special instance of the general principles involved in inbreeding and outbreeding. To fit it into its proper niche, we will trace first the evolution of our ideas on the effects of these two contrasting types of mating. Since our earliest breeding records seem limited to those of human beings and primitive deities, we will start with the breeding records of these two forms.

Hybrid vigor has been recognized in a great many plants during the last two hundred years. We will therefore describe briefly what was known of its influence on these plants. Because heterosis has reached its greatest development in *Zea mays*, we will trace briefly the pre-Mendelian genetics of this plant, and show how the facts were discovered which have been of such great scientific and economic importance.

The ill effects of too-close inbreeding have been known for a long time. Indeed, Charles Darwin (1868) believed that natural selection had produced in us an instinct against incest, and was effective in developing this instinct because of the greater survival value of the more vigorous offspring of exogamous matings. One of his contemporaries, Tylor (1865), noted that many savage tribes had tabooed the marriage of near relatives, and he assumed that they had done so because they had noticed the ill effects of inbreeding. The Greeks looked upon certain marriages between near relatives as crimes. This has been known almost universally ever since Freud popularized the tragedy of King Oedipus. At present, we outlaw close inbreeding in man, and our custom is scientifically sound.

We are apt to be mistaken, however, if we read into the standards of our distant preceptors the factual knowledge which we have today. The intellectual ancestors of European civilization approved of inbreeding and actually practiced it on supposedly eugenic grounds. The fact that their genetics was unsound and their eugenic notions impractical is irrelevant. They had their ideals, they were conscientious and they did their duties. The Pharaohs married their own sisters when possible so that their godlike blood would not be diluted. Marriage between half brother and sister was common in other royal families of the period. Actually, as we shall see, the two great pillars of European thought, Hebrew morality and Greek philosophy, endorsed inbreeding as a matter-of-course.

The Hebrews, who derived mankind from a single pair, were compelled to assume that the first men born had to marry their sisters—as there were then no other women on the earth. Indeed Adam and Eve themselves were not entirely unrelated. The marrying of a sister was obviously respectable, and it seems to have occurred routinely among the Hebrews and their ancestors for several thousand years. Abraham's wife, Sarah, was also his sister. At times even closer inbreeding took place. Abraham's nephew, Lot, impregnated his own two daughters. The latter instances occurred, however, under exceptional circumstances—and Lot was drunk. But as late as the time of King David, brother-sister marriages took place. The imbroglio between David's children, Tamar, Ammon, and Absalom, shows that a legal marriage between half-brother and sister would then have been a routine occurrence.

The Greeks also could hardly have had scruples against inbreeding, as evinced by the pedigrees they invented for their gods. Their theogony shows many instances of the closest inbreeding possible for either animals or gods in which the sexes are separate. Zeus, the great father of the gods, married his sister, Hera. Their parents, Kronos and Rhea, also were brother and sister, and were in turn descended from Ouranos and Gaea, again brother and sister. Thus the legitimate offspring of Zeus—Hebe, Ares, and Hephaestus—were the products of three generations of brother-sister mating. Moreover, the pedigrees of the Greek heroes show an amount of inbreeding comparable to that in our modern stud books for race horses. They were all related in one way or another and related to the gods in many ways. A single example will be cited. Zeus was the father of Herakles and also his great-great-grandfather on his mother's side. Herakles' great-great-grandmother, Danaë, who had found such favor in the eyes of Zeus, was herself descended from Zeus through two different lines. With immortals, backcrossing offered no real problems.

East and Jones (1919) have pointed out that close inbreeding was common among the Athenians even at the height of their civilization. These scientists were of the opinion that most of the freemen in Attica were rather closely related to each other. Marriage between half brother and sister was permitted, and marriage between uncle and niece fairly common. A Grecian heiress was nearly always taken as a wife by one of her kinsmen so that her property would not be lost to the family. Common as inbreeding was during the flowering of Greek culture, it was as nothing compared with the inbreeding which occurred in the period after the Trojan War and before the true historical period. In this intervening time, Greece was divided into innumerable independent political units, many of them minute. One island six miles long and two miles wide contained three separate kingdoms. Political boundaries as well as bays, mountains, and seas were functional, isolating mechanisms; and the Greeks were separated into many small breeding units for fifteen to twenty generations. Isolation was never complete, however, and there were enough wandering heroes to supply some genic migration. There were also some mass migrations and amalgamations of different tribes. The general situation was startlingly close to the conditions which Sewall Wright (1931) describes as the optimum for rapid evolution.

We may be tempted to explain as cause and effect what may be only an accidental relationship in time; and, while recognizing that it is far fetched, to ascribe the sudden appearance of what Galton called the ablest race in history to the ideal conditions for evolution which their ancestors had. We would also like to consider, as the necessary preliminary to the hybrid vigor, that period of inbreeding which preceded the flowering of Grecian culture. This hybrid vigor we would like to recognize as an important factor in the production of the great geniuses who flourished in the later, larger city states of Greece.

So much for the classical attitude toward endogamy. It slowly changed, and exogamy which had always existed became the exclusive custom. At the time of Sophocles, all forms of inbreeding were not considered ethical and pleasing to the gods. The sin of Oedipus lay in his having made a forbidden backcross rather than in mere inbreeding which was lawful. We do not find any records of degeneracy appearing in his children—indeed his daughter Antigone was a model of feminine virtue. It seems that close human inbreeding came to an end without its ill effects ever having been recognized.

The Nordics also were unaware of any degeneracy inherent in inbreeding. Their great god Wotan included a bit of inbreeding in his plan for creating a fearless hero who could save even the gods themselves from their impending fate. Wotan started the chain reaction by begetting Siegmund and Sieglinde, twin brother and sister. The twins were separated in infancy. They met again as adults and, recognizing their relationship, had an illegitimate affair—begetting the hero Siegfried. Although Siegfried was not exactly an intellectual type, he was certainly not a degenerate—representing rather the ideal male of a somewhat primitive culture.

As the centuries passed, incest was extended to cover brother-sister mating, even when the parties involved were unaware of their relationship. There is no need to cite here the many examples of the later tragedies based upon this plot. It soon became an almost universally accepted standard in literature, from epics to novels. The luckless Finnish hero, Kullervo (*The Kalevala*, Rune XXXV), thus brought disaster to his family by seducing his sister unknowingly. Defoe's long suffering heroine *Moll Flanders* (1722) had to abandon an apparently successful marriage when she discovered that her husband was her brother. On the other hand, as late as 1819, Lord Byron defended brother-sister marriage passionately in his drama *Cain*— but this was a scandalous exception to the rule. The marriage of kin nearer than first cousins had become legally and morally taboo. Perhaps we may follow Westermarck in assuming that endogamy became passé, not because its biological ill effects were recognized, but because men knew their kinswomen too well to marry one of them if they could possibly get a wife elsewhere.

It is possible that we have thus far paid too much attention to inbreeding and outbreeding in man. Our excuse is that there are almost no other records of inbreeding from classical times. There are no plant records, of course, for sex in plants was not understood in spite of the general practices of caprification and hand pollination of the date palm. Records of inbreeding and outcrossing in domestic animals are almost completely lacking even in the copious agricultural literature of the Romans. Aristotle's History of Animals. 576a15 (Thompson 1910) does state that horses will cover both their mothers and their daughters ". . . and, indeed, a troup of horses is only considered perfect when such promiscuity of intercourse occurs"—but he seems to be almost alone in referring to the subject. Later on in the same book (630b30) he cited a happening which we quote.

The male camel declines intercourse with its mother; if his keeper tries compulsion, he evinces disinclination. On one occasion, when intercourse was being declined by the young male, the keeper covered over the mother and put the young male to her; but, when after the intercourse the wrapping had been removed, though the operation was completed and could not be revoked, still by and by he bit his keeper to death. A story goes that the king of Scythia had a highly-bred mare, and that all her foals were splendid; that wishing to mate the best of the young males with the mother, he had him brought to the stall for the purpose; that the young horse declined; that, after the mother's head had been concealed in a wrapper he, in ignorance, had intercourse; and that, when immediately afterwards the wrapper was removed and the head of the mare was rendered visible, the young horse ran away and hurled himself down a precipice.

This behavior of the stallion was considered so remarkable that it was described by Aelian, Antigonus, Heirocles, Oppian, Pliny, and Varro. Varro confused the tradition and made the horse bite his keeper to death.

It is fairly safe for us to assume that in both classical and medieval times the flocks and herds were greatly inbred. Transportation difficulties would have insured inbreeding unless its evil effects were realized, and we have at least negative evidence that they were not. Varro, who gave many detailed directions for the breeding of all domestic animals, does not even mention the question of kinship between sire and dam. We do have an interesting literary allusion by Ovid, however, to the routine inbreeding of domestic animals in his account of the incest of Myrrha in the tenth book of the *Metamorphoses*. The affair between Myrrha and her father Cinyras was like that of Oedipus and his mother Jocasta. The fates had decreed that Myrrha should become the mistress of her father. Torn by her unholy desires she debates the matter with her conscience. Her better nature argues (From the metrical translation of Brookes More, 1922):

> But what more could be asked for, by the most
> Depraved? Think of the many sacred ties
> And loved names, you are dragging to the mire;
> The rival of your mother, will you be
> The mistress of your father, and be named
> The sister of your son, and make yourself
> The mother of your brother?

In stating the other side of the case Myrrha describes the "natural" inbreeding of animals.

> A crime so great—If it indeed is crime.
> I am not sure it is—I have not heard
> That any God or written law condemns
> The union of a parent and his child.
> All animals will mate as they desire—
> A heifer may endure her sire, and who
> Condemns it? And the happy stud is not
> Refused by his mare-daughters: the he-goat
> Consorts unthought-of with the flock of which
> He is the father; and the birds conceive
> Of those from whom they were themselves begot.
> Happy are they who have such privilege!
> Malignant men have given spiteful laws;
> And what is right to Nature is decreed
> Unnatural, by jealous laws of men.
>   But it is said there are some tribes today,
> In which the mother marries her own son;
> The daughter takes her father; and by this,
> The love kind nature gives them is increased
> Into a double bond.—Ah wretched me!

The debate ends as we would expect, and in due course Myrrha is delivered of an infant boy who certainly showed none of the ill effects of the inbreeding which produced him. He grew up to be quite an Adonis. In fact he *was* Adonis.

We can profitably skip to the late eighteenth century before we pursue further the matter of inbreeding. This was the period when Bakewell was emphasizing the importance of breeding in improving farm animals, when the various purebreds were beginning to emerge, and when the efficacy of artificial selection was beginning to be understood.

By the beginning of the nineteenth century, practical attempts to improve the different breeds of cattle led to intensive inbreeding. A prize bull would be bred to his own daughters and granddaughters. At first, the breeders seemed to believe that a selection of the very best individuals followed by intensive inbreeding was the quickest method for improving the stock. On theoretical grounds this seemed to be the case, and great advances were actually made by this method—but sooner or later something always happened. The inbred stock seemed to grow sterile, but vigor could be re-established by outcrossing. The actual cause of degeneracy in the inbreds was not understood until Mendelian inheritance was discovered, but the remedial procedures of the practical breeders could hardly have been improved on. We owe to them the basis of our finest stocks. They inbred to add up and concentrate desirable qualities and then crossbred to prevent degeneration, then inbred again and crossed again, all the time selecting their breeding stocks most carefully. Charles Darwin (1868) described this process most accurately and listed the pertinent publications.

There was a striking divergence in this work between theory and practice, which is just as well, as the only theories available at the time were inadequate. Those breeders who held that inbreeding was the *summum bonum* did not hesitate to crossbreed when the occasion demanded, and those who emphasized the virtues of hybridization inbred whenever inbreeding gave them the opportunity of adding up desirable qualities. Darwin, himself, stated, "Although free crossing is a danger on the one side which everyone can see, too close inbreeding is a hidden danger on the other." We await the twentieth century for a real improvement in breeding methods.

The first plant hybrid was described as such in 1716, and during the next forty-five years many descriptions of hybrid plants were published. Some attempts were even made to produce new varieties, but in retrospect the work seems somewhat dilettante.

From 1761 to 1766, Josef Gottlieb Koelreuter (1766) published the several parts of his well-known classic, and plant hybridization was put upon a different and more scientific basis. His investigation of hybridization was intensive, systematic, and scientific. He described, among other things, hybrid vigor in interspecific crosses in Nicotiana, Dianthus, Verbascum, Mirabilis, Datura, and other genera (East and Jones, 1919). He also observed floral mechanisms which insured cross pollination and assumed in consequence that nature had designed plants to benefit from crossbreeding. It is worth emphasizing that hybrid vigor in plants was first described by the person who first investigated plant hybrids in detail. Koelreuter continued to publish papers on plant hybrids until the early nineteenth century.

Meanwhile other contributions had been made to our knowledge of the effects of outcrossing and the mechanism for securing it. In 1793, Sprengel depicted the structure of flowers in great and accurate detail, and showed how self pollination was generally avoided. In 1799, Thomas Andrew Knight described hybrid vigor as a normal consequence of crossing varieties and developed from this his principle of anti-inbreeding. Other hybridizers noted the exceptional vigor of many of their creations. Indeed, hybrid vigor in plants was becoming a commonplace. Among the botanists who recorded this vigor were: Mauz (1825), Sageret (1826), Berthollet (1827), Wiegmann (1828), Herbert (1837), and Lecoq (1845). Gärtner (1849) was especially struck by the vegetative luxuriance, root development, height, number of flowers and hardiness of many of his hybrids.

Naudin (1865) found hybrid vigor in twenty-four species crosses out of the thirty-five which he made within eleven genera. In Datura his results were spectacular. In reciprocal crosses between *D. Stramonium* and *D. Tatula* the offspring were twice the height of the parents. Knowledge of plant hybridization was increasing more rapidly at this time than the biologists knew, for this was the year in which Mendel's (1865) paper *Versuche über Pflanzen-Hybriden* appeared. Mendel discovered hybrid vigor in his pea hybrids and described it as follows:

> The longer of the two parental stems is usually exceeded by the hybrid, a fact which is possibly only attributable to the greater luxuriance which appears in all parts of the plants when stems of very different lengths are crossed. Thus, for instance, in repeated experiments, stems of 1 ft. and 6 ft. in length yielded without exception hybrids which varied in length between 6 ft. and 7½ ft.

We shall cite but one more scientist who wrote on the general subject of hybrid vigor in plants. This is Charles Darwin, whose *Cross and Self Fertilization in the Vegetable Kingdom* appeared in 1876. This was a book of great importance and influence, but no attempt will be made here to summarize this work of nearly five hundred pages. At the beginning of his concluding chapter, Darwin stated:

> The first and most important conclusion which may be drawn from the observations given in this volume, is that cross-fertilization is generally beneficial and self-fertilization injurious.

There is a special reason why this book of Darwin's is of such great importance for any historical background to heterosis. Darwin worked carefully and quantitatively with many genera, including *Zea mays*. He measured accurately the amount of hybrid vigor he could induce, and he published his data in full. His work stands in the direct ancestral line to the twentieth century research on the subject, and the great advances made from 1908 to 1919 are based solidly on this work. There are no great gaps in the steady progress and no gaps in the literature.

Zea mays was brought to Europe in 1493 by Columbus on his homeward voyage. This was sometime before the great herbals were written, so our first descriptions of the new grain are to be found in the books of the travelers and explorers. Later, Indian corn appeared under various names in the early herbals, and it was described in detail in the famous *Krautebuch* of Tabernaemontanus, first published in 1588. The author obviously yielded to his enthusiasm in devoting five and a half folio pages to corn and including thirteen illustrations in his treatment. He was the first to describe the results of xenia—the occurrence of different colored grains on the same ear—but his explanation of the phenomenon has nothing to do with cross pollination. He ascribed it directly to God Almighty.

And one sees an especially great and wonderful mystery in these spikes, *Gott der Herr*, through the medium of nature which must serve everyone, disports himself and performs wonders in his works and so notably in the case of this plant that we must rightly be amazed and should learn to know the One True Eternal God even from his creatures alone. For some of the spikes of this plant, together with their fruit, are quite white, brown and blue intermixed. Thus, some rows are half white, a second series brown and the third blue; and some grains, accordingly are mixed with each other and transposed. Again, sometimes one, two, or three rows are white, the next rows blue, then again white and after that chestnut-brown; that is, they are interchanged on one row and run straight through on another. Some spikes and their grains are entirely yellow, others entirely brown, some are white, brown, and blue, others violet, white, black, and brown: of these the white and blue are prettily sprinkled with small dots, as if they had been artistically colored in this way by a painter. Some are red, black, and brown, with sometimes one color next to the other, while at other times two, three, even four colors, more or less, are found one next to another in this way.

During the next century and a half, many other descriptions of the occurrence of different colored grains on a single ear were published. I have found about forty of them and there are doubtless many more. The earliest correct interpretation of this phenomenon had to await the eighteenth century and is contained in a letter written by Cotton Mather in 1716. Here the different colored grains occurring together on an ear are ascribed to a wind-born intermixture of varieties. This letter is the first record we have of plant hybridization, and antedates Fairchild's description of a *Dianthus* hybrid by one year. In 1724, Paul Dudley also described hybridization in maize, and he was able to eliminate one of the hypotheses which had been used to explain the mixture. As a broad ditch of water lay between the mixing varieties, he could show that the mixed colors were not due to the rootlets of different strains fusing underground, a view held at the time by many New Englanders, both white and red.

Hybridization in maize was described again in 1745 by Benjamin Cooke, in 1750 by the great Swedish traveler and naturalist, Pehr Kalm, and in 1751 by William Douglass. By the early nineteenth century, knowledge of plant hybrids was widespread. Plant hybridization was becoming a routine practice, and there is little doubt that different varieties of maize were crossed many times by American farmers who did not record their breeding experiments in writing.

Brown and Anderson (1947, 1948) have recently shown that the modern races now grown in the corn belt are derived from both the northern flint and the southern dent varieties. Hybridization in corn was easy to perform and the results were easy to recognize. The intermixtures of colors were so spectacular that they were frequently described, by Gallesio (1806), Burger (1808), Sageret (1826), Gärtner (1827), and others.

We detour briefly here into some of the technical aspects of xenia. Double fertilization and the mixed nature of the endosperm were discovered by Nawaschin in 1899. In 1881, Focke introduced the term *xenia* but he used it to include what we now call *metaxenia*. Focke collected from the literature many supposed instances where the pollen influenced directly the color and form of the flowers, the flavor and shape of the fruits, and the color and content of the seeds. How many of these cases were really due to Mendelian segregation we will probably never know, since the investigators did not know enough to take proper precautions.

We can, however, divide the history of true xenia into three periods: first, when its visible effect was considered a *lusus naturae* (1588); second, when it was known to be caused by foreign pollen (1716); and third, when the embryo and endosperm were recognized as two different structures and when the influence of the pollen upon the latter was recorded specifically. In the paragraph on *Zea* in the section on xenia, Focke cites the work of Vilmorin (1867), Hildebrand (1868), and Körnicke (1876), who described the effect of pollen on the endosperm.

We should note a brief comment on the subject which has been overlooked and is earlier than the papers cited by Focke. In 1858, Asa Gray described xenia in maize. He reported starchy grains in ears of sweet corn and many different kinds and colors of grains on the same ear. He had two explanations for this occurrence: (1) cross pollination of the previous year and (2) direct action of the pollen on the ovules of the present year. It is obvious that by *ovules* he did not mean *embryos*. This may be the earliest authentic recognition of the real problem of xenia.

In reviewing the nineteenth century records of hybrid vigor in *Zea mays*, we start with those of Charles Darwin (1876). Darwin planned his experiments most carefully. He crossed and selfed plants from the same stock, and raised fifteen plants from each of the two types of seed he had obtained. He planted the seed from both the selfed and crossed plants in the same pots, from six to ten plants per pot. When the plants were between one and two feet in height, he measured them and found that the average height of the plants from the selfed seed was 17.57 inches, while that from the crossed seed was 20.19 inches or a ratio of 81 to 100. When mature, the two lots averaged 61.59 inches and 66.51 inches, respectively, a ratio of 93 to 100. In another experiment when the corn was planted in the ground, the ratio of the selfed to the crossed was 80 to 100. Darwin called in his cousin, Francis Galton, to check his results and Galton judged them to be very good after he had studied the curves that he drew.

The direct connection between Darwin's work and our present hybrid corn is shown by Darwin's influence on W. J. Beal who was the real leader in the American research designed to improve maize. Beal reviewed Darwin's book in 1878, and even wrote an article which was little more than a paraphrase of what Darwin had published. Beal's own contributions appeared a little later.

In 1880, Beal described how he had increased the yield of corn on a large scale. Two stocks of the same type of corn which had been grown a hundred miles apart for a number of years were planted together in alternate rows. All of one stock grown in this field was detasseled and thus it could not be self fertilized but could produce only hybrid seed. The tasseled stalks of the other lot would still be pure bred as there was no foreign pollen to contaminate their ears and they could again serve as a parent to a hybrid. A small amount of the first parental stock which furnished the detasseled stalks was grown apart for future hybridization. The hybrid seed was planted, and produced the main crop. Beal increased his yield by this method by as much as 151 exceeds 100. This method and these results, it should be emphasized, were published in 1880.

E. Lewis Sturtevant, the first director of the New York Agricultural Experiment Station, made a number of studies of corn hybrids starting in 1882. His findings are interesting and important but not directly applicable to heterosis. Singleton (1935) has called attention to this work and to the excellent genetic research which the western corn breeders were carrying on at this time—such geneticists as W. A. Kellerman, W. T. Swingle, and Willet M. Hays. They anticipated many of Mendel's findings and described dominance, the reappearance of recessives (atavisms), and even Mendelian ratios such as 1 to 1 and 3 to 1. They were all concerned with practical results. Hays (1889), in particular, tried to synthesize superior breeds of corn by hybridizing controlled varieties.

Sanborn (1890) confirmed Beal's results and reported that his own hybrid corn yielded in the ratio of 131 to 100 for his inbred. He also followed Beal's method of planting his parental stocks in alternate rows and of detasseling one of them. He made an additional observation which we know now is important:

It is this outcrossed seed which will give the great crops for the next year. It will be noted that I gained twelve bushels per acre by using crossed seed. The operation is simple and almost costless and will pay one hundred fold for the cost involved. *The cross must be made every year using new seed, the product of the outcross of two pure seed.* (Italics C. Z.)

If our farmers had known of this discovery reported in 1890 they might not have tried to use their own hybrid corn as seed.

Singleton (1941) also called attention to a pre-Mendelian interpretation of hybrid vigor by Johnson (1891) which, in the light of our present knowledge, deserves more than passing notice. We can state it in Johnson's own words:

That crossing commonly gives better offspring than in-and-in breeding is due to the fact that in the latter both parents are likely to possess by inheritance the same imperfections which are thus intensified in the progeny, while in cross breeding the parents more usually have different imperfections, which often, more or less, compensate each other in the immediate descendants.

We come next to a publication of G. W. McClure (1892). This paper is deservedly famous, and its many contributions are incorporated into our modern genetics literature. Here we shall cite only the observations which pertain to heterosis. McClure noted (1) that sterility and deformity often follow selfing, (2) that crossing imparts vigor, (3) that it is impossible to tell in advance what varieties will produce corn of increased size when crossed, (4) that what appears to be the best ear does not always produce the largest crops, and (5) nearly all of the hybrid corn grown a second year is smaller than that grown the first year, though most of it is yet larger than the average size of the parent varieties.

McClure also called attention to the fact that our fine varieties of fruits have to be propagated vegetatively, and hinted that the deteriorations of the seedlings from fruit trees was not unrelated to a like deterioration which occurred in the seedlings grown from hybrid corn.

The year following McClure's publication, Morrow and Gardiner (1893) recorded some very pertinent facts they had discovered as a result of their field experiments with corn. They reported that, "In every instance the yield from the cross is greater than the average from the parent varieties: the average increase per acre from the five crosses [they had made] being nine and a half bushels." They noted further in a paper published later the same year that, "It seems that cross bred corn gives larger yields at least for the first and second years after crossing than an average of the parent varieties, but how long this greater fruitfulness will last is undetermined." Gardiner continued the work and in 1895 published the data he obtained by repeating the experiments. He found that in four of six cases the yield was greater in the cross, the average being twelve bushels per acre.

We now come to the great corn breeding research project which was undertaken at the University of Illinois in 1895 by Eugene Davenport and P. G. Holden. Both of these scientists had been students of Beal and were interested in his work on inbreeding and cross breeding maize. We are indebted to Professor Holden for an account of this work which he printed privately in 1948. This account gives us valuable historic data not to be found elsewhere, as most of the University of Illinois records were destroyed by fire.

An intensive series of inbreeding experiments was undertaken by Holden, and later on the inbred lines were crossed. Hybrid vigor was noted, and it was found in addition that the crosses between different inbred lines differed widely in their yield and in their general desirability. The main purpose of the experiments was to find out how to use controlled crossing early and effectively. After Holden left Illinois in 1900, the project was taken over by C. G. Hopkins, a chemist, who was interested in increasing the protein content of maize. He hired as his assistant in 1900 a young chemist named Edward Murray East, whom we shall hear about later.

Our account of the background of heterosis is coming to an end as the beginning of the twentieth century makes a logical stopping point. We should mention, however, the great hybrid vigor discovered by Webber (1900) when he crossed a Peruvian corn, Cuzco, with a native variety, Hickory

King. The average height of the parental stocks was 8 feet 3 inches while the cross averaged 12 feet 4 inches, an increase of 4 feet 1 inch.

The next year Webber (1901) called attention to the marked loss of vigor in corn from inbreeding. From 100 stalks of selfed corn he obtained 46 ears weighing 9.33 pounds, while from 100 stalks obtained from crossing different seedlings he obtained 82 ears weighing 27.5 pounds. When he attempted to "fix" his Cuzco-Hickory King hybrid by selfing he got a great loss of vigor and almost complete sterility, but when he crossed the different seedlings there was little loss of vigor. He concluded that to fix hybrids one should not self the plants.

In 1900, the discovery of Mendel's long-forgotten paper was announced. Both Hugo de Vries and C. Correns, two of the three discoverers of Mendel, published papers on *Zea mays* and all future work on Indian Corn was on a somewhat different level.

SUMMARY OF KNOWLEDGE OF HYBRID VIGOR AT BEGINNING OF 20th CENTURY

1. Inbreeding reduces vigor and produces many defective and sterile individuals which automatically discard themselves.
2. Cross breeding greatly increases vigor both in interspecific and intervarietal hybrids. Crossing two inbred stocks restores the lost vigor and frequently produces more vigor than the stocks had originally.
3. All inbred stocks do not produce the same amount of vigor when crossed. Certain crosses are far more effective than others.
4. The simplest method of hybridizing *Zea* on a large scale is to plant two stocks in alternate rows and to detassel one stock. The hybrid corn grown from the detasseled stock produces the great yields.
5. Hybridization must be secured each generation if the yield is to be kept up, although a second generation of open pollinated corn may still be better than the original parental stocks.
6. In inbreeding, both parents are apt to have the same defects which are intensified in the offspring. The cause of hybrid vigor is that in crosses the parents usually have different defects which tend to compensate for each other in the immediate progeny.
7. The fact that hybrid vigor in *Zea* is not permanent but decreases if the hybrids are open-pollinated, seems to be related to the fact that fruit trees, whose desirable qualities are preserved by vegetative propagation, produce seedlings which are inferior.

GEORGE HARRISON SHULL
Princeton University

Chapter 2

Beginnings of the Heterosis Concept

The heterosis concept was first definitely recognized in the work with hybrid corn. Before attempting to define this concept, however, we will take a brief look at some of the observations of early workers which indicated the probable presence of heterosis, and where recognition of heterosis as an important biological principle might have been expected.

The first hybridizer of plants, Dr. J. G. Koelreuter, noted some impressive examples of excessive luxuriance in his Nicotiana hybrids. These were isolated observations which suggested no theory as to why these hybrids should exceed their parents in size and general vigor. Koelreuter cannot be said to have had a heterosis concept. Probably every conscious producer of hybrids since Koelreuter's time has made similar observations of the excessive vigor of some hybrids over their parents, so that such hybrid vigor has ceased to cause surprise. But the general acceptance of hybrid vigor as a normal phenomenon did not establish a heterosis concept. It was merely the summational effect of oft-repeated experience.

Thomas Andrew Knight noted the deterioration of some of the old standard horticultural varieties, and concluded that such varieties have a natural life-span and gradually decline as the result of advancing senility. He saw that such decline makes it necessary to develop new varieties which will start off with the vigor of youth. Although Knight himself produced many such new varieties, some of which were produced by hybridization, it is not apparent that he thought of hybridization as an agency for the production of such new vigor. Although he advanced a theory concerning physiological vigor and its decline, he did not recognize the heterosis concept.

Luther Burbank also produced numerous varieties, often following inten-

14

tional hybridizations, and it is easy to recognize heterosis as a potent factor in the remarkable values displayed by many of these new varieties. But while Burbank made great use of hybridizations in his plant breeding work, he did not recognize hybridization, as such, as the source of the large size and remarkable vigor of his new varieties. For him the role of hybridization, aside from the bringing together of desirable qualities possessed separately by the two chosen parents, was merely the "breaking of the types." In this way the variability in subsequent generations was greatly increased, thus enlarging the range of forms from among which to select the most desirable for recognition as *New Creations*.

There are many other important observations and philosophical considerations that bear a close relationship to our current understanding of heterosis, and which antedated the recognition of heterosis. It would take us too far afield, however, to discuss these related observations at length. We can make only this passing reference to the highly significant work of Charles Darwin in demonstrating that cross-fertilization results, in many cases, in increased size, vigor, and productiveness as compared with self-fertilization or with other close inbreeding within the same species.

Darwin did not recognize this increased vigor as identical with *hybrid vigor*, nor specifically attribute it to the differences between the uniting gametes. To him it only demonstrated a method which would inevitably preserve by natural selection any variation that might occur—whether mechanical or physiological—which would make cross-fertilization more likely or even an obligate method of reproduction. With heterosis established as a recognized pattern of behavior, or type of explanation, we can now interpret Darwin's demonstrated superiority of crossbreds as examples of the occurrence of heterosis. We may go even further and include the whole field of sexual reproduction in showing the advantages of heterosis. These result from the union of two cells—the egg and the sperm—extremely differentiated physiologically, and in all dioecious organisms also differentiated genetically.

Let us briefly consider several investigations which foreshadowed the procedures now used in growing hybrid corn—for somewhere in the course of this work with corn the heterosis principle was first definitely recognized.

Two techniques are characteristically associated with the work of the "hybrid-corn makers." Uncritical commentators have mistakenly considered these techniques synonymous with the development of the hybrid-corn program itself. These are (a) cross-pollination by interplanting two different lines or varieties, and the detasseling of one of these lines which then supplies the seed to be planted; and (b) controlled self-pollination.

In deciding what part these two methods played in the development of the heterosis concept, we must first consider why these methods were used by various workers and how their use affected the experimental conclusions.

Dr. William J. Beal, of Michigan Agricultural College, apparently was the first to make extensive use of controlled cross-pollination in the breeding of corn. Beal was a student of Asa Gray from 1862 to 1865, when the latter was in active correspondence with Charles Darwin. Darwin was beginning the studies on cross- and self-fertilization, which were reported in 1877 in an important book on the subject. It has been thought that Darwin's views on the significance of crossbreeding may have been instrumental in inciting and guiding Beal's experiments in the crossing of corn. There seems to be no supporting evidence, however, for such a surmise.

Beal's lectures before various farmers' institutes stressed the importance of being able to control the source of the pollen, so that the choice of good ears in the breeding program would not be nullified by pollen from barren stalks and other plants of inferior yielding capacity. On this point Professor Perry Greeley Holden, for several years assistant to Dr. Beal, has stated that controlled parentage, not heterosis, was the aim of the corn breeding program at Michigan and at Illinois before 1900.

In 1895 Holden was invited by Eugene Davenport to become professor of agricultural physics at the University of Illinois. Davenport also had served for several years as assistant to Dr. Beal at Michigan. Like Holden, he was very enthusiastic about the importance of Beal's program, so it was natural that Davenport and Holden should agree that corn improvement be a major undertaking of Holden's new department at the University of Illinois. On initiating this work at the University of Illinois, they learned that Morrow and Gardner already had tested Beal's variety crossing at Illinois before they got there, and with confirmatory results. Concerning the motivation of all this early work, both at Michigan and at Illinois, Holden says:

1. Hybrid corn [as we know it today] was unknown, not even dreamed of, previous to 1900. 2. *Controlled parentage* was the dominant purpose or object of this early corn improvement work.

Holden thus makes it clear that while heterosis was at play in all of this early work, it was not the result of, nor did it result in, a *heterosis concept*.

I refer next to the matter of inbreeding, which some writers have confused with the crossing that has brought the benefits of heterosis. Enough selfing had been done with corn prior to 1900 to convince all of those who had had experience with it that it resulted in notable *deterioration*. The results of these early observations are aptly summed up by Holden in the statement that "Inbreeding proved to be disastrous—the enemy of vigor and yield." Nowhere, so far as I have been able to determine, did any of the early inbreeders discover or conceive of the establishment of permanently viable pure lines as even a secondary effect of inbreeding.

In 1898 A. D. Shamel, then a Junior in the University of Illinois, offered himself to Holden as a volunteer assistant without pay. He did so well that when Holden severed his connection with the University in 1900, Shamel was appointed his successor, and continued in this capacity until 1902. He then transferred to the United States Department of Agriculture and did no further work with corn. In Shamel's final report of his own corn experiments (1905), he laid no stress on the positive gains which resulted from cross-breeding, but only on the injurious effects of inbreeding. His "frame of reference" was the normally vigorous crossbred (open-pollinated) corn, and the relation between self-fertilized and cross-fertilized corn was that of something *subtracted* from the crossbred level, not something *added* to the inbred level. The prime objective in a breeding program, he said, "is the prevention of the injurious effects of cross-fertilization between nearly related plants or inbreeding." In summing up the whole matter he said:

> In general, . . . it would seem that the improvement of our crops can be most rapidly effected with permanent beneficial results by following the practice of inbreeding, or crossing, to the degree in which these methods of fertilization are found to exist naturally in the kind of plant under consideration.

This means, for corn, practically no self-fertilization at all, and makes it obvious that, at least for Shamel, the heterosis concept had not yet arrived.

Edward Murray East was associated with the corn work at the University of Illinois, off and on, from 1900 to 1905. He worked mainly in the role of analytical chemist in connection with the breeding program of C. G. Hopkins and L. H. Smith. He must have been familiar with the inbreeding work of Shamel, if not with that of Holden. It is generally understood that he did no self-fertilizing of corn himself, until after he transferred to the Connecticut Agricultural Experiment Station in 1905. Some of his inbred lines at Connecticut may have had the inbreeding work at Illinois back of them, as he secured samples of seeds of the Illinois inbreds sent to him by Dr. H. H. Love, who assisted him for one year and succeeded him at Illinois. But according to his subsequently published records these older inbred lines did not enter to any important extent into his studies in Connecticut.

As reported in *Inbreeding and Outbreeding* (East and Jones, pp. 123, 124), "The original experiment began with four individual plants obtained from seed of a commercial variety grown in Illinois known as Leaming Dent." Table III (p. 124) presents the data for these four lines for the successive years from 1905 to 1917, and clearly indicates that the selfing was first made in 1905. East's work is so adequately presented in this excellent book that it seems unnecessary to comment on it further here except to recall that, as shown by his own specific statements, my paper on "The composition of a field of maize" gave him the viewpoint that made just the difference between repeated observations of heterosis and the heterosis concept. In proof of this we have not only his letter to me, dated February 12, 1908, in which he says: "Since studying your paper, I agree entirely with your conclusion, and wonder why I have been so stupid as not to see the fact myself"; but we also have the published statements of his views just before and just after the publication of my paper. Thus, we read in his Conn. Agr. Exp. Sta. Bull. 158,

"The relation of certain biological principles to plant breeding," which was published in 1907, only a few months before I read my paper in his presence in Washington, D.C., what seems like an echo of the final conclusion of Shamel, above cited. In this bulletin East urged that "corn breeders should discard the idea of forcing improvement along paths where nothing has been provided by nature," specifically rejecting a program of isolation of uniform types because of a "fear of the dangers of inbreeding," adding that he was "not able to give a reason for this belief beyond the common credence of the detrimental effects of inbreeding." He returned to this problem of the deterioration due to inbreeding in his Annual Report to the Conn. Agr. Exp. Sta. for 1907–8, prepared in 1908, with my paper before him. In this report he says:

> I thought that this deterioration was generally due to the establishment and enhancement of poor qualities common to the strain. . . . A recent paper by Dr. George H. Shull ("The composition of a field of maize") has given, I believe, the correct interpretation of this vexed question. His idea, although clearly and reasonably developed, was supported by few data; but as my own experience and experiments of many others are most logically interpreted in accordance with his conclusions, I wish here to discuss some corroboratory evidence.

We have thus far failed to recognize the existence of a general heterosis concept among plant breeders, prior to the reading of my paper on "The composition of a field of maize" in January, 1908, even when they were using the methods of inbreeding and controlled crossing in which such a concept could have developed. I must mention, however, a near approach to such a concept from the side of the animal breeders. Before the American Breeders' Association, meeting in Columbus, Ohio, 1907, Quintus I. Simpson, an animal breeder from Bear Creek Farm, Palmer, Illinois, read a paper which definitely recognized hybridization as a potent source of major economic gains beyond what could be secured from the pure breeds. The title of his paper, "Rejuvenation by hybridization," is more suggestive of the views of Thomas Andrew Knight than of the current students of heterosis, but the distinction seems to me to be very tenuous indeed.

Although I listened with great interest to Simpson's paper, I do not think that I recognized any direct applications of his views to my results with maize. I was working within the material of a single strain of a single species, and not with the hybridizations between different well established breeds to the superiority of whose hybrids Simpson called attention.

Students may make varying estimates as to how closely the work of men to whom I have referred approached the heterosis concept as we understand it today. But there can be no doubt that there was a *beginning* of this concept in the course of my own experiments with corn. At the beginning of 1907 I had not the slightest inkling of such a concept. By the end of 1907 I had written the paper that brought such concept clearly into recognition. At that time I knew nothing of the work of Beal, Holden, Morrow and Gardner,

McCluer, Shamel or East, in the selfing and crossing of the maize plant. This will become obvious as I explain the motivation and plan of procedure of my corn experiments.

Upon arriving at the Station for Experimental Evolution at Cold Spring Harbor on May 2, 1904, I found the laboratory building unfinished. It was in fact not ready for occupation until the following November. The potentially arable portion of the grounds was in part a swampy area in need of effective provision for drainage. The rest had been at one time used as a garden. But it had lain fallow for an unknown number of years, and was covered with a heavy sod that would need a considerable period of disintegration before it could be used satisfactorily as an experimental garden. The total area available was about an acre.

In the middle of this small garden plot was a group of lusty young spruce trees. These had to be removed in order to use the area for experimental planting the following spring. The ground was plowed, disked, and planted as soon as possible to potatoes, corn, sorghum, buckwheat, sugar beets, turnip beets, and many kinds of ordinary garden vegetables. None of them were designed as the beginning of a genetical experiment, but only as an excuse for keeping the ground properly tilled so it would be in best possible condition for use as an experimental garden later. Due to this fact, no adequate record was made of the origin of the several lots of seeds which were planted. This is unfortunate in the several cases in which some of these cultures did provide material for later experimental use.

There were two cultures of corn, one a white dent, the other a Corry sweet corn. These two varieties were planted at the special request of Dr. Davenport, who wished to have available for display to visitors the striking illustrations of Mendelian segregation of starchy and sugary grains on the single ears of the crossbred plants. I planted the white dent corn with my own hands on May 14, 1904, and must have known at the time that the grains came from a single ear. Although I have found no contemporary record to that effect, I am now convinced from a well-remembered conversation with Mrs. Davenport, that this ear of white dent corn came from the farm of her father, Mr. Crotty, who lived near Topeka, Kansas.

When I was last in Ames, after almost forty years of devotion to other lines of genetical experimentation, my memory played me false when Professor J. C. Cunningham asked me about the source of the foundation stock for my experimental work with corn, and I told him that my studies on corn began with some corn I had purchased in the local market as horse feed. I repeated the same unfortunate misstatement to several other highly reputable historians of science. I deeply regret this error because these men were trying so hard to get the record straight. My recollection was restored by finding the statement at the very beginning of the record of my formal corn studies under date Nov. 7, 1904: "Counted the rows on the ears of White dent corn raised in Carnegie garden this year." In fact, as I think of it now, I doubt that I could have bought white dent corn in the feed market of Long Island at that time.

I planted the Corry sweet corn on May 17. On July 18 I bagged the corn preparatory to making crosses between the two varieties. This crossing was carried out on the Corry sweet on July 25, and the crosses for the reciprocal combination were made on July 27 and 28. These were the first controlled pollinations I ever made in corn, and they were not part of a scientific experiment.

My interest in investigating the effects of cross- and self-fertilization in maize arose incidentally in connection with a projected experiment with evening primroses (Oenothera) to determine the effect, if any, of these two types of breeding on the kinds and the frequencies of occurrence of mutations. A critic of De Vries's mutation theory had urged that the mutations discovered by De Vries in *Oenothera lamarckiana* were artifacts produced by selfing a species which, in a natural state, had been always cross-fertilized. I developed a program to put this question to a crucial test. Then, it occurred to me that it would be interesting to run a parallel experiment to test the effects of crossing and selfing on the expressions of a purely fluctuating character. Since I had available this culture of white dent maize, I chose the grain-row numbers on the ears of corn as appropriate material for such a study. The Oenothera problems thus begun, continued to be a major interest throughout my genetical career, but it is not expedient to pursue them further here. It is important, however, to keep them in mind as a key to my motivation in launching my studies with maize.

In this double-barreled exploration of the genetical effects of cross-fertilization *versus* self-fertilization, I had no preconception as to what the outcome of these studies would be in either the mutational or the fluctuational field. Certainly they involved no plan for the demonstration of distinctive new biotypes, nor any thought of the possible economic advantages of either method of breeding. I was a faithful advocate of the early biometricians' slogan: *Ignoramus, in hoc signo laboremus.* Until the middle of summer of 1907, certainly, I had no premonition of the possible existence of a heterosis principle which would have important significance either scientifically or economically. I was forced to recognize this principle by direct observations of manifestations in my cultures which had not been anticipated, and therefore could not have been planned for.

Let us proceed then to a description of my experiments with corn which forced the recognition of this important phenomenon. The culture of white dent corn which we had growing, almost incidentally, on the Station grounds that first year, showed no variations that seemed to indicate the presence of any segregating characteristics. It appeared to be ideal material for the study of fluctuations of so definite and easily observed a quantitative character as the number of the rows of grains on the ears. The crop was carefully harvested and placed in a crib. On November 7, 1904, I counted the rows of grains on every ear, with the result shown in figure 2.1. The 524 ears ranged over the seven classes from 10-rowed to 22-rowed. The most populous classes

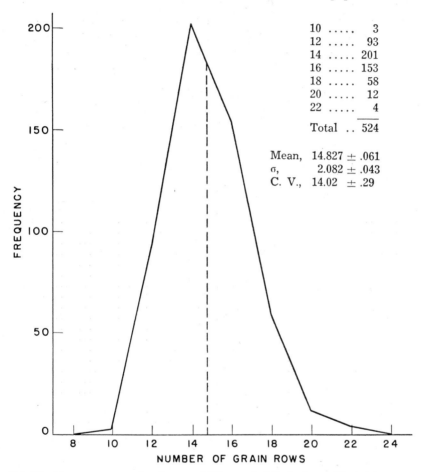

10	3
12	93
14	201
16	153
18	58
20	12
22	4
Total ..	524

Mean, 14.827 ± .061
σ, 2.082 ± .043
C. V., 14.02 ± .29

Fig. 2.1—Frequency curve of grain-rows of 524 ears of white dent corn. The total progeny of presumably a single ear of corn received from the Crotty farm near Topeka, Kansas, and grown at the Station for Experimental Evolution in 1904.

were the 14-rowed with a frequency of 201, and 16-rowed with 153 individual ears. The mean was 14.85 ± .06.

No photograph nor verbal description was made of the parent ear, since there was no intention at the time of its planting to use it in a breeding experiment. But its characteristics must have been accurately duplicated in all of the crossbred families subsequently grown, as well as in most of the F_1 hybrids between the several selfed lines. From each of the grain-row classes, several good ears were saved for planting in the spring of 1905, and the rest was used as horse feed.

The plantings from this material were made on May 25, 26, 27, 1905, again with my own hands, in the form of an ear-row planting. Two ears from each grain-row class of the 1904 crop were used. The seeds were taken from the mid-region of each seed ear. An additional row was planted from grains of each of the two parent ears with 16 grain-rows. Only modified basal grains and modified distal grains for the two halves of the same row in the field were used. In Table 2.1 these cultures from modified grains are indicated by

TABLE 2.1

GRAIN-ROW COUNTS OF PROGENIES GROWN IN 1905 FROM PARENT
EARS SELECTED FOR DIFFERENT NUMBERS OF
GRAIN-ROWS IN NOVEMBER, 1904

CULTURE NUMBERS	PARENTAL GRAIN-ROWS	FREQUENCIES OF PROGENY GRAIN-ROW NUMBERS									
		10	12	14	16	18	20	22	24	26	Totals
A1..........	10 A*	8	55	47	16	3	....	....	....	....	129
A2..........	10 B*	11	50	57	15	1	1	....	....	....	135
A3..........	12 A	12	36	45	10	1	....	....	....	....	104
A4..........	12 B	3	30	43	28	4	....	....	....	....	108
A5..........	14 A	7	32	58	13	5	....	....	....	....	115
A6..........	14 B	1	11	47	26	13	1	1	....	....	100
A7 and 8....	16 A	3	62	81	44	10	....	....	....	....	200
A9 and 10...	16 B	4	31	79	66	14	1	....	....	....	195
A11$_1$........	16 A_b†	3	7	19	7	2	....	....	....	....	38
A11$_2$........	16 A_p†	2	19	18	16	4	....	....	....	....	59
A12$_1$........	16 B_b	3	3	5	8	4	....	....	....	....	23
A12$_2$........	16 B_p	3	5	18	12	11	....	....	....	....	49
A13..........	18 A	....	12	36	39	17	3	1	....	....	108
A14..........	18 A	....	20	33	29	7	....	....	....	....	89
A15..........	20 A	....	3	28	38	14	2	1	....	....	86
A16..........	20 B	1	10	14	28	14	10	2	....	....	79
A17..........	22 A	....	2	9	21	27	19	7	....	....	85
A18..........	22 B	....	3	9	20	28	18	....	2	1	81
A19..........	22 C‡	....	2	12	32	24	16	3	1	1	91
Totals...		61	393	658	468	203	71	15	3	2	1,874

* The significance of the A and B in this column involved the plan to use the A rows for selfing and the B rows to be crossed with mixed pollen of plants in the corresponding A rows.

† The subscript b signifies the use for planting of only the modified basal grains of the given ear; and the subscript p refers to the planting only of modified grains at the "point" or distal end of the ear.

‡ C represents an added row grown to increase the probability of finding ears with still higher numbers of grain-rows.

A_b and B_b for the basal grains, and A_p and B_p for the modified "point" grains. A second row was planted from each of the two chosen ears having 16 grain-rows, and these additional rows (A8 and A10) were detasseled, beginning July 24, 1905, and received pollen from the intact plants in the corresponding rows (A7 and A9) beside them.

In harvesting these two pairs of rows, one detasseled, the other intact, the two rows from the same parent ear, through an oversight, were not kept separate. No further detasseling was done. Since the self-fertilized plants could not be detasseled and still utilized for selfing, the method of controlling cross-fertilization by detasseling would prove a distorting factor in comparing the effects of selfing and crossing.

Consequently, no detasseling was practiced in any of my subsequent experimental work with corn, but every pollination was controlled by bagging with glassine bags and manipulation by hand. The bags were tied in place by ordinary white wrapping-cord passed once around and tied with a loop for easy detachment. Each plant was labeled at the time of crossing with a wired tree-label attached to the stalk at the height of the operator's eyes, and marked with the exact identification of the plant to which it was attached and the source of the pollen which had been applied. On harvesting these hand-pollinated ears, the label was removed from the plant and attached securely to the ear, thus assuring that the ear and its label would remain permanently associated. A third row (A 19) from an ear having 22 grain-rows was added to improve the chances of finding ears with still higher numbers of grain-rows.

In November, 1905, these 19 pedigree cultures were carefully harvested by my own hands and the grain-rows counted, with the results tabulated in Table 2.1.

The only observation noted on these 1905 cultures was that there was no clear indication of mutations or segregations of any kind, but the aspect of the field was that of any ordinarily uniform field of corn. Row counts did show the expected indication of Galtonian regression, in that the parents with low numbers of grain-rows produced progenies having lower numbers of grain-rows than did the ears having higher than average numbers of grain-rows. Thus, the two ears with 10 rows of grains each had the average of 13.2 rows of grains on their progeny ears. The two 20-rowed ears showed an average of 15.5 rows of grains on their progeny ears. The three 22-rowed parent ears produced progenies with an average of 17.5 rows of grains.

The same general plan was followed in 1906, except that the pollen for the crossbred cultures was no longer taken from the plants set aside for selfing. The reason for this change, as specifically stated in my notes written at the end of the 1906 season, being "to avoid the deleterious effects of self-fertilization in the cross-fertilized series." This indicated that at the end of 1906 I had only the concept held by Holden, Shamel, East, and all other corn breeders who had had experience with the selfing of maize—that selfing has deleterious effects, not that crossing has advantageous effects other than the simple avoidance of the deleterious effects of selfing.

The new method of handling the crossbred cultures was to divide each such culture by a marker set at the midpoint of the row. All the plants in these rows were bagged. Mixed pollen from the plants in the first half of the row was collected and applied at the appropriate time to the silks of all the plants in the second half of the row. Then the mixed pollen from the plants in the second half of the row was applied in turn to the silks of all the plants in the first half of the row. It was realized that this still involved a considerable degree of inbreeding, but it seemed about the only way of carrying on a continuing program of crossing while still keeping the breeding completely under the operator's control.

Two major observations made on the 1906 crop were: (1) that every one of the seven families from selfed parents could be readily detected by their less height, more slender stalks, and greater susceptibility to the attack of *Ustilago maydis*. When the ears were harvested each lot was weighed and it was found that cross-fertilized rows produced on an average about three times as much grain as the self-fertilized. (2) The family A3, from a self-fertilized ear having 12 grain-rows, was practically all flint corn, showing that to be probably recessive. This occurrence of a rather obvious segregation in the 1906 crop remained at the end of the season only an isolated observation which led to no generalization. From the fall of 1905 until his retirement in 1943, Charles Leo Macy assisted me in many of the technical details of my experimental cultures. While I handled the planning and breeding operations as well as the actual pollinations, Macy prepared the plants for selfing and crossing, and counted the grain-rows and weighed the ear corn. The results of these counts for the 1906 crop are given in Table 2.2.

The following quotation from my notebook seems justified here, since it includes the first formulation of the considerations and conclusions which appeared in my report to the American Breeders' Association in 1908, on "The composition of a field of maize":

The same plan was continued, (in 1907 as in 1906), namely each self-fertilized row was the offspring of a single self-fertilized ear, and each cross-fertilized row was divided in half, each half coming from a single cross-fertilized ear, one ear in each such case coming from the first half of the corresponding row of the preceding year, the other ear coming from the second half. . . .

The obvious results were the same as in 1906, the self-fertilized rows being invariably smaller and weaker than the corresponding cross-fertilized. Ustilago is again much more in evidence on the self-fertilized. A very different explanation of the facts is forced upon me by the fact that the several self-fertilized rows differ from each other in a number of striking morphological characteristics, thus indicating that they belong to distinct elementary strains. The same point appeared last year in the case of the 12-row class which came almost a uniform flint corn, but the significance of this was not recognized at that time. It now appears that self-fertilization simply serves to purify the strains, and that my comparisons are not properly between cross- and self-fertilization, but between pure strains and their hybrids; and that a well regulated field of corn is a mass of very complex hybrids.

It may also be assumed that correct field practice in the breeding of corn must have as its object the maintenance of such hybrid combinations as prove to be most vigorous and productive and give all desirable qualities of ear and grain.

The ideas in this quotation represent a discovery in complete disagreement with my preconception that my white dent foundation stock, which had been the progeny of a single ear, was essentially a genetically pure strain. I had before me seven distinct biotypes, clearly distinguishable in their several morphological characteristics. They had been derived from seven separate self-pollinations of sibs in a family which I had reason to think was genetically homogeneous. This could not fail to make a great impression. Had these several pure-bred self-fertilized strains come from different breeders and from more or less disconnected experiments, as did the selfed

TABLE 2.2

GRAIN-ROW COUNTS AND YIELDS OF EAR CORN IN CULTURES OF WHITE DENT MAIZE GROWN AT THE STATION FOR EXPERIMENTAL EVOLUTION IN 1906

Culture Numbers	Parental Grain-Rows	Frequencies of Progeny Grain-Row Numbers													Totals	Weights Lbs. Av.	Yield Bu./A.
		8	10	12	14	16	18	20	22	24	26	28	30	32			
A1.1	10 selfed	4	36	62	14	1									117		
$A2.2_1$	10 crossed		3	32	25	7	1								68		
$A2.2_2$	10 crossed			2	26	29	11	1							69		
A3.3	12 selfed	5	13	40	19	4	1								82	21.6	37.7
$A4.4_1$	12 crossed			13	26	12	6	1							58	65.8	78.9
$A4.4_2$	12 crossed		1	16	34	9	1								61		
A5.5	14 selfed			12	41	34	15	4	1						107	33.6	44.9
$A6.6_1$	14 crossed			6	28	18	7								59	61.3	74.5
$A6.6_2$	14 crossed			6	17	19	12	4							58		
A7.7	16 selfed			8	17	28	17	4							74	29.6	59.1
$A9.8_1$	16 crossed			14	16	15	1	1							47	58.3	77.1
$A9.8_2$	16 crossed			5	16	28	11	1							61		
A19.9	16(22)×10			8	23	22	11	5	1	1					71	22.1	44.5
$A12_1.10_1$	16_b crossed			9	28	20	3								60		
$A12_2.10_2$	16_p crossed		1	20	23	15	4								63		
$A11_1$/$A12_1$ 11_1	16_p crossed			7	39	18	9	1							74		
$A11_1$/$A12_2$ 11_2	16_b crossed			10	22	18	5	2							57		
A13.12	18 selfed			2	8	6	5	3	2						26	9.6	52.9
A14.13	18 open-pol.				16	29	18	19	9	1	1	1			94	58.3	88.5
A15.14	20 selfed			6	11	23	18	10	4						72	23.6	46.9
$A16.15_1$	20 crossed				2	8	21	13	5	1					50	56.3	75.1
$A16.15_2$	20 crossed				3	17	20	13	4						57		
A17.16	22 selfed				1	4	10	17	13	7	3				55	24.1	62.4
A18.17	24 crossed				1	4	11	25	24	18	3	4	1		91	57.3	89.9
A19.18	24 open-pol.		1		3	12	14	17	11	6	2				66	32.6	70.6
A19.19	26 open-pol.					1	8	11	17	6	10	7			60	34.6	82.4
A18.20	26 open-pol.					5	9	14	19	13	5	1	1	1	68	40.6	85.4
A16.21	18 crossed				1	5	17	25	21	7	2				78		
A19.22	18(22)×10			16	29	20	6	1							72		
A19.23	14(22)×10		1	11	31	22	26	1							92	46.1	71.6
Totals		9	58	334	543	469	323	183	89	36	17	3	2	1	2,067		

lines available to Dr. East, the observation that they showed themselves to be genetically distinguishable biotypes would have given no cause for the special conclusions I drew from them. It would have been strange, indeed, if strains thus derived from heterogeneous sources had not been genetically different, one from another.

Comparison of the results for 1907, presented in Table 2.3, with those for 1906 in Table 2.2, shows a heavy accentuation of grain-row classes 8 and 10 and a marked decrease in classes 18 to 20, inclusive. There was also a significant increase in all higher classes, with further extension of the range from a maximum of 32 to about 40. The increase in the frequencies of the low grain-row classes was attributed in part to the fact that the 1907 season had seemed less favorable in general than 1906.

It was also noted, as a possible contributory condition, that this was the third season in which this corn was grown on the same area north of the laboratory building, and that "the yield may have been lessened by the gradual accumulation of injurious substances in the soil." The fact that the

Fig. 2.2—Young corn cultures growing in East Garden of the Station for Experimental Evolution in 1911, illustrating that no two were alike despite their descent from a single ear of 1904 by meticulously controlled pollinations that precluded the introduction of pollen from any other strain of corn.

average grain-row numbers were not significantly different in the two years— 15.8 in 1906, 16.0 in 1907—in fact a trifle higher in what was thought to have been the poorer year, does not seem to support these suggested explanations of the observed differences of distribution in the two years.

My contemporaneous notes proposed an additional explanation, namely, that "each successive generation of close inbreeding still further reduces the strains to their simple constituent biotypes, and as these are weaker than hybrid combinations, this too would tend to lessen the vigor, and this lessened vigor might readily be evidenced by a decrease in the average number of [grain-]rows and the total number of ears in the crop."

If we accept this latter suggestion as valid, it is clear that the occurrence of essentially the same average numbers of grain-rows in the two years gives only a specious indication of the relative climatic and soil effectiveness in these two seasons. It must mean simply that the diminution of grain-row numbers produced by increasing homozygosity happened to be balanced by the increased frequencies in the higher classes, produced by the gradual accumulation by selection of more potent hybrid combinations.

TABLE 2.3

GRAIN-ROW COUNTS AND HEIGHTS OF PLANTS IN
THE CULTURES OF 1907

Pedigree Numbers	Grain-Rows of Parents	Frequencies of Progeny Grain-Row Numbers																	Totals	Av. Ht. in Ft.
		8	10	12	14	16	18	20	22	24	26	28	30	32	34	36	38	40		
B1.1	10 selfed	20	25	20	2	1													68	7.25
B2₁.2₁	10 crossed	2	22	21	5														50	9.00
B2₂.2₂	10 crossed	6	28	18	5														57	
B1.3	8 selfed	23	48	17															88	7.63
B3.4	12 selfed	10	21	18	4	1													54	6.25
B4₁.5₁	12 crossed		1	16	19	13	3												52	8.00
B4₂.5₂	12 crossed	1		7	14	14	7	1											44	
B5.6	14 selfed		4	23	29	15	1	1											73	8.50
B6₁.7₁	14 crossed			5	15	19	7	1	1										48	9.67
B6₂.7₂	14 crossed			5	18	19	7	1	1										43	
B7.8	16 selfed			1	19	26	9												55	8.25
B8₁.9₁	16 crossed				2	8	14	7	3	3									37	8.75
B8₂.9₂	16 crossed					9	15	9	3										36	
B10₂.10₁	16 crossed				6	13	10	1	1										31	8.67
B10₁.10₂	16 crossed				11	15	9	1	1										37	
B12.11	18 selfed					5	7	1	2										15	7.00
B13.12	18 open-pol.				9	21	22	15	3	1									71	8.33
B14.13	20 selfed				5	8	21	11	6	1									52	7.25
B15₁.14₁	20 crossed				1	3	16	18	13	10	2								63	8.83
B15₂.14₂	20 crossed					4	10	13	16	8	1								52	
B16.15	22 selfed						6	9	17	8	5								45	7.00
B17.16	22 crossed					1	9	17	17	11	4	3	1						63	8.67
B15.17	20 crossed					1	7	22	17	11	4								62	8.83
B19.18	24 crossed						1	7	16	14	5	4	3						50	9.50
B20.19	32 open-pol.				3	6	8	8	7	4	2	2		1					41	9.50
B?.20	Branched ear				1	6	9	13	8	1	1								58	8.33
B17.21	30 open-pol.					2	5	12	17	11	9	1			1				58	8.33
B?.22	Branched ear					3	14	17	12	3									49	
B15.23	16 selfed					5	14	15	17	6	3	4							64	
B20.24	24 selfed						5	5	7	7	6	6							36	8.00
B20.25	26 selfed						3	2	2			1	2		1			1	12	7.83
Totals		62	150	204	236	282	228	189	108	49	22	6	3	3	1	1		1	1,545	

A truer measure of the relative favorableness of the two seasons for growth and productiveness of these cultures can be derived from a study of the middle classes with 12, 14, 16, and 18 grain-rows. These grain-row classes making up 80 per cent of the 1906 crop and 61.5 per cent of the 1907 crop, must be relatively free from most of the distortion assumed to be produced either by increasing homozygosity or by the accumulation of the more potent hybrid combinations. If we average these four grain-row classes by themselves for the two years, we find that in 1906 their average was 15.5 grain-rows, and for 1907 only 15.0, thus agreeing with my general impression that 1907 was the less favorable year.

With the fundamental change in my understanding of the nature of my corn population came a reorientation of the experiment. I found myself at the end of 1907 only ready to make a beginning on the problems of the relationship between pure lines and their hybrids, which I now saw was the crucial field that needed exploration.

As a first step in that direction, but without as yet a full comprehension of its importance, I made in July, 1907, pollinations between plants of C4, which I later designated "Strain A," and a plant of C6, which later became my "Strain B." I also made two sib crosses within these two strains. The cross of Strain A × Strain B, which gave rise in 1908 to F_1 family, D9, involved an 8-rowed ear of the former strain (from an original selection for 12 grain-rows) and a 12-rowed ear of Strain B which had originated in a selection for 14 grain-rows. The near-reciprocal cross (F_1 family, D13) resulted from the application of pollen from a 12-rowed plant of Strain A to silks of the same plant of Strain B, which supplied the pollen for the near-reciprocal cross.

At the time when these two near-reciprocal crosses were made between Strains A and B, the truth had not yet dawned upon me that I should do the same with all of my other selfed families. Aside from these two sets of crosses, the handling of the cultures was the same as in previous years. The results of the grain-row counts are given in Table 2.4. Unfortunately, there was considerable damage from crows, and failures to germinate for unknown reasons. The missing hills were replanted on June 8, 1908, and all of the new plantings made on this date seem to have reached maturity. To overcome the suggested deteriorating effect of soil depletion, the cultures were grown this year on the area east of the laboratory building (occasionally referred to in subsequent notes as "East Garden").

In summarizing the results for the year 1908, it may be noted first that the tendency to concentrate the frequencies of the grain-rows in the extremes of the range, at the expense of those in the middle, has continued strongly. As before, the most noteworthy concentration is at the lower extreme. All classes below 16 are considerably stronger in 1908 than in 1907 and the maximum frequency is now on 12 instead of 16. This is in part due to the fact that several of the lower-class families were grown in duplicate. Between classes 14 and 26 the relative strength of the classes was lessened in 1908. Above class 24 the frequencies were increased, there being 84 ears above class 24 in 1908 and only the equivalent of about 50 in the same region in 1907, when raised to the same total number. The highest number of grain-rows noted was 42.

The important new features brought in by the near-reciprocal crosses between Strain A and Strain B and a sib cross in Strain A are presented in my report to the American Breeders' Association at Columbia, Mo., in January, 1909, on "A pure line method in corn breeding." I find a discrepancy in that the 78 ears produced by the sib cross weighed only 16.25 pounds instead of 16.5, as stated in my 1909 paper. Whether by an oversight or intentionally,

I cannot now determine, the corresponding sib crosses in Strain B were not included in my 1909 report. The results were essentially the same as were reported for the sib cross in Strain A. Selfed Strain B (see Table 2.4, family C6.11) showed average heights of plants 2.3 meters, and yielded 66 ears weighing 13.0 pounds. The two sib crosses produced plants 2.5 meters tall and yielded 89 ears weighing 28.5 pounds. Distribution of the grain-row frequencies was closely similar in selfed and in sib-crossed Strain B, but significantly higher in the latter:

					Totals	Averages
Grain-rows..............	10	12	14	16	18	
Selfed...................	2	20	26	17	1	66	13.8
Sib-crossed.............	3	15	45	18	8	89	14.2

There was abundant evidence that the sib crosses showed a greatly restricted advantage over self-fertilization. It was also clearly indicated that

TABLE 2.4

GRAIN-ROW COUNTS, HEIGHTS, AND YIELDS OF
WHITE DENT MAIZE GROWN IN 1908

Pedigree Numbers	Grain-Rows of Parents	Frequencies of Progeny Grain-Row Numbers																		Totals	Av. Hts. in Dm.	Wts. in Lbs.	Yield Bu./A.
		8	10	12	14	16	18	20	22	24	26	28	30	32	34	36	38	40	42				
C3.1	10 selfed	52	39	13																104	19.5	31.5	43.3
C1.2	8 selfed	51	41	2																94	19.7	22.0	33.4
C2$_1$.3$_1$	8 crossed	6	29	14	2															51	23.4	25.0	70.7
C2$_2$.3$_2$	8 crossed	6	22	12	1	1														42		21.0	
C1.4	10 selfed	28	48	12	2															90	18.0	22.0	30.5
C2$_1$.5$_1$	10 crossed	9	32	9																50	21.5	20.8	59.8
C2$_2$.5$_2$	10 crossed	12	18	3																33		14.0	
C4.6	12 selfed	11	41	32	5															89	17.0	28.0	44.9
C4.7	10×sib	8	50	19	1															78	16.5	16.3	29.8
C4.8	8 selfed	65	6	2																73	16.5	12.0	23.5
C4.9	8×12		19	64	9															92	24.0	48.0	74.5
C5$_1$.10$_1$	12 crossed	2	9	31	15	1	1													59	24.5	34.8	84.1
C5$_2$.10$_2$	14 crossed	1	9	17	14	1														42	22.5	23.3	79.1
C6.11	14 selfed		2	20	26	17	1													66	23.0	13.0	28.1
C6.12$_1$	16×sib		2	4	25	11	5													47	25.0	16.8	50.9
C6.12$_2$	12×sib		1	11	20	7	3													42	25.0	11.8	40.0
C6.13	12×12	1	5	56	31	6	1													100	26.0	55.0	78.6
C7$_1$.14$_1$	14 crossed			18	28	11	2													59	25.0	30.0	72.6
C7$_2$.14$_2$	14 crossed		11	9	18	3	2													43	27.0	19.3	64.0
C8.15	16 selfed		1	31	32	28	1	1												94	24.4	31.5	47.9
C9$_1$.16$_1$	16 crossed			4	14	25	11		1											55	26.8	31.5	64.0
C9$_2$.16$_2$	16 crossed			6	18	13	4													41	25.2	20.0	69.7
C13.17	18 selfed			6	10	34	21	6												77	19.3	16.5	30.6
C12$_1$.18$_1$	18 crossed		1	6	20	16	12	1												56	23.5	31.3	79.7
C12$_2$.18$_2$	18 crossed		1	8	19	14	4													46	25.5	28.3	87.7
C13.19	20 selfed			2	15	39	23	6												85	21.6	23.0	38.7
C14$_1$.20$_1$	20 crossed				3	4	15	19	7	8	2									58	*	31.0	76.4
C14$_2$.20$_2$	20 crossed				2	6	17	10	11											46		24.5	79.2
C15.21	20 selfed				13	17	19	18	3											70		20.5	41.8
C16$_1$.22	22 crossed				3	9	20	24	13	10	4	1								84		48.3	82.1
C24.23	22 selfed				2	9	22	26	25	19	21									92		33.8	52.4
C18.24	28 crossed					3	4	21	16	24	7	3	1	3	1					83		43.3	74.4
C25.25	36? selfed	Grain-rows too difficult to count; silks shorter than husks.																					
C19.26	28(?)×26(?)						1	2	5	10	10	16	18	5	6	9	3		1	86		50.5	83.9
C22.27	Branched ear open-pol.			1	11	14	19	16	14	4	2	2								83		50.0	86.2
C22.28	20 open-pol.†			1	9	20	31	22	7	3										93		51.8	79.5
Totals		252	387	415	375	323	244	172	91	60	31	24	6	9	10	3			1	2,403			

* The remaining nine rows were not measured and described, "for lack of time."

† This plant carried four ears with 14, 14,16, and 20 rows of grains, of which only the twenty-rowed ear was used for planting.

Fig. 2.3—Vegetative habits of Strain A (*right*) and Strain B, drawn by J. Marion Shull from a photograph taken in the summer of 1908. At upper right typical ears of these two strains (*Strain A at right*) and between them their reciprocal F₁ hybrids, each hybrid standing nearest to its mother type.

if the advantage consisted solely of the effects of heterozygosity, both Strain A and Strain B were still a good way from being homozygous, Strain B being as yet more effectively heterozygous than Strain A.

In the reciprocal crosses between these nearly homozygous strains A and B, we have our first opportunity to arrive at an approximation to the actual amount of heterosis. The most important new discoveries these crosses made possible were: (1) As a result of such a cross it is possible to completely cancel in a single year the accumulated deterioration which had gradually accrued, although with lessening annual increments, over a period of several years; and (2) the approximate identity of the results of the reciprocal crosses gave assurance that the amount of heterosis resulting from a given hybridization is a specific function of the particular genetical combination involved in the cross.

Several new cultures of yellow- and red-grained corn were added to my experimental field in 1908, but these will not be followed here. They are mentioned only because they were included in my numbered pedigrees, and their omission in the following tables leaves a break in the series of numbered families which might lead to some question as to the reason for the apparent vacancies. The data from the 1909 cultures of white dent corn are presented in Table 2.5.

The families grown in 1909, as tabulated in Table 2.5, fall into three major classes: (1) Twelve families involve continuations of the original self-fertilized lines, whose average yields range from 18.8 to 41.2 bushels per acre, with the average for all twelve at 32.8 bushels per acre; (2) Twelve are continuations of crossbred families in which strictly controlled cross-fertilizations were made with mixtures of pollen taken from the other plants in the same crossbred strain. These yielded from 58.1 to 83.3 bushels per acre with the average of all at 73.3 bushels per acre; and (3) there were fourteen F_1 hybrid families from crosses between pairs of individuals representing two different selfed lines. The yields of these range from 60.3 to 87.5 bushels per acre, the average for all fourteen being 78.6 bushels per acre. As stated in my 1910 paper, the three highest yields of any of these cultures were from the families produced by crossing representatives of different selfed strains (see D8.13, D8.16, and D11.21).

Besides these, there were two cousin crosses involving matings between different families of the same selfed line. These produced, respectively, 27.1 and 44.6 bushels per acre. One cross between two sibs in Strain A gave 26.0 bushels per acre. The other cross was two F_2 families, each from crosses with mixed pollen within one of the F_1 families of my 1908 cultures. These F_2 families yielded 54.2 bushels per acre from the $(A \times B)F_2$, and 70.6 from the $(B \times A)F_2$. These yields should be compared with those of the corresponding F_1 families grown in the same season, in which $(A \times B)F_1$ yielded 74.9 and 83.5 bushels in two different families, and $(B \times A)F_1$ produced 82.6 bushels per acre.

In 1910 I was absent from the Station for Experimental Evolution during the entire summer and my experiments with corn, evening primroses, Lychnis, etc., were continued by an assistant, R. Catlin Rose, assisted by Mr. Macy, who carried out the operations meticulously described by myself in more than one thousand typewritten lines of detailed instructions.

The data on the white dent corn grown in 1910 are presented here in

TABLE 2.5

GRAIN-ROW COUNTS, HEIGHTS OF STALKS, AND YIELDS OF EARS OF WHITE DENT CORN IN 1909

Pedigree Numbers	Grain-Rows of Parents	Frequencies of Progeny Grain-Row Numbers																	Totals	Hts. in Dms.	Wts. in Lbs.	Yield Bu./A.
		8	10	12	14	16	18	20	22	24	26	28	30	32	34	36	38	40				
D1.1	8 selfed	21	51	30															102	18	24.0	53.0
D2.2	8 selfed	29	70	6															105	20	24.8	33.7
D3₁.3₁	8 crossed	18	25	12															55	21	21.0	59.2
D3₂.3₂	8 crossed	8	39	3															50	22	22.5	
D4.4	10×12	30	55	21															106	20	44.8	60.3
D4.5	10×14		8	44	11														63	24	35.3	80.0
D4.6	10×sib	10	53	32	1														96	17	17.5	26.0
D4.7	10 selfed	7	32	55	4														98	19	25.0	56.4
D5₁.8₁	10 crossed	3	23	17	1														44	24	17.3	59.7
D5₂.8₂	10 crossed	4	22	15															41	24	18.3	
D6.9	12 selfed	5	50	35	4														94	18	23.5	35.7
D7.10₁	12×cousins	1	31	18															50	19	9.5	27.1
D7.10₂	12×cousins	3	29	20	1														53	19	10.3	27.6
D8.11	A selfed	66	5	3															74	17	9.8	18.8
D8.12	A×20			4	40	45	9												96	24	54.0	80.4
D8.13	A×22			1	44	50	7												102	26	60.0	84.0
D8.14₁	A×B			2	18	9	2												31	24	16.3	74.9
D8.14₂	A×20				21	33	5	1											60	26	29.8	70.8
D8.15	A×16	1	1	74	32	7													115	28	61.3	76.2
D8.16	A×B	2	8	71	5														86	27	50.3	83.5
D9.17	(A×B)F₁ sibs	3	32	57	11	2	3												108	25	41.0	54.2
D10₁.18₁	12 crossed	2	5	28	16														51	25	29.5	83.3
D10₂.18₂	12 crossed		5	25	17	3	1												51	23	30.0	
D11.19	B selfed			10	18	12													40	26	7.3	25.9
D11.20	B×A		19	58	9														86	28	49.8	82.6
D11.21	B×20			6	20	38	15	1											80	28	49.0	87.5
D13.22	(B×A)F₁ sibs			1	26	40	15	2											84	27	41.5	70.6
D14₁.23₁	14 crossed			2	13	23	10												48	28	23.8	71.4
D14₂.23₂	14 crossed			14	18	8	1												41	29	20.8	
D15.24	16 selfed			1	25	51	4												81	24	21.0	37.0
D16₁.25₁	16 crossed				2	11	9	8	4	1									35	25	22.5	80.0
D16₂.25₂	16 crossed				4	19	19	6											48	26	24.0	
D17.26	18 selfed				2	14	42	15											73	20	17.3	33.8
D17.27	20×16				1	4	27	43	18	3									96	27	53.8	80.0
D17.28	20×A	1				16	46	22											85	24	46.0	77.3
D17.29	16×cousin				3	9	19	4	1										36	23	11.3	44.6
D18₁.30₁	18 crossed				5	18	17	5	1		1								47	28	26.0	79.4
D18₂.30₂	18 crossed				5	18	23	4	1										51	28	28.5	
D19.31	20 selfed					2	14	36	27	8									87	24	33.3	33.3
D19.32	20×16				1	12	54	36	9	1									113	28	63.3	80.0
D20₁.33₁	20 crossed					2	12	23	8	5	2								52	30	29.0	76.5
D20₂.33₂	20 crossed					5	19	21	14	7	1								67	29	34.8	
D21.34	22 selfed						4	30	41	12	4								91	26	25.3	39.6
D22.35₁	22 crossed							5	12	11	4								32	25	17.5	83.2
D22.35₂	22 crossed			1	6	5	8	10	8	2	1	2	1						44	27	26.8	
D23.36	24 selfed					5	22	36	16	12	5	1							97	23	28.0	41.3
D24.37₁	24 crossed							2	10	7	11	3	1						34	27	14.8	71.4
D24.37₂	24 crossed							2	5	3	7	2	2						21	27	12.8	
D25.39	30 selfed							2	1	4	12	14	9	11	4	4	3	4	68	25	11.5	24.2
D26.40₁	28 crossed						3	4	5	4	7	8	5	3					39	29	14.3	58.1
D26.40₂	28 crossed					2	2	4	4	6	7	8	5	3	1	2			44	28	19.5	
D27.41	22 crossed				5	23	31	27	11	2		1							100	29	37.3	81.8
D28.42	24 crossed				3	18	22	28	21	7	4		1						104	29	53.5	73.5
Totals		214	570	846	588	497	341	261	123	73	48	36	24	16	5	6	3	4	3655			

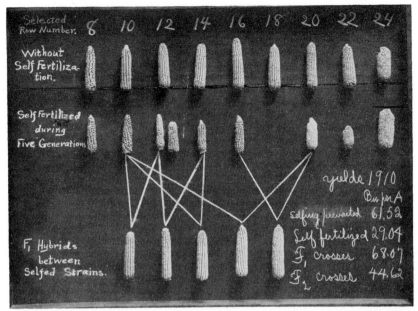

FIG. 2.4—An exhibit set up in the Genetics Department of Cornell University in 1910, displaying materials grown at the Station for Experimental Evolution in 1909.

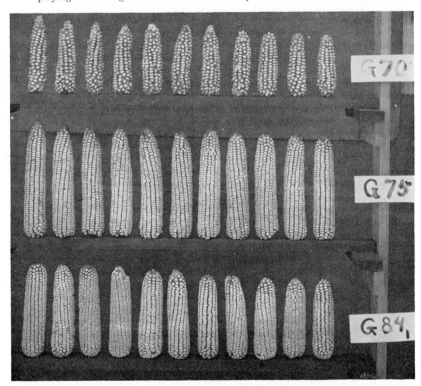

FIG. 2.5—The best eleven ears of the highest-yielding selfed line (F 29.70 in Table 2.7) grown in 1911 (*top row*); the best eleven ears of the best F_1 hybrid grown in the same year (F 32.75 in Table 2.7); and the best eleven ears of a crossbred strain (F 55.84 in Table 2.7) in which selfing was completely prevented during five years. This shows the relative variability which is characteristic of these three types of families, the F_1 being no more variable than the inbred, while the crossbred is quite noticeably more variable.

summary form. Some 73 ears were selected for planting, and 5,343 ears were harvested. The complete grain-row distribution was as follows:

Grain-rows.....	8	10	12	14	16	18	20	22	24	26	28	30	32	34	36	38	40	42	Total
Frequencies....	401	812	1271	921	716	476	275	141	118	74	53	41	24	8	6	4	1	1	5343
Percentages....	7.5	15.2	23.8	17.2	13.4	8.9	5.2	2.6	2.2	1.4	1.0	0.8	0.5	0.2	0.1	0.1	0.0	0.0	100.0

To save space and still indicate as completely as possible the significant results of these studies in 1910, the data from the several kinds of families of white dent corn grown at the Station for Experimental Evolution that year are presented in the form of averages in Table 2.6. The several quantitative indicators of physiological vigor, namely, the average number of grain-rows, heights of stalks, and bushels of ear-corn per acre, can be readily compared as follows:

Types of Families	No. of Families	Av. No. of Grain-Rows	Av. Heights in Dms.	Av. Yields in Bu./A.
Inbreds selfed............	10	12.6	19.3	25.0
Inbreds×sibs............	8	13.7	19.8	28.7
Crossbreds..............	11	16.9	23.5	63.5
F_1 between inbreds.......	6	15.2	25.7	71.4
F_2 from F_1 selfed.........	11	13.3	23.3	42.6
F_2 from F_1×sibs.........	11	13.5	23.1	47.9

Six interesting comparisons can be made among these summaries: (1) comparisons between inbreds selfed and inbreds crossed with pollen from one or more of their sibs; (2) comparisons between inbreds and crossbreds in which selfing has been completely prevented, but which still represent a (fairly low) degree of inbreeding; (3) comparisons between inbreds and their F_1 hybrids; (4) comparisons between the crossbreds in which selfing has been prevented through six generations and the F_1 hybrids in which five successive generations of selfing have been succeeded by a single cross; (5) comparisons between the F_1 and the F_2 hybrids of the inbreds; and (6) comparisons between F_2 hybrid families produced by selfing the F_1 and those F_2 families produced by sibcrosses in the F_1.

On making these comparisons we see that the evidence for residual heterozygosity in the inbreds is indicated by excesses in the sibcrossed families of the inbreds over the selfed inbreds of 8.7 per cent in grain-row number, 2.8 per cent in heights of stalks, and 14.7 per cent in yield of ear-corn. In the F_2 families (sections E and F, of Table 2.6) those produced from sibcrosses in the F_1 surpass those families produced from selfings in the F_1 by 0.9 per cent in grain-row number and 12.5 per cent in yield.

The average heights of stalks reverse the expectation by showing an insignificantly less height from the sibcrossed matings than from the selfings, the difference being 0.9 per cent. The contrast between the results of six successive selfings and the continued prevention of selfing for the same six

TABLE 2.6

AVERAGE VALUES IN THE FAMILIES OF WHITE DENT MAIZE GROWN IN 1910, GROUPED ACCORDING TO THE TYPES OF MATING OF THE PARENTS

Pedigree Numbers	Parental Grain-Rows	Number of Stalks	Av. No. of Grain-Rows	Heights in Dms.	Wts. in Lbs. Av.	Yields Bu./A.
(A) Families from Inbreds Selfed						
E1.16........	8 selfed	57	10.0	17	9.8	24.4
E2.19........	8 selfed	83	9.0	18	22.0	39.6
E7.29........	10 selfed	79	11.1	20	18.3	33.9
E9.32........	12 selfed	80	12.3	17	11.4	20.9
E11.34.......	A(8) selfed	75	8.8	16.5	9.1	18.1
E19.47.......	B(14) selfed	53	12.9	24	7.3	11.0
E24.54.......	14 selfed	66	13.8	23	16.3	25.8
E26.56.......	18 selfed	82	15.2	19	15.3	22.9
E34.67.......	22 selfed	62	17.9	19	11.0	19.2
E36.71.......	26, 28 selfed	72	15.2	19	17.5	34.2
Unweighted averages		71	12.6	19.3	10.7	25.0
(B) Families from Inbreds Pollinated by Sibs; Selfing Prevented						
E1.17........	10×sibs	61	10.2	19	13.8	29.8
E2.20........	10×sib	75	9.9	18	21.0	39.5
E7.30........	12×sib	85	11.0	22	18.3	37.3
E11.35.......	A(8)×sib	55	9.5	16	7.5	16.0
E19.48.......	B(12)×sib	54	12.7	24	5.3	7.8
E26.57.......	18×sib	89	15.8	20	24.5	37.8
E34.68.......	20×sib	65	17.9	20	15.3	25.6
E36.72.......	?(fasc.)×sib	73	22.5	20	18.3	35.2
Unweighted averages		61	13.7	19.8	15.5	28.7
(C) Families from Parents Given Mixed Pollen in Each Generation; Selfing Prevented						
E3.23........	8, 10 crossbred	88	9.5	22	30.8	49.9
E8.31........	10 crossed	65	10.3	22	31.0	68.1
E18.46.......	12 crossed	91	13.2	24	51.0	80.1
E23.53.......	14 crossed	94	13.7	27	49.0	74.5
E25.55.......	16 crossed	95	14.9	28	48.8	73.3
E30.63.......	18 crossed	202	16.0	22.5	76.8	54.3
E33.66.......	20 crossed	100	18.5	23	35.8	51.1
E35.70.......	20, 22 crossed	45	20.0	21	26.3	83.3
E37.73.......	24, 20 crossed	69	24.2	22	24.5	50.7
E40.75.......	32 crossed	56	19.2	24	22.5	57.4
E40.76.......	32 crossed	99	26.2	23	39.0	56.3
Unweighted averages		91.3	16.9	23.5	39.6	63.5

TABLE 2.6—*Continued*

Pedigree Numbers	Parental Grain-Rows	Number of Stalks	Av. No. of Grain-Rows	Heights in Dms.	Wts. in Lbs. Av.	Yields Bu./A.
(D) F₁ Hybrids between Different Inbred Lines					
E2.21.........	A(10)×16	95	13.8	24	50.3	75.6
E2.22.........	A(10)×B	94	12.8	28	50.0	76.0
E11.36........	A(8)×10	95	11.0	25	33.5	51.5
E11.37........	A(8)×B	84	12.3	25	28.5	48.5
E26.58........	18×14	109	17.8	27	60.8	79.6
E34.69........	18×26±(fasc.)	92	23.3	25	62.5	97.1
Unweighted averages		93	15.2	25.7	47.6	71.4
(E) F₂ Families from F₁×Self					
E4.24.........	(10×A)F₁ selfed	86	10.6	21	30.8	51.1
E5.26.........	(10×14)F₁ selfed	86	12.1	22	29.8	49.4
E12.38........	(A×20)F₁ selfed	76	13.9	19.5	20.5	38.5
E13.40........	(A×22)F₁ selfed	83	12.8	24	18.8	31.4
E15.42........	(A×16)F₁ selfed	94	12.8	25	33.5	50.9
E16.44........	(A×B)F₁ selfed	96	12.0	25	24.0	35.7
E20.49........	(B×A)F₁ selfed	95	11.7	24	25.3	38.0
E21.51........	(B×20)F₁ selfed	92	15.1	25	28.0	43.5
E27.59........	(20×16)F₁ selfed	97	16.6	25	35.3	51.9
E28.61........	(20×A)F₁ selfed	95	13.0	22	22.0	33.1
E32.64........	(20×16)F₁ selfed	93	15.9	24	29.5	45.3
Unweighted averages		90.3	13.3	23.3	27.0	42.6
(F) F₂ Families from F₁×Sibs					
E4.25.........	(10×12)F₁×sibs	85	10.7	21	31.3	52.5
E5.27.........	(10×14)F₁×sibs	83	12.2	22	35.0	60.2
E12.39........	(A×20)F₁×sibs	80	14.2	21	28.8	51.3
E13.41........	(A×22)F₁×sibs	96	13.4	25	27.0	40.2
E15.43........	(A×16)F₁×sibs	95	12.3	23	37.3	56.0
E16.45........	(A×B)F₁×sibs	93	11.8	24	21.0	32.3
E20.50........	(B×A)F₁×sibs	80	11.6	24	23.5	42.0
E21.52........	(B×20)F₁×sibs	93	15.5	25	31.8	48.8
E27.60........	(20×16)F₁×sibs	89	17.2	25	37.3	59.8
E28.62........	(20×A)F₁×sibs	92	13.7	23	30.0	46.6
E32.65........	(20×16)F₁×sibs	97	15.4	21	25.3	37.6
Unweighted averages		89.4	13.5	23.1	29.8	47.9

years (sections A and C, Table 2.6) shows the latter in excess of the former by 34.0 per cent in grain-row number, 22.1 per cent in height of stalks, and 154.2 per cent in per acre yields of ears. The superiority of the F_1 hybrids between different inbreds and the families in which selfing had been prevented during six generations of controlled breeding (sections D and C, Table 2.6), is indicated by an excess in heights of stalks of the F_1 families over the crossbreds, of 9.4 per cent, and in yields of ear-corn per acre of 12.3 per cent. But here there is a notable reversal in grain-row numbers. Notwithstanding these proofs of the superior vigor of the F_1's over the crossbreds, the latter exceed the former in grain-row number by 10.8 per cent.

The reason for this reversal is easily recognized when we consider that parents were selected in these studies for their grain-row numbers, with no noticeable selection for heights and yields. In section D of Table 2.6, we note that only one parent of any of the F_1 families had a grain-row number in excess of 18. The crossbred families ranged in parental grain-row numbers from 8 to 32. Five of the families came from parents having more than 18 rows of grains.

To make a fair comparison between the two types of breeding in their relation to grain-row number, it is necessary to use only the crossbred families having parents with no more than 18 grain-rows. When we make such a limitation, we find the average grain-row number for the remaining six crossbred families is only 12.9. The grain-row average for the six F_1 families, namely, 15.2, exceeds the crossbreds by 17.1 per cent. Limiting the other indicators of physiological vigor to the same six crossbred families, we find that the F_1's exceed the corresponding crossbreds on the average by 6.3 per cent in height of stalks and 7.0 per cent in yield of ear-corn.

In 1911 I was again in full personal charge of the corn experiments at the Station for Experimental Evolution, and was able to expand the work considerably, both quantitatively and in the types of matings studied. We planted 84 cultures in the white dent series as well as 25 cultures of other types of corn. The total number of white dent ears of which the grain-rows were counted was 6,508 which showed the following frequencies:

Grain-rows	8	10	12	14	16	18	20	22	24	26	28	30	32	34	36	Total
Frequencies	267	767	1725	1298	931	683	363	164	114	95	65	23	7	3	3	6508
Percentages	4.1	11.8	26.5	19.9	14.3	10.5	5.6	2.5	1.8	1.5	0.9	0.4	0.1	0.1	0.1	99.9

In Table 2.7 the 1911 results are presented in condensed form. Families are grouped in eleven sections representing fairly homogeneous groups, mostly based on the types of matings involved. Sections D and E are both made up of the same five families of F_2 hybrids produced by selfing the same number of different F_1's. For these families each seed ear was used to plant two rows. The one row of each such family was grown with the other cultures, as usual, in the East Garden. The second row of each of these families was

TABLE 2.7

AVERAGE GRAIN-ROW NUMBERS AND YIELDS PER ACRE OF WHITE
DENT MAIZE GROWN IN 1911 GROUPED ACCORDING TO THE
TYPES OF MATINGS OF THE PARENTS

Pedigree Numbers	Parental Strains Involved	Number of Stalks	Av. Number Grain-Rows	Weights in Lbs.	Yields Bu./A.
	(A) Families from Inbreds Selfed				
F16.68$_1$.....	8 selfed	12	8.7	1.5	17.9
E2.68$_2$......	8 selfed	44	9.0	6.0	19.5
F29.70......	10 selfed	89	10.9	16.5	26.5
F32.73.......	12 selfed	95	11.8	11.3	16.9
F34.76......	Strain A selfed	98	8.4	8.3	12.1
F0.77.......	A from L. H. Smith	101	8.9	8.8	12.4
E19.79$_1$.....	B selfed	3	Not counted nor weighed		
F47.79$_2$.....	B selfed	46	Not counted nor weighed		
F0.80.......	B from L. H. Smith	95	14.3	4.3	6.8
E24.82......	16 selfed	84	14.0	7.5	12.8
F56.85......	20 selfed	90	15.3	13.8	21.8
E36.92......	26, 28 selfed	79	22.7	11.5	20.8
F74.94......	*"Cobs" selfed	64	Not counted nor weighed		
	Unweighted averages (omitting the three uncounted families)	78.7	12.4	8.9	16.7
	(B) Families from Parents Given Mixed Pollen in Each Generation; Selfing Prevented				
F23.69......	8 crossed	71	10.4	30.3	60.2
F31.72......	10 crossed	95	10.7	30.3	45.5
F46.78......	12 crossed	92	12.2	44.5	69.1
F53.81......	14 crossed	97	13.7	40.8	60.0
F55.84......	16 crossed	101	15.2	33.0	46.7
F63$_2$.86.....	18 crossed	105	18.2	42.5	51.8
F66.87......	20 crossed	99	19.4	40.0	57.7
F70$_1$.91.....	22 crossed	63	22.3	20.8	45.9
F73.93......	24 crossed	68	23.8	34.5	72.5
F76.96......	32 crossed	94	25.2	50.5	60.4
	Unweighted averages	88.5	17.0	36.7	57.0
	(C) F$_1$ Hybrids between Different Inbreds				
F29.71......	(10×12)F$_1$	62	12.2	24.5	56.5
F32.74......	(10×B)F$_1$	106	12.8	65.3	87.9
F32.75......	(10×16)F$_1$	100	14.3	63.0	90.0
F54.83......	(16×20)F$_1$	100	18.4	58.2	83.2
	Unweighted averages	92	14.4	52.7	79.4

* This was a slightly fasciated brevistylis type, with silks about half as long as the husks. Usually it produced no grains except when given artificial help.

TABLE 2.7—*Continue*

Pedigree Number	Parental Strains Involved	Number of Stalks	Av. Number Grain-Rows	Weights in Lbs.	Yields Bu./A.
	(D) F₂ Families from F₁ Selfed, Grown in Annex No. 1				
F21.24......	(8×20)F₁ selfed	69	13.8	23.0	47.6
F22.28......	(8×B)F₁ selfed	61	13.4	31.3	73.2
F36.31......	(A×10)F₁ selfed	99	11.3	33.3	48.0
F37.36......	(A×B)F₁ selfed	93	11.8	17.0	29.3
F58.54......	(20×16)F₁ selfed	103	16.2	54.3	47.5
	Unweighted averages	83	13.3	31.8	49.1
	(E) Same Families as in (D), but Grown in East Garden				
F21.24......	(8×20)F₁ selfed	98	13.4	36.0	52.5
F22.28......	(8×B)F₁ selfed	101	13.4	56.0	79.2
F36.31......	(A×10)F₁ selfed	98	11.1	31.3	45.9
F37.36......	(A×B)F₁ selfed	76	11.0	15.3	28.7
F58.54......	(20×16)F₁ selfed	97	16.8	34.3	50.8
	Unweighted averages	94	13.2	34.6	51.4
	(F) F₂ Families from F₁×sibs, All Grown in East Garden				
F21.25......	(8×20)F₁×sib	59	12.9	22.0	53.3
F22.29......	(8×B)F₁×sib	97	12.8	42.8	63.0
F36.34......	(A×10)F₁×sibs	93	10.8	26.3	40.3
F37.37......	(A×B)F₁×sib	71	11.3	18.5	37.2
F58.55......	(20×16)F₁×sib	110	16.0	35.0	45.5
	Unweighted averages	86	12.8	28.9	47.9
	(G) F₃ Families from F₂ Selfed				
F38.39......	(A×20)F₂ selfed	84	13.0	9.8	16.6
F40.42......	(A×22)F₂ selfed	108	11.6	19.3	25.5
F42.45......	(A×16)F₂ selfed	67	10.2	10.5	22.4
F44.46......	(A×B)F₂ selfed	92	11.0	6.0	9.3
F49.49......	(16×A)F₂ selfed	112	11.4	24.3	30.9
F51.52......	(16×20)F₂ selfed	95	15.0	23.8	35.7
F59.57†.....	(20×16)F₂ selfed	100	15.9	24.5	35.0
F59.57......	(20×16)F₂ selfed	100	16.4	25.5	36.4
F61.59......	(20×A)F₂ selfed	117	12.0	9.8	13.6
F64.62......	(B×16)F₂ selfed	107	17.0	12.5	16.7
	Unweighted averages	98.2	13.3	16.6	24.2

† This family was divided and this section was grown in the North Hill-field. All of the other families were grown, as usual, in East Garden.

TABLE 2.7—*Continued*

Pedigree Numbers	Parental Strains Involved	Number of Stalks	Av. Number Grain-Rows	Weights in Lbs.	Yields Bu./A.
	(H) F₃ Families from F₂×Sibs				
F38.40......	(A×20)F$_2$×sib	106	13.5	26.0	35.0
F40.43......	(A×22)F$_2$×sib	112	11.9	26.5	33.8
F44.47......	(A×B)F$_2$×sib	94	11.2	21.8	33.1
F49.50......	(16×A)F$_2$×sib	104	11.8	29.8	40.9
F59.58......	(20×16)F$_2$×sib	90	16.5	38.5	61.1
F61.60......	(20×A)F$_2$×sib	111	13.8	25.0	32.2
F64.63......	(B×16)F$_2$×sib	104	15.1	27.5	37.8
	Unweighted averages	103	13.4	27.9	39.1
	(I) Families from "Three-Way" and Iterative Crosses				
F58.56......	(20×16)F$_1$×22	114	18.9	61.8	77.4
F74.95......	"Cobs"×(20×16)F$_1$	29	20.6	23.3	114.5
F21.27......	(8×20)F$_1$×20	67	15.0	28.5	60.8
F22.30......	(8×B)F$_1$×B	103	14.3	37.8	52.4
F36.33......	(A×B)F$_1$×A	84	10.5	23.0	39.1
F27.38......	(A×B)F$_1$×B	79	12.8	23.5	29.8
F51.53......	(16×20)F$_2$×20	108	17.1	42.3	55.9
	Unweighted averages (three-way)	71.5	19.7	42.5	96.0
	Unweighted averages‡ (iterative)	83.3	13.1	28.2	45.5
	(K) Families from "Four-Way" Crosses, the So-called "Double-Cross"				
F21.26......	(8×20)F$_1$×(A×10)F$_1$	67	12.7	28.5	60.8
F36.35......	(A×10)F$_1$×(20×16)F$_1$	106	12.8	47.0	63.3
F69.66......	(22×"Cobs")F$_1$×(8×10)F$_1$	75	16.3	58.5	111.4
F36.32§....	(A×10)F$_1$×(A×B)F$_1$	102	11.2	45.5	63.7
	Unweighted averages	87.5	14.3	44.9	74.8
	(L) F₃ Families from Four-Way F₂ Crosses, and Imperfect Iteratives of Same Form				
F61.61......	(20×A)F$_2$×(B×16)F$_2$	102	15.3	31.8	44.5
F38.41......	(A×20)F$_2$×(A×22)F$_2$	103	12.9	27.0	37.5
F40.44......	(A×22)F$_2$×(A×16)F$_2$	110	13.2	43.5	56.5
F44.48......	(A×B)F$_2$×(16×A)F$_2$	78	11.4	28.0	51.3
F49.51......	(16×A)F$_2$×(16×20)F$_2$	117	13.3	44.3	61.6
	Unweighted averages	102	13.2	34.9	50.3

‡ Does not include F51.53.

§F36.32 is an imperfect 4-way, being partly iterative, involving only 3 inbreds.

planted in new plots of ground about one-fourth mile north of the original Station grounds.

The purpose of this replication was to determine the degree of consistency of results secured in these new locations with those recorded for the cultures grown in the different conditions of soil, drainage, exposure, lighting, etc., in the East Garden. Summaries of these two sections of Table 2.7 show the cultures grown in the new plot with average grain-row number 1.29 per cent higher than in the same families grown in the East Garden. However, the East Garden cultures produced a higher average yield of ear-corn by 4.70 per cent.

Comparison between selfing and sibcrossing was made a subject of special study in the inbred and F_1 families in 1910. This was not continued in 1911 in the inbreds, but was given a further test in the derivation of the F_2 families from the F_1, and was carried forward to the derivation of F_3 families from the F_2. These comparisons as they relate to F_1 families are given in sections E and F of Table 2.7. They show the F_2 families derived from selfing their F_1 parents slightly superior to those F_2 families produced from sibcrosses in the F_1. This is indicated by an average grain-row number 3.1 per cent higher and average yield 7.5 per cent higher in the F_2 families from selfed F_1 parents, thus reversing the indications from the 1910 cultures.

The comparison of selfing *versus* sibcrossing in the production of the F_3 by these two methods of breeding in F_2 can be derived from section G for selfings and section H for the sibcrosses. Summaries of these two sections show a superiority from sibcrosses of 0.4 per cent in average grain-row number and 61.6 per cent in yield. A part of this discrepancy is clearly due to the inclusion of families in the selfed group which had no direct counterpart in the sibcrossed group. If we limit the comparison to the families which are represented in both groups, we can avoid this cause of distortion. We then find the sibcrossed families superior to the selfed by 1.5 per cent in grain-row number, and 48.6 per cent in yields.

Comparative values between inbreds and crossbreds, as shown in sections A and B of Table 2.7, and between crossbreds and F_1 hybrids, are essentially the same as in 1910. The ratios of inbreds, crossbreds, and F_1 hybrids, with respect to yields, is 0.29 to 1.00 to 1.22. Again the average grain-row number is less in the F_1 than in the crossbreds, and for the same reason. This particular group of F_1 families came from parents with low average grain-row numbers, as compared with the broader parentage of the crossbreds.

The relationship of F_3 to F_2 can now be noted by comparing the results in sections G and H of Table 2.7, with sections D, E, and F. There are several ways in which such comparisons can be made. Perhaps as good a way as any is simply to combine all of the F_2's together, regardless of the considerations which led these to be tabulated in three separate sections, and compare the results with all the F_3 families of sections G and H likewise averaged in an undivided population. When treated in this way, we find that the F_2's have an average grain-row number of 13.1 and average yields of 49.5 bushels per acre, while the F_3 had an average of 13.4 grain-rows and produced an average of 30.4 bushels per acre. If we associate the average yield of the F_1 families, 79.0 with these values for F_2 and F_3, we see the beginning of the characteristic curve in which the loss of yield from one generation to the next is about twice as great as the loss for the next following generation.

It remains to consider the last three sections of Table 2.7, in which are

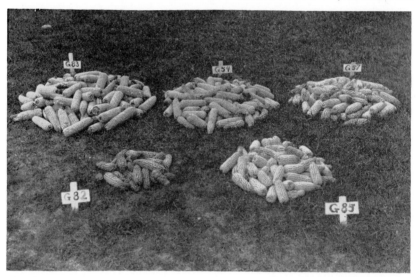

FIG. 2.6—Total yields of ear corn of two selfed strains, Strain 16 and Strain 20, in the foreground (exaggerated, of course, by foreshortening), and their F_1, F_2, and F_3 hybrids, left to right, successively, in the background. As may be seen in Table 2.7, these yields, calculated in terms of bushels per acre, are 12.76 and 21.82 for the two inbreds, and 83.21, 50.81, and 36.43 for the three hybrid families.

included the results of more complicated crossing which had become possible through the accumulation of simpler crossing in preceding years. In section I are given two "three-way" crosses and four iterative crosses involving F_1 combinations and one iterative cross involving an F_2 combination, each representing a cross between a hybrid and an inbred. As might be expected, these seven families although similar in form show no special consistency, since they involve various combinations of five different inbreds and five different hybrids.

In Table 2.7, section K, are presented what I believe to be the first "four-way" or so-called "double crosses" ever made among inbreds. The elements of one of these double crosses are shown in Figure 2.7. These double crosses were made some five or six years before Dr. D. F. Jones pointed out the potentialities of such crosses in producing hybridized seed corn at a price

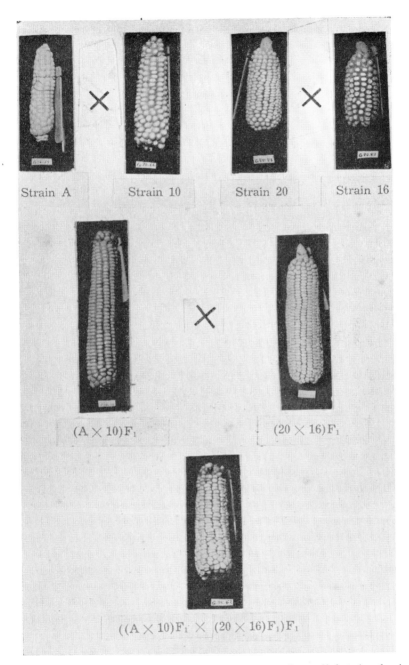

Strain A   Strain 10   Strain 20   Strain 16

(A × 10) F₁   (20 × 16) F₁

((A × 10) F₁ × (20 × 16) F₁) F₁

FIG. 2.7—One of the first *four-way* or *double crosses* ever grown from selfed strains of maize. The single crosses for this double cross were made in 1909, the cross between the F₁'s was made in 1910, and the double-cross ear at bottom (G35.62) was grown in 1911 and grains from it were used for planting in 1912.

that could make the pure-line method of corn production practical. No credit is sought for the fact that I made these four-way crosses some years prior to the similar combinations made by Dr. Jones. They are presented here only because they belong in a historical account.

In the last section of Table 2.7 I have entered five families which have the form of four-way crosses, but in which the single crossings used were F_2 instead of F_1. Only the first of these five families actually involved four different inbreds, the others being partially iterative, in that only three inbreds contributed to each. A comparison of the double crosses both of F_1 and F_2, with the corresponding single crosses, is instructive. Comparison of the summary of section C with that of section K shows the double cross families slightly inferior to the single cross families, as indicated by a 1 per cent higher grain-row number and 6 per cent higher yield of the single cross families over the double cross. Comparing sections L and E, it is to be noted that the double cross retains the vigor of the F_2, instead of declining to the vigor of the F_3 families produced by the usual methods, as seen in sections G and H, Table 2.7.

In 1911 I realized that the effective exposition of the important discoveries we were making required photographs of prepared exhibits. A number of such exhibits were set up and photographed, and have been presented in lantern slides on many occasions. I have included the most instructive of these here.

Here the detailed account of these studies must end, for although they were continued in 1912, I have been unable to locate the field and harvesting notes including grain-row counts and weighings for the 1912 cultures. These 1912 cultures were especially designed to explore the evidences of Mendelian segregations in the F_2 and the F_3 families, with respect to grain-row numbers and yields. They included 11 families of the breeding $F_1 \times$ self, 8 families of $F_1 \times$ sib, 21 $F_2 \times$ self, 10 $F_2 \times$ sibs, and five families of $F_3 \times$ self. There was also an interesting pair of approximations to eight-way combinations or quadruple crosses produced by reciprocal combinations of the four-way crosses included in the 1911 cultures. While these had the form of quadruple crosses, they were imperfect in that one of the inbreds was repeated, so that only seven different inbreds were represented, instead of eight. This was inevitable since I initiated only seven inbred lines in the beginning of these experiments.

The 1912 crop completed the experimental work with corn at the Station for Experimental Evolution, and I spent the next year in Berlin, Germany. In a lecture I gave at Göttingen about three weeks before the beginning of the first World War the word *heterosis* was first proposed. I used the occasion to discuss the bearing of the results of these studies on the practical work of breeders of various classes of organisms, both plant and animal. I stressed the point that the breeder should not be content, as had long been the case, to seek merely to avoid the deterioration incident to inbreeding, but should

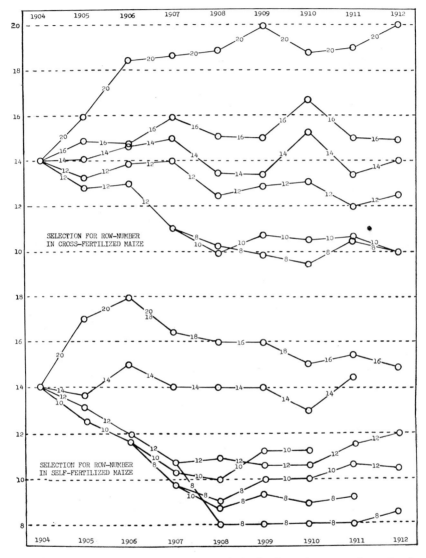

FIG. 2.8—Diagrams of the progressive results of selection for grain-row number under the two systems of breeding: selfing completely prevented in the upper diagram; selfing the sole method of breeding in the lower. The numbers on the lines indicate the numbers of rows of grains on the parent ears. The circles show by their position on the scale at left the average grain-row numbers of the resulting progenies.

recognize in heterosis a potent source of practical gains, to be investigated, understood, and utilized as a new tool in deriving from plant and animal life their maximum contributions in the service of man.

Although no further experimental work was done with corn at the Station for Experimental Evolution after 1912, I tried to resume the work in my first two years at Princeton University, by planting 77 cultures of pedigreed

S. A   S A x B A   B A x S A   B. A   B A x B   S B.

FIG. 2.9—Ears of my white dent "strain" of corn grown at Princeton University in 1916. The ears, each typical of the progeny to which it belonged, are from left to right: SA, Shull's Strain A; SA × BA, F₁ hybrid between Shull's Strain A and Blakeslee's "branch" of the same strain; BA × SA, reciprocal of the last; BA, Shull's Strain A, after two successive selfings by Dr. A. F. Blakeslee; BA × B, F₁ between Blakeslee's branch of Strain A and Shull's Strain B; and SB, Shull's Strain B. About as much heterosis is shown by a cross between two sub-lines of Strain A as between one of these sub-lines and Strain B, the implication being that something more specific may be involved in this example of heterosis than the mere number of genetic differences. (Photo by W. Ralph Singleton in 1945.)

corn in 1916 and 65 in 1917. I used some of the materials from these cultures for laboratory studies in biometry in my classes in genetics. The interesting results shown in Figure 2.9 are from my 1916 crop at Princeton. The plantings at Princeton were made late and the young plants were decimated by pigeons and crows, so that some valuable connections were lost, and with them some of my interest in their continuation.

As we all know, heterosis is not limited to corn, and my own interest in the matter was in no wise restricted to its manifestation in corn. There were examples presented in many other of my genetical experiments. I was particularly interested in the discovery of such special mechanisms as balanced lethal genes in the Oenotheras and self-sterility genes in *Capsella grandiflora*

which, along with many types of asexual reproduction including parthenogenesis, specifically enable the organisms possessing these special mechanisms to maintain the full advantages of heterosis. On one occasion, one of
my new hybrid combinations in Oenothera happened to be planted through
an area in my experimental field where the soil had become so impoverished
that none of my other cultures reached their normal growth. Many of the

FIG. 2.10—The F$_1$ hybrids between a cultivated form of *Helianthus annuus* and a wild form
of the same species received from Kansas. This photograph, taken at the Station for Experimental Evolution in 1906, shows the author affixing a glassine bag to a head of one of the
hybrid plants. The two parents of this hybrid averaged from 5 to 6 feet tall, while 51 of
these F$_1$ hybrids, measured on August 28, 1906, ranged in height from 6.7 to 14.25 feet, the
average being 10.46 feet. This may be considered my first experience with *hybrid vigor*.

plants remained rosettes or formed only weak depauperate stems. But this new hybrid became a vigorous upstanding form in this impoverished area as well as on better soil elsewhere. I recorded this as a notable example of making heterosis take the place of manure or commercial fertilizers.

Figure 2.10 is a notable hybrid, which represents my first direct personal contact with a recognized case of hybrid vigor. This hybrid resulted from a cross I made in 1905 between the so-called "Russian" sunflower and the wild *Helianthus annuus* of our western prairies. Both of these forms have been referred, botanically, to the same species. Both are of approximately equal height, scarcely as tall as the six-foot step-ladder shown in the figure. The tallest of these F_1 hybrids was 14.25 feet in height.

Returning now to the question which I sidestepped in the beginning— what we mean by the expression *the heterosis concept*—I suggest that it is the interpretation of increased vigor, size, fruitfulness, speed of development, resistance to disease and to insect pests, or to climatic rigors of any kind, manifested by crossbred organisms as compared with corresponding inbreds, as the specific results of unlikeness in the constitutions of the uniting parental gametes.

I think the first clear approach to this concept was involved in a statement which I have already quoted, that "a different explanation was forced upon me" (in my comparisons of cross-fertilized and self-fertilized strains of maize). That is, "that self-fertilization simply serves to purify the strains, and that my comparisons are not properly between cross- and self-fertilization, but between pure strains and their hybrids." Since heterosis is recognized as the result of the interaction of unlike gametes, it is closely related to the well known cases of complementary genes. It differs from such complementary genes, however, mainly in being a more "diffuse" phenomenon incapable of analysis into the interactions of specific individual genes, even though it may conceivably consist in whole or in part of such individual gene interactions.

H. K. HAYES
University of Minnesota

Chapter 3

Development of
the Heterosis Concept

Hybrid vigor in artificial plant hybrids was first studied by Koelreuter in 1763 (East and Hayes, 1912). The rediscovery of Mendel's Laws in 1900 focused the attention of the biological world on problems of heredity and led to renewed interest in hybrid vigor as one phase of quantitative inheritance.

Today it is accepted that the characters of plants, animals, and human beings are the result of the action, reaction, and interaction of countless numbers of genes. What is inherited, however, is not the character but the manner of reaction under conditions of environment. At this time, when variability is being expressed as genetic plus environmental variance, one may say that genetic variance is the expression of variability due to genotypic causes. It is that part of the total variance that remains after eliminating environmental variance, as estimated from studying the variances of homozygous lines and F_1 crosses between them.

Early in the present century, East, at the Connecticut Agricultural Experiment Station, and G. H. Shull at Cold Spring Harbor, started their studies of the effects of cross- and self-fertilization in maize. The writer has first-hand knowledge of East's work in this field as he became East's assistant in July, 1909, and continued to work with him through 1914. In 1909, East stated that studies of the effects of self- and cross-pollination in maize were started with the view that this type of information was essential to a sound method of maize breeding. In addition to studies of maize, which is normally cross-pollinated, East carried out studies in tobacco of crosses between varieties and species. This gave an opportunity of studying the effects of self- and cross-pollination with a self-pollinated plant. A 1912 publication of East and Hayes made the following statement:

> The decrease in vigor due to inbreeding naturally cross-fertilized species and the increase in vigor due to crossing naturally self-fertilized species are manifestations of one phenomenon. This phenomenon is heterozygosis. Crossing produces heterozygosis in all characters by which the parent plants differ. Inbreeding tends to produce homozygosis automatically.

Several photographs from this bulletin are of some interest. A picture of two inbred lines of maize and their F_1 cross was one of the first published field views of hybrid vigor from crossing inbred lines of maize. East told me that such a demonstration of hybrid vigor would create a sensation if the material had been grown in the corn belt.

Some F_1 crosses between species and sub-species in tobacco gave large increases in vigor. Some species crosses were sterile. Some varietal crosses within species showed little or no increase in vigor, other crosses gave an average increase of 25 per cent in height over the average of their parents. A few wide species crosses were very low in vigor. One such cross beween *Nicotiana tabacum* and *Nicotiana alata grandiflora* was sterile and very weak in growth. Photographs of the parents and hybrids bring out the fact that a lack of vigor in a few cases was known to accompany the heterozygous condition. Naturally such undesirable combinations had little importance either to the plant breeder or as a basis for evolution.

In 1910, G. H. Shull summarized the effects of inbreeding and crossbreeding in maize in a clear, concise, and definite manner. The student of heredity in this early period had little conception of the complexity of inheritance. Hybrid vigor was in many cases not clearly Mendelian. The term heterosis was coined by Shull and first proposed in 1914. He used the term to avoid the implication that hybrid vigor was entirely Mendelian in nature and to furnish a convenient term to take the place of such phrases as "the stimulus of heterozygosis."

At this time it was usually stated that increased vigor in hybrids was due to a more rapid cell division as stimulated by the heterozygous condition of the genotype. A. F. Shull in 1912 attributed the vigor "to the effect of a changed nucleus and a (relatively) unaltered cytoplasm upon each other."

The purpose of this chapter is to discuss some phases of the development of the heterosis concept since 1910. Three main topics will be presented covering utilization, breeding methods, and genetic concepts with particular reference to practical applications and to genetic explanations.

UTILIZATION OF HETEROSIS BY THE PRODUCER

The presentation of East and Hayes in 1912 emphasized the probable practical value of heterozygosis. A review of experiments with maize was made. In discussing Shull's (1909) plan for the use of single crosses between inbred lines, it was stated that the procedure was desirable in theory but difficult of application. At this early time the inbred lines of maize that were available seemed so lacking in vigor that the use of F_1 crosses between selfed lines in maize for the commercial crop seemed impractical. Both Shull and East believed that some method of direct utilization of hybrid vigor in maize would be found.

One is inclined to forget that the inbred lines of maize of today are markedly superior, on the average, to those of 1910. Jones's discovery about 1917 of the double cross plan of producing hybrid seed in maize, and the subsequent proof by many workers that double crosses can be obtained that closely approach the vigor of F_1 crosses between selfed lines, furnished the basis for the utilization of hybrid vigor in field corn. With sweet corn, however, F_1 crosses between selfed lines are used very widely today for the commercial crop.

East and Hayes emphasized that F_1 crosses probably would be of commercial value in some truck crops where crossing was easy. Eggplants, tomatoes, pumpkins, and squashes were considered to offer promise for a practical use of such vigor. The writers also mentioned the fact that heterozygosis had been used in vegetatively propagated plants, though not purposely, and that it seemed feasible to make a practical application in the field of forestry.

The use of heterosis in practical plant and animal improvement has borne out and surpassed these early predictions as shown in Table 3.1.

TABLE 3.1

USE OF HETEROSIS IN CROP PLANTS AND LIVESTOCK

Farm crops:	Maize, sugar beets, sorghums, forage crops, and grasses
Horticultural crops:	Tomatoes, squashes, cucumbers, eggplants, onions, annual ornamentals
Silkworms	
Livestock:	Swine, poultry, beef and milk cattle
Vegetatively propagated plants	

In the corn belt of the United States nearly 100 per cent of all maize is hybrid. Hybrid corn is rapidly being developed in other countries of the world, and is one of the best illustrations of the practical utilization of modern genetics. Considerable evidence leads to the conclusion that heterosis can be used extensively in farm crops, including such widely different plants as sugar beets, sorghums, tobacco, forage crops, and grasses.

With horticultural plants, where the individual plant is of rather great value, planned heterosis has proven worth while. First generation crosses of tomatoes, onions, egg plants, cucumbers, and squashes have proven their value and are being grown extensively by home and truck gardeners. Similar use is being made of heterosis in some annual ornamentals.

Heterosis has become an important tool of the animal breeder. Its use in silkworm breeding is well known. Practical utilization of hybrid vigor has been made in swine and poultry, and applications are being studied with beef cattle, dairy cattle, and sheep. A somewhat better understanding of the effects of inbreeding and crossing by the breeder has aided in applications with livestock. As in plants, inbreeding makes controlled selection possible, while controlled crosses may be grown to utilize favorable gene combinations.

METHODS OF BREEDING FOR HETEROSIS

In general there is a much closer relation between the characters of parents and of their F_1 crosses in self-pollinated plants than between the characters of inbred lines of cross-pollinated plants and their F_1 crosses.

Characters of Parents and F_1 Crosses in Self-pollinated Plants

A recent study by Carnahan (1947) in flax, which is normally self-pollinated, may be used for illustrative purposes. Four varieties of flax were selected to represent desirable parental varieties. Each was crossed with four other varieties, of different genetic origin from the first group, to be used as testers. Sufficient seed for F_1 and F_2 progenies was produced so that all

TABLE 3.2

PARENT AND F_1 CROSSES, YIELD
IN BUSHELS PER ACRE*

Parent Varieties		Tester Varieties			
		5	6	7	8
		16	14	17	13
1	19	31	25	22	19
2	18	24	26	19	20
3	13	26	24	20	18
4	17	22	21	20	19

*Parent yields outside rectangle, F_1 crosses within.

progenies could be planted in replicated, 8-foot rows at the rate of 200 seeds per row. Combining ability was studied in F_1 and F_2 in comparison with the parents for yield of seed, number of seeds per boll, number of bolls per plant, weight of 1000 seeds, date of full bloom, and plant height.

As shown in Table 3.2, each F_1 cross yielded more than its highest yielding parent, although for one cross the difference was only slightly in favor of the F_1. For an average of all crosses, the F_1 yielded 40 per cent more than the average of the parents, and the F_2, 26 per cent more. The lowest yielding cross, 3×8, was produced from a cross of the two lowest yielding parents. The highest yielding cross, 1×5, however, could have been selected only by actual trial. It was obtained by crossing the highest yielding selected variety with the second highest yielding tester variety.

There was excellent agreement, on the average, for each of the characters studied between the average expression of the characters of the parents and their F_1 crosses. Carnahan concluded that for each character studied there appeared to be a good relationship between the performance of the parents and the average performance of their F_1 crosses. The characters of the parents in this study were as good or better indication of the combining ability of a parental variety as that obtained from a study of average combining ability in four crosses.

Powers (1945) obtained also relatively good agreement in tomatoes between the parental yield of 10 varieties and that of all possible F_1 crosses between the 10 varieties (see Table 3.3).

Moore and Currence (1950) in tomatoes made a somewhat comparable study to that of Carnahan with flax. They used two three-way crosses as testers for a preliminary evaluation of combining ability of 27 varieties. Based on this, eight varieties were selected that gave a wide range in average combining ability for several characters including early yield and total yield. These varieties were crossed in all combinations, and yield trials of the

TABLE 3.3

YIELD OF RIPE FRUIT IN GRAMS
IN TOMATOES (AFTER POWERS)

VARIETY OR INBRED	YIELD OF RIPE FRUITS (PER PLANT)	
	Variety or Inbred Grams	9 Crosses (av.) Grams
L. esculentum		
Bounty 4101........	513 ± 39	1280 ± 53
4102........	607 ± 86	1267 ± 46
4105........	332 ± 64	1081 ± 33
4106........	828 ± 108	1236 ± 45
Es.$\times$L. pim		
4103........	1066 ± 159	1597 ± 54
4104........	808 ± 114	1340 ± 44
4107........	801 ± 111	1181 ± 47
4108........	857 ± 108	1192 ± 41
4109........	1364 ± 151	1968 ± 46
4110........	1868 ± 149	2231 ± 52

varieties and F_1 crosses were made. There was relatively good agreement between the early test for combining ability and the average yield of F_1 crosses, but the relationship did not seem superior to the varietal performance as a means of predicting combining ability in crosses. In the studies by Carnahan, Moore, Currence, and Powers the only means of selecting the most desirable F_1 cross was by actual trial.

Characters of Inbred Lines and Their F_1 Crosses in Maize

Numerous studies have been made with maize of the relation between characters of inbred lines and of their F_1 crosses. There usually have been indications of significant correlations for most characters of inbred lines and their F_1 crosses. In most cases, however, the relationship was not very large or highly important when one studied individual characters, or the more complex character—yield of grain. The studies have been reviewed by numerous workers (see Sprague, 1946b).

Hayes and Johnson (1939) in Minnesota studied the relation between the characters of 110 inbred lines of maize and their performance in top crosses. The characters studied in selfed lines in replicated yield trials are given in Table 3.4.

All possible correlations were made between the individual characters of the inbreds and of these characters and the yield of grain of top crosses. The

TABLE 3.4

CHARACTERS OF 110 INBRED LINES IN
CORN CORRELATED WITH INBRED-
VARIETY YIELDING ABILITY

1. Date silked	7. Stalk diameter
2. Plant height	8. Total brace roots
3. Ear height	9. Tassel index
4. Leaf area	10. Pollen yield
5. Pulling resistance	11. Grain yield
6. Root volume	12. Ear length

TABLE 3.5

TOTAL CORRELATIONS BETWEEN CHARACTERS OF 110 INBREDS,
LABELED 1 TO 12, AND YIELDING ABILITY OF INBRED-
VARIETY CROSSES DESIGNATED AS 15

	2	3	4	5	6	7	8	9	10	11	12	15
1	0.51	0.61	0.48	0.65	0.62	0.55	0.38	0.37	0.22	0.07	−0.06	0.47
2		0.76	0.44	0.48	0.43	0.40	0.26	0.19	0.36	0.25	0.08	0.27
3			0.43	0.54	0.50	0.41	0.35	0.33	0.22	0.15	−0.01	0.41
4				0.50	0.44	0.48	0.40	0.29	0.18	0.20	0.08	0.29
5					0.76	0.51	0.60	0.41	0.21	0.15	0.04	0.45
6						0.55	0.74	0.39	0.29	0.19	0.03	0.54
7							0.54	0.24	0.27	0.21	0.15	0.41
8	Multiple value of R							0.26	0.22	0.20	0.07	0.45
9	for inbred-variety yield								0.20	−0.00	0.03	0.19
10	and twelve characters of									0.35	0.32	0.26
11	inbred=0.67										0.64	0.25
12												0.28

CHARACTERS CORRELATED

Significant value of r for P of .05 = 0.19.
Significant value of r for P of .01 = 0.25.

characters, in general, were those that were considered to evaluate the inbreds in developmental vigor.

The total correlations between characters are summarized in Table 3.5. Most correlations were significant at the 5 per cent or 1 per cent point except the relation between ear length and other characters of the inbreds. All relationships between the characters of the inbreds, including grain yield, and the yield of top crosses were significant at the 1 per cent point except for tassel index of the inbreds, and that was significant at the 5 per cent point. The multiple correlation coefficient of 0.67 indicated that under the conditions of the experiment about 45 per cent of the variability of inbred-variety yield was directly related to characters of the inbreds. These relationships between the parents and their F_1 crosses were somewhat larger than those obtained by others with maize. Nevertheless, relationships were much smaller than has been obtained in similar studies with self-pollinated plants.

Richey (1945b) compared the yield of inbred parents in the S_3 and S_4 generations of selfing with the mean yield of their single crosses from data taken by Jenkins and Brunson. Similar comparisons were made between the yield in top crosses and the mean yield in single crosses (see Table 3.6).

Although for various reasons the r values are not strictly comparable, the yield of inbreds was as strongly correlated with the mean yield of their single crosses as the yield in top crosses was correlated with the mean yield of single crosses.

TABLE 3.6

CORRELATION COEFFICIENTS FOR YIELDS OF
INBRED PARENTS OR TOP CROSSES WITH
MEAN YIELDS OF SINGLE CROSSES*

Hybrids Correlated with	Previous Generations of Inbreeding	
	S_3†	S_4
Inbred parents	.25, .64, .67	.41, .45
Top crosses	.53	.53

* After Richey, after Jenkins and Brunson.
† S_3 = three years selfed, etc.

Comparison of Methods with Self- and Cross-pollinated Plants

In self-pollinated plants it seems probable that the first natural step in the utilization of heterosis normally may consist of the selection of available parental varieties that in themselves produce the best combination of characters. It seems important to continue breeding for the best combination of genes that can be obtained in relatively homozygous varieties. Where hybrid seed can be produced cheaply enough, or new methods can be found to make crosses more easily, heterosis can be used to obtain from the hybrid an advance in productivity over the homozygous condition.

In cross-pollinated plants two general methods of breeding for heterosis are now being widely utilized. One consists, as in maize, of the selection within and between selfed lines and the use of single, three-way, or double crosses for the commercial crop. The second general method consists of selecting or breeding desirable clones of perennial crops. These are evaluated for combining ability by polycross, or other similar methods, and the desirable clones used to produce F_1 crosses, double crosses, or synthetic varieties.

There seems to be some difference of opinion regarding the selection process in its application to maize improvement. One school of thought practices a somewhat similar method of breeding selfed lines as is used in self-pollinated plants, with the viewpoint that controlled selection makes it possible to isolate in the inbred lines the genes for characters needed in the hybrids. Apparently the relationship between the characters of inbreds and their F_1 crosses will become greater as inbred lines themselves improve. The other extreme of viewpoint (Hull, 1945a) is that the greater part of hybrid vigor is due to interallelic interaction of genes to such an extent that selection based on appearance may be harmful. In a recurrent selection program Hull, therefore, does not recommend selection for vigor of growth, although he states that plants showing pest or weather damage should be avoided.

It is probable that differences between these two so-called schools may have been overstated. Both believe that the actual test for combining ability in hybrid combination is necessary. The stage in the breeding program when such test should be made will depend on the material worked with and the nature of the breeding program. In both cross- and self-pollinated plants an actual trial will be needed to determine the combination that excels in heterosis.

Where clonal lines can be propagated vegetatively, a method of selecting for heterosis in alfalfa was suggested by Tysdal, Kiesselbach, and Westover (1942), by means of polycross trials. The method is being used extensively today with perennial forage crops that normally are cross-pollinated. The writer is studying the method with early generation selfed lines of rye. With perennial crop plants, selection for combining ability is made for heterozygous parent clones. Where disease and insect resistance or winter hardiness are important, it may be essential to insure that the clones used in the polycross trials excel for these characters. Polycross seed is produced on selected clones under open-pollinated conditions where the clones are planted together at random under isolation.

In one study of progenies of eight clones by Tysdal and Crandall (1948) yields were determined from polycross seed in comparison with top cross seed when each of the clones was planted in isolation with Arizona common alfalfa (see Table 3.7). The agreement for combining ability was relatively good in the two trials.

An early suggestion of utilization of heterosis in alfalfa was by double crosses, from single crosses between vegetatively propagated clones, without entire control of cross-pollination. Synthetic varieties also have been suggested as a means of the partial utilization of heterosis. In one comparison the progeny of a synthetic combination of four clones of high combining ability yielded 11 per cent more forage than a similar combination of four clones of low yielding ability. A recent comparison of eight synthetics led Tysdal and Crandall to conclude that the first synthetic and second synthetic seed progenies gave about the same forage yield. In this comparison, heterosis continued through the second seed increase of the high yielding synthetic.

Other Studies with Maize

Combining ability, that is ability to yield in hybrid combination, has been shown by various workers to be an inherited character (Hayes and Johnson, 1939), (Cowan, 1943), (Green, 1948). It seems feasible to breed for high combining ability as for other quantitative characters. In the breeding program

TABLE 3.7

FORAGE YIELDS OF POLY-
CROSSES COMPARED TO
TOP CROSSES OF THE
SAME CLONES*

CLONE No.	YIELD RELATIVE TO GRIMM AS 100	
	Polycross	Arizona Top Cross
1..........	121	130
2..........	111	122
3..........	101	117
4..........	99	103
5..........	97	105
6..........	96	101
7..........	89	101
8..........	76	101

* After Tysdal and Crandall.

for the production of improved inbred lines, it is often possible to select as parents of crosses, select lines having high combining ability as parents of crosses, in addition to selection for other characters that are desired. In breeding for heterosis, however, it seems evident that genetic diversity of parentage is equally as important as combining ability (see Hayes and Immer, 1942; Sprague, 1946b).

All relatively homozygous, inbred lines in maize are much less vigorous than the better F_1 crosses. It is apparent that heterosis is of great importance in crosses with inbred lines of maize.

Inbred lines that have undesirable characters may be easily improved by the application of any one of several methods of breeding. The breeder may select for each problem the method or methods that seem to him most applicable. In breeding selfed lines the selection of parents that have complementary characters that together include the characters desired in the improved inbred is a natural first step. Subsequent methods of breeding may be used according to the viewpoint of the breeder and the particular problem to be solved.

While combining ability is an inherited character, it seems of special interest that single crosses of high × high combiners have not been greatly superior in yield, on the average, to crosses of high × low. Both, however, were clearly higher in yielding ability than low × low crosses (Johnson and Hayes, 1940), (Cowan, 1943), (Green, 1948). An illustration from Johnson and Hayes (Table 3.8) shows the type of results obtained. The crosses were classified for yielding ability in comparison with recommended double crosses of similar maturity.

Two recent studies in Minnesota may be used to illustrate other breeding problems. A further study was made by Johnson (1950) of the combining ability of F_4 lines that were studied in earlier generations by Payne and Hayes (1949). Yield relations in the double cross Min. 608 (A344 × A340) (A357 × A392) are illustrated in Table 3.9.

TABLE 3.8

FREQUENCY DISTRIBUTION FOR YIELD OF SINGLE CROSSES
OF SIMILAR MATURITY IN COMPARISON WITH
RECOMMENDED DOUBLE CROSSES AS 0

Type of Cross	Class Centers of −1 to −2, +1 to +2, etc. Times the S.E. of a Difference									Total	Mean
	−7 −8	−5 −6	−3 −4	−1 −2	0	+1 +2	+3 +4	+5 +6	+7 +8		
Low × low.....	....	1	1	2	4	4	....	....	....	12	−0.5±0.7
Low × high.....	1	3	....	11	6	16	9	5	1	52	+1.1±0.4
High × high.....	....	1	5	12	8	33	20	4	....	83	+1.1±0.2

TABLE 3.9

YIELD RELATIONS IN MIN. 608
(A334×A340)(A357×A392)

	% M.	Yield (Bu.)
A334×A357 and A392.....	19.6	66.8
A340×A357 and A392.....	18.5	62.4
Average..............	19.0	64.6
A357×A334 and A340.....	19.5	66.0
A392×A334 and A340.....	18.6	63.2
Average..............	19.0	64.6
Min. 608.............	19.0	64.0

In these studies the usual method of predicting combining ability of a double cross gave excellent agreement between both predictions and the actual double cross yield.

The studies of the performance in early and later tests of F_2 to F_4 lines from L317 × A116 when crossed with (A334 × A340) in comparison with A357(A334 × A340) were carried out by Payne and Johnson. The methods of comparing combining ability in different generations were adapted by the writer, who alone is responsible for the conclusions drawn. The lines were first placed in +1, −1, etc. × L.S.D. at the 5 per cent point with the performance of A357(A334 × A340) as 0. Classes for performance of individual lines were made by adding the yield class of a line to its moisture class with the sign of the latter changed.

The F_2 and F_3 crosses were both grown the same year, the F_3 and F_4 were grown in different years, and the F_4 and the top crosses were grown the same year (see Tables 3.10, 3.11, 3.12).

In these studies no new lines seemed markedly superior to A357 in com-

TABLE 3.10

COMBINING ABILITY RELATION OF F_2 AND F_3 LINES
OF (L317×A116) IN CROSSES WITH (A334×A340)
GROWN IN SAME TRIAL IN 1947

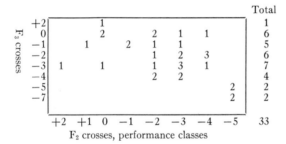

F_3 crosses	+2	+1	0	−1	−2	−3	−4	−5	Total
+2		1							1
0		2		2	1	1			6
−1			1	2	1	1			5
−2					1	2	3		6
−3	1		1		1	3	1		7
−4					2	2			4
−5							2		2
−7							2		2
	+2	+1	0	−1	−2	−3	−4	−5	33

F_2 crosses, performance classes

TABLE 3.11

COMBINING ABILITY RELATION OF F_3 AND F_4 LINES
OF (L317×A116) IN CROSSES WITH (A334×A340)
F_3 GROWN IN 1947, F_4 IN 1949

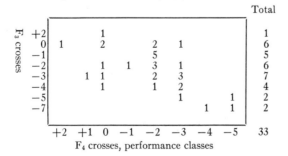

F_3 crosses	+2	+1	0	−1	−2	−3	−4	−5	Total
+2			1						1
0	1		2	2	1				6
−1					5				5
−2			1	1	3	1			6
−3			1	1	2	3			7
−4			1		1	2			4
−5					1		1		2
−7							1	1	2
	+2	+1	0	−1	−2	−3	−4	−5	33

F_4 crosses, performance classes

bining ability with (A334 × A340). As A357 is rather outstanding in combining ability the result may not be so surprising. There was much greater relation between the combining ability of F_3 and F_4 lines and of F_4 with top crosses than between F_2 and F_3.

In an unpublished study of gamete selection, with a different but highly desirable double cross, there was an indication that a lower yielding inbred could be improved by an application of gamete selection (Stadler, 1944). The study is from one phase of a breeding program to improve Min. 406. The yield relations of inbreds in an average of single crosses are given in Table 3.13.

Approximately 60 F_1 plants of A25 × Golden King were selfed and top crossed with A73 × A375. Thirty-two of the more desirable plants were selected to study in yield trials. In this study both yield and moisture classes of plus 1, plus 2, etc. × L.S.D. at 5 per cent were used around the mean of

TABLE 3.12

COMBINING ABILITY RELATION OF F_4 LINES OF
(L317×A116) IN CROSSES WITH (A334×A340) AND
WITH GOLDEN KING. GROWN IN 1949

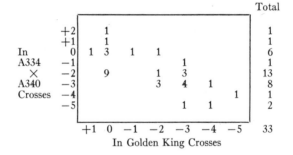

TABLE 3.13

GAMETE SELECTION IN THE IMPROVE-
MENT OF MINHYBRID 406
(A25×A334)(A73×A375)

	Av. of Crosses	
	%M.	Bu.
A25×A73, A375.......	24.6	76.2
A334×A73, A375......	24.7	79.4
A73×A25, A334.......	24.6	74.8
A375×A25, A334......	24.7	80.8

Proposal for improvement of A25 and A73:
A25× G. King gametes
A73×Murdock gametes

A25 × tester as 0. The results (see Table 3.14) indicate that gametes from Golden King are a desirable source of improvement of A25 in crosses with A73 × A375.

From this first trial three high and three low yielding lines were selected, and selfed progeny grown in S_1. Plants in each of the three S_1 high and three low combining lines were selected, selfed, and again top crossed on A73 × A375. The agreement for S_0 and S_1 lines was very good (see Table 3.15). It appears that gamete selection is an excellent breeding method for the early selection of material to improve the specific combining ability of a known inbred.

SOME GENETIC CONCEPTS OF HETEROSIS

It seems very evident to the writer that heterosis, the increased vigor of F_1 over the mean of the parents or over the better parent, whichever definition is used, is not due to any single genetic cause. A brief summary of various

TABLE 3.14

DISTRIBUTION OF % MOISTURE AND YIELD OF 32 S_0 PLANTS OF A25×G. KING CROSSED TO A73×A375. CLASSES OF L.S.D. 5% AROUND MEAN OF A25× TESTER

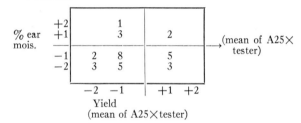

TABLE 3.15

PERFORMANCE INDICES OF S_0 AND S_1 LINES FROM A25×G. KING WHEN CROSSED TO A73×A375 TESTER AND COMPARED WITH A25×TESTER

GAMETE NUMBER	S_0		S_1	No. OF S_1's
	1947	1949	1949	
19 H.....	+11	+19	+25	5
20 H.....	+14	+ 9	+14	7
36 H.....	+ 9	+16	+11	7
5 L.....	−11	− 3	+ 5	7
29 L.....	−11	− 1	− 0	1
46 L.....	− 5	+ 1	+ 2	7

theories advanced to explain heterosis seems desirable to set the stage for later discussions. Bruce (1910) explained heterosis on the combined action of favorable dominant or partially dominant factors, based as Richey (1945a) has emphasized on mathematical expectations.

Keeble and Pellew (1910) used a similar hypothesis on a di-hybrid basis to explain hybrid vigor in peas. East and G. H. Shull (1910–1914) believed vigor was dependent on heterozygosis on the basis that the stimulus of hybridity was not entirely Mendelian. A. F. Shull (1912) preferred the explanation that heterosis was due to a stimulus resulting from a changed nucleus on a relatively unaltered cytoplasm. Jones (1917) restated Bruce's concept and added the concept of linkage.

Collins (1921) and Richey (1945) have pointed out that where large numbers of factor pairs are involved it would be very difficult to recover all factors in a favorable condition in F_2, or in later segregating generations. With multiple factors involved, however, linkage must of necessity make the recombination of factors more difficult. East (1936) presented a Mendelian concept of the interaction of alleles at the same locus to explain heterosis, where two alleles of a particular gene pair had each developed a divergent physiological function. The writer believes he continued also to accept the previous explanation that heterosis was dependent on the cumulative effect of dominant or partially dominant linked genes.

Gustafsson (1947), Hull (1945a), Jones (1945), Castle (1946), and others have emphasized the importance of interallelic action in relation to heterosis. Castle has suggested also that the effect of interallelic action of a single pair of genes "is similar to that of the killer mutation of Sonneborn, except that the action induced in the dominant gene by its sensitized recessive, instead of being harmful, in this case is beneficial."

In certain cases a homozygous recessive pair of genes may completely modify the normal expression of either a homozygous or heterozygous organism. Homozygous dwarfs in maize condition such a result. A cross between two different dwarfs, however, releases the inhibition of each dwarf and results in marked heterosis. Both dominant factors, where two dwarfs are crossed, appear to be necessary to condition normal development. In this case the dominant conditions of both factor pairs act as complementary factors for normal growth.

It is evident that genes are greatly affected in their expression by differences in both external and internal environment. Cytoplasmic inheritance of male sterility may be used for illustrative purposes. Several cases of male sterility in sugar beets and onions, for example, are known that are due to maternal cytoplasmic inheritance which may be modified in expression by the dominant or recessive condition of one or more factor pairs.

Recently Hsu (1950) at Minnesota has studied the effect of two pairs of dwarf factors of maize in their homozygous dominant and recessive conditions, and also when heterozygous in near isogenic, homozygous, and highly heterozygous backgrounds.

The factor pair for D_1d_1 was studied in the near isogenic background of inbred A188, that of D_xd_x in the near isogenic background of A95–344, and both factor pairs were studied in crosses between A188 × A95. Particular attention was given to total dry matter produced at various periods of growth under field conditions and to the growth in length of the coleoptile and meso-cotyl under controlled laboratory conditions.

One comparison of the growth of the mesocotyl during a 12-day period for D_1D_1 and D_1d_1 on three different near isogenic backgrounds will be con-sidered: the near isogenic background, A188, and the highly heterozygous backgrounds of A188 × A95 in the presence of D_xD_x and D_xd_x, respec-tively. While D_1 conditioned greater growth of mesocotyl in length than d_1, D_x conditioned less development of the mesocotyl in length than d_x.

The mesocotyl length of six strains consisting of comparisons of D_1D_1 with D_1d_1 on three different backgrounds was taken as 100. The comparisons are summarized in Table 3.16 and in Figure 3.1.

It is apparent that the superiority of D_1D_1 over D_1d_1 in mesocotyl length becomes less in the highly heterozygous background than in the homozygous background of A188. This may be more evident from the diagram in Fig-ure 3.1.

TABLE 3.16

COMPARATIVE LENGTH OF MESOCOT-
YL FOR SIX STRAINS OF CORN

Background	Percentage Difference in Mesocotyl Length, D_1D_1 minus D_1d_1	Percentage Expression of Background
A188..............	19	89
A188×A95 D_xD_x...	16	101
A188×A95 D_xd_x....	4	110

It seems of some interest that the differences between D_1D_1 and D_1d_1 were smaller in the highly heterozygous background than in the homozygous background, and that in the presence of D_xd_x that the differences were further reduced over those in the presence of D_xD_x. It may be well to recall that d_x conditioned greater length of mesocotyl than D_x.

Reference may be made to an explanation by Torssell (1948) of the decline in green weight or length of stem in alfalfa in different generations of in-breeding. It was not greatest in the first inbred generation. He suggests there was a surplus of vigor genes in a heterozygous condition in the early genera-tions of selfing, and that great loss of vigor was not observed until about I_3

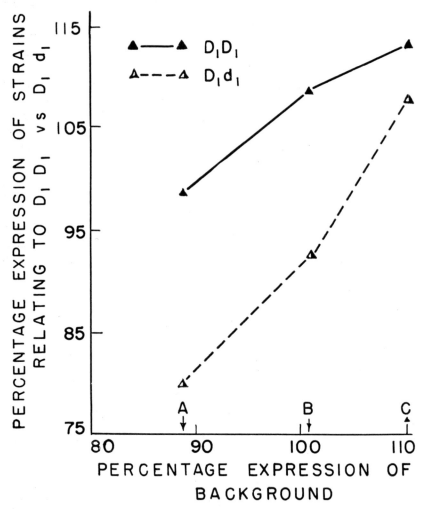

Fig. 3.1—Relative expression of D_1D_1 vs. D_1d_1 regarding final length of mesocotyl on various backgrounds: (A, A188; B, A188 × A95-344 carrying D_xD_x; C, A188 × A95-344 D_xd_x).

when selfing reduced the necessary genes below a stage needed by the organism. The following quotation from Thorssell emphasizes the viewpoint that the relative importance of genes controlling heterosis is greatly influenced by other factors of the organism:

The cumulative effect of heritable characters, however, brings it about that development, that is to say green weight, does not stand in arithmetical proportion to the number of pairs of the dominant genes in question. From this it follows also that the said number can be reduced within a certain limit without perceptible or any great influence upon green weight. If this limit is exceeded, a considerable degeneration sets in.

The speaker has chosen to consider heterosis as the normal expression of a complex character when the genes concerned are in a highly heterozygous condition. As most normal characters are the end result of the action, reaction, and interaction of countless numbers of genes, and as gene mutation constantly occurs although relatively infrequently, it may be impossible to obtain all essential genes in the most favorable homozygous state. After selecting the best homozygous combinations, further vigor will be obtained due to heterozygous combinations of factors. Dominance or partial dominance seems of great importance as an explanation of hybrid vigor. In some cases there may be extra vigor correlated with the heterozygous condition of pairs of alleles. The types of response of inter and intra allelic factor interactions are without doubt dependent upon both external and internal environment.

M. M. RHOADES
University of Illinois

Chapter 4

Preferential
Segregation in Maize

The outstanding example of the utilization of heterosis in plant improvement is that of hybrid corn. Extensive studies on maize genetics have clearly demonstrated that chromosome and gene segregation are in accordance with Mendel's laws of segregation and recombination. It would appear, therefore, that any unusual mechanism operating in maize to produce deviations from normal Mendelian behavior should be worthy of our consideration, even though the principles involved have no bearing on the nature or manifestation of heterosis. The purpose of this section is to present data on preferential segregation in maize and to offer a tentative interpretation of this phenomenon.

Two kinds of chromosome 10, the shortest member of the haploid set of ten, are found in populations of maize. The common or normal type gives typical Mendelian ratios when the two homologues are heterozygous for mutant loci. The second kind of chromosome 10, which has been found in a number of races from Latin America and the southwestern United States, also gives normal Mendelian ratios for chromosome 10 loci in plants homozygous for this chromosome. This second or abnormal kind of chromosome 10 differs from the normal chromosome 10 by a large, chiefly heterochromatic segment of chromatin attached to the end of the long arm and also in the chromomeric structure of the distal one-sixth of the long arm (see Fig. 4.1 and Fig. 1 of Plate I). As is illustrated in Figure 4.1 the chromomeres in this region are larger and more deeply staining than are the correspondingly situated chromomeres of the normal homologue.

Although normal Mendelian ratios are obtained for segregating loci in chromosome 10 in both kinds of homozygotes, we were able to show in an earlier paper (Rhoades, 1941) that preferential segregation occurs at mega-

66

FIG. 4.1—Camera lucida sketch at pachynema of bivalent consisting of one normal and one abnormal chromosome 10. Note the dissimilarity in chromomere pattern in the distal one-sixth of the long arm. The identical chromomere pattern found in the remainder of the chromosomes is not figured here.

FIG. 4.2—Anaphase I of cell illustrated in Figure 4 of Plate I. Some of the disjoining dyads are normal appearing while others have active neo-centric regions.

FIG. 4.3—Metaphase I with eleven dyads. Five of the dyads have precocious neo-centromeres at sub-terminal portions of their long arms.

FIG. 4.4—Anaphase II of cell illustrated in Figure 7 of Plate II. In some of the inverted V-shaped monads the true centric regions are attracted toward the opposite pole.

sporogenesis in plants heterozygous for a normal and an abnormal type of chromosome 10. Approximately 70 per cent of the functioning megaspores possessed the abnormal 10 instead of the usual 50 per cent. The excess of female gametes with the abnormal 10 was not due to lethal factors or to megaspore competition. The disjunction of the two dyads comprising the heteromorphic bivalent at anaphase I, and of the two monads of each dyad at anaphase II, was such that an abnormal 10 chromosome tended to pass with a high frequency to the basal spore of the linear set of four.

The factor or factors responsible for this preferential segregation reside in the chromatin segments which differentiate the two kinds of chromosome 10. Whether the distal one-sixth of the long arm or the large heterochromatic piece of extra chromatin carries the causative genes for preferential segregation has not yet been determined—since these two regions of the abnormal chromosome 10 have never been separated by crossing over. The locus of the gene R is in the long arm of chromosome 10. There is approximately 1 per cent recombination between R and the end of the long arm in plants heterozygous for the two kinds of chromosome 10; but every crossover distal to R occurred to the left of the dissimilar chromomeres in the distal one-sixth of the long arm. Apparently little or no crossing over takes place here, although pairing at pachytene is intimate.

Strictly terminal chiasmata in the long arm have not been observed at diakinesis in heterozygous plants. The close linkage of the R locus with the extra segment of abnormal 10 is due to a suppression of crossing over in the end regions of the long arm. E. G. Anderson (unpublished) has studied a reciprocal translocation involving normal 10 with the break distal to R, and found 5 per cent recombination between R and the translocation point. There is an undetermined amount of crossing over between the translocation point and the end of the chromosome. It should be possible to locate the region or regions in abnormal 10 responsible for preferential segregation by obtaining successively larger terminal deficiencies, but this has not been attempted.

The dissimilarity in chromomere pattern in the distal portion of the long arms of the abnormal and normal chromosomes 10, together with the lack of crossing over in this region, suggest the possibility that the gene content may not be identical in the two kinds of chromosome 10. Inasmuch as plants homozygous for the abnormal chromosome 10 are not noticeably different in growth habit and general appearance from sibs carrying only the normal 10, it would appear that some kind of structural modification was responsible for the suppression of crossing over. To assume that this distal region consists of non-homologous loci in the two types of chromosome would mean that plants with two abnormal 10 chromosomes would be homozygous deficient for certain loci found in the comparable region of normal 10. This appears unlikely.

That a structural difference, aside from the extra chromatin of abnormal 10, exists between the two kinds of chromosome 10 also is indicated by the pairing relationships in plants trisomic for chromosome 10. In plants with two normal and one abnormal chromosome 10, trivalent associations were observed in 251 (60.2 per cent) among a total of 417 microsporocytes. When a chain of 3 was found at diakinesis, the abnormal 10 occupied a terminal position in 90 per cent of the cells. It was united with a normal chromosome 10 by a chiasma in the short arm. A univalent chromosome 10 was found at diakinesis in 39.8 per cent of the pollen mother cells.

If pairing, as reflected by chiasmata formation, were random among the three chromosomes, the ratio of normal:abnormal chromosomes 10 in the univalent class should be 2:1. Actually the unpaired chromosome was a normal 10 in 28 cells among a total of 166, while in the remaining 138 cells the univalent was an abnormal 10. In individuals again trisomic for chromosome 10, but possessing one normal and two abnormal chromosomes, the percentage of trivalent associations at diakinesis was 57.9 in a total of 513 cells. In the chains of 3, the two abnormal homologues were adjacent members, joined by a chiasma between their long arms, in 70 per cent of the cases. An unpaired chromosome 10 was found in 42.1 per cent of the microsporocytes.

If pairing were random, two times as many abnormal 10's as normal 10's should be found as univalents; but in a total of 216 cells an abnormal 10 was the univalent in 69, while a normal chromosome 10 was the univalent in 147. Chiasma formation among the three chromosomes 10 of trisomic plants clearly is not at random. There is a marked preference for exchanges in the long arm between the two structurally identical homologues. If synapsis usually begins at the ends and progresses proximally, the non-random associations found in trisomic plants become understandable. Normal recombination values for the li-g_1 and g_1-R regions which lie proximal to R (see Table 4.1 for g_1-R data) indicate that any suppression of crossing over is confined to the region beyond the R locus in disomic plants heterozygous for the two kinds of chromosome 10. It is no doubt significant that differences in chromomeric structure are not found in regions proximal to the R locus.

Inasmuch as the R locus is closely linked with the extra chromatin of abnormal 10, the ratio of R:r gametes from heterozygous plants gives a good approximation of the frequency with which the abnormal chromosome passes to the basal megaspore. The genetic length of the long arm of chromosome 10 is such that at least one chiasma is found in the arm. If one chiasma invariably occurs in the long arm of heteromorphic bivalents, each of the two disjoining dyads of anaphase I will possess one normal chromatid and one abnormal chromatid. Preferential segregation would be restricted to the second meiotic division, and occur only if the orientation of the dyad on the spindle of metaphase II were such that the abnormal chromatid passed to the lower pole of the spindle. Normal segregation would occur in those megasporocytes which had homomorphic dyads.

If the terminal segment of abnormal 10 determines preferential segregation, it follows that loci near the end of the long arm will be preferentially segregated more frequently than loci further removed from the end of the chromosome. From the data in Tables 4.1 and 4.2 it is evident that the distortion from a 1:1 ratio is greater for the R locus than for the more proximally situated g_1 locus. The li locus which is proximal to g_1 was less affected than g_1.

Longley (1945) reported non-random segregation at megasporogenesis for chromosome pairs other than chromosome 10 when one of the two homologues had a prominent knob and the other was knobless. Segregation was random for these heteromorphic bivalents in plants homozygous for the normal chromosome 10, and non-random if abnormal 10 was heterozygous. He studied preferential segregation of chromosomes 9 and 6. The data for chromosome 9 are the most instructive. Some strains of maize have a chromosome 9 with a knob at the end of the short arm, others have a knobless chromosome 9. The C, Sh, and Wx loci lie in the short arm of this chromosome, with Wx nearer to the centromere. C and Sh are in the distal one-third of the short arm. Approximately 44 per cent recombination occurs between Wx and the terminal knob—they approach independence—while C and Sh are 23 and 26 recombination units distant from the knob.

When plants of knob-C/knobless-c constitution, which were also heterozygous for abnormal 10, were pollinated by recessive c, 64 per cent of the functioning megaspores possessed the C allele. The Sh locus, close to C, showed a similar degree of preferential segregation in comparable tests, but the Wx locus was little affected. Such a progressive decrease in effect is expected if the terminal knob on the short arm is instrumental in producing preferential segregation. The part played by the knob of chromosome 9 was wholly unexpected. Obviously this heterochromatic structure can no longer be considered as genetically inert. The data on various loci in chromosomes 9 and 10 prove that the degree of preferential segregation of a locus is a function of its linkage with heterochromatic regions which, in some way, are concerned with non-random segregation.

The data presented above show that alternative alleles are not present in equal numbers among the female gametes when abnormal 10 is heterozygous. We have here an exception to Mendel's first law. Are deviations from Mendel's second law, the independent assortment of factor pairs on non-homologous chromosomes, also occurring? This question is answered by Longley's data where the C and R loci are both segregating preferentially. In separate experiments he found the C locus was included in 64 per cent and the R locus in 69 per cent of the functioning megaspores. Assuming that these percentages hold in plants where both are simultaneously segregating, the observed

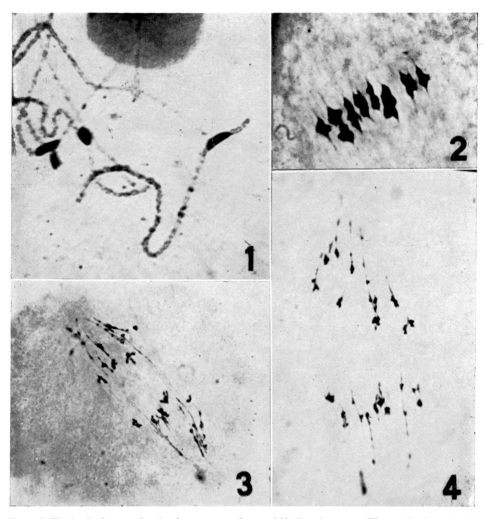

PLATE I: Fig. 1—Pachytene showing homozygous abnormal 10. Carmine smear. The proximal portion of the extra chromatin is euchromatic as is a smaller distal piece. A large and conspicuous knob lies between the two euchromatic portions. Fig. 2—Metaphase I in microsporocyte homozygous for abnormal 10. Carmine smear. The ten bivalents each have their true centric regions co-oriented on the spindle. The onset of neo-centric activity is manifest in the second, sixth, and seventh bivalents from the right. The third and fourth bivalents from the right are somewhat superimposed. Figs. 3 and 4—Anaphase I in microsporocyte homozygous for abnormal 10. Carmine smear. Some of the dyads are undergoing a normal anaphase separation while in others the neo-centric regions are pulling the ends poleward. Note that the normal appearing dyads are slower in their poleward migration. Fig. 4.2 is a drawing of Fig. 4 above.

PLATE II: Figs. 1 and 2—Metaphase II in plant homozygous for abnormal 10. Carmine smear. Precocious poleward movement of neo-centric regions is clearly evident. One dyad has a single neo-centric region (Fig. 4.5, dyad No. 8) while the left-most dyad has a neo-centric region in both long arms (Fig. 4.5, dyad No. 7). This cell was figured in Rhoades and Vilkomerson 1942. Figs. 3 and 4—Anaphase II in plant homozygous for abnormal 10. Carmine smear. Note that the rod-shaped monads with precocious neo-centromeres are the first to reach the poles. Fig. 5—Metaphase II in plant homozygous for abnormal 10. Carmine smear. The only chromosome of the haploid complement which can be recognized at metaphase II is chromosome 6 which has a satellite at the end of the short arm. In this cell the chromosome 6 dyad is the second from the left. That the terminal chromosome of the satellite is actually a small knob is indicated by the formation of neo-centric regions at the end of the short arm. Fig. 6—Early anaphase II in plant heterozygous for abnormal 10. Carmine smear. That the poleward movement of neo-centric regions is less rapid in heterozygous than in homozygous abnormal 10 plants is indicated here by the relatively slight attenuation of the rod-shaped monads. Fig.—7 Late anaphase II in plant homozygous for abnormal 10. Carmine smear. The previously greatly stretched rod monads with precocious neo-centromeres have contracted. Note the inverted V-shaped chromatids. This is the same cell shown in Figure 4.4. Fig. 8—Side view of metaphase I in a normal plant showing the fibrillar nature of the chromosomal fibers. Fixed in Benda, stained with haemotoxylin. Paraffine section. The only chromosomal fibers present are those formed by the true cen-tromeres. Ordinarily chromosomal fibers are not evident in carmine smears since they are destroyed by acetic-alcohol fixation and it is necessary to use special techniques to demon-strate them. Similar fibrillar chromosomal fibers are found at neo-centric regions when proper fixation and staining methods are employed. Fig. 9 (top)—Polar view of meta-phase I in normal plant. Fixed in Benda, stained with haemotoxylin. Paraffine section. Note the arrangement of the ten bivalents on the equatorial plate. This microsporocyte was cut slightly above the metaphase plate. The next section, which includes the remaining portion of this cell, is a cross section through the ten sets of chromosomal fibers.

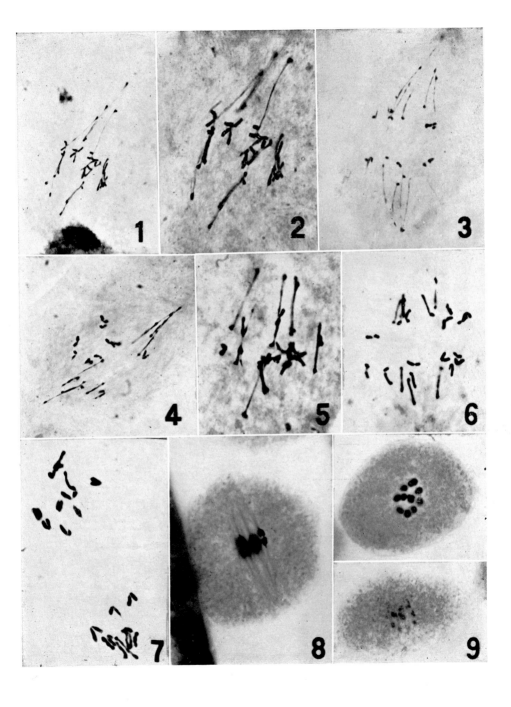

TABLE 4.1

LINKAGE DATA FROM THE CROSS OF $G\,r$ ABNORMAL/$g\,R$ NORMAL $\times\,g\,r\;\male\male$

LINKAGE PHASE	CONSTITUTION OF CHROMOSOMES					RATIO OF $R:r$ ON EAR
	(o) G r	(o) g R	(x) G R	(x) g r	Total	
Repulsion						
	243	138	29	49	459	186R:326r
	102	86	9	13	210	136R:319r
	150	114	18	20	302	145R:288r
	396	50	7	59	512	169R:588r
	154	81	11	29	275	120R:277r
	169	90	21	30	310	127R:223r
	215	61	24	77	377	102R:338r
	231	79	35	81	426	133R:358r
	1660	699	154	358	2871	1118R:2717r

%R in total = 29.7   %g in total = 36.8   29.2% R
%R in non-crossover classes = 29.6
%R in crossover classes = 30.1
$G - R$ recombination = 17.8%

TABLE 4.2

LINKAGE DATA FROM THE CROSS OF $G\,r$ NORMAL/$g\,R$ ABNORMAL $\times\,g\,r$

LINKAGE PHASE	CONSTITUTION OF CHROMOSOMES					RATIO OF $R:r$ ON EAR
	(o) G r	(o) g R	(x) G R	(x) g r	Total	
Repulsion						
	12	87	13	1	113	182R: 42r
	38	96	29	6	169	188R: 59r
	35	86	33	7	161	230R: 74r
	39	107	21	9	176	241R: 77r
	124	376	96	23	619	841R:252r

%r seeds in total = 23.8
%r seeds in non-crossover classes = 24.8
%r seeds in crossover classes = 19.3
$G - R$ recombination = 19.2%

frequencies of F_2 phenotypes can be compared with those calculated on the assumption of independent assortment. The two values agreed very closely, indicating little or no deviation from the law of independent assortment. His data, from plants where loci in chromosomes 9 and 6 are both segregating preferentially, likewise permit such a conclusion to be drawn.

In my 1942 paper on preferential segregation the statement was made that the chromosomes in plants with the abnormal chromosome 10 formed extra chromosomal (half spindle) fibers at regions other than the true centromere region. Rhoades and Vilkomerson (1942) found these supernumerary chromosomal fibers were produced only in plants homozygous or heterozygous for the abnormal 10, and that sister plants homozygous for the normal 10 had chromosomal fibers originating solely from the localized centric region in an orthodox manner (see Fig. 8 of Plate II). Although the abnormal chromosome 10 was clearly responsible for the formation of these neo-centric regions, they were not restricted to this chromosome since many of the non-homologous chromosomes had supernumerary chromosomal fibers. The abnormal chromosome 10 is thus responsible for the formation of neo-centric regions, as well as for preferential segregation. Since 1942, a considerable body of data has been obtained bearing on the behavior of abnormal 10. Some of the more pertinent observations have suggested a cytological mechanism for the phenomenon of preferential segregation.

The unorthodox formation of supernumerary chromosomal fibers from neo-centric regions is limited to the two meiotic divisions. (For a description of normal meiosis in maize see Rhoades, 1950.) The first meiotic division is in no way exceptional until metaphase I is reached. Normal appearing bivalents are co-oriented on the spindle figure in a regular manner with the half spindle fibers, arising from the true centric regions, extending poleward. Normally these fibers effect the anaphase movement of the disjoining dyads with the localized centromere region leading the journey to the spindle pole. However, in plants with the abnormal 10, chromosomal fibers arise from distal regions of the chromosome while the bivalents are still co-oriented on the spindle at metaphase I. The neo-centric regions are drawn poleward more rapidly than the true centric regions. Consequently the distal ends, instead of being directed toward the spindle plate during anaphase I, lead the way to the pole.

The appearance of many disjoining dyads at anaphase I suggests that their poleward migration is due largely, even exclusively, to the fibers originating from the neo-centric regions. The primary centric region appears to play no active role even though it possessed chromosomal fibers at metaphase I when the tetrad (bivalent) was co-oriented. At mid-anaphase there is no indication of the presence of these fibers in many of the dyads with the precocious neo-centric regions.

Figure 4.5 and Figures 3 and 4 of Plate I illustrate some of the observed

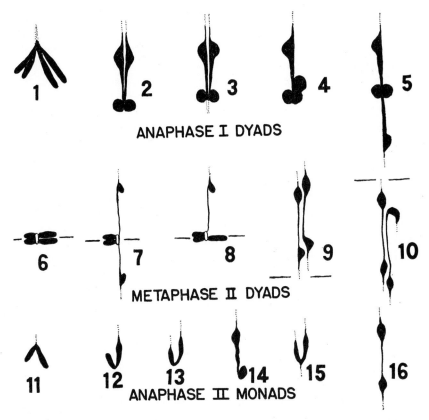

ANAPHASE I DYADS

METAPHASE II DYADS

ANAPHASE II MONADS

Fɪɢ. 4.5—All figures are from carmine smears of homozygous abnormal 10 plants. Figures 1–5 represent various configurations found at anaphase I. Figure 1 is a normal dyad with chromosomal fibers formed only at the true centric region. In Figure 2, two arms have formed neo-centric regions. The true centric regions appear to be inactive. Figure 3 shows a dyad with two neo-centric regions and an active true centric region whose chromosomal fibers are directed away from the nearest pole. Figure 4 is a dyad with a single neo-centric region. In Figure 5 the two neo-centric regions are directed to opposite poles. Figures 6–7 illustrate various metaphase II dyads. The location of the equatorial plate is represented by horizontal lines. Figure 6 is essentially normal with no formation of neo-centromeres. Figure 7 is a dyad with two neo-centric regions directed toward opposite poles. There is a single neo-centric region in Figure 8. Figure 9 is a dyad which is displaced from the equatorial plate. The true centric region has divided to form two independent monads. Each monad has formed two neo-centric regions which are oriented toward opposite poles. In Figure 10 one of the monads has its two neo-centromeres directed to opposite poles. Figures 11–16 are illustrations of monads found at anaphase II. Figure 11 is a normally disjoining monad. In Figure 12 a single neo-centromere is evident. Figure 13 shows two neo-centric regions. Figure 14 has a single neo-centromere which was active at metaphase II. In Figure 15, chromosomal fibers have arisen from two neo-centric regions and also from the true centric region. The true centric region and the neo-centromeres are acting in opposite directions. Figure 16 shows a monad with two neo-centric regions which are directed toward opposite poles. This type of monad is derived from those shown in Figure 9.

anaphase I configurations. Chromosomal fibers may arise from one or both of the long arms of each dyad at late metaphase or early anaphase I. Although it was not always possible to differentiate between long and short arms, the neo-centric regions in general appear to be confined to the long arm. When both long arms of the two chromatids of a dyad possessed a neo-centric region, the chromosomal fibers arising from these centric regions were usually directed toward the same pole. Occasionally they were oriented to opposite poles thus causing a great attenuation. In such cases, however, those chromosomal fibers nearest to one pole were powerful enough to overcome the oppositely directed force of the second neo-centromere. Despite the great complexity of configurations at anaphase I resulting from interacting and conflicting half-spindle fibers arising from both the true and neo-centric regions, the end of anaphase I usually finds ten dyads at each pole. Sometimes, however, greatly stretched chromosomes undergo breakage. This breakage doubtless accounts for the higher pollen abortion (about 10 per cent) found in homozygous abnormal 10 plants as contrasted to the lower (0–5 per cent) pollen abortion of normal sibs.

Even though one or two arms of some dyads are markedly stretched at anaphase I, the ensuing telophase is normal. All four arms of each dyad contract to form a spherical mass of chromatin which is loosely enveloped by the lightly-staining matrical substance. The chromonemata uncoil during interphase and early prophase II finds each daughter cell with ten, long X-shaped dyads of typical appearance. The two chromatids comprising each dyad are conjoined by the undivided primary centric region. There is no indication of neo-centric regions, although some of the long arms possessed chromosomal fibers at the preceding anaphase.

The onset of metaphase II sometimes occurs before the dyads have undergone their usual contraction. Occasionally chromosomal fibers arising from neo-centric regions in the long arms are found at late prophase II. These precociously acting fibers produce an extension of the long arms before any spindle is visible. This observation is of singular importance. Some authorities believe that the centromere region is attracted (whatever this term may signify) to the spindle pole. Here we have a movement produced by the chromosomal fibers of neo-centric regions in the absence of an organized spindle. The way in which these neo-centric fibers act can only be conjectured, but no interaction between centric regions and spindle pole is essential. It is, indeed, probable that the only role of a bipolar spindle is to provide a structural frame which channels the chromosomes to the spindle poles. Clark's (1940) studies on divergent spindles are pertinent in this respect.

The objection may be raised that the chromosomal fibers of neo-centric regions are not comparable to those arising from the true centric region. I do not believe this is a valid criticism. Not only are both kinds of fibers concerned with chromosome movement, but, as will be shown in a later section, the fiber-producing activity of the neo-centric regions is a product of the true centric region.

The appearance of neo-centric fibers in prophase II is not the rule. Usually the dyads come to lie with the true centric region on the spindle plate at metaphase II before any pronounced activity of neo-centric regions is apparent. Before the primary centric region divides, thus permitting a normal anaphase, chromosomal fibers again arise near the distal ends of the long arms of some dyads. These newly formed fibers move the long arms poleward while the dyad is still held on the metaphase plate by the undivided true centric region. This poleward movement is so rapid that the ends of the chromosomes may reach the spindle poles before the true anaphase occurs. Eventually the true centric region becomes functionally split, and the two monads fall apart and pass poleward. It is evident from Figures 4.4 and 4.5 and Figure 7 of Plate II that the configurations of the disjoining monads (chromatids) at anaphase II are greatly different from normal.

Neo-centric activity, as shown by formation of additional chromosomal fibers, occurs in plants both homozygous and heterozygous for the abnormal 10, but it is much more striking in homozygous plants. Plants trisomic for abnormal 10 were not greatly different from homozygous disomic sibs.

Precocious chromosomal fiber formation by neo-centromeres at metaphase II appears in general to be confined to the long arms of the dyads, although it is often difficult to differentiate between two unequal arms when one is stretched poleward. Some chromosomes have arm ratios so extreme that the distinction between long and short arms is clear, and in these chromosomes the precocious fibers at metaphase II arise from the long arms. It is perhaps significant that, with the exception of the terminal knob on the short arm of chromosome 9, all remaining knobs in our material were situated in the long arms. (Chromosome 6 had two small knobs in its long arm but a maximum of one knob was present in the other chromosomes.) Correspondingly, only one of the two arms of any chromatid had neo-centric activity at metaphase II.[1] The number of dyads with precocious spindle fibers, as judged by the number of arms pulled poleward at metaphase II, varied in different strains. The maximum number in some plants was seven, in others five, etc. Plants with seven knobbed chromosomes had a maximum of seven dyads with arms stretched poleward at metaphase II. Those with four knobs had four such dyads. That is, a strong correlation exists between knob number and the number of dyads with neo-centric activity at metaphase II.

A further observation of some interest was that in plants homozygous for all knobs both homologous arms of a dyad usually were pulled poleward at metaphase II; while in plants heterozygous for some knobs many of the dyads had only one arm with neo-centric activity (see Figure 4.5 and Figures

1. With the possible exception of chromosome 6. See Figure 5 of Plate II.

1 and 2 of Plate II). It is not unreasonable to assume that dyads with both homologous arms exhibiting neo-centromeres at metaphase II carried a knob in each chromatid, while dyads with one neo-centromere consisted of one knobbed and one knobless chromatid. Such heteromorphic dyads would arise from heteromorphic bivalents by a crossover between the true centromere and the knob. We believe that only knobbed chromatids have active neo-centromeres at metaphase II, and that knobless ones are normal at this stage. Unfortunately, knobs cannot be recognized at metaphase II, and the validity of the above assumptions rests upon indirect but convincing evidence.

Two types of disjoining monads are found at anaphase II, those which are rod-shaped and those which are V-shaped. Monads which had one arm extending poleward at metaphase II are rod-shaped. They are the first to reach the pole. Indeed distal portions of such chromatids already had arrived there during metaphase II owing to the early action of their neo-centromeres. The V-shaped monads of anaphase II are derived from those chromatids devoid of neo-centromeres at metaphase II. The poleward migration of some monads is first begun by the chromosomal fibers emanating from the true centric region, but shortly after anaphase is initiated chromosomal fibers may arise from the ends of both arms. These terminally placed fibers, which are directed to the same pole, propel their ends poleward with such rapidity that the ends first overtake and then pass the centric region in the course of anaphase migration. Consequently these monads reach the poles as inverted V-shaped chromosomes (see Fig. 4.4). The spindle fibers from the true centric region now are directed toward the spindle plate rather than to the pole—they have reversed their orientation. This would be impossible if chromosomal fibers were of a thread-like structure. It is more likely that these fibers represent nothing more than lines of force emanating from the centromere. Inverted V-shaped chromatids are not invariably found at anaphase II.

Some monads have chromosomal fibers only at the true centric region and move poleward in a normal fashion. Either neo-centric regions are not present, or else arise too late to be effective. It should be emphasized that a fundamental distinction exists between the rod and inverted V chromatids found at anaphase II. The rod-shaped monads come from dyads with neo-centric activity at metaphase II. Their supernumerary chromosomal fibers arise from one arm. Their sub-terminal location suggests they may arise adjacent to the knob, but this is merely a conjecture. The later-formed extra chromosomal fibers of the inverted V chromatids, which are knobless, are terminal and arise from both arms.

If a dyad is oriented on the spindle plate at metaphase II before the onset of precocious neo-centromere activity, the supernumerary chromosomal fibers arising from the knobbed arm of the chromatid situated slightly above the spindle plate are directed toward the upper (nearest) pole, and those from the bottom chromatid go to the lower pole—they are co-oriented (see

Fig. 4.3). No such regularity is found in those infrequently occurring dyads which are longitudinally displaced from the spindle plate at metaphase II. Their true centric regions divide prematurely. Consequently, the two chromatids of these displaced dyads no longer remain conjoined, but fall apart to become independent monads which lie side-by-side, parallel with the longitudinal axis of the spindle.

The neo-centric activity which these monads now manifest is similar to that found at anaphase II for those monads derived from normally oriented dyads lacking precocious neo-centromeres at metaphase II, in that neo-centromeres may arise from the ends of both arms. When this occurs, the orientation of the two neo-centromeres of each monad is usually to opposite poles, but sometimes both ends of a monad are directed toward the same pole. Although the monads from displaced dyads have neo-centromeres at the end of each arm, one end being attracted to the nearest pole and the other to the more distant pole, normal disjunction usually occurs. This requires one monad to move away from the nearest pole toward which one of its ends is attracted, and to pass to the more distant pole, while the other monad goes to the nearest pole. It is difficult to interpret this phenomenon in terms of strength of attraction as a function of distance from centromere to pole.

The formation of neo-centric regions requires the presence of the abnormal chromosome 10. In its absence, no such regions are found. It appears highly probable that heterochromatic knobs located on other chromosomes also are concerned in the formation of precocious centric regions at both meiotic metaphases, since the cytological observations show a correlation between number of knobs and number of precocious centric regions. Knobless arms later form neo-centric regions, but not until anaphase movement has already been initiated by the true centric region.

It is possible that maize chromosomes possess latent centric regions which are activated by the abnormal 10. It has been demonstrated, however, that the true centric region is involved in the formation of neo-centromeres. Plants homozygous for abnormal 10 and heterozygous for the long paracentric inversion in chromosome 4, studied by McClintock (1938) and Morgan (1950), were obtained. Both the normal and inverted chromosome 4 carried a large knob in the long arm which is included in the inverted segment. Single crossovers within the inversion give rise to two non-crossover monocentric chromatids, one dicentric chromatid which forms a bridge at anaphase I, and an acentric fragment. The knobbed acentric fragment lies passively on the spindle with no indication of spindle fiber activity. Neo-centromeres arise from the same chromatin segments comprising the acentric fragment when they constitute a portion of a whole chromosome 4. It follows that the true or primary centromere plays an essential role in the production of neo-centromeres.

The localized centromeres of maize chromosomes are concerned with the elaboration of fiber-producing material. Normally this unique substance is confined to the true centric region, hence chromosomal fibers arise solely from this part of the chromosome.

It is our belief: (1) that these centric regions produce an over-abundance of fiber-forming material if abnormal 10 is present in the nucleus; (2) that a portion of this substance escapes from the confines of the centric regions and moves distally along the chromosome to produce supernumerary chromosomal fibers; and (3) that the knobs either stimulate centric activity or else cause the excess fiber-forming substance to move preferentially along knob-bearing arms so that neo-centric activity is first manifested by these arms.

The failure of the acentric fragment to form chromosomal fibers suggests that the postulated movement of the material from the true centric region occurs after crossing over has taken place. If it happened prior to pachytene, the regions which later constitute the acentric fragments would receive some of this fiber-producing substance which subsequently could form spindle fibers. In support of the above interpretation is the observation that small aggregations of a substance similar in appearance to that located in the true centric region are sometimes found near the distal regions of some chromosomes at metaphase I and metaphase II. This observation is subject to various interpretations. But in conjunction with the behavior of acentric fragments, it strengthens the hypothesis that the production of neo-centromeres is intimately related to the presence or activity of the primary centric region. It is obvious that the presumed movement of the products of the centromere along the arms of the chromosome has a bearing on the kinetic theory of Position Effect.

Evidence has been presented that the abnormal chromosome 10 produces the phenomenon of preferential segregation, and that it also causes the formation of neo-centromeres. Are these two phenomena related—does preferential segregation occur as a consequence of neo-centric activity? While no definite answer can be given at this time a tentative hypothesis has been developed. Sturtevant and Beadle (1936), seeking to account for the absence of egg and larvae mortality following single crossovers in paracentric inversions in Drosophila, postulated that the crossover chromatids were selectively eliminated from the egg nucleus. The two spindles of the second meiotic division in Drosophila eggs are arranged in tandem. Following a crossover within the inverted segment, the tetrad at metaphase I consists of two non-crossover chromatids, a dicentric and an acentric chromatid.

They assumed that the chromatin bridge arising from the dicentric chromatid, when the homologous centromeres pass to opposite poles at anaphase I, ties its two centromeres together. The spatial arrangement thus produced is such that the two monocentric chromatids lie nearer the two poles than does the dicentric chromatid.

The persistence of this relationship into the second division results in a non-random orientation on the metaphase II spindles. The monocentric, non-crossover chromatids are free to pass to the two terminal poles, while the two centromeres from the dicentric chromatid are directed to the two inner poles. Consequently, at anaphase II the terminal poles each receive a non-crossover chromatid. Since the egg nucleus arises from the innermost terminal pole it would contain a non-crossover chromatid with a full set of genes. The correctness of this ingenious hypothesis was established by Darlington and La Cour (1941) in Lilium and Tulipa and by Carson (1946) in Sciara.

It is possible that a somewhat similar mechanism is operating in Zea to produce preferential segregation. In maize, as in Drosophila, the two spindles of the second meiotic division of megasporogenesis are arranged in a linear order. The basal megaspore of the linear set of four develops into the female gametophyte, the remaining three aborting. We know that in plants heterozygous for knobbed and knobless chromosomes, one arm of some of the disjoining dyads at anaphase I possess precociously-acting chromosomal fibers not present in the homologous arm. There is reason to believe that the knobbed arms form precocious neo-centromeres while knobless arms do not. Owing to the rapidity with which neo-centric regions pass poleward at anaphase I, those chromatids with neo-centromeres reach the pole in advance of knobless arms lacking neo-centromeres. In a dyad consisting of one knobbed and one knobless chromatid, the knobbed chromatid would come to lie closer to the pole, while the knobless one would face the spindle plate.

In order to account for preferential segregation, it is necessary to assume that this orientation persists until the second metaphase, and that it results in the knobbed chromatids facing the two terminal poles while the two knobless ones would be oriented toward the two inner poles. On such a mechanism, preferential segregation would occur only when a crossover takes place between the knob and the true centromere in a heterozygous bivalent. The extent of preferential segregation would be a direct function of the amount of crossing over in the knob-centromere region.

Such an explanation can only be considered as a working hypothesis. It can be critically tested, however, and such experiments are being conducted by Jean Werner Morgan, who also participated in the studies reported here. They include varying the crossover distance between knob and centromere by translocation and inversion, testing for preferential segregation of heteromorphic chromosomes other than chromosome 10 in plants homozygous for abnormal 10, determining neo-centric activity in chromatids with knobs in both the long and short arm, etc. I prefer not to mention her incomplete findings at this time, since to do so would detract from continued interest in her work.

The phenomenon of preferential segregation is by no means confined to maize. Sturtevant (1936) found a non-random segregation of three chromosomes IV in Drosophila. Bridges, in Morgan, Bridges, and Sturtevant (1925), established that the distribution of the chromosomes in triploid Drosophila was not according to chance. Beadle (1935) reported that crossing over in triploid Drosophila near the centromere region between one member of attached -X's and a free X chromosome was correlated with autosomal disjunction. Lower crossover values were found in $1X\ 2A$ and $\widehat{XX}\ 1A$ combinations than in $1X\ 1A$ and $\widehat{XX}\ 2A$ gametes. This non-random distribution indicates a correlated orientation of non-homologous chromosomes on the equatorial plate.

In Sciara the paternal set of chromosomes moves away from the pole of the monocentric spindle of the primary spermatocyte. The two sister X chromosomes pass to the same pole at the second spermatocyte division (Metz, 1938). Schrader (1931) observed a non-random orientation in Protortonia which led to selective distribution in secondary spermatocytes. Catcheside (1944), in an analysis of Zickler's data on spore arrangement in the Ascomycete *Bombardia lunata*, found that certain genes were preferentially segregated. Not all of the above examples are strictly comparable to the situations found in maize, Sciara, and Bombardia. In the latter cases a specific spindle pole receives a certain chromosome or set of chromosomes, while in the Drosophila cases particular chromosomes pass preferentially together, but presumably at random, to either pole.

The neo-centromeres arising from chromosome ends, reported in rye by Prakken and Muntzing (1942) and Östergren and Prakken (1946), closely resemble those found in maize. In both maize and rye the neo-centric regions are found on arms possessing knobs (heterochromatin), and the poleward movement of neo-centromeres is precocious in both plants. Unfortunately, nothing is known about preferential segregation in rye, but it should occur if our hypothesis is correct.

R. A. BRINK
University of Wisconsin

Chapter 5

Inbreeding and Crossbreeding in Seed Development[*]

It is now generally recognized that the effects on growth of inbreeding and crossbreeding are intimately interwoven in the whole complex fabric of development and reproduction. Not only are the effects widespread and often of major consequence in the economy of the organism, but sometimes they are manifested in devious ways. Such is the case in the seed of flowering plants.

The success or failure of seed development turns primarily, not on the embryo which embodies the line of descent, but upon an accessory organ of reproduction, the endosperm. The novel origin and sensitivity of this latter tissue to changes in genetic composition render early seed development one of the critical stages in the life cycle of flowering plants. My colleague, D. C. Cooper, and I have been exploring these relations during the past decade. An attempt will be made here to review some of the evidence upon which our point of view rests, and to call attention to some of the broader implications of the main facts.

As a means of bringing the important aspects of the problem in flowering plants into focus, seed development in the angiosperms and gymnosperms will be compared. Essential features of the general hypothesis by which we have been guided will then be set forth. The central role of the endosperm in formation of the angiosperm seed and the responsiveness of this tissue to variations in genetic composition will be illustrated by a consideration of the immediate effects of self- and cross-fertilization in alfalfa. It will then be shown that the means by which the embryo in the common dandelion, an autonomous apomict, is nourished is of a type which would be expected according to the hypothesis proposed.

[*] Paper from the Department of Genetics, College of Agriculture, University of Wisconsin, No. 432.

An illustration will next be given of endosperm failure as an isolating mechanism. Finally, the significance of the present results for the problem of artificially rearing embryos whose development in the seed is blocked by endosperm disfunction will be pointed out.

Complete literature citations are not given. These may be found in the summary paper (Brink and Cooper, 1947) in which much additional evidence bearing on the present thesis also is presented.

The endosperm is a special structure intercalated between the female parent and the embryo, serving to mediate the relations between the two. The tissue originates from the central cell of the female gametophyte, following a fertilization distinct from that giving rise to the embryo. The secondary fertilization is unusual in that two identical haploid nuclei of maternal origin are united with one contributed by the pollen. The endosperm thus becomes $3x$ in chromosome number in contrast with the $2x$ condition of the embryo and the mother plant, respectively. Endosperm and embryo carry the same kinds of genes, but the genic balance may be unlike in the two tissues by virtue of the double contribution to the endosperm from the maternal parent. A further element of genetic heterogeneity in the seed arises from the fact that nucellus and integuments, which are maternal structures, may differ in genotype from the endosperm and embryo which they enclose, since they belong to the previous generation.

These facts, of course, have long been known. Certain of their implications, however, are only now becoming apparent. Particularly is this true of the secondary fertilization on which our attention will be focussed.

A word should be said at this point concerning the manner in which the endosperm should be visualized. Many are familiar with the tissue only in the mature seeds of species in which the endosperm persists as a storage organ. This condition, well known in the cereals, for example, is exceptional among flowering plants, and represents a secondary adaptation of significance mainly for the future seedling. In most species the endosperm either does not persist in the fully developed seed or occurs therein as a residue only. On the other hand, the endosperm is regularly a prominent organ in the juvenile seed. It is especially active directly following fertilization, during what may be termed the lag phase of embryo growth. This period is seldom longer than a few days, and varies according to the species. In spite of its typically ephemeral character, the endosperm plays a critical role in (1) transforming the mature ovule into a young seed and (2) nourishing the embryo during its initial period of growth. We are here concerned with the endosperm in these two relationships only.

THE SEED IN GYMNOSPERMS AND ANGIOSPERMS

It is helpful in understanding the significance of the secondary fertilization to compare the circumstances of seed development in the angiosperms with those in the other great class of seed forming plants, the gymnosperms. A secondary fertilization does not occur in the gymnosperms. The endosperm is a haploid tissue derived from the megaspore by continuous cell division. The tissue is a part of the gametophyte rather than an integral structure distinct from both gametophyte and sporophyte, as in the angiosperms.

On the other hand, the endosperms in the two classes of seed plants have an important common function, namely, nourishment of their respective associated embryos. The genetic equipment with which the two kinds of endosperms are furnished differs in a fundamental respect. That of the gymnosperm is a sample half of the mother plant's inheritance, whereas the angiosperm endosperm, being of biparental derivation, has two chances instead of only one of receiving a physiologically effective genic complement. Insofar as the two tissues are autonomous in their functional properties, the angiosperm endosperm, therefore, is equipped to meet much more exacting requirements than its counterpart in the gymnosperms. A summary review of the differences in the gymnosperm and angiosperm ovules and seeds at fertilization, and during the immediately subsequent period, shows the importance of (or necessity for) a secondary fertilization in the flowering plants in order to maintain continuity of the life cycle at this stage.

The differences between the mature ovules of gymnosperms and angiosperms which appear to have a direct bearing on the present problem may be summarized as follows:

1. The seed coat in the gymnosperms approaches its mature size at the fertilization stage. The angiosperm seed coat undergoes extensive growth subsequent to fertilization. These facts are of interest in relation to the total food requirements of the two respective classes of growing seeds and the post-fertilization distribution of nutrients between the seed coat and the enclosed tissues.

2. The female gametophyte in the gymnosperms is an extensively developed multicellular (multinucleate, in some higher forms) structure. Its counterpart in the angiosperms typically consists of only seven cells. The potential disadvantage of the extreme reduction of the female gametophyte in the flowering plants will be considered below.

3. Generally speaking, the gymnosperm ovule is rich in food reserves, whereas the angiosperm ovule is sparsely supplied. This means that in the latter, the large volume of nutrients required for growth of the endosperm, embryo, and seed coat must be moved in from other parts of the plant. In the gymnosperms an extensive supply is directly at hand.

4. So far as may be inferred from the published accounts, fertilization in the gymnosperms initiates a new cycle of growth in the embryo only. Other parts of the ovule do not appear to be stimulated. Double fertilization in the angiosperms, in contrast, not only marks the inception of endosperm and embryo formation, but also incites pronounced mitotic activity and en-

largement of the cells in the integuments. Thus, with the exception of the nucellus which is broken down and absorbed by the rapidly expanding endosperm, all the elements of the young seed which were previously quiescent, suddenly spring into active growth following syngamy.

Consideration of these differences between the seeds of gymnosperms and angiosperms led us some ten years ago to explore the hypothesis that the secondary fertilization in angiosperms is essentially a means of enhancing the competitive power of the endosperm relative to the maternal portions of the seed—by conferring upon the endosperm the advantages of hybridity. The nutritive requirements of the young seed suddenly are raised from a low to a high level since fertilization starts a new cycle of growth in the massive integuments. The nutrient supply, on the other hand, quickly falls to the plane which can be maintained by movement of foods into the seed from other parts of the plant as a result of exhaustion of the limited ovule reserves.

It seemed reasonable to assume that, within the seed, the incoming nutrients would tend to be partitioned between the different tissues according to the respective amounts of growth occurring in them. On this basis, the extensively developed integuments would consume the major portion. The diminutive endosperm and embryo would receive but a small fraction of the total. Under these conditions, failure of the young seed through starvation of the embryo could arise, unless the endosperm—as the nutritive agent of the embryo—were endowed with special properties which offset its initially small size. It seemed essential that the endosperm, by one means or another, be enabled to quickly acquire a position of physiological dominance in the juvenile seed in order to insure continued development.

Two genetic characteristics of the endosperm suggest themselves as being important in this connection. The first is the triploid condition of the nuclei. Little is known of the physiological effects of ploidy in general, and virtually nothing of its meaning in special situations of this kind. One suspects, however, that the endosperm gains some advantage from its extra chromosome garniture, as such, in mediating the relations between the diploid maternal parent and the young diploid embryo. It is also probably significant that, whereas the embryo inherits equally from the two parents, two-thirds of the endosperm's genic complement is derived from the plant upon which it is nutritionally dependent and one-third of the complement from the male parent.

Heterozygosis is the second characteristic of the endosperm which might enhance the inherent physiological efficiency of this tissue. The possibility of heterozygosity arises, of course, from the biparental origin of the endosperm mother nucleus. The condition is realized in matings between genetically different plants. Haploidy of the endosperm, as occurs in the gymnosperms, appears to be genetically insufficient for seed development in the flowering plants. Early post-fertilization circumstances, particularly the dependence upon and competition for an outside nutrient supply in the latter, require that the tissue shall share in the advantages of sexuality. The advantage gained is not that of amphimixis in general, as in the embryo, but solely the extra vigor of growth associated with the union of unlike nuclei in the mother cell. Thus hybrid vigor in the endosperm has some claim to uniqueness. The sole object gained by entry of a sperm into the nuclear makeup of this sterile tissue is the added vigor of growth thus acquired. Some of the evidence by which the validity of this point of view may be tested will now be considered.

INBREEDING AND CROSSBREEDING EFFECT ON
SEED COLLAPSE IN MEDICAGO SATIVA

Two classes of matings on seven alfalfa plants were carried out under favorable growth conditions in a greenhouse. After removal of the anthers from the flowers used, a part of the flowers were pollinated with pollen from the same respective plants. This constitutes the self-fertilized series. Other flowers on the same plants were cross-pollinated, the pollen being derived in each case from an unrelated plant within the group. These matings comprise the cross-fertilized series.

Since alfalfa is regularly cross-fertilized, the second series of matings is designed to maintain the level of heterozygosity normal to the endosperm and embryo in this species. The enforced self-fertilization, on the other hand, would be expected to reduce heterozygosity in the endosperm mother nucleus and the zygote by 50 per cent. It is proposed to review the consequences for seed development of this sharp reduction in heterozygosis.

Following the above two series of matings, the pistils were collected at 30, 48, 72, 96, 120, and 144 hours and imbedded in paraffin. After sectioning and staining, data were taken on fertility of the ovules, frequency of fertile ovules collapsing, number of cells in the embryo, and number of nuclei in the endosperm. Detailed observations were made subsequently on growth of the integuments.

Alfalfa was known previously to be partially self-incompatible. It was not unexpected, therefore, to find that only 15 per cent of the ovules became fertile after selfing in contrast to 66 per cent after cross-pollination. The new fact which emerged was the much higher incidence of collapse of ovules subsequent to fertilization in the selfed than in the crossed group. The data are summarized in Table 5.1. Fertilization occurred within about 30 hours after pollination under the prevailing conditions. It was somewhat delayed after selfing. Little evidence of breakdown of the seeds was found at 48 hours. In the 72 hour and subsequent collections, however, the phenomenon was common. The results presented in the table cover the period from 72 hours to 144 hours, inclusive, and are based upon 433 seeds and 1682 seeds in the selfed and crossed series, respectively.

Growth of the young seed at this stage appears to be quite independent of that of its neighbors in the same ovary. Furthermore, the quickly succeeding secondary effects of fertilization, such as enlargement of the surrounding fruit, are at a minimum. Studies on the reproductive physiology of the flowering plants are rendered difficult by the multiplicity of changes which are eventually set in motion in the tissues of the seed, the fruit, and the maternal plant following fertilization. The sequence and interrelations of the events immediately subsequent to syngamy are simpler to analyze than those which occur later, in view of the fact that each very young seed may be considered to behave independently of the others.

The data in Table 5.1 show that, for each of the seven plants tested, the

TABLE 5.1

FREQUENCY OF FERTILE OVULES COLLAPSING IN SEVEN ALFALFA PLANTS FOLLOWING SELF- AND CROSS-FERTILIZATION. DATA BASED ON COLLECTIONS AT 72, 96, 120, AND 144 HOURS AFTER POLLINATION (AFTER COOPER AND BRINK, 1940)

	SELF-FERTILIZATION			CROSS-FERTILIZATION			
Plant Selfed	No. of Fertile Ovules		Percentage Collapsing	Plants Crossed	No. of Fertile Ovules		Percentage Collapsing
	Total	Collapsing			Total	Collapsing	
A........	37	9	24.3	A×B.....	187	13	7.0
B........	37	19	51.4	B×C.....	110	5	4.5
C........	20	7	35.0	C×D.....	171	13	7.6
D........	17	7	41.2	D×E.....	171	16	9.4
E........	39	8	20.5	E×A.....	146	9	6.2
F........	109	39	35.8	F×G.....	228	14	6.1
G........	55	19	34.5	G×F.....	198	16	8.1
Total..	314	108	34.4	Total..	1211	86	7.1

frequency of seeds collapsing is much higher in the selfed than in the crossed series. The proportions vary in different individuals from about 3 to 1 to over 11 to 1. On the average, approximately five times as many seeds containing inbred endosperms and embryos collapse within the first six days after pollination as in the crossbred group. Since other factors were not varied, the decrease in survival in the selfed series must be attributed to the inbreeding.

The evidence, both general and particular, points to the endosperm rather than the embryo as the seat of the inbreeding depression effect. The endosperm in alfalfa is free nucleate up to about 144 hours after pollination, although it develops as a cellular tissue thereafter. Successive waves of mitotic divisions traverse the tissue, the number of nuclei being doubled in each cycle. Thus growth during this period proceeds at an exponential rate.

The concurrent development of the embryo, on the other hand, is relatively slow. The zygote divides to form a two-celled proembryo. Successive divisions of the apical cell give rise first to a six-celled proembryo and then to the initials of the definitive embryo.

The pronounced difference in rate of development of the two tissues is illustrated by the fact that at 144 hours the modal number of cells in the embryo is only 16, whereas the typical number of nuclei in the endosperm at this time is 128. Rapid and precocious development of the endosperm as seen in alfalfa is characteristic of the angiosperms in general. The much higher level of activity of the endosperm is presumptive evidence that this tissue, rather than the embryo, is especially subject to developmental upsets in the young seed. Data available in the present instance provide direct confirmation of this interpretation.

The comparative rates of growth of endosperm and embryo in the selfed and crossed alfalfa series up to 144 hours after pollination are illustrated in Figure 5.1. Not only are the values for the embryo low, but also there is little difference between those for the inbred and crossbred series. The conclusion appears warranted that the direct effect of inbreeding on the embryo at this stage, if indeed there is a demonstrable effect, is too small to account for the high frequency of seed collapse. In contrast, there is a very sharp decline in rate of nuclear division in the endosperm, following enforced self-fertilization of this naturally cross-fertilized plant. The lower rate is shown from the first division onward. There are about twice as many nuclei present at 144 hours in the crossbred as in the inbred endosperms.

Due to the partial self-incompatibility in alfalfa, fertilization on the average, is slightly delayed following selfing. A comparison of the rate of growth of the two classes of endosperms independent of time as shown in Figure 5.2, however, establishes the reality of the difference in rate of growth between the inbred and crossbred endosperms. When the seeds are arrayed in terms of cell numbers of the enclosed embryo, it is found that for all nine classes occurring in the material the endosperms are more advanced in the crossbred than in the inbred series. That is to say, the embryos at a given stage of development have associated with them more vigorously growing endosperms following cross-fertilization than after selfing. Moreover, the decrease in size resulting from the inbreeding is so large that one is led immediately to suspect that herein lies the primary cause of the frequent seed collapse following selfing.

Why should impairment in rate of endosperm growth lead to arrested seed development? The answer in the present case is clear. As was pointed out earlier, double fertilization initiates not only endosperm and embryo development, but also a new cycle of growth in the integuments. The latter compete directly with the endosperm for the nutrients moving into the young seed. If the endosperm is developing subnormally, a disproportionate amount of the incoming nutrients is diverted to the integuments. As a result this tissue frequently becomes hyperplastic. The overgrowth in the case of al- falfa characterizes the inner integument. As Dr. Cooper observed, it begins at a point opposite the distal end of the vascular bundle where the concen- tration of nutrients may be assumed to be the greatest. The inner integument, which is normally two cell layers in thickness, becomes multilayered and somewhat callus-like in the region of the greatest mitotic activity. This pro- nounced overgrowth of the inner integument quickly reacts upon the endo- sperm, further impairing its development. In the seeds which fail, a complete

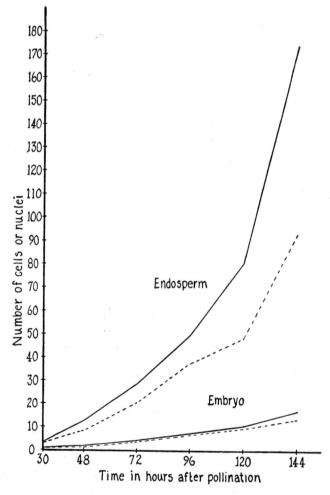

FIG. 5.1—Increase in number of cells in embryo and in number of nuclei in endosperm following self- (*broken line*) and cross-fertilization (*continuous line*). After Brink and Cooper, 1940.

collapse of the endosperm then ensues. Significantly, breakdown of the endosperm tissue begins in the region opposite the end of the vascular bundle where the inner integument is especially hyperactive. Following collapse of the endosperm, the young seed dies.

SEED DEVELOPMENT WITHOUT FERTILIZATION

There are a few species of flowering plants in which both endosperm and embryo develop without fertilization. These so-called autonomous apomicts

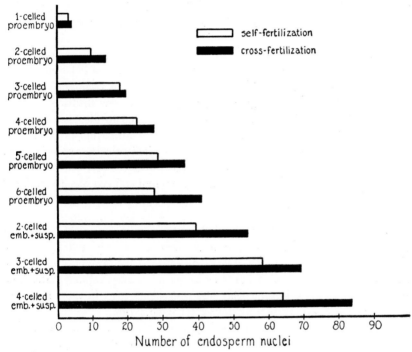

FIG. 5.2—Number of endosperm nuclei associated with proembryos and embryos at various stages of development following self- and cross-fertilization. After Brink and Cooper, 1940.

should provide an independent test of the hypothesis that aggressive development of the endosperm is requisite to seed development, and that the secondary fertilization is a device by which aggressiveness of the tissue is enhanced. On the basis of the reasoning applied to sexual species, one would expect to find in autonomous apomicts that the embryo is not basically dependent on an active endosperm for its nourishment. So far as I am aware, the evidence bearing directly on this question is limited to a single study which Cooper and I carried out on the common dandelion, *Taraxacum officinale* (Cooper and Brink, 1949).

The common dandelion is triploid ($3x = 24$). The regularity and abundance of seed production in the plant is well known. A full complement of seed forms in the absence of pollination, as may be demonstrated easily by re-moving the corollas and anthers—by cutting off the distal portion of the head in the bud stage. Ordinarily the anthers do not open in the intact mature flower.

The female gametophyte is formed without reduction in chromosome number of the nuclei. Otherwise it is a typical eight-nucleate, seven-celled structure lying in direct contact in the mature ovule with the innermost layer of cells of the single thick integument. The polar nuclei fuse to give a hexaploid primary endosperm nucleus. The single layer of cells comprising the nucellus disintegrates during formation of the embryo sac.

Sexual forms of the common dandelion are not known to occur. Accordingly another species, *T. kok-saghyz*, the Russian dandelion, was examined as a control. *T. kok-saghyz* is diploid ($2x = 16$) and, since it is self-incompatible, requires cross-pollination for seed formation. A comparative study of *T. officinale* and *T. kok-saghyz* was made with a view to discovering, if possible, the means by which the former is enabled to dispense with the secondary fertilization, which is essential to seed formation in the latter. Heads were collected at four stages: late bud, just prior to anthesis, open flower, and with seeds ranging up to six days of age. After sectioning and staining, the number of cells in the endosperm and embryo was determined, and observations were made on the amount and distribution of food materials.

Seed formation in *T. kok-saghyz* follows the course typical of the angiosperms. Endosperm and embryo development are initiated by double fertilization. Subsequently, the two tissues grow very rapidly, and in tune with each other. Cell number in the endosperm increases exponentially. The endosperm, however, is somewhat less precocious than in most flowering plants. The seed is mature 9–12 days after fertilization.

A markedly different set of relations present themselves in the seed of the apomictic *T. officinale*. The seed in this species begins development when the flowers are in the late bud stage. By the time the flowers open, there may be 100 cells or more in the endosperm, the embryo, or in both tissues in some seeds. A further significant fact is the extraordinary amount of variability in the size ratios of endosperm and embryo from seed to seed of even age. There is a positive relation between cell number in endosperm and embryo over the period studied—as would be expected in view of the fact that in most seeds both tissues are growing. As measured by the correlation co-efficient, this value is low ($r = .57$) compared with that for *T. kok-saghyz* ($r = .76$).

Average cell number in the embryo in relation to endosperm size is depicted for the two species in Figure 5.3. Cell number in the endosperm increases geometrically, so that size of the tissue may be expressed appropriately in terms of division cycles. Embryo cell number, in contrast, increases arithmetically. It will be noted from Figure 5.3 that the mean embryo cell number in *T. officinale*, before the endosperm mother cell divides (0 cycle), is about 16. The corresponding value *T. kok-saghyz* is 1. This is a reflection of the fact that the embryo in the apomictic species usually starts growth in advance of the endosperm. Although they start from different levels, the two curves are not greatly dissimilar. The embryo in the common dandelion, on the average, is consistently larger in the young seed than that of *T. kok-saghyz*, relative to given stages in endosperm development.

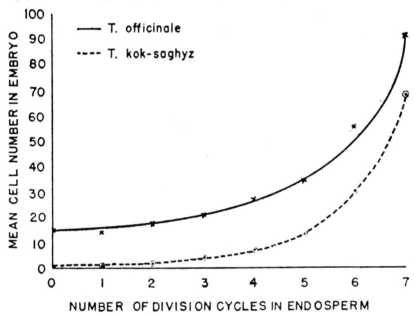

FIG. 5.3—Early growth of embryo of *T. kok-saghyz* and *T. officinale* in relation to endosperm size. After Cooper and Brink, 1949.

More instructive than the mean values on which Figure 5.3 are based, is the variability in the frequency distributions concerned. The data are summarized in Table 5.2. A logarithmic scale was used in expressing embryo sizes merely as a convenient way of summarizing the widely dispersed values. As mentioned above, growth of the embryo during this period is approximately linear.

Table 2 reveals that the variability is low in embryo cell number at successive stages of endosperm development in *T. kok-saghyz*. This means that embryo and endosperm are closely synchronized in their growth in the sexual species. The variability in embryo size in the apomict, on the other hand, is enormous. For example, in seeds in which the endosperm is still at the mother cell stage (0 cycle), the associated embryos are distributed over all size classes from 1 to 128. The standard deviation for embryo cell number is

15.6, a value equal to the mean. The range is even greater in the class of seeds having 128-cell endosperms, and the standard deviation rises to 51 cells.

The extreme variability in embryo size for given stages of endosperm development in *T. officinale* is a fact of cardinal importance in the present analysis. Inspection of Table 5.2 reveals certain details which emphasize the significance of the summary data on dispersion. Note, for instance, that

TABLE 5.2

DISTRIBUTION OF EMBRYOS BY CELL NUMBER RELA-
TIVE TO ENDOSPERM DIVISION CYCLE
(AFTER COOPER AND BRINK, 1949)

Endo-sperm Division Cycle	Species	Total Seeds Examined	Embryo Cell Number—Logarithmic Class Values									Standard Deviation
			1	2	4	8	16	32	64	128	256	
0.......	*T. officinale*	227	9	16	33	57	66	38	7	1	....	15.6
	T. kok-saghyz	All	All	....	....	....	....	....	....	....	....	0
1.......	*T. officinale*	253	23	11	37	70	55	50	6	1	....	13.6
	T. kok-saghyz	77	31	46	....	....	....	....	....	....	....	0.5
2.......	*T. officinale*	145	18	11	7	23	43	33	9	1	....	17.0
	T. kok-saghyz	32	1	31	....	....	....	....	....	....	....	0.2
3.......	*T. officinale*	108	12	6	6	19	27	25	12	1	....	21.1
	T. kok-saghyz	25	....	....	22	3	....	....	....	....	....	0.7
4.......	*T. officinale*	111	4	1	2	9	39	40	14	2	....	19.2
	T. kok-saghyz	34	....	....	5	27	·2	....	....	....	....	1.9
5.......	*T. officinale*	115	6	....	4	4	23	50	23	5	....	24.2
	T. kok-saghyz	68	....	....	....	24	40	4	....	....	....	4.1
6.......	*T. officinale*	99	1	1	....	....	7	31	46	13	....	29.9
	T. kok-saghyz	55	....	....	....	....	10	41	4	....	....	9.0
7.......	*T. officinale*	60	2	....	1	....	1	8	17	28	3	51.0
	T. kok-saghyz	19	....	....	....	....	....	3	16	....	....	16.7

among the seeds still in the endosperm mother cell stage (0 cycle) one contains an embryo in the 128-cell class and seven have embryos in the 64-cell class. Similar, although less extreme, cases occur in the 1-cycle and 2-cycle endosperm distributions. Study of the histological preparations shows that the seeds in which the embryos are found are growing vigorously and appear capable of completing development. This can mean only that either very small endosperms in *T. officinale* are extraordinarily efficient structures, or embryo growth in this species is not dependent on an endosperm.

At the opposite corner of the table, on the diagonal, two seeds are entered in the 7-cycle endosperm array in which the embryos are still in the one-cell stage. These seeds also appeared to be healthy and capable of continued development. These extreme examples point unmistakably to the conclusion that in the apomictic dandelion the endosperm, as the master tissue in the young seed, has been disestablished. Embryo growth must be sustained by other means.

The substitute arrangement for nourishing the embryo in *T. officinale* was disclosed by a histological study of the ovules of this species and *T. kok-saghyz*. Basically the structure of the ovule is the same in both. As the female gametophyte expands, the nucellus disintegrates so that the gametophyte comes to lie in direct contact with the endothelium which comprises the innermost layer of cells of the massive integument. The endothelium persists and appears to function in the transfer of nutrients during the course of seed development. In *T. kok-saghyz* the inner layers of integumentary cells adjacent to the endothelium lose their contents during formation of the gametophyte, and contain shrunken and misshapen nuclei when the ovule is mature. The cells of the integument immediately surrounding this depleted region are densely cytoplasmic and possess well-defined nuclei. The outermost parenchymatous cells of the integument are highly vacuolate. The single vascular bundle makes an arc about the greatest circumference of the ovule in both species. Only limited amounts of stainable reserve food materials occur anywhere in the *T. kok-saghyz* ovule.

The *T. officinale* ovule differs conspicuously from that of *T. kok-saghyz* in possessing an abundance of reserve food. The cells of the integument just outside the endothelium enlarge as the ovule matures and become gorged with a homogeneous material which appears to be proteinaceous in composition. This substance also extends between the cells at the outer edge of the storage region proper.

This extensive prestorage of protein-rich food material in the integument provides an explanation of the fact that embryo development in the apomict may proceed normally in spite of very limited endosperm growth. The conditions render superfluous an aggressively functioning endosperm. The embryo draws directly on a food supply already at hand. From the physiological point of view, the nutritive mechanism in the apomict is analogous to that in the gymnosperms. In both these classes of plants certain of the processes essential to seed development, which follow double fertilization in sexual species of flowering plants, are pushed back into the ovule. The secondary fertilization, which through its effect on vigor of endosperm growth may be looked upon as a means of offsetting the tardy provision of nourishment for the embryo, thus can be dispensed with.

SEED DEVELOPMENT GRADE AND EMBRYO GROWTH POTENTIALITIES

The conclusion that growth of the angiosperm seed is basically controlled by the endosperm has an interesting corollary. That is, that the grade of seed development attained after a given mating is not a definitive index of the intrinsic vigor of the embryo. This statement is not intended to imply that the two phenomena are unrelated, but rather that they vary independently of each other to a significant degree. Many interspecific matings, for example, yield poorly developed seeds. Often the embryos in these seeds give rise to relatively weak plants. Sometimes, however, the embryos within such seeds are capable of forming plants of great vegetative vigor. In other words, the fact that development of the seed is impaired, even to a degree that calls for special methods of propagation, does not necessarily mean that the embryo is intrinsically weak. The hybrid during the seed stage may merely be the victim of a faulty endosperm. Only when released from this stricture can the inherent potentialities of the new individual be expressed.

Two examples of such intrinsically vigorous hybrids in which the conditions of seed development have been explored will be briefly mentioned. They differ in the grade of seed development attained. Small but nevertheless germinable seeds are formed in the one case, whereas in the other the embryo egularly dies unless special precautions are taken to save it.

Cooper and I found that when the diploid ($2n = 24$) Red Currant tomato, *Lycopersicon pimpinellifolium*, is pollinated with a particular strain of *L. peruvianum*, likewise a diploid, fertilization occurs with high frequency but all the seeds collapse before the fruit is ripe. Seed development follows a familiar pattern. The endosperm grows less vigorously than in normal *L. pimpinellifolium* seeds, and the endothelium enclosing it tends to become hyperplastic. Endosperm cells become highly vacuolate and starved in appearance. Densely staining granules of unknown composition accumulate in the chalazal region just outside the endosperm, suggesting that the latter tissue is incapable of absorbing the available supply of nutrients. All the seeds in the ripe fruit are shrivelled and incapable of germination.

Following the application of pollen from the same diploid strain of *L. peruvianum* to a tetraploid ($2n = 48$) race of *L. pimpinellifolium*, about one-half the fertile ovules develop into small but germinable seeds containing triploid embryos. The other seeds collapse at various stages of growth. Histological examination of the $4n$ *L. pimpinellifolium* × $2n$ *L. peruvianum* seeds shows retarded embryo development and a less rapid endosperm growth than occurs in the normally pollinated tetraploid parent. The endosperm in sixteen-day-old hybrid seeds lacks the rather densely packed starch reserves characteristic of tomato seeds at this stage. The peripheral layers of endosperm cells adjacent to the endothelium break down. An unusually large cavity is formed in the interior of the tissue as a result of digestion of the cells by the slowly differentiating embryo. Endosperm function is markedly impaired in this cross, but in many seeds remains somewhat above the threshold at which complete failure occurs.

The triploid plants resulting from germinable $4n$ *L. pimpinellifolium* × $2n$ *L. peruvianum* seeds are extraordinarily vigorous. Although partially sterile, they considerably exceed both the parents in capacity for vegetative growth. The inference is clear that the genic combination resulting from this cross yields markedly different results in the endosperm and the sister sporophyte. The difference in part may be a consequence of the 2:1 balance of *L. pimpinellifolium* and *L. peruvianum* genes in the embryo as compared with the 4:1 ratio in the endosperm. The important point, however, is that the mechanism of seed formation in the flowering plants is such that the two products of a given double fertilization may be quite differently endowed in terms of the genes necessary to perform their respective functions.

The second example to be discussed in this connection will enable us to visualize the limits which may be reached in endosperm disfunction with retention of embryo viability.

Fertilization freely occurs when squirrel-tail barley, *Hordeum jubatum* is pollinated by cultivated rye, *Secale cereale*. The resulting seeds all die, however, within less than two weeks. Space does not permit me to recount here the steps leading to the breakdown. They have been described in detail elsewhere (Cooper & Brink, 1944; Brink & Cooper, 1944). The endosperm early becomes completely disorganized. Some of the embryos formed, however, reach a stage previous to collapse at which time they may be dissected from the seed and successfully reared on an artificial nutrient medium. A single plant was grown to maturity from an embryo treated in this way. The plant was thrifty, although sterile. Representatives of the parent species grown under comparable conditions were not available, so that a valid comparison of relative vigor could not be made. The hybrid, however, appeared to be intermediate in stature and number of tillers.

The extreme character of the endosperm disturbances in the *H. jubatum* × *S. cereale* seed indicates that this hybrid could not arise under field conditions. Although the embryo is demonstrably capable of continued development its growth is terminated in the seed due to failure of the associated endosperm. Death of the embryo, as an indirect result of endosperm disfunction following wide crosses, appears to be commoner than was thought before the physiological implications of the secondary fertilization in flowering plants were recognized. Realization of this fact has stimulated additional interest in circumventing the phenomenon by excising such embryos from the seed and rearing them artificially.

Artificial methods of cultivating embryos removed from abortive seeds often have been used to extend the area within which gene transfers may be effected. Numerous interspecific hybrids have thus been grown which otherwise are not realizable. The nature of the general problem involved may now be seen in somewhat broader perspective. Two points of particular interest may be noted.

The first, briefly adverted to above, is that the frequency with which embryos are formed following matings between distantly related plants is much higher than earlier believed. Various investigators have expressed the opinion that the mere presence of growing pollen tubes in the style causes enlargement of the ovules. This view now appears to be incorrect.

On the other hand, there is a steadily increasing amount of evidence to show that the incipient growth of the ovules, following many interspecific matings which do not yield functional seeds, is a response to fertilization. That is to say, the block in the reproductive cycle which was assumed to intervene prior to fertilization actually occurs following syngamy. Embryos are formed in these cases, but they perish when the young seed fails to develop. Some rather extreme examples of this phenomenon which have been observed in our laboratory include *Nicotiana glutinosa* × *Petunia violacea*, *N. glutinosa* × *Lycopersicon esculentum*, and *Medicago sativa* × *M. scutellata*.

It is not to be inferred that all hybrid embryos of this general class are capable of growing into mature plants. The fact that the seeds containing them collapse is not proof, however, of intrinsic inviability. An unknown but probably significant proportion of these novel zygotic combinations are potentially propagable. The problem is to discover the means by which they may be reared. This brings us to the second point—the nature of the problem to be faced in growing very small excised embryos.

With few exceptions, the embryos which have been successfully cultivated artificially have been removed from the seed at rather advanced stages of development. Unless they are multicellular and differentiation has at least begun, the embryos usually do not grow on the media which thus far have been devised. There are reasons for thinking that the nutritional requirements of these older embryos are simpler than those in a juvenile condition. Histological evidence shows that at the early stages of seed development the embryo is enclosed, or nearly enclosed, in the highly active, young endosperm. The endosperm cells adjacent to the proembryo and the very young embryo remain intact. A little later, as the embryo enlarges, these cells begin to break down and their contents disappear. Eventually all the endosperm tissue is consumed in most species.

One may infer from these facts that the embryo is dependent upon the endosperm for certain metabolites which initially the embryo is quite incapable of synthesizing. The endosperm may be pictured as secreting the needed materials at the early post-fertilization stage, and yielding them later in a more passive fashion as the tissue becomes lysed. Meanwhile the embryo becomes progressively less dependent upon the endosperm by acquiring for itself the synthetic capabilities previously limited to the nurse tissue. On this view the very young embryo is an obligate parasite on the endosperm. Once past the state of obligate parasitism, growth of the embryo may be effectively supported by comparatively simple nutrients such as may be provided in artificial culture media.

Visualized in those terms, the problem of cultivating very young, excised embryos resolves itself into the discovery of means of duplicating the un-known but presumably special nutritive functions of the normal endosperm. Two possibilities suggest themselves in this connection. One is to determine natural sources of the special metabolites produced by the endosperm and then add these materials to the nutrient medium. Van Overbeek (1942) ob-tained significant improvement in the growth of small *Datura stramonium* embryos by supplying them with unautoclaved coconut milk. Blakeslee and Satina (1944) later reported that the coconut milk could be replaced by un-autoclaved malt extract. The other possibility is to cultivate the embryos artificially in association with actively functioning endosperm tissue. Cur-rent findings offer some encouragement that the latter procedure may prove efficacious.

Dr. Nancy Ziebur, working in our laboratory, recently has shown that the growth of very young embryos of common barley (0.3–1.1 mm. long) may be greatly improved by surrounding them on a nutrient agar medium with aseptically excised endosperms. The basic medium employed permits a satisfactory growth of older barley embryos but does not yield transplantable seedlings from embryos shorter than about 0.6 mm. except in conjunction with endosperms. Coconut milk and malt extract are ineffective with barley embryos. Water extracts of fresh barley endosperms gave positive, although smaller effects than the intact tissue. Further exploration of the living endo-sperm as a source of nutrients for very young, excised embryos should prove rewarding. The interrelationships of these two tissues in the juvenile seed give strong credence to this approach. The success which has so often at-tended efforts to grow older embryos artificially on rather simple media may have blinded us to the fact that the young embryo, divorced from the endo-sperm, may have quite different requirements.

W. GORDON WHALEY

*The Plant Research Institute of the University of Texas and
the Clayton Foundation for Research*

Chapter 6

Physiology of Gene
Action in Hybrids

The physiology of gene action in hybrids is not a subject apart from the physiology of gene action in organisms in general. The approach to specific problems of gene action is probably better made in non-hybrid organisms than in hybrids. Hybrids do, however, represent one type of genetic situation which in certain instances is particularly favorable for the study of gene action. Most useful in this respect are those hybrids which exhibit the phenomenon referred to, often rather loosely, as hybrid vigor. The terms hybrid vigor and heterosis often are used synonymously. A more precise usage, and one in accord with the original definitions, refers to the developed superiority of hybrids as hybrid vigor, and to the mechanism by which the superiority is developed as heterosis. By this definition, hybrid vigor is heterosis manifest. Because in studies of growth and development it is often desirable to distinguish clearly between mechanism and end result, this use of the two terms will be followed in this chapter.

Heterosis has been the subject of many experiments and a great deal of speculation on the part of geneticists. The concern has been mostly with the genetic bases of heterosis, and relatively little attention has been given to the physiological mechanisms involved. As a matter of fact, the literature on heterosis mirrors faithfully the changing emphasis in genetics in the last two or three decades. Practically all of the early investigations of heterosis had to do with the comparison of mature characteristics of inbred lines and their vigorous hybrids, and then with attempts to formulate genetic schemes in explanation of the differences. Gradually, the focus of investigation has turned to a study of developmental differences responsible for the hybrid vigor, and more recently to the gene action bases of these developmental differences.

It is a fair hope that from detailed studies of the nature and development of heterosis, much will in time be revealed about specific gene action. Unfortunately, most of the studies up to the present time have been directed to general rather than to specific considerations. It has been necessary to deal in terms of size differences, yield differences, and growth rate differences, until enough of the pattern should appear to indicate what specific physiological considerations are likely to be involved in heterosis. Because we have come only to this point and have proceeded but a little way in an analysis of these specific physiological considerations, this chapter will have to deal more with suggestions of the likely mechanisms than with data from investigations of them.

It is neither possible nor desirable to separate wholly the consideration of the physiological mechanisms of heterosis from the genetic bases. Our main concern will ultimately be with the genes involved and the nature of their action.

The word hybrid has no good, definitive genetic meaning. It can be used with equal propriety to refer to organisms which approach complete heterozygosity or to organisms which are heterozygous for only a small number of genes.

There is at least a rough relationship between the amount of heterosis in a hybrid and the extent of the genetic differences between the parents. Physiological and morphological diversity are dependent both upon the number of allelic differences between organisms and upon the nature of the action of the particular genes among which these allelic differences exist. It is quite possible that organisms differing by only a few genes may be more widely separated in certain characteristics than are organisms differing by many more genes—the actions of which are of less fundamental significance for the control of the developmental pattern.

In our approach to questions of hybrid vigor, we may be concerned with different degrees of hybridity. Consideration of this factor must involve not only the number of genes but also the nature of the action of the particular genes. Nor is this all, for the action of any specific allele is conditioned by the genetic background in which it occurs in a particular individual. Hence, the relations among genes may often be of critical importance.

Of tremendous import, too, are the interactions between the activities of the genes and the environment. In speaking of hybrid vigor, we are generally concerned with such characteristics as size and yield, but these are merely end products of the metabolic processes. Patterns of these metabolic processes are set by the genes, but the processes themselves may be either accelerated, inhibited, or otherwise modified by the effects of environmental factors. Hybrids which are particularly vigorous under certain conditions may show relatively little vigor under other environmental conditions. It is true that the enhanced vigor of hybrids frequently gives to them a wide range of environmental adaptability. It is equally true that certain hybrids exhibit vigor within only relatively narrow environmental limits. For lack of evidence it must be assumed that the distinction lies in the differences between the patterns of hybridity and in the action of the genes responsible for the hybrid advantages.

Any attempt to explain the genetic basis of heterosis must make initial recognition of one fact. The phenomenon can involve only the recombination of alleles already existing in the population or populations from which the hybrid organisms have been developed; unless, by rare chance, mutation should take place just prior to or just after the actual crossing. We are thus concerned with an interpretation limited to different types of recombinations, and to different kinds of gene action resulting from these recombinations.

GENETIC MECHANISM OF HETEROSIS

Consideration of the characteristics of dominance and heterozygosity has been of primary importance to investigators concerned with interpretation of the genetic mechanism of heterosis. Jones's dominance of linked factors hypothesis (1917) probably is still the most popular explanation of the genetic basis of heterosis.

Dobzhansky (1941) and his co-workers, and many others, have recorded that in most species there has been, in the course of evolution, accumulation of deleterious recessive characters, which when homozygous reduce the efficiency of the organism—but which in the heterozygous condition are without efficiency-reducing effects. This revelation calls for a reshaping of notions regarding the nature of the favorable effects of the dominant alleles, but does not otherwise modify the structure of the explanation. The favorableness of the action of many of the dominant alleles probably is not the result either of directional mutation producing more favorable dominants or of selection tending to eliminate the unfavorable dominants. Instead, it may be due to the accumulation in populations of deleterious recessive mutations. These, if their effects are not too deleterious, often can be piled up in significant numbers.

The piling-up of such deleterious recessives is probably one of the reasons why heterosis is a much more important phenomenon in such a plant as corn than it is, for example, in the tomato. Corn has been handled for hundreds or even thousands of years in a manner that has made possible the accumulation in populations of relatively large numbers of deleterious recessive modifiers. The tomato is more than 90 per cent self-pollinated, and any great accumulation of deleterious modifiers is unlikely. Corn populations characteristically contain thousands of individuals, and wind pollination makes for maintenance of heterozygosity. In tomato, the effective breeding population size approaches one, and deleterious mutations would tend to become homozygous with sufficient frequency to bring about the elimination of many of them.

As a matter of observation, it would seem that a comparison of the occurrence and degree of heterosis in different species, along with a consideration of the reproductive mechanisms in the various species, supports the proposal that heterosis in many cases is the result of the covering up in the hybrids of deleterious recessive alleles with a consequent return to vigor. The often stated argument that hybrids of corn, for instance, frequently are more vigorous than the original open-pollinated populations from which the inbreds used in their production were derived, has no validity with respect to this situation. In the production of the inbreds there is invariably a reassorting of the alleles of the open-pollinated populations.

It is highly improbable, however, that dominant alleles operating either because of certain inherent favorable characteristics of their own, or simply to prevent the deleterious activity of recessives, present the only genetic basis of heterosis. Dominance is by no means the clear-cut feature described in Gregor Mendel's original paper. The dominance of a particular allele may be conditioned by the environment, or it may depend upon the genetic background in which the allele exists. A completely dominant effect of one allele over another, in the classic sense of our utilization of the word dominance, is by no means universal.

Rather unfortunately the so-called heterozygosity concept of heterosis has usually been introduced as being in opposition to the dominance explanation. Because the concepts of the features of dominance and recessiveness early put them into rigid categories, it has been difficult to postulate how a heterozygous condition with respect to one or more genes could render an organism more vigorous than the homozygous condition, usually of the dominant alleles.

Evidence of significance for the interpretation of the importance of heterozygosity in heterosis has been accumulated slowly. There is now, however, a fairly long list of instances in many different species in which the heterozygous condition for certain alleles is known to be superior to either the homozygous recessive or the homozygous dominant condition (Stubbe and Pirshcle, 1940; Singleton, 1943; Karper, 1930; Robertson, 1932; Robertson and Austin, 1935; Gustafsson, 1938, 1946; Nabours and Kingsley, 1934; Masing, 1938, 1939a, 1939b; Rasmusson, 1927; and Timofeef-Ressovsky, 1940.

The accumulation of data on these cases followed a long period during which all the investigations reported seemed to indicate no marked differences between organisms heterozygous for certain alleles and those with the dominant homozygous condition for these same alleles. At least, in no instance, was there any marked superiority referable to the heterozygous condition. Most of the genes involved in the more recent findings have been catalogued as having at least moderately deleterious effects in the mutated state. The characteristics controlled by them include: chlorophyll deficiencies, modifications of leaf form and pigmentation, stalk abnormalities, flowering pattern, and time of flowering.

The extent to which the actual nature of the genetic situation has been analyzed varies, but in several of the cases it seems clear that the mutation of a single gene is involved and that the F_1 hybrids are heterozygous only with respect to the alleles at this particular locus. The amount of heterosis manifest also varies greatly. Because of experimental differences, no accurate comparisons can be made, but in some instances the amount of hybrid vigor appears to be nearly comparable to that which occurs in crosses involving large numbers of allelic differences. The situation appears to be one in which a mutation takes place, and the mutated allele is definitely deleterious when homozygous. In individuals heterozygous for the particular gene, there appear none of the deleterious effects. Instead, a definite heterotic effect appears. Dominance is of no apparent importance, and the distinction between the vigorous hybrids and the less vigorous non-hybrids rests upon heterozygosity.

Jones (1944, 1945) has reported several cases of what he has called heterosis resulting from degenerative changes. He first suggested that these cases represented instances of heterosis with a genetic basis in the heterozygosity of certain of the mutated genes. More recently (private communication) Jones has concluded that these cases involve more than single gene differences, and that the results may be explained on the basis of an accumulation of favorable dominant effects.

The case of a *single locus heterosis* reported by Quinby and Karper (1946) involves alleles which do not produce any detectable deleteriousness, but in certain heterozygous combinations produce hybrid vigor comparable in amount to that in commercial hybrid corn. Quinby and Karper have referred the hybrid advantage in this case to a stimulation of meristematic growth in the heterozygous plants.

All of these instances involve specific allelic interactions and not superiority resulting from heterozygosity *per se*—as was postulated by some of the earlier workers concerned with the genetic interpretation of heterosis. These examples contribute to the increasing realization that the phenomenon of dominance is perhaps of less importance with respect to heterosis than has been supposed. There is no *a priori* reason why the interaction of a so-called recessive allele and a so-called dominant allele should not give results different from and metabolically superior to those which are conditioned by either two recessives or two dominants.

This situation bears closely upon the interpretation of heterosis set forth by East in 1936. East postulated that at the loci concerned with the mechanism of heterosis there might be a series of multiple alleles—with the combinations of different alleles giving results metabolically superior to those determined by the combinations of like alleles, and with no considerations of dominance being involved. In the light of existing evidence it seems a safe assumption that a considerable portion of hybrid vigor is the result of allelic interaction between different alleles at the same locus. Although the evidence as yet is scanty, it is certainly pertinent to suggest that some heterosis may result from the interaction of alleles at different loci, when such alleles are brought into new combinations in the hybrids.

Most of the recent studies of the relation of heterozygosity to heterosis have been concerned with the results of the action of single genes. Such studies have emphasized that heterosis need not have its basis in the action of large numbers of genes but can be, and apparently frequently is, a result of the combining of different alleles of a single gene. Any considerable amount of hybrid vigor resulting from the action of single genes would seem to indicate the involvement either of multiple effects of single genes or of genic action in the control of relatively fundamental metabolic processes. Both are likely probabilities.

The metabolic system of any organism which grows and functions in a satisfactory manner is an exceedingly complicated mechanism with a great number of carefully balanced, interrelated processes. The mutation of any gene which has control over any of the key processes or functions will almost certainly be reflected in a number of processes and activities. For example, if a change in the character of some fundamental enzyme system is involved, either the addition or subtraction of a functional step, or of a substance produced at a particular developmental stage, would be likely to enhance or inhibit a number of important processes in the general metabolism of the organism.

The equilibrium factor in genic action is obviously a consideration of great importance. If a mutation disturbs this equilibrium after it has become fairly well established through selection and elimination processes, the consequences may reduce the organism's vigor. If, in a hybrid, the mutation is then brought together with the original wild type or normal allele, the sum total of the actions of the mutated allele and the original allele may well be such as to exceed that of two copies of the original allele in the production of vigor in the organism.

When we give attention to physiology of gene action in hybrids which are heterotic, we must concern ourselves with all of these considerations including the fact that a single gene, the mutation of which affects some processes in a sufficiently fundamental stage of the organism's formation, may well have a greater end effect than a number of genes whose functions are concerned with more superficial developmental processes.

SEED AND EMBRYO DEVELOPMENT

The literature on heterosis contains a number of discussions concerning the relation between seed and embryo size and heterosis (Kiesselbach, 1926:

Ashby, 1930, 1932, 1937; East, 1936; Sprague, 1936; Copeland, 1940; Murdoch, 1940; Kempton and McLane, 1942; Whaley, 1944, 1950).

Most of the investigations have dealt with mature seed and embryo size. The evidence shows that in many instances hybrid vigor is associated with a high embryo weight. In some cases the initially high-weight embryo is found in a relatively large seed. There is, however, by no means a consistent correlation between either high embryo weight or large seed size and heterosis.

The results of studies on corn inbreds and hybrids in our own laboratory (Whaley, 1950) seem representative of the general findings. Among some ten inbred lines there occurred a great deal of variation from one line to another as to both embryo weight and seed weight. There was somewhat more variation with respect to embryo weight. Among the F_1 hybrids, all of which exhibited considerable vigor under central Texas conditions, there were a few with embryo weights which exceeded those of the larger-embryo parent. For the most part, the embryo weights were intermediate, and in one or two cases they were as low as that of the smaller-embryo parent. The weight of the seed tissues other than the embryo tended to follow that of the pistillate parent, but was generally somewhat higher. Double crosses which had vigorous F_1 hybrids as pistillate parents characteristically had large seeds with what were classified as medium-weight embryos.

The few reports, such as Copeland's (1940), concerning the development of embryos in inbred and hybrid corn, suggest that at the earlier stages of development some hybrid vigor is apparent in the hybrid embryos. The observations of hybrid vigor during early development of embryos and the absence of any size advantage at the time of seed maturity are not necessarily conflicting. In most plants, embryo and seed maturation represent fairly definite stages at which a certain degree of physiological maturity and of structural development has been attained. It is probably to be anticipated that even though certain heterotic hybrids show early embryo development advantages, these advantages may be ironed out by the time the embryo and the seed mature. The size of both the embryo and the other seed tissues is conditioned not only by the genotype of these tissues themselves, but also by the nutritional background furnished them by the plant on which they grow.

It is quite possible that this genotype-to-background relationship is an important consideration in the determination of whether or not hybrid vigor is exhibited in the development of the embryo and seed. The background provided by the pistillate parent might be such as to preclude the development of embryo vigor, even though the embryo genotype were of a definitely heterotic constitution. The fact that hybrid vigor is apparent during certain stages of embryo and seed development may or may not be related to an embryo or seed size advantage at maturity. Because of this, it seems doubtful that embryo or seed size is a reliable measure of hybrid vigor; and that the rate of development during the embryo and seed maturation period is of any critical importance with respect to the development of hybrid vigor during post-embryonic growth.

EARLY SEEDLING GROWTH AND HETEROSIS

There have been few studies of early postgermination growth in plants in relation to heterosis. It would seem that the usual failure to find higher growth rates during the grand period of growth, or longer continued growth periods in heterotic hybrids, would suggest that the answer to the development of hybrid vigor lies for the most part in the early postgermination growth stages. The work of Ashby and his co-workers (Ashby, 1930, 1932, 1936; Hatcher, 1939, 1940; Luckwill, 1937, 1939) emphasized that the hybrid advantage in their materials was either present in the resting embryo or became manifest in early postgermination growth. Its development was definitely not a characteristic of the later growth phases. This observation has now been made for many cases of hybrid vigor (Whaley, 1950). There are some instances in which hybrid vigor seems to be the result of longer-continued growth on the part of the hybrid. These probably have a different explanation from the majority of cases.

We have been concerned lately in our own laboratory with an analysis of the early postgermination growth of corn inbreds and single and double cross hybrids (Whaley, 1950). Studies of growth during the first ten to twelve days after germination have revealed that the hybrid advantage is largely the result of the heterotic hybrid plants reaching a high growth rate earlier than do the inbreds. Almost without exception, the development of the hybrid advantage takes place very rapidly in the early stages of germination and growth. Rarely have we seen evidence of the hybrids having higher growth rates during any later part of the developmental cycle. Neither are the hybrid growth periods extended appreciably beyond those of the inbreds. In most instances the hybrids mature somewhat more rapidly than the inbreds—a fact of common observation among plant breeders.

Since the attainment of the maximum growth rate takes place more quickly during the early stages of development, the hybrids do have a longer maximum growth rate period. During this period the early advantage is compounded, to give a considerably greater maturity advantage. When both the inbred lines and the hybrids used in our studies are considered, it is apparent that the rapid attainment of high early growth rates is correlated with relatively low embryo weights. This apparent higher efficiency of small embryos and its importance in relation to hybrid vigor requires further study.

On the basis of the data at hand one can suggest that the hybrid advantage lies in the more rapid unfolding of certain metabolic processes, a suggestion which receives support from the recorded studies of later growth.

LATER GROWTH AND HETEROSIS

It is unfortunate that most studies of the physiology of heterosis have been confined to the later growth period, and consequently do not include that part of the growth cycle during which the important differences seem to be developed. Nonetheless, we can learn much from these studies of later growth as to the nature of the physiological differences which may furnish bases for the development of hybrid vigor.

The early experiments on physiological differences between inbreds and hybrids were concerned mostly with the responses of the inbreds and the hybrids to different soil conditions. A few examples will serve to indicate the type of investigation and the character of the results. Hoffer (1926) determined the amounts of the constituents of the ash of heterotic hybrid corn to be generally intermediate between those of the parental types. He noted that iron and aluminum were present in the ash of the hybrids in smaller amounts than in the inbreds. His studies showed that although there were marked differences in the absorption of iron and aluminum in different soil types the vigorous hybrids tended to absorb less of both these elements than the less vigorous inbred lines.

In the same year Kiesselbach (1926) reported distinct differences in water requirements between selfed lines of corn and their heterotic F_1 hybrids. The low productivity inbreds had much higher water requirements than the vigorous F_1 hybrids, when water requirements were calculated on the basis of either water absorbed per gram of ear corn or water absorbed per gram of total dry matter. Barley inbreds and heterotic barley hybrids were shown by Gregory and Crowther (1928, 1931) to make distinctly different responses to various levels of available minerals. These investigators postulated that heterosis in barley might be directly related to differences in the ability of the hybrids and the inbreds to use certain nutrients. This suggestion has had a fairly adequate test, particularly with reference to nitrogen and phosphorus nutrition.

The work of DeTurk et al. (1933), Smith (1934), Lyness (1936), Harvey (1939), Burkholder and McVeigh (1940), and Rabideau et al. (1950), has provided a fairly adequate picture of the relation of phosphorus and nitrogen nutrition to the development of hybrid vigor. Smith demonstrated distinct differences among inbred corn lines with respect to phosphorus nutrition, noting that these differences were most apparent when the phosphorus supply was limited. He postulated that the higher phosphate utilization efficiency of the hybrids might be referred, at least in part, to the dominant inheritance in them of a much branched root system. Later studies have shown that the root growth pattern is certainly important in relation to heterosis.

Smith noted particularly that when inbred lines were inefficient in the utilization of phosphorus or nitrogen, crossing them failed to produce hybrids showing any evidence of physiological stimulation resulting in the more effective use of these elements. Lyness (1936) studied heterotic F_1 hybrids resulting from crosses between a low phosphorus-absorbing capacity inbred and a high phosphorus-absorbing capacity inbred. He found the heterotic F_1 plants to have high phosphorus-absorbing capacity. These results suggested that phosphorus-absorbing capacity in corn, in some instances at least, acts genetically as a dominant factor. Lyness also noted the relationship between high phosphorus absorption and the extent of root development. He supposed that the extent of root development might be responsible for varietal differences in phosphorus absorption, a supposition which is supported by later studies. The work of DeTurk *et al.* (1933) suggested that more than simply phosphorus-absorbing capacity is involved. This work revealed that the actual phosphorus content patterns of two F_1 hybrids of corn were quite different. By estimating the amount of phosphorus in various chemical fractions, De Turk and his coworkers were able to demonstrate marked phosphorus pattern differences and to associate these pattern differences with various phosphate fertilizer treatments.

In our laboratory we have made a study of the phosphorus-absorbing efficiency of corn inbreds and hybrids, and have attempted to correlate the findings of this study with developmental changes in the vascular system and with general growth (Whaley *et al.*, 1950; Heimsch *et al.*, 1950; Rabideau *et al.*, 1950). The data indicate that heterotic hybrids definitely absorb more radioactive phosphorus than their inbred parents. This advantage in absorption on the part of the hybrid is associated with more rapid early development, with earlier attainment of maturity, and with certain features of vascular organization. The greater absorption can be referred at least in part to better early development of the root system in the hybrids, and to a generally higher level of metabolic activity which presumably creates a greater phosphorus demand. The greater absorption of phosphorus by the hybrids is certainly one of the factors which compounds the heterotic effects, but it seems doubtful that it is a primary factor in the development of hybrid vigor.

Harvey's (1939) studies of nitrogen metabolism among inbreds and hybrids of both corn and tomato showed differences from one line to another with respect to the ability to use nitrate and ammonium nitrogen. The experiments were of such a nature as to make it clear that such differences in nutritional responses were results of differences in genetic constitution. The behavior of hybrids produced from the inbreds reflected a combination of the characteristics of the inbreds. Significantly, Harvey's study revealed that not only did differences exist among his inbreds and hybrids with respect to the ability to use different types of nitrogen, but that there were distinct genetic differences in the responses of the plants to various levels of nitrogen availability.

Somewhat similar differential responses to potassium availability were revealed by Harvey's studies on tomato inbreds and hybrids. Burkholder and McVeigh (1940) have also noted differences in responses of corn inbreds and hybrids to various levels of available nitrogen. These investigators correlated apical meristematic development, and the differentiation of the vascular system with the level of nitrogen nutrition, and the efficiency of different lines and hybrids in utilizing the available nitrogen. Their results indicate that hybrid vigor, involving superiority in the production of dry matter and the differentiation of organs, was not correlated with greater growth and development of the vascular system.

There definitely are vascular organization differences between the heterotic hybrids and the inbreds in the material we have studied. These vascular organization differences seem not to be the result of differences in mineral absorption and distribution, but rather to be one of the factors responsible for the differences in absorption and distribution. All the evidence seems to indicate that the greater absorption of minerals by heterotic hybrids can be referred to better developed root systems in the hybrids, probably also to the presence of more efficient transport systems, and to a generally higher level of metabolic activity.

Recently we have undertaken a rather extensive analysis of both the morphological and physiological characteristics of a tomato cross in which there is marked heterosis. We have found no significant differences between the inbreds and the hybrids as to total phosphorus content of the leaves, stems, or roots. There is some suggestion that the phosphorus content of the organs of the hybrids reaches a higher level earlier in growth than it does in the inbreds. Neither do the hybrid plants have any consistent advantage with respect to nitrogen content.

Analyses of the starch content of the leaves and stems suggest that the hybrid plants may have a slightly higher starch content than the inbreds during the early growth stages. In terms of average figures over the whole growth period, however, there are no marked differences between the inbreds and the hybrids. The same appears to be true of the sugar content. The hybrids have a somewhat higher sugar content, at least in the leaves, early in development. During the greater part of the growth cycle the hybrids do not have significantly more sugar than the inbreds. The only clear difference found between the inbreds and the hybrids is in the catalase activity of the shoot tips, the hybrids having an appreciably greater index of catalase activity than either of the inbred parents. The catalase activity differences are associated with much more active meristematic growth in the hybrid plants.

THE ROLE OF SPECIFIC SUBSTANCES IN HETEROSIS

Evidence for another sort of physiological differences possibly involved in heterosis is furnished by the work of Robbins (1940, 1941a) in assaying the growth-promoting activities of extracts from inbred and hybrid corn grains. Robbins' evidence indicates that a substance or substances, which he has designated as factor Z, may be synthesized in greater amounts by the hybrids than by the inbreds. He has stated that factor Z can be fractionated into Z_1, which is hypoxanthine; and Z_2, a still unidentified fraction. Robbins' work suggests that among the advantages possessed by heterotic hybrids may be the ability to synthesize certain growth substances which the inbreds either cannot synthesize or cannot synthesize as well.

Further evidence of a slightly different nature is provided by the root culture work of Robbins (1941b) and of Whaley and Long (1944). Robbins used cultures of a strain of *Lycopersicon pimpinellifolium* Mill., a strain of *L. esculentum* Mill., and their F_1 hybrid, in solutions supplemented by thiamin, thiamin and pyridoxine, or thiamin, pyridoxine, and nicotinamide. Robbins found that the F_1 roots grew much more rapidly and produced more dry matter than those of either parental line. He was able to show further that one parental line made a greater response to the presence of pyridoxine than did the other, while the roots of the second parental line made a greater response to nicotinamide than those of the first. This suggests the combination of complementary factors from the parents in the hybrid. Whaley and Long (1944) obtained essentially the same results with a cross involving two inbred lines of *L. esculentum*.

In the University of Texas tissue and organ culture laboratory, we have been exploring certain aspects of this problem. While the results are not sufficiently complete for publication, some facts are already clear. Among the roots of many inbred lines of tomatoes which we have been culturing, there are marked differences in growth responses associated with the availability or non-availability of thiamin, pyridoxine, niacin, and certain other substances. These differences appear definitely to be inherited and they can be studied in either the inbred lines or hybrids.

It is still too early to say what the inheritance pattern is, but consideration can be given to some aspects of the growth response patterns. One of the most significant revelations is that the responses of most of the roots to a specific substance are conditioned not only by the availability of that substance, but by the availability of the other substances and by the general composition of the culture medium. Heterosis in tomato root cultures is, like heterosis in whole plants, definitely relative, and conditioned, not only by the environment, but, with respect to any specific gene action, by the background of other gene actions taking place in the developing organism.

Heterosis in tomato root cultures is definitely related to the inheritance of the capacity to synthesize or utilize such substances as thiamin, pyridoxine, and niacin. This is not to suggest that heterosis in whole plants of tomato may have its basis in the genetic recombination of factors concerned in the control of thiamin, pyridoxine, or niacin metabolism. In intact plants, it is likely that the green parts supply these substances to their own tissues and to the roots, in amounts satisfactory for growth and development. The root tissue responses, however, are definitely heterotic in certain instances, and these mechanisms merit examination.

It seems pertinent to explore the role of these B vitamins in growth and development. Thiamin appears to be a metabolic requirement for all types of cells. Its metabolic activity apparently revolves around a role in enzyme systems. Thiamin pyrophosphate is the co-enzyme of the enzyme pyruvate carboxylase (Lohmann and Schuster, 1937). The enzyme carboxylase occurs in many plant tissues. The possible biochemical basis of thiamin action in plants has been set forth in some detail by Bonner and Wildman (1946), Vennesland and Felsher (1946), and Bonner and Bonner (1948). It is assumed that thiamin represents a step in the development of co-carboxylase which is active in one or more of the decarboxylating enzyme systems of the respiratory mechanism.

Pyridoxine also has an enzymatic role, apparently being important for its conversion to pyridoxal phosphate, which is a co-enzyme of one or more of the reactions in the nitrogen metabolism of the plant (Bonner and Bonner, 1948). As a co-enzyme active in nitrogen metabolism reactions, pyridoxine may be of extreme importance in amino acid-protein building, and hence active in conditioning fundamental growth activities.

Similarly, niacin activity is enzymatic in character. Niacin appears to be involved as a constituent of the nucleotide cozymase, and possibly of triphosphopyridine nucleotide. Cozymase is a co-enzyme for a whole series of dehydrogenase enzymes, including alcohol dehydrogenase, malic dehydrogenase, and glutamic dehydrogenase (Bonner and Bonner, 1948).

The genetic background of thiamin, pyridoxine, and niacin metabolism is thus a genetic background concerned with basic components of the plant's enzyme systems. Heterosis, which rests upon recombinations concerned with thiamin, pyridoxine, or niacin metabolism, quite obviously rests upon recombinations which are concerned with the acceleration, inhibition, or blocking of specific stages or developed substances in the basic enzyme system.

A considerable amount of supporting evidence for the involvement of such fundamental enzyme and other growth substance activities in the development of heterosis has been coming for some time from the work on Neurospora. In many heterocaryons of Neurospora, increased growth responses directly suggestive of heterosis have been observed. In a number of instances (Beadle and Coonradt, 1944), the growth responses depend upon the two types of nuclei in the heterocaryon—each carrying wild type alleles of deleterious mutant genes carried by the other nucleus. Such instances represent essentially the same situation as the recombination of favorable dominant alleles in normally diploid organisms.

In one case reported by Emerson (1948) a different situation obtains. A mutant strain of Neurospora which requires sulfonamides for growth at certain temperatures will grow satisfactorily in the absence of sulfonamides, provided that the concentration of available p-aminobenzoic acid is held at a particular level. Either higher or lower concentrations of p-aminobenzoic acid result in growth inhibitions. Emerson has made heterocaryons between a mutant strain carrying the sulfonamide-requiring gene (*sfo*) and a gene which prevents the synthesis of p-aminobenzoic acid (*pab*), and a strain carrying *sfo* and the wild type allele (+) of *pab*. The resultant heterocaryons grow vigorously on the minimal medium (without sulfonamides), whereas strains carrying *sfo* and *pab*, or *sfo* and +, make no appreciable growth on the minimal medium. Emerson's explanation of the growth of the heterocaryons is that it results from a balance between the production of p-aminobenzoic acid by one of the types of nuclei and the absence of production of p-aminobenzoic acid by the other type of nucleus; so that the total production of p-aminobenzoic acid is sufficient for growth but still within the range tolerated by strains carrying *sfo*. Heterosis-like effects of this sort are suggestive of the instances of heterosis related to the heterozygosity of particular genes in diploid organisms.

We thus have in Neurospora, heterosis-like effects assignable both to a recombination of dominant alleles basis and to a heterozygosity basis. More important for this discussion is the fact that these instances are all concerned with facilitation in the hybrid of the production or utilization of substances which are components of the basic enzyme or other growth substance pattern of the organisms.

Various investigations of heterosis in Drosophila, while for the most part not concerned with specific growth substances, have nonetheless assigned manifestation of heterosis to a background in the fundamental biochemical activities of the organisms. Inasmuch as these investigations are discussed in detail in another chapter, they will not be treated here.

THE PHYSIOLOGICAL BASIS OF HETEROSIS

From consideration of the pertinent data, a definite pattern emerges. This associates the development of heterosis with the ability of the hybrid to synthesize or to utilize one or several specific substances involved in the fundamental growth processes of the organisms. Nutritional factors, water absorption factors, and the other more gross considerations with which investigators have been particularly concerned seem to be secondary factors—perhaps responsible for compounding the heterotic effects but probably not responsible for their initial development. Much of the evidence agrees with the assumption that the primary heterotic effect is concerned with growth substances whose predominant activity is registered in the early part of the developmental cycle; in plants, especially in early postgermination growth. Into this category fall the enzymes, the auxins, and the other "physiological key" substances.

Many heterotic hybrid plants seem to gain their advantage within the first few hours after germination. This advantage may not be shown as statistically significant until it has been further heightened by subsequent growth. The primary growth activities during this period are those involved in the unfolding of the enzymatic pattern; the mobilization, transformation, and utilization of stored materials, and the building up of active protoplasmic synthesis. It seems definitely to be here that the hybrid advantage lies. By the time growth is well under way, the hybrid advantage is already well developed.

Structural differences between inbreds and heterotic hybrids shown by the studies of Burkholder and McVeigh (1940), Weaver (1946), and the members of our laboratory (Whaley et al., 1950; Heimsch et al., 1950; Rabideau et al., 1950) are apparently to be regarded as results of heterosis rather than as causal factors. The evidence suggests that heterosis is concerned primarily with growth processes and that differentiation activities are most likely involved secondarily rather than primarily. What seems to be indicated is the assignment of the physiological basis of heterosis to the activity of one or more of the so-called physiologically active substances involved in early growth.

Much of the apparent hybrid vigor is assignable to these activities only in a secondary fashion. Once the advantage of a larger number of growing centers or of heightened meristematic activity is established, the greater availability of nutrients, the greater amount of protoplasm involved in further protoplasm building, and other general advantages tend to increase the initial differences. To the general evidence in favor of this supposition can be added the specific evidence of the few cases in which the physiological action of particular alleles is known. Where these alleles in combination are responsible for heterosis, they have—when studied in sufficient detail—invariably been shown to be alleles whose action involves basic enzyme or other growth substance activity.

If we are to make significant headway in understanding the physiological mechanism of heterosis, we shall have to concentrate on a detailed study of the developmental physiology of early growth. Much of the general knowledge we already have can contribute toward this understanding if we translate it into terms signifying that when we speak of quantitative differences—size, yield, or of rate differences—we are really concerned with differences in the level of metabolism. We must recognize that these differences in the level of metabolism are bound to vary against different environmental backgrounds, and where the particular genes involved are associated with different genetic backgrounds.

Our approach to the heterosis problem has been complicated by common insistence upon attempts to find a single genetic mechanism. It has suffered, too, from failure to recognize that between the gene and the final mature organism there lies a system of developmental processes of great complexity. The complexity of this system is formidable but it surely can be analyzed, at least with respect to its most significant features, if it is taken part by part.

SUMMARY

The evidence relating to heterosis suggests that the phenomenon is to be explained genetically in terms of various recombination effects. In some cases, dominance is the important consideration, while in other cases, heterozygosity must be considered. In any event, it is the resulting specific gene action which lies at the basis of the physiological advantage or advantages which give rise to hybrid vigor. One or many genes may be involved. Considerations of genetic balance and genotype-environment balance are important. Probably most cases of heterosis are to be explained physiologically in terms of differences in the more fundamental aspects of the metabolic pattern, particularly those concerned with enzyme, auxin, and other growth substance activity in plants and with enzyme and hormonal activities in animals.

To clarify the mechanism further, studies must be concerned primarily with the genetics and physiology of early development. We have been concerned with mature characteristics of size and yield, with the inheritance of so-called quantitative genes, and with analyses by the classic methods of genetics. These studies have brought us close enough to an understanding of the phenomenon of heterosis to indicate that its further analysis by techniques now at hand will uncover facts of tremendous importance for genetics, physiology, and other studies of development, some of them considerably afield from heterosis itself.

WILLIAM J. ROBBINS

Columbia University and New York Botanical Garden

Chapter 7

Hybrid Nutritional Requirements

Hybrid vigor has been recognized for more than a century. It has been considered from a genetic, morphological, developmental, physiological, and commercial standpoint. Although a great deal of information has been accumulated about the phenomenon, we are still unable to define exactly why a hybrid grows better than the parents from which it comes.

It is obvious that the cause is physiological—the hybrid functions more effectively or for a longer period of time, and accumulates a greater mass of cell substance. Its metabolic efficiency is greater (East, 1936). It would be illuminating if we could locate specifically the physiological processes which are responsible for the greater vigor of the hybrid—recognizing that they may be numerous and complex rather than single and simple, and that they may not be the same for all examples of hybrid vigor.

For many years I have been interested in the factors which determine why one plant species, variety, or strain grows slowly in a given environment where another flourishes. I have dealt mainly with microorganisms, especially the filamentous fungi, because the external environment can be more easily controlled and photosynthesis is not a complicating factor. From my experience, as well as from the work of others, it is clear that in many instances growth—the accumulation of cell substance—is limited by the efficiency of the organism's metabolic machinery, especially the activity of one or more enzyme systems. Whether this concept can be applied also to the phenomenon of hybrid vigor is still to be determined. However, it is a hypothesis which deserves exploration.

Let us begin with a simple example of growth-limitation. *Aspergillus niger* grows well in a liquid medium of sugar, mineral salts, and asparagine. In the same medium *Phycomyces Blakesleeanus* will not grow at all.

114

Does Phycomyces fail to grow in the basal solution because of the absence of something essential which it needs for growth, or because of the presence of something detrimental? Does *Aspergillus niger* grow in the basal solution because it does not need to be furnished with the "essential" substance, or because it is more resistant to the supposed injurious ingredient?

For the example cited, we have a definite and well demonstrated explanation. Phycomyces fails to grow in the basal medium because it requires the vitamin, thiamine—which it is unable to make from sugar, mineral salts, and asparagine. *Aspergillus niger* also needs thiamine, but it constructs the vitamin from the elementary materials present in the basal solution. In this instance, therefore, the failure to grow is due to the lack of something essential for growth; namely, thiamine, the precursor of co-carboxylase.

This is not an isolated example. Many species of fungi grow slowly, or not at all, in a basal medium because of their inability to make one or more of the essential metabolites. These metabolites may include various vitamins, purine and pyrimidine bases, amino acids, fatty acids, or substances as yet unidentified.

ESSENTIAL METABOLITES—RELATION TO GROWTH

It may be assumed that the complex chemical compounds which make up the cell substance of a living organism are constructed by the organism from simpler compounds. A series of intermediate chemical compounds are formed between the original simple foods and nutrients and the final product, cell substance. This step-wise progression from simple to complex is made possible by a series of enzymes, also made by the organism, which operate on each stage as that stage is completed. Although synthesis is likely to be emphasized in considering growth, there are other subsidiary processes—necessary concomitants for the building up of new cell substance. The catabolic processes of digestion and respiration also occur in steps, and are made possible by the action of a series of enzyme systems.

Any substance playing a necessary part directly or indirectly in the chain of reactions which end in the synthesis of new cell substance is an essential metabolite. Unless each essential metabolite, each chemical substance in the step-wise process of growth, each enzyme which facilitates the chemical reactions concerned, is made within the organism or supplied from without, the series is interrupted. New cell substance is not made, and growth does not occur. If not enough of an essential metabolite is made, growth will be slowed.

Of course, this is an oversimplified statement of a very complicated process. The reactions concerned in growth probably do not occur in a straight line. Some steps may be bypassed and side reactions may occur, all of which may affect the speed and character of the growth which results.

It would be difficult to estimate the number of essential metabolites involved in the growth of even the simplest organism, or to put a limit on the number for which some organism may not eventually be found to exhibit a deficiency.

Some species or strains exhibit a complete deficiency for one or more essential metabolites. They are unable to synthesize any of the substances in question and do not grow unless the substances are supplied in the medium in which they are cultivated (Robbins and Ma, 1942). Others suffer from partial deficiencies, that is, they grow slowly in the absence of a particular

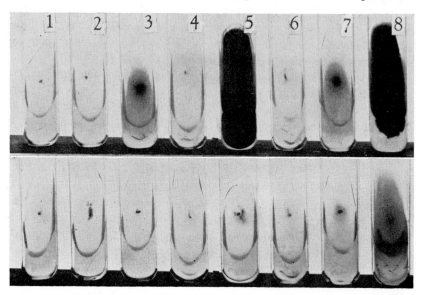

Fig. 7.1—Growth affected by complete and partial deficiencies for essential metabolites. Fungi grown on mineral-dextrose medium containing asparagine and purified agar and supplemented as follows: (1) no addition; (2) thiamine; (3) pyridoxine; (4) biotin; (5) thiamine and pyridoxine; (6) thiamine and biotin; (7) pyridoxine and biotin; (8) all three vitamins. Above, *Ceratostomella multiannulata*, complete deficiency for pyridoxine, partial for thiamine; below, *C. microspora*, complete deficiency for thiamine, biotin, and pyridoxine.

essential metabolite but more rapidly if it is added to the medium (Fig. 7.1).

For example, the clone of excised tomato roots, with which we have worked for many years, suffers from a complete deficiency of thiamine and a partial deficiency of pyridoxine. It will not grow unless the medium contains thiamine or its equivalent. When pyridoxine is added to a medium containing thiamine, the growth of the excised roots is markedly increased.

In a sugar, mineral-salt solution, the growth of our clone of excised tomato roots is limited by its ability to synthesize thiamine. In a thiamine solution, growth is limited by the ability of the roots to synthesize pyridoxine (Robbins, 1946). We have not been able to define what limits the growth of the root in a solution which contains both thiamine and pyridoxine. Other examples of partial deficiencies could be cited. Their effect is to decrease the rate of growth but not to inhibit it entirely.

As a result of investigations which have extended over the past decade or two, we know of many examples in which poor growth or failure to grow in a specific environment is due to the inability of the organism to synthesize adequate quantities of one or more essential metabolites. The metabolic machinery lacks a part, or some part works slowly, with the result that the organism does not make sufficient quantities of one or more growth essentials, and unless supplied with the missing materials from without, grows slowly, or not at all.

Not all instances of failure to grow or of poor growth in a given environment are explainable on the basis of deficiencies of essential metabolites. In some instances growth may be limited by autogenic growth inhibitors.

AUTOGENIC INHIBITORS

Zalokar (1948), Emerson (1947, 1948), and others have described a mutant strain of Neurospora which grows poorly at high temperatures. Growth occurs if sulfonamide is added to the medium. One might conclude that sulfonamide acts for this organism as an essential metabolite. It appears, however, that this mutant produces growth inhibitors which are antagonized in some way by the sulfonamide. This seems to be an example of poor growth caused by the accumulation of autogenic growth inhibitors, and not because of the lack of an essential metabolite.

Information on the role of autogenic inhibitors in limiting growth is less specific and more difficult to obtain than evidence for the limitation of growth due to a deficiency of an essential metabolite. How commonly do internally produced inhibitors reduce growth? What is the nature of these substances?

From the investigation of antibiotic substances we know that many organisms form metabolic products, highly inhibitory for organisms other than themselves. Do they also produce substances which limit their own growth? The role of autogenic inhibitors in limiting growth deserves much more attention than it has received.

It is well known that minute amounts of specific chemical compounds materially modify the amount and nature of growth in plants. Zimmerman and Hitchcock (1949) treated Kalanchoe plants with small amounts of the ortho, para, and meta forms of chlorophenoxyacetic acid. The para form caused the apical meristem to develop into a spathe-like organ which could be cut off and rooted. It had little resemblance to Kalanchoe. The ortho and meta forms of this compound did not have this effect. This modification was not a mutation. The effect wore off as the chemical in the plant disappeared, and the Kalanchoe eventually returned to its normal growth pattern. If the change had been permanent, we would have been inclined to call it a mutation and look for a genic explanation; i.e., look for a gene which controlled the production of para-chlorophenoxyacetic acid. We might say that this compound and the Kalanchoe plant acted temporarily as linked genes.

Many other kinds of abnormal growth in plants are probably the result of the effect of minute amounts of specific chemical compounds. Insect galls are characterized by an abnormal but specific growth pattern superimposed on normal tissue by the presence of a foreign living organism. It seems very likely from the observations of Boysen Jensen that the abnormal growth of insect galls is caused by specific chemical compounds produced by the larvae which inhabit the galls.

It must be emphasized that growth is an extremely complex process, not just a series of chemical reactions. To consider it as such is admittedly an oversimplification giving no thought to the organization in which these reactions occur, or to the structural elements, physical processes, and chemical reactions which must play a role.

The concept of growth as a series of catalyzed reactions is useful and stimulating, however, in considering the role of essential metabolites—especially enzymes—and the action of inhibitors and minute amounts of specific chemical compounds.

HYBRID VIGOR

Some years ago I attempted to determine whether hybrid corn contains a greater quantity of substances which stimulate the early growth of *Phycomyces Blakesleeanus* than the inbred parents. The effect of extracts of air dry grains and of partially germinated grains of the hybrid corn and its inbred parents was determined on the growth of Phycomyces in the presence of thiamine (Robbins, 1940, 1941a).

When compared on the basis of extract per grain, I found that the extracts of the grains of the hybrid corn gave a greater dry weight of mycelium of Phycomyces than those of either of the inbred parents (Fig. 7.2). The stimulating material seemed to be present in both the embryo and the endosperm. Since the solution in which the beneficial effects of the extracts were exhibited contained sugar, asparagine, mineral salts, and thiamine, it appeared that the effect was produced by unidentified growth substances. These were termed for convenience, factor Z.

After estimating the amount of factor Z present—from the effects of the extracts of the corn grains on the early growth of Phycomyces in the presence of thiamine—the following generalities seemed permissible. The amount of factor Z increased with the time of the germination of the corn grains, at least up to seventy-two hours' germination. The quantity of Z was greater per endosperm than per embryo, and was greater in the grains of the hybrid than in those of either parent. The amount of thiamine and its intermediates in the embryo and endosperm of the grains of the hybrid and its parents was not correlated with the amount of factor Z, nor did the amount of biotin in the extracts appear to be correlated with the amount of factor Z.

These results suggest that there is present in the grains of corn, material which stimulates the early growth of Phycomyces in the presence of thiamine, and that there is more of this material per grain in heterotic hybrids than in those of the inbred parents.

Interpretation of these results depends in part on the identity of factor Z.

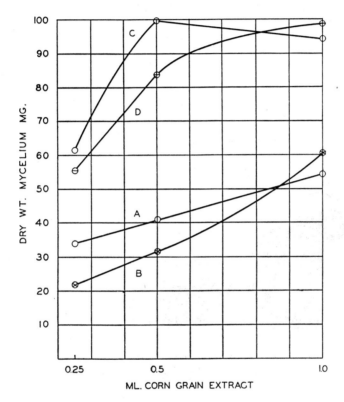

Fig. 7.2—Increase in dry weight of *Phycomyces* produced by extracts of air dry grains of maize. Extracts added to medium of sugar, minerals, asparagine, and thiamine. A = line 4–8; B = line 187; C = 985, 4–8 × 187; D = 995, 187 × 4–8. 1 ml. extract = 1 grain.

Unfortunately, we do not know what factor Z is. We succeeded in dividing it. We demonstrated that factor Z is multiple, and separated it into a fraction adsorbed on charcoal, factor Z_1, and a filtrate fraction, factor Z_2. Factor Z_1 was identified as hypoxanthine. Factor Z_2 may be a mixture of amino acids.

Although this problem is left in an uncertain and unsatisfactory condition, it suggests a line of attack. This would be an investigation of heterosis by studying the effect of extracts of parents and of heterotic hybrids on the growth of other organisms. This may serve as a means of bioassay for favorable or unfavorable growth factors.

Vigor in Heterocaryons

Observations of Dodge (1942) on heterocaryosis in Neurospora are of interest to the general problem of heterosis. Dodge inoculated three petri dishes, one with his Dwarf 16 strain of *Neurospora tetrasperma*, one with race C-8, and the third with mixed mycelium or conidia of both the dwarf and the C-8 races. He observed that the mycelium of the mixed culture grew much more rapidly and produced more abundant conidia than the mycelium of either the dwarf or the C-8 races (Fig. 7.3).

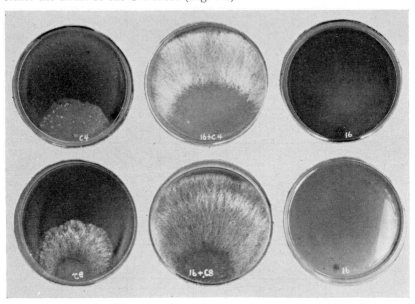

Fig. 7.3—Heterocaryotic vigor in *Neurospora tetrasperma*. Growth in 34 hours at room temperature in petri dishes. The mycelium of the two heterocaryotic races (*16 + C 4* and *16 + C8*) has nearly covered the medium in the dishes; *C4* and *C8* have not grown halfway across the medium and *Dwarf 16* has made no visible growth.

When two races of *Neurospora tetrasperma* are grown together, there is a migration of nuclei through the openings at the points of hyphal anastomoses. The races need not be of opposite sex. After nuclear migration, the cells of the resulting mycelium are heterocaryotic. They contain two kinds of haploid nuclei. The greater vigor of the mixed culture referred to above appears to be the result of the presence in a common cytoplasm of two kinds of nuclei.

Heterocaryotic vigor does not always accompany heterocaryosis. Dodge (1942) observed heterocaryotic vigor when the two races, Dwarf 16 and C-4, were grown together. But heterocaryosis for races C-4 and C-8 did not result in increased vigor in the mixed culture. Not all dwarf races act as race 16 does. Some of them evidence heterocaryotic vigor with both C-4 and C-8, others with C-4 but not with C-8, and still others develop none with either C-4 or C-8.

Dodge has suggested that the heterocaryotic hybrid may synthesize a full quantity of growth substances or essential metabolites. Whereas the growth of each of the parents is limited by their inability to synthesize adequate quantities of one or more essential metabolites.

Dwarf 16, for example, may be able to make adequate quantities of essential metabolites 1, 2, 3, and 4, but unable to construct enough of 5, 6, 7, and 8. On the other hand, race C-4 may be unable to synthesize enough of 1, 2, 3, and 4, but be capable of producing an adequate supply of 5, 6, 7, and 8. When nuclei of the two races are brought together in a common cytoplasm, the essential metabolites synthesized by one of the nuclear components supplement those synthesized by the other component. The heterocaryotic mycelium is then supplied with adequate quantities of all the essential metabolites necessary for rapid growth.

We have tried to test this hypothesis by supplementing with various substances the medium on which race 16 and other dwarf races were grown. If it were possible to increase materially the growth rate of the dwarf race by supplements in the medium, without introducing the heterocaryotic condition, the limiting factors for dwarfness could be identified and the stimulus involved in the heterocaryotic condition identified.

A basal agar medium containing mineral salts, dextrose, asparagine, neopeptone, and thiamine was supplemented by a mixture of purine and pyrimidine bases; by a vitamin mixture containing PAB, calcium pantothenate, inositol, nicotinic acid, pyridoxine, riboflavin, thiamine, guanine, hypoxanthine, and 2-methyl-1, 4-naphthohydroquinone diacetate; by malt extract, casein hydrolysate, cow's milk, dried yeast, choline, a-tocopherol, hemin, oleic acid, ascorbic acid (filtered sterile), coconut milk, Taka-diastase (filtered sterile), water extracts of the mycelium of Neurospora, liver extracts (both filtered sterile and heated), adrenal cortical extract (unheated), estrogenic substance, progesterone, anterior pituitary extract, posterior pituitary extract, whey, or potato extract.

None of the substances or combinations of them as used increased the growth rates of any of the dwarf races to an extent adequate to explain heterocaryotic vigor. Some beneficial effects, usually noted only in older cultures, were obtained from cow's milk and from liver extract. These effects were not sufficiently marked to suggest that either supplement supplied the missing factors.

We were unsuccessful, therefore, in defining the factors limiting the growth of the dwarf races and conversely those effective in inducing more rapid growth in the heterocaryotic mycelium.

Our failure may be explained in various ways. We may not have included in our various supplements the missing essential metabolites. These metabo-

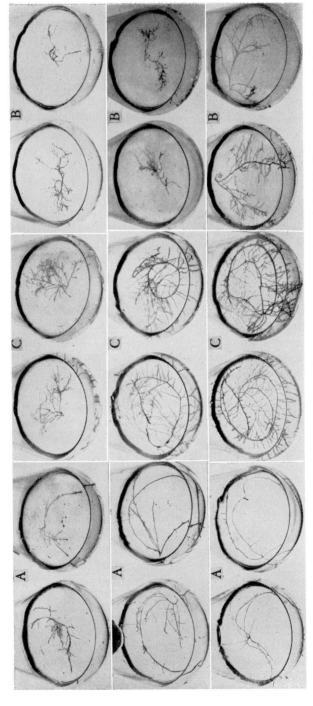

FIG. 7.4—Heterotic vigor in excised tomato roots. *A*, Johannesfeur; *B*, Red Currant; *C*, the heterotic hybrid. Above, grown in solutions supplemented with thiamine; center, thiamine and pyridoxine; bottom, thiamine, pyridoxine, and nicotinamide.

lites may be non-diffusible or very labile substances such as enzyme proteins, which could only be introduced into the cell through inserting a nucleus and its genes. The original hypothesis may be in error. We may not be dealing with limiting quantities of essential metabolites but with inhibitors. We might assume that the growth of one or both of the parents is limited by autogenic inhibitors, and the presence of both kinds of nuclei in a common cytoplasm results in the neutralization in some fashion of the inhibitors.

Emerson (1948) has succeeded in producing heterocaryons in which one kind of haploid nucleus neutralizes the effect of the other. The augmented growth of the heterocaryon, as compared to that of strains which are homozygous, reminds one, says Emerson, of instances of single gene heterosis in maize reported by Jones.

The importance of internal factors in heterosis is suggested by the results I obtained on the growth of the excised roots of a heterotic tomato hybrid and its inbred parents (Robbins, 1941b). The hybrid roots and the roots of the two inbred parents were grown in liquid culture which contained mineral salts and cane sugar. This basal medium was supplemented with thiamine, with thiamine and pyridoxine, and with thiamine, pyridoxine, and nicotinamide.

Growth of the roots of the hybrid exceeded that of either of the inbred parents in all three types of media (Fig. 7.4). Growth of one parent was improved by the addition of pyridoxine to the thiamine solution, but a further supplement of the medium with nicotinamide had little effect. Growth of the second inbred parent was little affected by the addition of pyridoxine to the thiamine medium, but was improved by the further addition of nicotinamide to the thiamine and pyridoxine solution.

These results suggest that the greater vigor of growth of the heterotic hybrid is determined in part by its greater ability to synthesize pyridoxine and nicotinamide. That is evidently not the whole story, because its growth exceeded that of the inbred parents in media containing all three vitamins.

Although heterosis may be considered and should be considered from the genetical standpoint, it should also be studied from the physiological standpoint. I have suggested that it may be important to devote attention to the question of what the internal factors are which limit growth, what they are in inbreds, and how they are removed in heterotic hybrids. We should consider in such investigations the role of essential metabolites, of growth inhibitors, and of other specific chemical compounds which materially modify growth. Microorganisms might be utilized as tools for the detection of growth stimulators or growth inhibitors.

EDGAR ANDERSON
Missouri Botanical Garden
and
WILLIAM L. BROWN
Pioneer Hybrid Corn Company

Chapter 8

Origin of Corn Belt Maize and Its Genetic Significance

Several ends were in view when a general survey of the races and varieties of *Zea mays* was initiated somewhat over a decade ago (Anderson and Cutler, 1942). Maize, along with Drosophila, had been one of the chief tools of modern genetics. If one were to use the results of maize genetics most efficiently in building up general evolutionary theories, he needed to understand what was general and what was peculiar in the make-up of *Zea mays*. Secondly, since maize is one of the world's oldest and most important crops, it seemed that a detailed understanding of *Zea mays* throughout its entire range might be useful in interpreting the histories of the peoples who have and are using it. Finally, since maize is one of our greatest national resources, a survey of its kinds might well produce results of economic importance, either directly or indirectly.

Early in the survey it became apparent that one of the most significant sub-problems was the origin and relationships of the common yellow dent corns of the United States Corn Belt. Nothing exactly like them was known elsewhere in the world. Their history, though embracing scarcely more than a century, was imperfectly recorded and exasperatingly scattered. For some time it seemed as if we might be able to treat the problem only inferentially, from data derived from the inbred descendants of these same golden dent corns. Finally, however, we have been able to put together an encouragingly complete history of this important group of maize varieties, and to confirm our historical research with genetical and cytological evidence.

An even approximate survey of *Zea mays*-as-a-whole remains a goal for the distant future, but our understanding of Corn Belt dent corns is already more complete than we had originally hoped. Since our evidence is detailed and of various kinds, it may make the presentation somewhat easier to follow if we give a brief description of the pre-hybrid commercial yellow dents of the United States Corn Belt, review their history in broad outline, and then proceed to an examination of the various kinds of evidence on which these generalizations have been built.

Corn Belt dents, the commercial varieties which dominated the chief centers of corn production in the United States for over half a century preceding the advent of hybrid corn, were variable open-pollinated varieties. They varied from plant to plant, from field to field of the same variety, and from variety to variety. Figure 8.1, based upon an examination of a field of Golden Queen, one of the lesser known of these varieties, will indicate the kind of variation which characterized the fields of that day.

In spite of this variation, or one might almost say, impressed on top of it, was a remarkably persistent combination of generally prevalent characters. Considered from plant to plant or from field to field, *as individuals*, these varieties seemed ephemeral and unimportant. *Seen as populations*, as collections of inter-breeding individuals, the Corn Belt dents as a whole were a well-marked and definite entity, particularly when contrasted with maize in other parts of the world. They tended to have one well-developed ear, frequently accompanied by a small ear at the node below this primary one. The ears had large, nearly cylindrical cobs with red or reddish glumes. The usually golden yellow kernels, pronouncedly dented at the tip, had a pericarp frequently roughened by tiny wrinkles. They were set in from 14 to 22 straight rows with little external indication of the fact that the rows were in pairs. The mathematical perfection of the ear was frequently lessened by a slight tendency for the whole ear to taper toward the apex, and for the rowing of the kernels and the diameter of the cob to be somewhat differentiated in its lowermost quarter.

Characteristically, the plant on which this ear was borne had a single, upright stem, leaves with tight sheaths and strong, arching blades, and a heavy, many-branched tassel. Kernel color was remarkably standardized, a faint flush of coppery red in the pericarp and a yellow endosperm, combining to give varying shades of deep, golden color. Epidermal color was apparent on the culm and leaves at the base of the plant, but seldom or never were there to be found the brilliant reds, dark purples, and other foliage colors which are so characteristic of maize in various parts of Latin America. While there was some variation in anther color and silk color, pinks and dull reds were commonest though greens and bright reds were not unknown.

As we have shown elsewhere (Anderson and Brown, 1950) there cannot be the slightest doubt that these widespread and standardized Corn Belt varieties were the creation of the nineteenth century. They came in large part

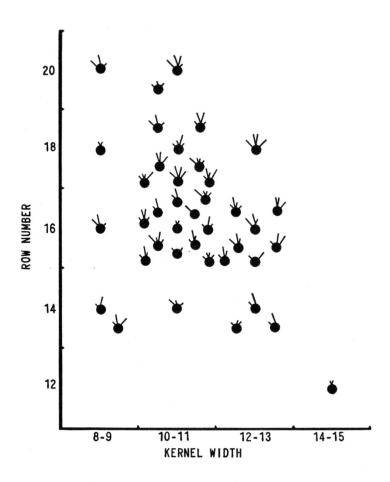

Fig. 8.1—Pictorialized diagram showing relationship between numbers of rows of kernels, kernel width, tassel branch number, glume length, pith diameter, and ear length in an open-pollinated sample of Golden Queen dent corn.

from crosses between White Southern Dents, mostly of Mexican origin, and the long, slender Northern Flints which had dominated the eastern United States for at least some hundreds of years preceding the discovery of America. While these two complexes were of primary importance in the creation of Corn Belt corn, it should be pointed out that germ plasm of other types of maize has undoubtedly filtered into Corn Belt mixtures. Compared to Southern Dents and Northern Flints, these certainly are of minor importance. There are, nevertheless, to be found among dent inbreds of the Corn Belt certain strains which exhibit Caribbean influence and others which seem to contain germ plasm of southwestern United States or western Mexican varieties.

Although the following discussion does not go into detail regarding the influence of these secondary sources of germ plasm on Corn Belt corn, the effects of such influences are important and we have already made small beginnings at studying them. The Northern Flints are in some ways strikingly similar to the common yellow flints of the Guatemalan highlands, strikingly unlike most Mexican maize. They are one of several cultural traits which apparently spread from the Mayan area to the eastern United States without leaving any clear record of the route by which they came. In their general appearance, as well as in technical botanical details, the Northern Flints were very different from the Southern Dents. The hybrid vigor which resulted from mixing these diverse types was soon noted by alert agriculturists. While some of the blending of flints and dents may have been haphazard and accidental, much of it was directed and purposeful. The benefits to be gained were listed in public, and the exact effects of continued mixing and of backcrossing were discussed in detail as early as 1825 (Lorain, 1825). This intelligent, controlled hybridizing proceeded for at least a half century until the new yellow dents were so ubiquitous and everyday that their very origin was forgotten.

For theoretical reasons this neglect of historical tradition was unfortunate. Maize breeders have not understood that the heterosis they now capitalize is largely the dispersed heterosis of the open-pollinated flint-dent mongrels. Maize geneticists are for the most part unaware that the germ plasm they use for fundamental generalizations is grossly atypical of germ plasms in general. We shall return to a detailed discussion of these two points after referring briefly to the evidence concerning the origin of Corn Belt maize.

Though there is abundant evidence that our Corn Belt dents came from mixtures of Northern Flints and Southern White Dents, the evidence concerning these two regional types is very one-sided. The Northern Flints (Brown and Anderson, 1947) were remarkably uniform from place to place and from century to century. The archaeological record is rich going back to early pre-Columbian times and there are numerous naïve but accurate descriptions of these varieties in colonial accounts.

The Southern Dents (Brown and Anderson, 1948) are much more variable. For over a century their variability has been stressed by all those who have discussed them. The samples which we obtained from the South differed from field to field, and from variety to variety. For an accurate understanding of them and their history, we would like many more archaeological specimens than we have for the flints, and many more colonial descriptions. Instead, we have as yet no archaeological record, merely two accounts in early colonial times—one from Louisiana and the other from Virginia. There is one passing mention in a pre-revolutionary diary, and then a truly remarkable discussion by Lorain in 1825. Finally, the United States Patent Office report for 1850 gives us, for region after region, a detailed picture of the extent to which this purposeful mixing had proceeded by that time.

To summarize the historical evidence, the Northern Flints were once the prevailing type of maize throughout the eastern United States (Brown and Anderson, 1947) with an archaeological record going back at least to A.D. 1000. There is as yet no archaeological evidence for their having been preceded in most of that area by any other type of maize, or of Mexican-like dents having been used there in pre-Columbian times. The Northern Flints belong to a type of maize rare or unknown over most of Mexico, but common in the highlands of Guatemala. The Southern Dents, on the contrary, obviously are largely derived from Mexican sources, and by 1700 were being grown as far north as Louisiana and Virginia (Brown and Anderson, 1948). As to how and when they spread north from Mexico, we have no evidence other than the negative fact that they are not known archaeologically from the eastern United States, and are not represented in the collections of early Indian varieties from that region.

As early as 1800, the benefits of crossbreeding these two different types of maize were appreciated by at least a few experts. By 1850 the process was actively under way from Pennsylvania to Iowa, and south to the Gulf states. By the '70's and '80's, a new type of corn had emerged from this blending, although crossing and re-crossing of various strains continued up to the advent of hybrid corn. During the latter half of the process, the origin of Corn Belt dents from 50 to 100 generations of selective breeding of crosses of Northern Flints and Southern Dents was almost completely forgotten. Having at length resurrected the evidence (Anderson and Brown, 1950) for this mingling of two fundamentally different types of maize, we shall now turn to the genetical and cytological evidence which first called the phenomenon to our attention and led us to search for historical proof.

CYTOLOGY

The most important cytological contribution on the origin of Corn Belt maize is found in a comparison of the numbers and distribution of chromosome knobs in the Northeastern Flints, open-pollinated varieties of Southern

Dents, and inbred strains of Corn Belt dents. As has been shown previously (Longley, 1938) and (Reeves, 1944), chromosome knobs may be an important tool in studying relationships in maize. Our work with North American corn not only supports this contention, but suggests that knob data may be even more important than has previously been supposed.

The 8–10 rowed flint and flour varieties of New York, Pennsylvania, and New England are nearly knobless. In the material we have examined, they have 0 to 2 knobs. These observations are in agreement with Longley's earlier conclusions that maize varieties of the northern Indians were characterized by having few knobs. Longley's material, however, included no strains from northeastern United States—the area in which the flint ancestors of Corn Belt corn were highly concentrated. It is interesting, moreover, to note that varieties from this segment of North America have even fewer knobs than do the strains from most Northern Plains Indian tribes.

In contrast, many more knobs were to be found in the open pollinated varieties of Southern Dent corn. In these strains we have found numbers ranging from 5 to 12, for those varieties representing the least contaminated segment of present-day Southern Dent corn. These cytological data are in complete agreement with the known facts regarding the history of Northern Flints and Southern Dents.

There seems little doubt that the Gourdseed-like Dents[1] of the southeastern United States have stemmed directly from Mexico where morphologically and cytologically similar corns can be found even today. Likewise, we have found in highland Guatemala varieties of maize with ear characteristics strikingly similar to Northern Flints and with as few as three knobs. Insofar as cytology is concerned, therefore, it is not at all difficult to visualize a Guatemalan origin for Northeastern Flint corn. The Corn Belt inbreds with which we have worked (Brown, 1949) have knob numbers of 1 to 8. The distribution of numbers in these strains is almost exactly intermediate between that of Northern Flints and Southern Dents (Fig. 8.2). This evidence, based on a character which certainly has not been intentionally altered by selection, strongly fortifies the archaeological and historical facts pointing to a hybrid origin of Corn Belt dent corns.

GENETIC EVIDENCE

The genetical evidence for the origin of Corn Belt maize from mixtures of Northern Flints and Southern Dents is of various kinds. In its totality, it is so strong that, had we not been able to find the actual historical evidence, we could have determined what had happened from genetic data alone. In the first place we have demonstrated, by repeating the cross, that it is possible to synthesize Corn Belt dents from hybrids between Southern Dents

[1] The name "Gourdseed" has been used since colonial times to describe the extremely long seeded, white Southern Dents, whose kernels are indeed not so different in appearance from the seeds of gourds of the genus Lagenaria.

and Northern Flints. Our experiments in crossing a typical white gourdseed from Texas and a typical yellow flint from New York State are now only in the third generation and are being continued. However, it is already evident that some of the segregates from this cross are within the range of variation of Corn Belt dents (Fig. 8.3).

In spite of the 50 to 100 generations of mixing which has taken place, the characters of Northern Flints and Southern Dents still tend to be associated in Corn Belt dents. Anderson (1939) has shown that in crosses between species

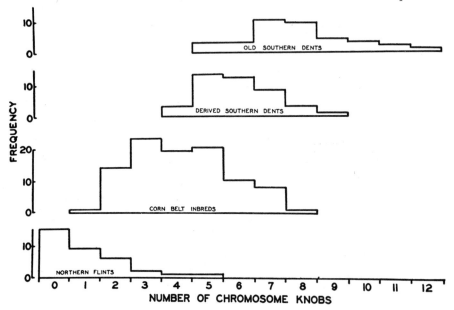

Fig. 8.2—Frequency distribution of chromosome knobs in Northern Flints, Southern Dents, and Corn Belt inbreds.

or between races, all the multiple factor characters which characterize each are partially linked with one another and tend to remain associated, even after generations of controlled breeding. More recently he has used this principle in the development of *the method of extrapolated correlates* (Anderson, 1949) by which the original characteristics can be deduced from the mixtures even when previously unknown.

Using this method in a relatively crude form, we were able (in advance of our historical evidence) to demonstrate (Brown, 1949) in Corn Belt inbreds, the association of low knob numbers, flag leaves, cylindrical ears, few tassel branches, and flinty kernels—all characteristics which typify the Northern Flints. Similarly, it was possible to show the association among these 98 Corn Belt inbreds of high knob numbers, no flag leaves, tapering ears, dented kernels, and many tassel branches—a combination of characters which is typical of the Southern Dents. As a matter of fact, by this technique Brown predicted the knob numbers of the Northern Flints, even when that fact was unknown to us.

The association of characters in actual open-pollinated fields of Corn Belt dents is so complex that one might suppose any study of it would be hopeless. However, from a study of character association in an open-pollinated field

FIG. 8.3—Corn Belt Dent-like segregates from an F_2 generation of cross of Longfellow Flint $\times$ Gourdseed Dent.

of Golden Queen Dent (Fig. 8.1) we were able to demonstrate the association of: (1) wide kernels, (2) low row numbers, (3) short glumes, (4) few tassel branches, (5) long ears, and (6) narrow central pith in the ear—all of these characterizing Northern Flints. The opposing combination: (1) narrow kernels, (2) high row numbers, (3) long glumes, (4) many tassel branches, (5) short ears, and (6) wide central pith also tended to be associated and is characteristic of Southern Dents. In other words, some of the characters which went in together from flints and dents were still in this open-pollinated variety tending to stay together on the average. The existence of such character complexes has been appreciated by experienced corn breeders, though apparently it has never been commented on in print. Of course, corn breeders and corn geneticists differ in their endowments for apprehending such phenomena in advance of the published facts, and the existence of these strong linkages has been more apparent to some than to others.

WIDTH OF CROSS

The demonstration that Corn Belt dents largely are derived from hybridization between Southern Dents and Northern Flints is of particular importance because this is such a wide cross. Our evidence for this assertion is largely morphological, though there is supporting evidence from cytology and genetics.

In nearly all species of cultivated plants there are conspicuous differences in color and shape. These differences give the various cultivated varieties of a species a false aspect of difference from one another, and from their wild progenitors. False, because these differences are usually due to a few genes, if not being actually monofactorial. The striking differences between such varieties are therefore no true indication of the distinctness of their germ plasms.

On the other hand, there are subtle differences in form, proportion, and indument which, though difficult for a novice to apprehend, are more like the differences which distinguish distinct species of the same genus. These taxonomically important differences have proven valid criteria for indicating the diversity of germ plasms. So it has been proven that the subtle taxonomic differences between the Old World and New World cottons are much more representative of the genetic diversity and relationships of these two groups of varieties than are the conspicuous differences in color and leaf-shape which are found within each group. In the Cucurbits the striking differences in color and form of fruit, which differentiate the varieties of *Cucurbita Pepo* and of *C. moschata*, are superficial compared to the taxonomically significant features which separate these two groups. The latter, moreover, have been proved to be a significant index of genetic diversity, either between these two groups of Cucurbits or in assaying the variation within *C. Pepo* itself (Shifriss, 1947) (Whitaker and Bohn, 1950).

The difficulty in relying upon such taxonomic criteria is that the method is highly subjective. Taxonomy is of necessity still more of an art than a science. This means that one must personally examine the evidence if his opinion is to be worth anything. It also means that the worker's opinion is worth no more than his understanding of the taxonomic entities included in his judgment. However, until more objective criteria are evolved for this field, we shall have to use fairly traditional taxonomic methods for want of anything better. Accordingly, the senior author has for two years spent one day a week in a technical, agrostological, herbarium survey of all the grasses conceivably related to *Zea mays*—all the genera in the tribes Andropogoneae and Maydeae. With that background, his judgments may well be mistaken but they are certainly informed.

From this point of view, the variation within *Zea mays* is without parallel, not only in the cultivated cereals but in any other domesticated plant or animal. There are such superficial characters as aleurone color, pericarp color, plant color, carbohydrate composition, and such amazing single factor differences as tunicate and teopod. In addition, there are a whole battery of characters which are difficult to work with genetically, but which are the kinds of differences that agrostologists find significant in the deployment of species and genera: spikelet shape and venation, spikelet arrangement, rachis morphology, pubescence, leaf-shape, internode proportions, etc. Using such criteria, the hybridization of the Southern Dents and the Northern Flints represents the mingling of two basically different germ plasms.

For evidences of relationship, the male inflorescence of maize (the tassel) is of particular importance. Inflorescence differences generally have proved to be of primary taxonomic importance in the Gramineae. Variation in the male inflorescence of Zea would likely be less obscured by domestication than the female inflorescence (the ear) which has been deliberately selected for various peculiarities. The entire male inflorescence of the Southern Dents has been extensively modified by condensation (Anderson, 1944), a sort of fasciation which telescopes adjacent nodes, and in the ear produces increases in row number. It is an abnormality conditioned by at least two pairs of recessive genes and its expression is certainly modified by still other genes.

Tassels of the Northern Flints are without any condensation. Though condensation modifies the general aspect of the tassel, it is relatively superficial. The presence of so much condensation renders difficult the demonstration of a much more fundamental difference. The central spike of the Northern Flints is decussately arranged. That is, the pairs of spikelets are in alternate whorls of two; whereas the spike of the Southern Dents (allowing for the modifications produced by extreme condensation) is fundamentally in whorls of 3, or mixtures of whorls of 3 and whorls of 2. The rachis of the Northern Flints is slender with long internodes, that of the Southern Dents is short and flattened (Fig. 8.5). Pedicels of the upper spikelets always are long in the Northern Flints. In the Southern Dents they may be so short that one cannot distinguish the normally pedicellate spikelet from its sessile partner.

Correlated differences are seen in the ear. That of the Northern Flints has a narrow central pith and is long and slender, characteristically with 8–10 rows. The ear of the Southern Dents is short and thick with a wide central pith, and with from 16 to 30 or more rows. Pairing of the rows is markedly evident in the Northern Flints, even when they are pushed closer together in those occasional ears with 10 or 12 rows (Fig. 8.4). There is little or no row pairing in the Southern Dents. The kernel of the Southern Dents is long, flat, and narrow. Its largest diameter is near the base. By contrast, the kernel of the Northern Flints is wider than it is high, and is considerably thicker at the apex than it is at the base.

The ear of Zea mays is terminal on a secondary branch, which is hidden by

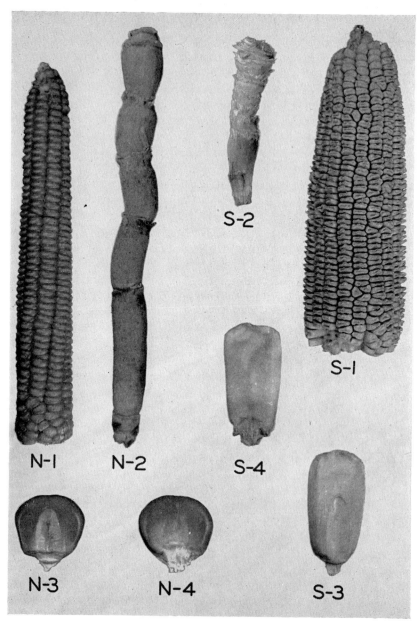

FIG. 8.4—Typical ears (*1*), shanks (*2*), and seeds (*3* and *4*) of Northern Flint (*N*), and Southern Dent (*S*).

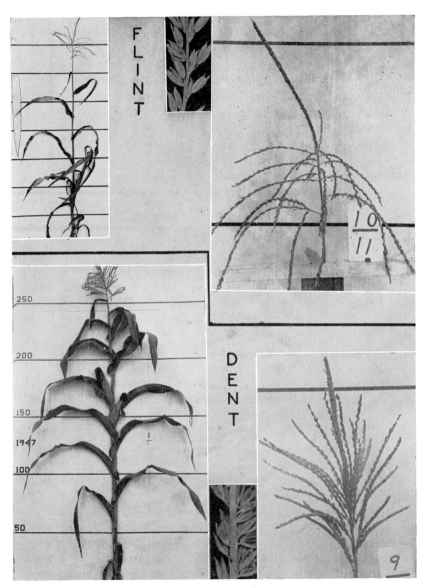

FIG. 8.5—Typical plants, tassels, and staminate spikelets of Northern Flint and Southern Dent.

its specialized leaves or husks. When dissected out, these ear shoots (or shanks) are diagnostically different in Northern Flints and Southern Dents (Fig. 8.4). In the former they are long, with elongated internodes which are *widest* between the nodes, and which have a smooth surface upon drying. In the latter they are very short, frequently *wider* at the nodes than between them, and have a characteristically ribbed surface upon drying.

The leaves of the Northern Flints are long and slender and frequently a light green. Those of the Southern Dents are proportionately wider and shorter and are often dark green. They are set upon culms whose internodes are proportionately longer and more slender in the Northern Flints, and less prone to become greatly shortened at the internodes immediately above the ear.

If we ignore such abnormalities as differences in carbohydrate composition and condensation, these two races of *Zea mays* still are widely different from one another—as compared to differences between their wild relatives in the Andropogoneae or the Maydeae. The differences in internode pattern and proportion and in leaf shape are similar to those frequently found between species of the same genus. The differences in pedicellation of the upper spikelet would be more characteristic of genera and sub-genera. On the other hand, in the whorling of the central spike (whorls of 2 versus whorls of 3) is the kind of difference which would ordinarily separate genera or even groups of genera. On a par with this difference are those in the cupule (the bony cup in which the kernels are attached in pairs). They are so difficult to observe that we cannot discuss these until the general morphology of this organ has been described. If we sum up the morphological evidence, it is clear that the fundamental differences between the Northern Flints and the Southern Dents are similar to those which differentiate distantly related species (or even genera) among related wild grasses. There is every morphological indication, therefore, that we are dealing with two fundamentally different germ plasms.

The cytological facts reported above lend further weight to the conclusion that the Northern Flints are basically different from the Southern Dents. The former have chromosomes which are essentially knobless at pachytene. The latter average nearly one knob per chromosome (Fig. 8.2). Heterochromatic knobs are known in other grasses besides *Zea mays*. In these other genera, their presence or absence, from such evidence as is available, seems to be characteristic of whole species or groups of species. Such a difference between the Flints and Dents indicates that we are dealing with two fundamentally different germ plasms. It has been shown in Guatemala (Mangelsdorf and Cameron, 1942) and in Mexico (Anderson, 1946) that the varieties with many knobs are morphologically and ecologically different from those with low numbers of knobs.

A further indication that these two germ plasms are physiologically dif-

ferent is given by their pachytene behavior. The pachytene chromosomes of
the Northern Flints are easy to smear and give sharp fixation images. Southern Dents are more difficult to smear. The chromosomes do not spread out
well and do not stain sharply. This is not a result of differences in knob number, since some of the Mexican Dents with few knobs are equally difficult to
smear. Whatever the physiological significance of this reaction, it is direct
evidence for a difference in the chemistry of the germ cells. Again such differences in stainability are more often met with, between genera, than they
are in different strains of the same species.

There is genetic evidence for the difference between Southern Dents and
Northern Flints, in the behavior of crosses between them. The F_1's are fully

TABLE 8.1

PERCENTAGE OF STERILE OR BARREN PLANTS IN
GOURDSEED, LONGFELLOW, AND F_2 GENERATION
OF CROSS GOURDSEED × LONGFELLOW

	Sterile or Barren	Normal Ear	Total Number of Plants
Gourdseed...................	37	63	46
Longfellow...................	2	98	58
F_2 Gourdseed×Longfellow.....	52	48	101

fertile and exhibit extreme hybrid vigor. The F_2's show a high percentage of
completely barren plants—plants which formed ears but set little or no seeds,
either because of sterility or because they were too weak to mature successfully—and plants which managed to set seeds, though their growth habit
indicates fundamental disharmonies of development.

Table 8.1 shows the percentages of good ears and plants which were either
without ears or on which the ears had failed to set any seed, for Gourdseed-
Dent, Longfellow Flint, and their F_2, when grown in Iowa. Like Southern
Dents generally, the Gourdseed is less adapted to central Iowa than is Longfellow Flint. An F_2 between these two varieties, however, has a much greater
percentage than either parent of plants which are so ill-adapted that they
either produce no visible ear, or set no seed if an ear is produced. Similar
results were obtained in other crosses between Northern Flints and Southern
Dents, both in Missouri and in Iowa. From this we conclude that they are
so genetically different from one another that a high percentage of their F_2
recombinations are not able to produce seed, even when the plants are carefully grown and given individual attention.

SUMMARY

The common dent corns of the United States Corn Belt were created
de novo by American farmers and plant breeders during the nineteenth cen-

tury. They resulted in a large measure from deliberate crossing and re-crossing of two races of maize (the Northern Flints and the Southern Dents) so different that, were they wild grasses, they would be considered as totally different species and might well be placed in different genera. The origin of two so-different races within cultivated maize is an even larger problem and one outside the scope of this discussion. It may be pointed out parenthetically that the Tripsacum hypothesis (Mangelsdorf and Reeves, 1945) would not only account for variation of this magnitude, it would even explain the actual direction of the difference between these two races of maize. However, the relation between maize and Tripsacum on any hypothesis is certainly a most complicated one (Anderson, 1949). It would be more effective to postpone detailed discussions of this relationship until the comparative morphology of the inflorescences of maize and of Tripsacum is far better understood than it is at present.

SIGNIFICANCE TO MAIZE BREEDING

Derivation of the commercial field corns of the United States by the deliberate mingling of Northern Flints and Southern Dents is a fact. Unfortunately, it is a fact which had passed out of common knowledge before the present generation of maize breeders was educated. From the point of view of practical maize breeding, either hybrid or open-pollinated, it is of central importance. Briefly, it means that the maize germ plasms now being worked with by plant breeders are not varying at random. They are strongly centered about two main centers or complexes. Such practical problems as the development and maintenance of inbreds, the detection of combining ability, and the most effective utilization of hybrid vigor need to be rethought from this point of view. Detailed experiments to provide information for such practical questions already are well under way. While these experiments are not yet far enough along to give definite answers, they have progressed far enough to allow us to speak with some authority on these matters.

HETEROSIS

The heterosis of American Corn Belt dents acquires a new significance in the light of these results, and practical suggestions as to its most efficient utilization take on a new direction. We are immediately led to the hypothesis that the heterosis we are working with is, in part at least, the heterosis acquired by mingling the germ plasms of the Northern Flints and the Southern Dents.

Insofar as hybrid vigor is concerned, the hybrid corn program largely has served to gather *some* of the dispersed vigor of the open-pollinated dents. Preliminary results indicate that this has not been done efficiently in terms of what might be accomplished with somewhat more orientation.

The early days of the hybrid corn program were dominated by the hypothesis that one could inbreed this vigorous crop, identify the inferior strains in it, and then set up an elite cross-pollinated germ plasm. This hypothesis was clearly and definitely stated by East and Jones (*Inbreeding and Outbreeding*, 1919, pp. 216–17).

Experiments with maize show that undesirable qualities are brought to light by self-fertilization which either eliminate themselves or can be rejected by selection. The final result is a number of distinct types which are constant and uniform and able to persist indefinitely. They have gone through a process of purification such that only those individuals which possess much of the best that was in the variety at the beginning can survive. The characters which they (pure lines) have, can now be estimated more nearly at their true worth. By crossing, the best qualities which have been distributed to the several inbred strains can be gathered together again and a new variety recreated. After the most desirable combinations are isolated, their recombination into a new and better variety, which could be maintained by seed propagation, would be a comparatively easy undertaking.

Though other corn breeders and corn geneticists may not have committed themselves so definitely in print, such a notion was once almost universal among hybrid corn experts. Modified versions of it still influence breeding programs and are even incorporated in elementary courses in maize breeding.

The facts reported above would lead us to believe that heterosis, having resulted from the mingling of two widely different germ plasms, will probably have many genes associated with characters which in their relatively homozygous state are far from the Corn Belt ideal of what a corn plant should look like. It is highly probable that much of the so-called "junk" revealed by inbreeding was extreme segregants from this wide cross, and that it was closely associated with the genes which gave open-pollinated dents their dispersed vigor. It is significant that some very valuable inbreds (L317 is a typical example) have many undesirable features. For this reason, many such inbreds are automatically eliminated even before reaching the testing stage.

If one accepts the fact that Corn Belt dents resulted from the comparatively recent mingling of two extremely different races of maize, then on the simplest and most orthodox genetic hypotheses, the greatest heterosis could be expected to result from crosses between inbreds resembling the Southern Dents and inbreds resembling the Northern Flints. If heterosis (as its name implies) is due to heterozygous genes or segments, then with Corn Belt corn on the whole we would expect to find the greatest number of differing genes when we reassembled two inbreds—one resembling the Northern Flint, the other resembling the original Southern Dent.

Theory (Anderson, 1939a), experiment (Anderson, 1939b; Brown, 1949), and the results of practical breeding show that linkage systems as differentiated as these break up very slowly. On the whole, the genes which went in together with the Northern Flints still tend to stay together as we have demonstrated above. This would suggest that in selecting inbreds, far from trying to eliminate all of the supposed "junk," we might well attempt to breed for inbreds which, though they have good agronomic characters like stiffness of the stalk, nevertheless resemble Northern Flints. On the other hand, we should breed also for those which resemble Southern Dents as closely as they can and still be relatively easy to grow and to harvest. It would seem as if the opposite generally has been done. A deliberate attempt has been made to produce inbreds which look as much as possible like good Corn Belt maize in spite of being inbreds.

There are, of course, practical necessities in breeding. In this direction the work of corn breeders is a remarkable achievement. Strong attention to lodging resistance, to desirable kernel shapes and sizes, and to resistance to drought and disease has achieved real progress. The inbred-hybrid method has permitted much stronger selection for these necessary characters than was possible with open-pollinated maize. Most Corn Belt dents now plant well, stand well, and harvest well.

Perhaps partly because of these practical points there has been a conscious and unconscious attempt on the part of many breeders to select for inbreds which are like the Corn Belt ideal in all characters, trivial and practical alike. The corn shows are now out-moded, but corn show ideals still influence corn breeding. For instance, there has been an effort to produce plants with greatly arching leaves, whose margins are uniformly ruffled. Such characters are certainly of a trivial nature and of secondary importance in practical programs. Any potential heterosis closely associated with upright leaves, yellow green leaves, tillering, or blades on the husk leaves has seldom had a chance to get into inbreds where it could be tested on a basis of achievement. It would seem highly probable that, in not basing the selection of inbreds more soundly on performance, we have let much potential heterosis slip through our sieve of selection.

Heterosis Reserves

These considerations lead us to believe that there is probably a good deal of useful heterozygosis still ungathered in high yielding open-pollinated varieties. There is also a distinct possibility that still more could be added by going back to the Northern Flints and Southern Dents with the specific object of bringing in maximum heterozygosity. From our experience it is more likely that superior heterosis is to be found among the best flints than among the best dents. On the whole, the Northern Flints have been farthest from the corn breeders' notion of what a good corn plant should look like. Flint-like characteristics (tillering, for example) have been most strongly selected against, both in the open-pollinated varieties and the inbreds derived from them.

Several of the widely recognized sources of good combining inbreds are open-pollinated varieties with a stronger infusion of Northern Flints than was general in the Corn Belt. This is particularly true of Lancaster Surecrop, the excellence of whose inbreds was early recognized by several breeders in the United States Department of Agriculture. In our opinion, it is probable that the greater proportion of flint germ plasm in Lancaster Surecrop has made it an outstanding source of inbreds of proven highly specific combining ability when used with other Corn Belt inbreds. This is not an isolated example, and even more extreme cases could be cited. We think it is a reasonable working hypothesis that Northern Flint varieties of superior productivity might be efficient sources of improved heterozygosity for the United States Corn Belt.

Morphological Characters as Related to Heterosis

To put this hypothesis in different language, morphological characters, if carefully chosen, may be used as criteria of specific combining ability in Corn Belt inbreds. Before presenting data bearing directly on this hypothesis, two points need to be emphasized and discussed: (1) the effective selection of morphological criteria, and (2) the relativity of all measures of effective combining ability.

Previous studies (Kiesselbach, 1922; Jenkins, 1929; and others) have indicated that the only positive correlations between the morphology of inbreds and their combining ability are those involving characters of the inbreds which are indicative of plant vigor. Reference to these investigations shows that the characters chosen were such superficial measurements as date of silking and tasseling, plant height, number of nodes, number of ears, ear diameter, etc. Unfortunately, the morphology of the maize plant is not a simple matter. It is so complex that one needs technical help on morphology quite as much as he would in biochemistry were he studying the concentrations of amino acids in the developing kernel.

Accordingly, we first familiarized ourselves thoroughly with the technical agrostological facts concerning the detailed gross morphology of grasses in general and Zea in particular. Just as in the case of a biochemical study of the kernel, we found that further original research was necessary if the investigation was to be carried on effectively. We have accordingly undertaken detailed studies of internode patterns and branching of the inflorescence; the venation, size, and shape of the male spikelet, the development of the husk leaf blades, the external anatomy of the cob, and the morphology of the shank. Some of these investigations are still continuing, and must continue if inbred morphology and combining ability are to be effectively correlated.

It is impossible to produce an absolute measure of combining ability. When one speaks of combining ability of two inbreds, he always refers to their behavior with each other compared to their behavior with certain other inbreds or open-pollinated varieties. This is such a relative measure that the scoring of a particular F_1 cross as very low or very high in combining ability might depend solely upon our previous experience with the two inbreds. We may illustrate this point with an extreme example. Let us suppose that we have inbreds 1F and 2F derived directly from Northern Flints, and inbreds 10D and 11D derived from Southern Dents. Were we to cross 1F $\times$ 2F and

10D × 11D we would expect relatively little heterosis within either of the crosses. Accordingly, when we crossed 2F × 11D we would rate this cross as having high specific combining ability. On the other hand, had we originally crossed 2F × 10D and 11D × 1F, then there would probably have been almost equally great heterosis in each of the crosses. Had these been used as a basis for comparing the heterosis of 2F × 11D, then our notion as to the amount of heterosis in these crosses would have been very different than it would have been had comparisons been made with 1F × 2F or 10D × 11D.

If the germ plasms of the two main races of maize involved in Corn Belt dents are still partially intact as a result of linkages, it should be possible to classify inbreds on the basis of morphological differences according to their flint and dent tendencies. If this can be done, and if genetic diversity is important in bringing about a heterotic effect in hybrids, one should be able to predict with some accuracy the relative degree of heterosis to be expected from crossing any two inbred lines. With this hypothesis as a background, a series of experiments was started three years ago to determine whether or not hybrid vigor in maize, as expressed in terms of grain yield, could be predicted on the basis of morphological differences of inbreds making up the F_1 hybrids.

Fifty-six relatively homozygous inbred lines consisting of eighteen U.S.D.A. or experiment station lines, and thirty-eight strains developed by the Pioneer Hi-Bred Corn Company were scored for the following characteristics: row number, kernel length, denting, development of husk leaf blades, number of secondary tassel branches, glume length, and chromosome knob number. For each of these characteristics the two extremes in the eastern United States are to be found in Southern Dents and Northeastern Flints. At least twelve plants of each of the fifty-six inbreds were scored, and these scores were then averaged to give a mean value for the line. The resulting means were translated into numerical index values, in which a low value represents Northern Flint–like tendencies, and a high value Southern Dent–like tendencies. For example, the mean row number values for the inbreds studied ranged from 11.2 to 19.5. These were arranged in the following index classes.

1	2	3	4	5	6	7
11.2–11.7	11.8–12.3	12.4–12.9	13.0–13.5	13.6–14.1	14.2–14.7	14.8–15.3

8	9	10	11	12	13	14
15.4–15.9	16.0–16.5	16.6–17.1	17.2–17.7	17.8–18.3	18.4–18.9	19.0–19.5

Index values for the other characteristics were arranged similarly, and from the individual characteristic inbred indices (each being given equal weight) a total "Inbred Index" was determined as is shown by example in Table 8.2.

After index values had been determined for the inbreds, single cross combinations were made and these tested for yield. In 1948, sixty-six single crosses were grown in yield tests in Iowa and in Illinois. Each F_1 hybrid was replicated six times in each test. At the end of the season, yield of grain was determined on the basis of 15 per cent moisture corn. Actual yields in bushels per acre and morphological differences of the inbreds involved in each of the crosses were then plotted on a scatter diagram as shown in Figure 8.6. It will be noted that although the observations exhibit considerable scatter, there is a tendency for grain yields in single crosses to increase as the morphological differences between the inbreds making up the crosses become greater. Actually the correlation coefficient between yield and index differences in this case was $r = +.39$.

The experiment was continued in 1949, in which 100 F_1 hybrids were tested for yield. In this experiment three characters only were used to deter-

TABLE 8.2

INBRED INDICES BASED ON SEVEN CHARACTERS

Inbreds	Row No.	Kernel Length	Denting	Husk Leaves	Tassel Branches	Spikelet Length	Chromosome Knobs	Inbred Index	Sums of 7 Differences without Signs
Hy.....	9	14	4	14	5	6	12	64	41
Oh40b..	2	8	4	1	4	1	3	23	30 / 59
MY1...	14	11	14	14	14	6	9	82	

mine the index of relationship between the inbreds used. These were row number, kernel length, and degree of development of husk leaf blades. Elimination in this experiment of certain morphological characteristics used previously was done largely to facilitate ease and speed of scoring. It had been determined previously that, of the several characteristics used, those having the highest correlation with yield were differences in row number, kernel length, and husk leaf blades. There was likewise known to be a rather strong association between each of these characteristics and tassel branch number, denting, glume length, internode pattern, and chromosome knob number. Therefore the scoring of these three characteristics probably covers indirectly nearly as large a segment of the germ plasm as would scores based on all seven characteristics.

The 1949 tests in which each entry was replicated six times in each location were again grown both in Iowa and Illinois. Yields from these tests, plotted against index differences of the inbreds, are shown in Figure 8.7. As in the previous year's data, a pronounced tendency was shown for hybrids made up of inbreds of diverse morphology to produce higher grain yields than hybrids consisting of morphologically similar inbreds. The correlation co-

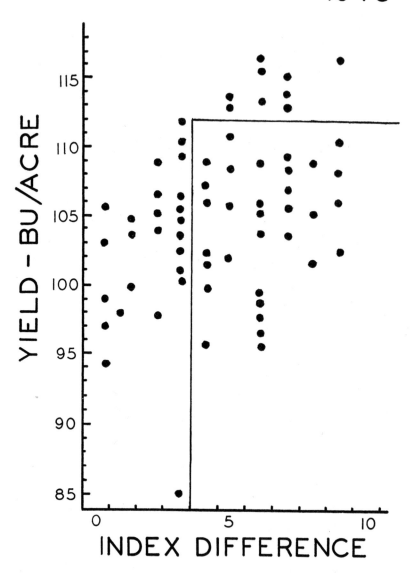

1948

r = +.38 *

Fig. 8.6—Scatter diagram depicting relationship between grain yields of 66 single cross hybrids and morphological differences of inbred parents of the hybrids. Explanation in text.

efficient between yield and index differences is $r = +.40$, a significant value statistically.

In terms of practical corn breeding, the distribution of single crosses in Figures 8.6 and 8.7 is of particular significance. If these observations are critical (we have produced a repeatable result) it means that one could have eliminated from the testing program the lower one-third of the crosses on the basis of index differences, without losing any of the top 10 per cent of the highest yielding hybrids. In the case of the 100 hybrids in Figure 8.7, one could have eliminated from testing 35 per cent of the crosses, thereby permitting the inclusion of 35 additional hybrids in this particular testing area. If further

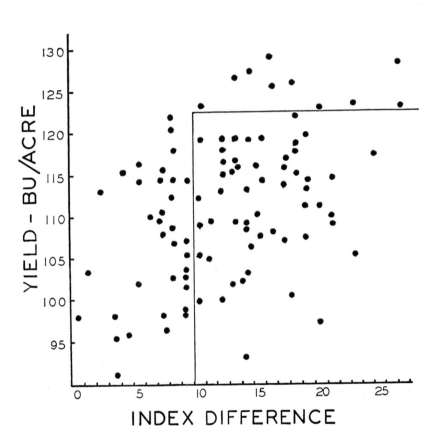

FIG. 8.7—Scatter diagram depicting relationship between grain yields of 100 single cross hybrids and morphological differences of inbred parents of the hybrids. Explanation in text.

experiments show that the method is reliable, such a procedure should expedite most corn breeding programs.

Our method of scoring does not take into account the variation brought about by the infusion of germ plasm other than that from Northern Flints and Southern Dents. Perhaps this is one reason why we have not obtained higher correlations between differences in inbred morphology and yield. There are a few inbreds in the Corn Belt which appear to be affiliated either with Caribbean flints or the Basketmaker complex. Scoring of such inbreds on a scale designed for Northern Flints and Southern Dents undoubtedly leads to conflicting results. It is hoped that experiments now in progress will aid in clarifying this situation.

SIGNIFICANCE OF FLINT-DENT ANCESTRY
IN CORN BREEDING

The Flint-Dent ancestry of Corn Belt maize bears upon many other breeding problems besides those concerned with heterosis. Its widest usefulness is in giving a frame of reference for observing and thinking about the manifold and confusing variation of Corn Belt maize. When one becomes interested in any particular character of the corn plant, he no longer needs to examine large numbers of inbreds to understand its range of variation and its general over-all direction. He merely needs to examine a few inbreds, and a Northern Flint and a Southern Dent. A good part of the variation will then be seen to fall into a relatively simple series from an extreme Northern Flint type to the opposite Southern Dent extreme, with various intermediates and recombinations in between. This is quite as true for physiological or biochemical characters as for glumes, lemmas, or other morphological characters. One is then ready to study further inbreds with a framework in his mind for sorting out and remembering the variation which he finds.

The actual breeding plot efficiency of this understanding will be clearer if we cite a practical example. Now that corn is picked mechanically, the size, shape, texture, and strength of shank are important. When maize was picked by hand, the hand had a brain behind it. Variations in ear height, in the stance of the ear, and in the strength and shape of the shank were of minor significance. Now that machines do the work, it is of the utmost practical importance to have the shank standardized to a type adapted to machine harvesting. When this necessity was brought to our attention a few years ago, there were few published facts relating to variation in the shank. Examination of a few inbreds showed that though this organ varied somewhat within inbreds, it varied more from one line to another than almost any other simple feature of the plant. We accordingly harvested typical shanks from each of 164 inbreds being grown for observation in the breeding plots of the Pioneer Hi-Bred Corn Company. We also examined a number of Northern Flints, and had they been available, we would have studied the shanks on typical Southern Dents. However, simply by using the hypothesis that one extreme would have to come in from the Northern Flints, the other from the Southern Dents, we were able within one working day to tabulate measurable features of these shanks and to incorporate all the facts in a

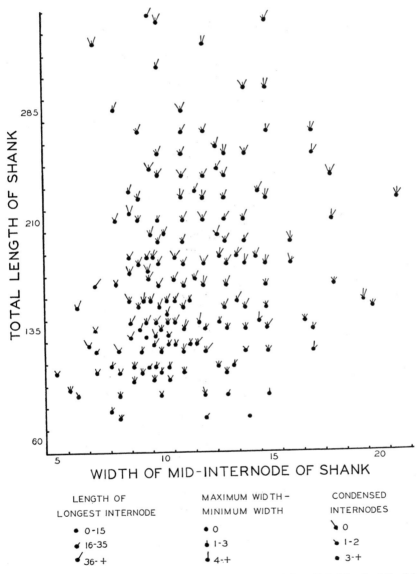

FIG. 8.8—Pictorialized diagram showing relationship in 164 Corn Belt inbreds of the following shank characters: total length, width of mid internode, length of longest internode, maximum width minus minimum width, and number of condensed internodes.

pictorialized scatter diagram (Fig. 8.8). Using the method of Extrapolated Correlates we were able to reconstruct the probable shank type of the Southern Dents. (We later grew and examined them and verified our predictions.) We arranged most of the facts concerning variation in shank type in United States inbreds in a single, easily grasped diagram. All the technical information needed as a background for breeding was available after two days' work by two people. Without the Northern Flint–Southern Dent frame of reference for these miscellaneous facts, we might have worked around the problem for several breeding seasons before comprehending this general, overall picture.

SUMMARY

1. Archaeological and historical evidence shows that the common dent corns of the United States Corn Belt originated mainly from the purposeful mixing of the Northern Flints and the Southern Dents.

2. Cytological and genetic evidence point in the same direction and were used in the earlier stages of our investigations before the complete historical evidence had been located.

3. The Northern Flints and Southern Dents belong to races of maize so different that, were they wild grasses, they would certainly be assigned to different species and perhaps to different genera. Such cytological and genetical evidence as is available is in accord with this conclusion.

4. The significance of these facts to maize breeding problems is outlined. In the light of this information, the heterosis of Corn Belt maize would seem to be largely the heterosis acquired by mingling the germ plasms of the Northern Flints and Southern Dents. It is pointed out that most breeding programs have been so oriented as to be inefficient in assembling the dispersed heterosis of the open-pollinated varieties of the Corn Belt. The possibility of gathering more heterosis from the same sources is discussed and it is suggested that more might be obtained, particularly among the Northern Flints.

5. Morphological characters of dents and flints, if carefully chosen, should be useful criteria for specific combining ability. The problem of selecting such characters is described. Two seasons' results in correlating combining ability and flint-dent differences are reported. They are shown to be statistically significant and of probable practical importance.

6. The practical advantages of understanding the flint-dent ancestry of Corn Belt maize are discussed and illustrated by example. In brief these facts provide a "frame of reference" for detecting, organizing, and understanding much of the manifold variability in Corn Belt maize.

ADRIANO A. BUZZATI-TRAVERSO
Universita, Istituto di Genetica, Pavia, Italy

Chapter 9

Heterosis in
Population Genetics

Population genetics is the study of the genetic structure of populations. Such a statement may look at first to be a truism, a tautology. The subject matter of our research becomes very intricate, however, as soon as we try to specify what we mean by the above definition. The terms "genetic structure" and "population" may have different meanings according to what we are willing to indicate by such words. It therefore seems convenient to start with an analysis of the terms we are using. Such discussion will give us a chance to see how the problem of heterosis is intimately connected with the general theme of population-genetical studies. A few experimental data will be used to illustrate such points.

Let us consider first what we mean by population. If we take a dictionary definition, we find in Webster's that population is "all the people or inhabitants in a country or section." It means, in this sense, the sum of individuals present at a certain moment over a more or less arbitrarily limited territory. But this definition does not correspond to the requirements of our studies, as I have tried to show elsewhere (Buzzati-Traverso, 1950). Such a definition is a static one, while the population, as considered in the field of population genetics, is a dynamic concept. We are interested not in the number of individuals present at a certain time in a certain place and their morphological and physiological characteristics. Instead, we are concerned with the underlying mechanisms which bring about such characteristics, and the particular size the population reaches at any particular moment. Since such mechanisms depend upon the numerical dynamics of the population and upon heredity, it follows that our concept of population is typically dynamic. On this view, then, *a population is an array of interbreeding individuals, continuous along the time coordinate.*

Consideration of a population as a phenomenon continuously occurring in time makes it impossible for the experimental student of population genetics to get a direct and complete picture of what is occurring within a population at any particular moment. We can attempt to collect data on the population under study only by freezing such flowing processes at particular time intervals. Collecting observations on a population at different times gives us a chance to extrapolate the direction and rate of the processes that have occurred within the population during the time elapsed between two successive sets of observations. If the samples studied are large enough and give an unbiased picture of the total population at the time when the sample is being drawn, this experimental procedure may give us a fairly adequate idea of what is going on within the array of interbreeding individuals continuous along the time coordinate. That sum of individuals at a definite time, which one usually means by *population*, is of interest to the population geneticist only as an index of the particular evolutionary stage reached by the array of interbreeding individuals. Since there are actual breeding and genetic relationships between the individuals of any such array, of any such population, the population can be considered as the natural unit of our studies.

If we consider now what we mean by "genetic structure," our task becomes much more complex. At first we could assume that the genetic structure of a population could be properly described in terms of the gene frequencies present at a certain time within a population. But this is only part of the picture.

For the total description of the genetic structure of a population we have to consider not only the frequencies of existing genes, but how these are fitted within the chromosomes, how these allow the release of variability by means of recombinations, how large is the amount of new variability produced by mutations, and several other factors which we cannot analyze now. In a few words, the study of population genetics aims at the knowledge of the breeding system of populations. This, as we shall see, is a rather difficult task because of the complexity of factors responsible for the origin and evolution of such systems.

EVOLUTIONARY FACTORS INVOLVED

When we take into consideration a species or a natural population at a certain stage, we have to assume that such a natural entity is the product of a series of evolutionary factors that have been at work in previous times and that some, or all of them, are still operating on the population while we are studying it. This means that we should try to explain the genetic structure of the population in terms of such evolutionary factors.

Now, if we are willing to examine the nature of the known evolutionary agencies, we conclude that these can be classified into two types. On one side we find, in sexually reproducing organisms, a limited number of chromosomes, linkage between genes, sterility mechanisms, mating discriminations, devices favoring inbreeding, and other conservative forces that aim at the preservation of certain constellations of genes over a large number of generations. On the other side we find mutation pressure, recombination between chromosomes, recombination among genes due to crossing over, outbreeding devices, migration pressure, and other revolutionary forces that aim at the production of genetic novelty.

It seems reasonable to maintain that, at any particular time, a species or a natural population can be considered as a sort of compromise between the two conflicting forces—a compromise that is brought about through the action of natural selection. In other words, the fine adjustment or adaptation of a population to its environment is the expression of such compromise. At any particular time the terms of the compromise between the conflicting forces are always different as compared to other moments, as the compromise itself is a dynamic process.

In order to reach the highest possible level of adaptation with respect to a certain set of environmental conditions, natural selection is discriminating not only for or against a certain individual genetic constitution, but for or against a group of individuals, as well. Sometimes selection acts at the level of the individual, sometimes it operates at some higher level. If we consider a genotype that insures resistance against an infectious disease, present in a certain area of distribution of a species, it will be obvious that an individual carrying it shall directly benefit by it. But if we consider a genotype producing fecundity higher than the average of the population, this will be selected by the mere fact that a larger number of individuals having such genetic constitution will be present in the next generation. These, in their turn, shall have a chance of being represented in the next generation greater than that of individuals having a less fertile genotype. The individual itself, though, obtains no direct advantage from such selection.

The next extreme condition we can consider is the one occurring when the advantage of the individual is in conflict with the advantage of the group. This is the case, for instance, of a genotype that would extend the span of life far beyond the period of sexual activity—or higher fertility linked with antisocial attitudes in the case of man. In both cases, natural selection favoring the preservation of the group will discriminate against the individual. A similar mechanism must have played a great role in various critical periods of organic evolution. When intergroup selective pressure is in the opposite direction from intragroup selection, a sort of compromise has to be reached between the two conflicting tendencies. This can be reached in many different ways that are best illustrated by the great variety of life histories and mating systems to be found in the living world.

Those factors which we have classified as conservative tend to produce genetic homogeneity, or what is technically known as homozygosis. Factors that we have named revolutionary tend to produce genetic heterogeneity or heterozygosis. Thus we come to the conclusion that the mentioned compromise brought about by selection consists of the pursuit of an optimum level of hybridity with respect to the conditions under which the organism lives. Such a hybridity optimum is the product, not only of the mutation rate and selective value of single genes, but also depends largely upon the genetic system and the mating system—the breeding system—of the considered species or population.

The genetic structure of natural populations cannot be solved only in terms of individual variations observable in the group. Instead, it must be integrated into a unitary research on changes in gene frequencies as related to the underlying breeding systems. This is why we are justified in considering the natural population as a unit, since individual variations must be referred to the genetic balance of the whole aggregate of individuals.

What is that hybridity optimum I was speaking about but heterosis? How else could heterosis be defined in population problems other than that type and amount of heterozygosity that gives the population or the individual the best adaptive value with respect to the conditions in which the organism lives? With this view, then, it becomes feasible to analyze experimentally what morphological and physiological characteristics of the hybrids produce the better adaptation.

MECHANISMS WHICH PROMOTE HYBRIDITY

In studying how heterosis mechanisms are brought about in living creatures, we may attempt a sort of classification of the devices present in plants and animals insuring hybridity. Starting from the most complex and proceeding to the less complex cases, we can distinguish three types of mechanisms: (1) mating systems, (2) chromosome mechanisms, and (3) gene effects.

We will not discuss in detail all the devices insuring hybridity found in plants and animals. We will mention a few, in order to show how many different paths have been followed in evolution to reach the same sort of results.

Under the heading "mating systems" we may mention homo- and heterothally among fungi; monoecism and dioecism, incompatibility mechanisms, and heterostyly among flowering plants. Here, in some cases such as *Primula scotica*, there is close relation between the variability of ecological conditions, and, therefore, of selection pressure and the efficiency of the incompatibility mechanisms. Other species of this genus present in England are characterized by heterostyly and incompatibility devices to insure the occurrence of outcrossing, apparently necessary to meet the requirements of varied ecological conditions. *Primula scotica*, living in a very specialized ecological niche, shows that such a mechanism has broken down. In fact, it looks as if the requirements of a constant environment are met better by populations genetically less diversified.

Among animals, the largest part of which are not sessile and therefore not bound to the ground, the differentiation into two sexes offers the best solution to the problem of insuring a wide range of crossing among different genotypes. But even here we see that special behavior patterns have been developed for this purpose. These may be courtship relationships, sexual selection, dominance relationships among a group of animals, or protandry mechanisms, where the presence of two sexes in hermaphrodites could reduce the amount of outcrossing and therefore endanger the survival of the species. Even among parthenogenetic animals, such as Cladoceran crustacea, the appearance of sexual generations after a long succession of asexual ones seems to depend upon extreme environmental conditions. For its survival, the species must shift over to sexual reproduction in order to obtain a wider range of genetic combinations, some of which might be able to survive under the new set of conditions.

At the level of the chromosome mechanisms, several examples of permanent hybrids are known well enough to be sure that they play an important role for the survival of some flowering plants. In animals, too, some similar mechanism may be present. In a European species of Drosophila which we are studying now, *Drosophila subobscura*, one finds that practically every individual found in nature is heterozygous for one or more inversions. It looks as if the species were a permanent hybrid.

Rarely, though, one finds individuals giving progeny with homozygous gene arrangement. Such cases have been observed only three times: once in Sweden, once in Switzerland, once in Italy; and they are very peculiar in one respect. The three homozygous gene arrangements are the same, even though the ecological and climatic conditions of the three original populations were as different as they could be. It looks as if the species could originate only one gene arrangement viable in homozygous condition, and that this may occur sporadically throughout its vast distribution range (Buzzati-Traverso, unpublished).

At this level too is the fine example of heterozygous inversions from the classical studies of Dobzhansky (1943–1947). They have demonstrated that wild populations of *Drosophila pseudoobscura* show different frequencies of inversions at different altitudes or in the same locality at different times of the year. Variation in the frequency of inversions could be reproduced experimentally in population cages by varying environmental factors such as temperature. It is shown in such a case that natural selection controls the increase or decrease of inversions determining an interesting type of balanced polymorphism. Finally, according to the investigations of Mather (1942–1943) on the mechanism of polygenic inheritance, it appears that linkage relationships within one chromosome, even in the absence of heterozygous inversions, tend to maintain a balance of plus and minus loci controlling quantitative characters.

We come then to the third level, that of gene effects. Here it is well known that heterozygotes for a certain locus sometimes show a higher viability or a better adaptation to the environment than either homozygote. The most extreme examples are those of the widespread occurrence of lethals in wild populations of Drosophila, noted in the next section.

Every population of plants and animals that has been studied from the genetic viewpoint has proved to be heterozygous for several loci. We have now at our disposal a large series of data showing that the phenomenon of genetic polymorphism is frequent in plants, animals, and man. These offer to the student of evolutionary mechanisms the best opportunities to test his hypotheses concerning the relative importance of selection, mutation pressure, migration, and genetic drift as factors of evolution. Wherever we find a well established example of balanced polymorphism, such as that of blood groups and taste sensitivity in man, it seems safe to assume that this is due to selection in favor of the heterozygote. How this selection actually may produce an increase in the chances of survival of the heterozygote, as compared to both homozygotes, is an open question. When the characters favored by natural or artificial selection are the result of several genes in heterozygous condition, the analysis becomes very difficult indeed, as the experience of plant and animal breeders clearly shows.

EXPERIMENTS WITH HETEROSIS

The importance of the problem of heterosis for population-genetical studies is clearly shown, not only by such general considerations and by the few examples mentioned, but also by the everyday experience of people interested in such lines of work. I have come across problems involving heterosis several times and shall describe some results we have obtained which may be of interest for the problem under discussion, especially at the level of single gene differences.

Several Drosophila workers have been able to show the occurrence of heterosis in the fruit flies. L'Heritier and Teissier (1933), Kalmus (1945), and Teissier (1947a, b) have shown that some visible recessive mutants of *Drosophila melanogaster* such as *ebony* and *sepia* have a higher selective value in heterozygous condition than either of the corresponding homozygotes under laboratory conditions. Dobzhansky and collaborators in *Drosophila pseudoobscura*, Plough, Ives, and Child, as well as other American and Russian workers in *Drosophila melanogaster*, have shown that recessive lethals are widely spread in natural populations. It is generally accepted that such genes are being maintained in the population because the heterozygotes are being selected. Teissier (1942, 1944) has brought similar evidence under laboratory conditions for *Drosophila melanogaster*.

It has been shown in several populations of species of the genus Drosophila that heterozygous inversions are being selected, under natural and experimental conditions. It seems, however, that the study of selection in favor of the heterozygote for single loci deserves more careful analysis. The whole problem of heterosis for several genes affecting quantitative characters will be solved, I think, only when the more simple cases of heterosis where single gene differences are involved shall be cleared up. I have been lucky enough to come across some useful experimental material for the purpose.

For a number of years I have kept about one hundred different wild stocks of *Drosophila melanogaster* coming from different geographical localities. Such stocks were maintained by the usual Drosophila technique of transferring about once a month some 30–40 flies from one old vial to a new one with fresh food. About twice a year I look at the flies under the microscope. Since all such stocks were wild type, no change by contamination was expected, as these stocks were phenotypically alike. Contamination by mutants kept in the laboratory could not have produced any appreciable result, owing to the well known fact that both under laboratory and natural conditions mutants are generally less viable than the normal type. To my surprise, however, I happened to observe at two different times, in two different wild stocks, that a fairly large number of the flies showed an eye color much lighter than the normal. These two mutants proved to be indistinguishable recessive alleles at the same locus in the third chromosome. The presence of the homozygotes has been checked at different times over a number of years.

In the summer of 1947 while collecting flies in the wild for other purposes, I found in the neighborhood of Suna, a small village on the western shore of the Lake Maggiore, in Northern Italy, several individuals of both sexes showing the same eye color. From these a homozygous stock for such mutant was obtained. Crossing tests proved that it was another allele of the same locus as the above mentioned. The occurrence of several individuals mutant for an autosomal recessive within a free living population was remarkable enough. But finding that the same gene was concerned as in the laboratory stocks, I suspected that such a mutant might have a positive selective value, both under laboratory and natural conditions.

I began an experiment to check this point. Two populations in numerical equilibrium were started, applying the method previously used by Pearl for the study of population dynamics of Drosophila, described in detail elsewhere (1947a). Sixteen light-eyed individuals, eight males and eight females, were put together in one vial with sixteen wild type flies. The gene frequency at the beginning of the experiment was therefore .5. Under the experimental conditions the population reached an equilibrium in respect to the amount of available food at about 700–900 flies per vial. After about twenty generations, assuming that each generation takes 15 days, the frequency of recessive homozygotes was about 40 per cent. Assuming random mating within the population, taking the square root of .40 one gets a gene frequency for the light-eyed gene of about .63. Since in both parallel populations the gene frequency was similar, one could conclude that selection had favored the mutant type, shifting its frequency from .5 to .63 in the course of about twenty generations.

Such an experiment did prove that the mutant gene had a positive selective value. It was impossible to know whether in the long run it would have eventually eliminated its normal allele from the population. At this stage, I

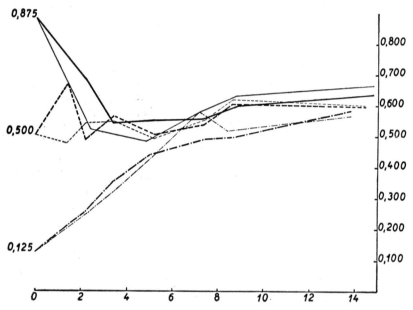

Fig. 9.1—Variation in the frequency of the light-eyed gene in selection experiments. In the abscissae is the number of generations, in the ordinates the gene frequency. Each line represents a single experiment on an artificial population.

have begun a new experiment along the same lines, but with different gene frequencies to start with. Two populations were started with 2 males and 2 females of the mutant type, plus 14 males and 14 females of the normal type. Two populations were started with 16 mutant and 16 wild flies, and two populations with 28 mutant and 4 wild type flies.

I had, therefore, at the beginning of the experiment six populations. Two had a gene frequency of the light-eyed mutant approximately equal to .125. Two had a gene frequency of .5, and two had a gene frequency of .875. Figure 9.1 shows the result of such an experiment after about fifteen generations. Crossings of wild type males, taken from the populations, with homozygous recessive females showed that there was no significant departure from random mating within the population. The gene frequencies indicated on the ordinates were obtained by taking the square root of the observed frequencies of homozygous recessives.

The following conclusions can be drawn: (1) the three experimental populations, each being run in duplicate, have reached the same gene frequency at about the .579 point; (2) natural selection has been acting on the three populations producing the same end results, irrespective of the initial gene frequency; (3) natural selection has been acting in favor of the heterozygous flies; and (4) the homozygous mutant seems to be slightly superior in its survival value to the homozygous normal allele.

It was of considerable interest to determine whether the intensity of selection operating in the three experiments was the same. Since the three experimental curves (each being the mean of the two duplicate populations) could not be compared directly, Dr. L. L. Cavalli elaborated a mathematical analysis of the problem (Cavalli, 1950). The function of gene frequency linear with time Y, when the heterozygote is at an advantage, is given by:

$$Y = q_e \log p + p_e \log q - \log [p_e - p],$$

where p and q are the gene frequencies at the beginning of the experiment in a random breeding population, and p_e and q_e are the equilibrium frequencies. By means of this function it is possible to transform the experimental curves to linear ones. Results can then be plotted graphically for the three experiments. Fitting straight lines with the method of maximum likelihood, one obtains the following values for the constants of the linear regression equation:

Experiment	Initial Gene Frequency (Observed)	Slope	Position	Initial Gene Frequency (Theoretical)
1.........	.500	.0879	+1.21	.425
2.........	.125	.0631	− .41	.100
3.........	.875	.0726	+ .27	.830

The *position* is the transformed value of the initial gene frequency which is given in the last column, and is in good agreement with the experimental value. If one tests the parallelism of the three regression lines so obtained, one gets a chi square of 4.0 with two degrees of freedom. Parallelism therefore seems to be satisfactory. This implies that the intensity of selection is independent of initial conditions.

If we take these results together with the two independent occurrences of the same mutant gene in different genotypical milieus, it seems safe to maintain that such a gene has a positive selective value with respect to its normal allele, and that selection is acting mainly through a typical heterosis mechanism. It is worth while to stress that this gene was found both in natural and experimental conditions. The exceptional occurrence of many mutant individuals in a free living population can be accounted for by assuming that they have a higher selective value.

BASIS FOR SUPERIORITY OF THE HETEROZYGOTE

It would be interesting to try to find out how selection discriminates against both normal and mutant homozygotes. I am just beginning to attack this problem.

Dr. E. Caspari has some interesting results on a similar problem, and I wish to thank him for permission to quote them (Caspari, 1950). In free living populations of the moth *Ephestia kühniella*, this author has observed a balanced polymorphism, whereby individuals having brown colored and red colored testes occur in various numbers. The character brown behaves as a complete dominant with respect to red. The polymorphism seems to be determined by a higher selective value of the heterozygote. It has been possible to show that the heterozygote is equal or superior to the homozygous recessive and the latter is superior to the homozygous dominant with respect to viability. It was found that, while the heterozygote is equal or superior to the homozygous dominant, the homozygous brown is superior to the homozygous red with respect to mating activity. The dominance relationships of such two physiological characters are therefore reversed.

There is no decisive evidence for heterosis for any of the characters studied. The recessive for the testis color acts as dominant with respect to viability, and the dominant testis color acts as dominant with respect to mating behavior. The net result is a selective advantage of the heterozygote that can account for the observed polymorphism. This seems a good example of how a heterosis mechanism can be determined by the behavior of two visible alleles in heterozygous condition. It is hoped that similar analyses will be developed for other cases of balanced polymorphism.

The search for clear-cut examples of heterosis depending on single genes seems to me the most promising line of attack on the general problem under discussion. If I could find another gene behaving in a way similar to the one I have studied in *Drosophila melanogaster*, and could study the interaction of the two, it would be possible to go a step further in the analysis of heterosis mechanisms. The evidence derived from such single genes being favored in heterozygous condition is likely to be very useful in more complex conditions where the action of several genes is involved.

When we come to consider the selective advantage of polygenic characters, even in such an easy experimental object as Drosophila, the problem becomes very entangled indeed. In recent years I have been studying, for example, a number of quantitative characters being favored by natural selection in artificial populations in numerical equilibrium, such as the ones I have been speaking about. I have set in competition at the beginning of one experiment two stocks differing for visible mutants. One stock was *white*- and *Bar*-eyed, the other stock was normal for both characters. The two stocks differed, too, in a number of quantitative characters such as fecundity, fertility, rate of development, longevity, and size.

After about thirty generations the two mutant genes had been wiped out. This could have been expected on the basis of previous data of L'Heritier and Teissier on the elimination of such genes in artificial populations. At that time, however, I did not discard the populations, but kept them going for some seventy more generations. All the individuals present in the populations were phenotypically normal. But testing from time to time the values of the above mentioned characters, I could establish that natural selection was continuously operating and favoring higher fecundity, higher fertility, higher longevity, and quicker developmental rate throughout the four years that the experiment lasted. At the end, the flies present in the population were superior by a factor of more than six to the mean of the considered characters in the two original parental stocks. When I measured such values in the F_1 hybrids between the two stocks I could observe values higher than those obtained after more than one hundred generations of selection.

The selection experiment could then be interpreted in two different ways. Either (a) selection had picked up a new genotype made out of a new combination of polygenes derived from the two parental stocks, or (b) selection had just preserved by means of a heterosis mechanism a certain amount of heterozygosity, which was at its highest value at the beginning of the experiment. The fact that in the course of the experiment the factors had been steadily improving seemed to be against hypothesis b, but I could not be sure that was the case.

I then set up a new selection experiment, whereby I put in competition the original stock *white Bar* with the normal type derived from the population which had been subjected to natural selection for more than one hundred generations. The result was clear. The genes *white* and *Bar* were eliminated in this second experiment at a much higher rate than in the first experiment. In the first experiment the gene frequency of the gene *Bar* after ten generations had dropped from .50 to .15. In the second experiment, after as many generations, the *Bar* gene frequency had dropped from .50 to .03. It seems that the genotype produced by a hundred generations of natural selection under constant conditions was so much better adapted to its environment that it could get rid of the competing genes with much greater ease than the original wild type flies. But could it not be that all or at least part of this result could be accounted for by the action of some heterosis effect?

Another example of a similarly puzzling condition is an experiment on artificial populations under way now in my laboratory. I would like to find out whether it is possible to produce so-called small mutations or polygenic mutations with X-rays, and whether an increase in the mutation rate may speed up the evolutionary rate under selection pressure.

For this purpose I have set up four artificial populations starting from an isogenic stock of *Drosophila melanogaster*. One of these is being kept as control while the other three get, every two weeks, 500, 1000, and 2000 r-units respectively. At the start, and at various intervals, I am measuring fecundity, fertility, and longevity of the flies. The few data so far collected show clearly that in the irradiated populations the percentage of eggs that do not develop is much higher than in the control. This is due to the effect of dominant and recessive lethals. But the startling result is that the fecundity, measured by the number of eggs laid per day by single females of the irradiated populations, is higher than in the control series. Probably X-rays have produced a number of mutations for higher fecundity which have been accumulated by natural selection in the course of the experiment. But, are specific mutations for higher fecundity being produced, or am I dealing with heterosis phenomena dependent upon nonspecific mutants?

These few examples from my own experience with population-genetical studies show, I think, how important the heterosis phenomenon can be in our field of work. Both in natural and artificial populations, heterosis seems to be at work, making our analysis rather difficult, but stimulating as well. Closer contacts between students of selection and heterosis in plant and animal breeding and students of evolutionary problems are to be wished. Let us hope that a higher level of hybridization between various lines of investigation might become permanent, since it surely will make our studies more vigorous and better adapted to the requirements of a rapidly growing science.

HAROLD H. SMITH
Cornell University

Chapter 10

Fixing Transgressive Vigor
in Nicotiana Rustica*

Hybrid vigor has been observed to varying degrees among certain inter-varietal hybrids of the self-pollinated cultivated species *Nicotiana rustica* L. (Bolsunow, 1944; East, 1921). In experiments undertaken to obtain a larger *N. rustica* plant giving increased yield of nicotine, it was reported (Smith and Bacon, 1941) that inbred lines derived as selections from hybrids among three varieties exceeded the parents and F_1's in plant height, number of leaves, or size of the largest leaf.

The general experience of breeders of self-pollinated plants has been that improved varieties can be developed through hybridization followed by selection and inbreeding, to fix desirable transgressive characteristics. Yet it is difficult to find data from which quantitative relationships of parents, F_1, and transgressive inbred can be adequately evaluated; as from replicated and randomized experiments in which the generations have been grown at the same time under comparable conditions. In view of the increasing number of reports on hybrid vigor in self-pollinated crop plants and its suggested utilization (Ashton, 1946), it was considered opportune to present relevant data accumulated on *N. rustica*.

Since methods of partitioning phenotypic variance have become generally available there was additional interest in making further study of the *N. rustica* material. Breeding results obtained in advanced selections could be related to the heritability estimated from data on early generations.

MATERIALS AND METHODS

Four varieties of *Nicotiana rustica* were used in these experiments. Three of them—*brasilia* strain 34753, Olson 68, and tall type have been described

* Published as Paper No. 261, Department of Plant Breeding, Cornell University, Ithaca New York.

in Smith and Bacon (1941). The fourth was received originally from the director of the Tabak-Forschungsinstitut, Baden, Germany, under the name of texana, a designation which we have retained. It is a small, early-maturing type. The four parental varieties were of highly inbred stocks maintained by the Division of Tobacco, Medicinal and Special Crops of the United States Department of Agriculture. The earlier part of the breeding program was carried out while the writer was associated with this organization.

The advanced selection, designated A1, used in these experiments has a complex genetic history of crossing, backcrossing, and inbreeding. This can be briefly summarized by stating that its ultimate composition was, on an average, 60 per cent 34753, 22 per cent Olson, 12 per cent tall type, and 6 per cent texana. About 82 per cent of the A1 genotype was, on chance alone, contributed by the two most vigorous parents, 34753 and Olson 68. This calculation does not take into account any differential effect of selection on changing the frequency of genes introduced from diverse parental origins. Observation of the A1 phenotype led us to believe that selection had further increased the proportion of genes from the two most vigorous parents.

In 1947 the four parents, the six possible F_1's, the three double crosses, and the F_4 generation (preceded by three generations of inbreeding) of line A1 were grown in a randomized complete block design with fifteen plants in each plot and replicated six times. In 1949 the two most vigorous varieties (Olson 68 and 34753), the F_1, F_2, backcrosses of the F_1 to each of its parents, and the F_6 generation of line A1 were grown in a randomized complete block design with twenty plants in each plot and replicated eight times.

Measurements were made on plant height, number of leaves or nodes, and length of the largest leaf. In addition, data were taken on the width of the largest leaf, number of days from planting to appearance of the first flower, and total green weight of individual plants.

Typical plants of Olson 68, 34753, the F_1 between these two varieties, and selection A1 are illustrated in Figure 10.1.

EXPERIMENTAL RESULTS

Data obtained from the 1947 and 1949 plantings are summarized in Tables 10.1 and 10.2, respectively.

Phenotype-Genotype Relations

Preceding further biometrical analysis of the data, tests for evidence of differential environmental effects and genetic interactions were made. For the former, the relation between genotype mean and non-heritable variability was determined by comparing means and variances of the parents and F_1 (1949 data, Table 10.2). For the characters plant height and leaf length, the variances were unrelated to the means and the parental variances were not significantly different from each other. For node number, however, the

Fig. 10.1—Typical field-grown (1949) plants of *Nicotiana rustica*. *Left to right:* Olson 68, *brasilia* strain 34753, F₁ Olson 68 × 34753, and selection A1(F₆). The scale shown at the left is in inches.

TABLE 10.1

PLANT CHARACTERISTICS IN PARENTAL VARIETIES, HYBRIDS, AND AN INBRED SELECTION OF *NICOTIANA RUSTICA**

Generation	Type	Plant Height Mean	Total within Plot d.f.	Total within Plot Var.	Leaf Number Mean	Total within Plot d.f.	Total within Plot Var.	Leaf Length Mean	Total within Plot d.f.	Total within Plot Var.	Mean Leaf Width	Mean Days to Mature	Mean Green Wgt. Per Plant
		in.						in.			in.		lbs.
P₁	Olson 68 (A)	49.9	73	17.8	18.8	72	4.68	11.7	72	1.07	8.7	70.1	1.51
	34753 (B)	29.0	84	20.0	15.8	82	7.96	8.7	82	1.43	7.5	66.6	0.89
	Tall type (C)	46.7	83	30.3	16.0	83	1.36	6.2	83	1.24	5.5	48.0	0.51
	Texana (D)	33.6	83	11.1	12.7	83	1.04	6.6	83	1.01	5.4	40.9	0.48
	Average	39.8	...	19.8	15.8	...	3.76	8.3	...	1.19	6.8	56.4	0.85
F₁	Olson×34753 (A×B)	48.5	74	58.3	16.8	74	7.18	10.8	74	1.92	8.7	75.0	1.47
	Olson×tall (A×C)	42.9	80	25.4	13.0	80	7.74	10.1	80	1.82	9.6	65.1	1.16
	Olson×texana (A×D)	40.1	81	20.8	11.2	81	4.99	10.6	81	1.49	9.7	70.6	1.13
	34753×tall (B×C)	47.1	84	45.2	16.6	84	1.77	7.8	84	1.37	6.7	50.5	0.76
	34753×texana (B×D)	40.3	83	28.1	14.4	83	6.34	8.7	83	2.30	7.4	60.0	0.93
	Tall×texana (C×D)	44.2	84	29.3	15.5	83	1.49	7.7	83	1.88	7.0	51.8	0.95
	Average	43.8	...	34.5	14.6	...	4.92	9.3	...	1.80	8.2	62.2	1.07
F₁×F₁	(A×B)×(C×D)	41.9	74	25.1	14.0	74	10.60	8.8	74	2.36	7.7	61.9	0.86
	(A×C)×(B×D)	39.6	82	61.1	12.4	79	9.29	9.8	79	3.11	8.8	66.0	0.99
	(A×D)×(B×C)	42.5	81	39.9	13.9	80	10.80	9.7	80	2.50	8.7	60.4	1.06
	Average	41.3	...	42.0	13.4	...	10.23	9.4	...	2.66	8.4	62.8	0.97
F₄	Selection A1	54.9	78	78.8	19.9	77	5.28	10.4	77	1.51	8.0	79.6	1.83
Least significant diff. at	5% level	2.68	...	......	1.22	...	......	0.89	...	......	0.76	4.11	0.25
	1% level	3.56	...	......	1.62	...	......	1.19	...	......	1.00	5.46	0.34

* Summary of 1947 data.

means and non-heritable variances were linearly related for both 1947 and 1949 data, and the parental variances were significantly different.

Tests to reveal the presence or absence of non-allelic interactions were then made according to the method proposed by Mather (1949). Results are shown in Table 10.3. No significant deviations from zero were found if the level of significance was taken as $P \gtreqless .01$. In each test, however, the P values for number of nodes were less than for plant height or leaf length, possibly owing to non-additive gene effects.

It was concluded, on the basis of these tests, that for the two characters

TABLE 10.2

PLANT CHARACTERS IN THE TWO MOST VIGOROUS VARIETIES OF
$N.$ $RUSTICA$, THEIR F_1, F_2, AND FIRST BACKCROSS PROGENY
AND IN SELECTION $A1(F_6)$*

GEN-ERA-TION	TYPE	PLANT HEIGHT			NO. OF NODES			LEAF LENGTH		
		Mean	Total within Plot		Mean	Total within Plot		Mean	Total within Plot	
			d.f.	Var.		d.f.	Var.		d.f.	Var.
		in.						in.		
P_1	Olson 68.........	47.8	141	15.46	24.5	136	3.45	11.6	142	0.68
P_2	34753.............	28.7	143	22.63	21.8	106	10.10	10.5	127	0.81
F_1	Olson 68×34753.....	43.2	140	39.18	22.5	110	8.60	11.1	131	0.63
F_2	(Olson×34753) self...	40.6	149	99.19	23.7	119	10.52	11.2	142	1.08
B_1	F_1×Olson 68.......	47.3	149	40.28	24.9	138	10.49	11.8	144	1.10
B_2	F_1×34753.........	36.2	148	101.50	21.6	117	9.45	10.8	135	0.95
F_6	Selection A1........	55.6	133	29.77	31.0	126	6.44	12.0	141	0.69

Least significant diff. at				
5% level................	2.55		1.37	0.49
1% level................	3.42		1.83	0.66

* Summary of 1949 data.

TABLE 10.3

SCALING TESTS FOR AVERAGE ADDITIVENESS OF GENE EFFECTS*

CHARACTER	TEST A				TEST B				TEST C			
	Dev.	Var.	Dev./S.E.	P	Dev.	Var.	Dev./S.E.	P	Dev.	Var.	Dev./S.E.	P
Plant height.	3.6	2.86	2.13	.03–.04	0.5	4.13	0.25	.80–.81	−0.5	15.48	0.13	.89–.90
No. nodes...	2.8	1.50	2.30	.02–.03	−1.1	1.71	0.84	.40–.41	3.5	6.18	1.40	.16–.17
Leaf length..	0.9	0.47	1.32	.18–.19	0.0	0.47	0.00	1.00	0.5	1.77	0.38	.70–.71

* Based on 1949 means.

plant height and leaf length, the data, as taken, could be used without serious error in partitioning the variance of segregating generations. For node number it was indicated that some correction should be made with the data before further biometrical analysis was undertaken.

Mather suggested that difficulties of the sort encountered in these data with node number may be overcome by finding a transformation of scale on which they would be minimized. The transformations $\sqrt{X}$, X^2, X^3, and $\sqrt{a + bx}$ on the individual measurements were made. In the latter transformation b is the linear regression coefficient and a the intercept. Also, for $\sqrt{a + bx} = K$, $\sqrt{-K}$ was taken as $-\sqrt{K}$. In some cases the transformations reduced the departure from the preferred relationship in one test, only to make the transformed data less preferable by another test. No transformation tried resulted in a consistent improvement over the original scale, and consequently none was used.

It is evident that the significantly different variances in node number of the two parental types were due mainly to different interactions between genotype and environment. From previous experience we know that under ideal conditions of growth, Olson 68 and strain 34753 show approximately the same variability. The adverse weather conditions of the 1949 season were observed to have a more deleterious effect on leaf number in strain 34753. Consequently it was considered that the greater variability of this variety, compared to Olson 68, could be attributed to a greater phenotypic interaction between genotype and environment. In view of these relationships, the analysis of the data on node number was approached in another way, as mentioned below under "Partitioning Phenotypic Variance."

First Generation Hybrids

Deviations of the F_1 means from mid-parent values (arithmetical average between parental means) can be used to estimate the preponderance of dominant gene effects, acting in one direction, at loci by which the parental complements differ. Mid-parent values were calculated from the 1947 data on the four original varieties. The results for each line are summarized in Table 10.4. The data shown were obtained by first calculating the difference between the F_1 mean and the mid-parent $(\overline{F_1} - \overline{MP})$ for each cross, then taking the average of the differences for each group of three F_1's involving the parent variety under consideration. The ratio of the deviation of the F_1 from the mid-parent to half the parental difference, $\overline{F_1} - \overline{MP}/\frac{1}{2}(\overline{P_2} - \overline{P_1})$, is a measure of the relative potence (Mather, 1949; Wigan, 1944) of the gene sets. Potence ratios, calculated from averages, are shown in Table 10.4. For plant height and leaf length the F_1 means fall, on an average, about .6 of the distance from the mid-parent toward the larger parent. For leaf number the F_1 means fall, on an average, about .7 of the distance from the mid-parent toward the smaller parent.

The F_1's were taller and had larger leaves, on an average, than the mid-parent. It was concluded, therefore, that a preponderance of dominant+ genes was involved in determining differences in plant height and leaf length. In the development of the parent varieties, selection resulted in the accumulation of dominant+modifiers, as is usually the case in naturally cross-pollinated plants.

The result with the character leaf number was different in that the F_1 had fewer leaves, on an average, than the mid-parent. Evidently, in the evolution of the varietal gene sets, there had been accumulated a preponderance of recessive+modifiers (or dominant genes for *fewer* leaves) at the loci by which

TABLE 10.4

DIFFERENCE BETWEEN THE F_1 AND MID-PARENT ($\overline{F_1 - MP}$) AND THE POTENCE† RATIO IN INTERVARIETAL HYBRIDS. BOTH VALUES ARE EXPRESSED AS THE AVERAGE FOR EACH VARIETY IN CROSSES WITH THE OTHER THREE VARIETIES*

VARIETY	PLANT HEIGHT		NO. LEAVES		LEAF LENGTH	
	F_1-MP	Potence†	F_1-MP	Potence	F_1-MP	Potence
	in.				in.	
Olson 68........	+0.7	+0.10	−3.2	−1.62	+0.9	+0.43
34753..........	+9.1	+1.26	+0.1	+0.09	+0.3	+0.33
Tall...........	+2.6	+0.46	−0.9	−0.87	+0.8	+0.63
Texana........	+3.8	+0.68	−1.1	−0.53	+1.1	+0.97
Average....	+4.0	+0.62	−1.2	−0.73	+0.8	+0.59

* 1947 data.
† Potence $= \overline{F_1 - MP}/\frac{1}{2}(\overline{P_2 - P_1})$.

the parents differed. There can be little doubt that selection for *many* leaves was practiced in producing the parent types. This is especially true for Olson 68 which was developed from hybrid origin by the late Mr. Otto Olson (Smith and Bacon, 1941) by selection for plants yielding large amounts of nicotine. In crosses with Olson 68, the F_1 was consistently below the mid-parent. This result, interpretable as due to an accumulation of a preponderance of recessive genes for the character favored by selection, might be expected occasionally in naturally self-pollinated plants. Dominance is of less importance here than in cross-pollinated organisms, since selection is largely a matter of sorting out superior homozygous combinations.

The 1949 results (Table 10.2) on Olson 68 × 34753 were consistent with those of 1947 discussed above.

Double Crosses

The three possible double crosses involving all six F_1 hybrids of four varieties were grown in 1947 in order to obtain evidence on genic interactions by comparing experimental results with predicted values. The latter were made in the manner employed in corn breeding, namely Jenkins' method, in which the average of the four F_1's not contributing to the double cross was used. These comparisons are shown in Table 10.5 for the three plant characters studied. The differences between observed means and predicted values in the nine comparisons made were all within the limits required for odds of 19:1. It was concluded that the double cross means for plant height, number of leaves, and leaf length in *N. rustica* could be predicted with a high degree of precision by Jenkins' method. The results indicated that there were no

TABLE 10.5

COMPARISON BETWEEN PREDICTED AND OBSERVED VALUES FOR PLANT HEIGHT, NUMBER OF LEAVES, AND LEAF LENGTH IN THREE DOUBLE CROSSES INVOLVING FOUR VARIETIES OF *N. RUSTICA*

Double Cross	Observed	Predicted	Difference, Obs.-Pred.
Plant height (in.):			
$(A \times B) \times (C \times D)$	41.9 ± 2.68	42.6 ± 1.34	-0.7 ± 3.00
$(A \times C) \times (B \times D)$	39.6 ± 2.68	45.0 ± 1.34	-5.4 ± 3.00
$(A \times D) \times (B \times C)$	42.5 ± 2.68	44.0 ± 1.34	-1.5 ± 3.00
Average	41.3	43.8	-2.5
No. leaves:			
$(A \times B) \times (C \times D)$	14.0 ± 1.22	13.8 ± 0.61	$+0.2 \pm 1.36$
$(A \times C) \times (B \times D)$	12.4 ± 1.22	15.0 ± 0.61	-2.6 ± 1.36
$(A \times D) \times (B \times C)$	13.9 ± 1.22	14.9 ± 0.61	-1.0 ± 1.36
Average	13.4	14.6	-1.2
Leaf length (in.):			
$(A \times B) \times (C \times D)$	8.8 ± 0.89	9.3 ± 0.44	-0.5 ± 0.99
$(A \times C) \times (B \times D)$	9.8 ± 0.89	9.2 ± 0.44	$+0.6 \pm 0.99$
$(A \times D) \times (B \times C)$	9.7 ± 0.89	9.3 ± 0.44	$+0.4 \pm 0.99$
Average	9.4	9.3	$+0.1$

A, B, C, D represent the parent varieties as shown in Table 10.1.

marked interactions between the genes or gene sets from the four varieties when combined in a variety of associations.

To illustrate this point, let us assume that each parent is homozygous for a different allele at each of two independent loci so that $A = XXYY$, $B = X^1X^1Y^1Y^1$, $C = X^2X^2Y^2Y^2$, and $D = X^3X^3Y^3Y^3$. The F_1's represent six different combinations of these alleles. Each double cross contains all four alleles of each locus in four particular combinations. For example, the population $(A \times B) \times (C \times D)$ is $1/4XX^2 + 1/4XX^3 + 1/4X^1X^2 + 1/4X^1X^3$ for the X locus and $1/4YY^2 + 1/4YY^3 + 1/4Y^1Y^2 + 1/4Y^1Y^3$ for the Y locus. Sixteen different combinations of alleles at the two loci are possible in this double cross. Accurate prediction of the double cross value on the basis of only four of these combinations, namely: F_1's $A \times C$, $A \times D$, $B \times C$, and $B \times D$, indicates that the other 12 possible combinations do not introduce any significant non-additive effects.

Another indication that epistatic effects were unimportant in the inheritance of plant height, leaf number, and leaf length was afforded by the evidence that the means of the double crosses did not differ significantly from each other (Table 10.1).

The average variance of the double crosses was greater than that of the parents or F_1's (Table 10.1), as would be expected from segregation.

Partitioning Phenotypic Variance, Heritability, and Number of Effective Factors

Estimates of the magnitude of the non-heritable variation (σ_E^2), in populations involving Olson 68 and 34753 (1949 data), were obtained by taking

TABLE 10.6

ESTIMATES OF COMPONENTS OF VARIABILITY, NUMBER OF EFFECTIVE FACTORS (K_1), HERITABILITY, AND GAIN FOR PLANT HEIGHT, LEAF LENGTH, AND NUMBER OF NODES IN THE *N. RUSTICA* CROSS OLSON 68 × BRASILIA, STRAIN 34753*

Character	σ_E^2	σ_D^2	σ_G^2	K_1	Heritability Per Cent	Gain
Plant height....	25.76±15.3	67.32±53.5	113.20±71.3	0.81	54.9	1.74
Leaf length.....	0.71± 0.45	1.04± 1.05	0.22± 0.69	1.38	11.2	0.91
Node number...	7.38± 4.38	8.16±13.00	2.20± 8.11	0.83	12.4	2.42

* 1949 data.

an average of the total within plot variance of the non-segregating families—P_1, P_2, and F_1. As shown in Table 10.6, the values obtained were 25.76 for plant height, 0.71 for leaf length, and 7.38 for number of nodes.

The following symbols are used for the components of heritable variance (total phenotypic minus environmental): σ_G^2 = variance depending on additive gene effects, σ_D^2 = variance depending on dominance. The heritable variance of the F_2 was calculated and equated to: $1/2\sigma_G^2 + 1/4\sigma_D^2$. The pooled heritable variance of the two first backcrosses was equated to $1/2\sigma_G^2 + 1/2\sigma_D^2$. Solving for σ_D^2, the values obtained were 67.32 for plant height, 1.04 for leaf length, and 8.16 for number of nodes. Values for σ_G^2, as calculated by substitution, were 113.20 for plant height, 0.22 for leaf length, and 2.20 for number of nodes.

In view of the influence on node number of a differential interaction of the two parental genotypes with environment, an additional way of approaching an analysis of the data on this character was tried. If a simple relation between the environmental variances of the P_1, P_2, and F_1 is assumed, so that σ_E^2 of the $F_1 = 1/2(\sigma_E^2$ of $P_1 + \sigma_E^2$ of $P_2)$, then σ_E^2 of the $F_1 = 6.78$. The environmental variance of B_1 may then be equated to $1/2$ (variance of P_1+variance of F_1), which is 5.12. By a similar relation, the environmental variance of B_2 is equal to 8.44. The pooled heritable variance of $B_1 + B_2$, $i.e.$, $1/2\sigma_G^2 + 1/2\sigma_D^2$, may be equated to: $(10.49 - 5.12) + (9.45 - 8.44)$. This gave 6.38. The heritable variance of the F_2, $i.e.$, $1/2\sigma_G^2 + 1/4\sigma_D^2$, may be equated to $(10.52 - 6.78)$. This gave 3.74. Solving: $\sigma_D^2 = 10.56$ and $\sigma_G^2 = 2.20$. The former, σ_D^2, has a somewhat larger value than that obtained by the original analysis (8.16, Table 10.6); the latter, σ_G^2, is the same.

Heritability of a character was estimated as the ratio, expressed in per cent, of the variance component due to additive, fixable gene effects (σ_G^2) to the sum, $\sigma_G^2 + \sigma_D^2 + \sigma_E^2$. Heritability of plant height was calculated to be 54.9 per cent, of leaf length 11.5 per cent, and of node number 12.4 per cent.

Estimates of the number of effective factors (K_1) were made on the assumptions inherent in the equation $K_1 = (\bar{P}_1 - \bar{P}_2)^2/4\sigma_G^2$. The values obtained (Table 10.6) were 0.81 for plant height, 1.38 for leaf length, and 0.83 for number of nodes. These estimates were undoubtedly too low, due in part to non-isodirectional distributions of $+$ and $-$ genes in the parents. Experimental evidence of non-isodirectional distribution was afforded by the fixing of transgressive characteristics in inbred selections following hybridization between varieties. Some $+$ genes were contributed by each parent, and consequently could not have been concentrated in one. Linkage in coupling phase and/or differences in magnitude of effect of the individual genes or gene blocks might also have contributed to the low estimates of the number of effective factors.

In the absence of data on F_3's, biparental progenies, and double backcrosses (Mather, 1949), the errors of the estimates of σ_E^2, σ_D^2, and σ_G^2 for each character were computed as follows. From the eight replications, four means were calculated by grouping replications 1 and 2, 3 and 4, 5 and 6, and 7 and 8. The standard error of the four independent means was then obtained (Table 10.6). These errors are maximum estimates since there was a pronounced gradient of environmental effects from replication 1 to replication 8.

Mather (1949) is in the process of making an extensive biometrical genetic analysis of plant height in a *Nicotiana rustica* cross, and it was of interest to compare his published results with corresponding statistics presented in this study. From his data so far reported, the average values (mean of 1946 and 1947) for components of variance for plant height are: 9.30 for σ_E^2, 9.25 for σ_D^2, and 18.05 for σ_G^2. The heritability calculated from these estimates is 44.1 per cent. The results reported in this discussion are similar in that heritability is high and σ_G^2 has about twice the value of σ_D^2.

Results of Selection
The result of selection for tall plants with many, large leaves can be seen by comparing the means of A1 with those of the parental and hybrid generations in Tables 10.1 and 10.2.

From the 1947 data it is evident that in the F_4 generation of selection A1 a significant increase had been obtained over the parents and F_1's in plant height and green weight. This was accompanied by a lengthening in time required to reach maturity. With regard to this latter character, it was noted that the average time for reaching maturity in five of the six F_1's was later than the average of their respective parents. This is contrary to the usual result in first generation hybrids of certain other plants, as maize and tomatoes; and, where early maturity is an important economic character, would generally not be considered a manifestation of hybrid vigor, at least in a "beneficial" sense.

The number of leaves in selection A1 was significantly higher ($P < .05$) than in any of the F_1's, and all but the most vigorous parent, Olson 68. Leaves of the selection were shorter than the parent with the longest leaves (Olson 68), not significantly different from the three F_1's that involved this parent, and longer than in the other three parents and three F_1's.

The 1949 data (Table 10.2) corroborated the 1947 results. There was a significant increase ($P \leq .01$) in plant height and in number of nodes over the two main parents and their F_1. Number of nodes, rather than of leaves, was used since it is a more reliable criterion of the same character. As in 1947, there was a less marked effect of selection on leaf length, though there appeared to be an increase in A1 from the F_4 to the F_6. For this character the selection was superior to 34753 and the F_1, but not significantly different from Olson 68, although a close approach to significance at the 5 per cent level of probability was reached.

The total within plot variances of selection A1(F_6) for plant height, number of nodes, and leaf length were in no case significantly higher than for the more variable parent. It was deduced, therefore, that the inbred selection had reached relative homozygosity.

The general conclusions were that an inbred selection had been produced which had increased plant height, more nodes, heavier green weight, and a longer growth period than any parent or F_1. Length of leaf had been maintained at least at the level of the best parent variety.

It was also noted, though no quantitative data were taken, that selection A1 had markedly less vigorous *sucker* growth at *topping* time than any of the other varieties or hybrids. This is an important agronomic character.

Heritability and Gain
One of the objectives in conducting these experiments was to attempt to determine to what extent the progress realized in actual selection experi-

ments could be related to the heritability of a character as determined from F_2 and first backcross data.

Results on the three main characters studied were similar in that there was no indication of complex genic interactions, and that estimates of the number of effective factors were low and of the same order of magnitude in each. If we wish to assume that the "reach" or selection differential (in terms of standard deviations) was the same for each character, and this is approximately correct though exact records on this point are lacking, then the gain (in terms of standard deviations) due to selection should be roughly proportional to the heritability. The gain was calculated as the difference between the mean of selection A1 and the mid-parent value, divided by the standard deviation of the F_2 (1949 data, Table 10.2).

The relationships between heritabilities and gains can be observed by comparing the last two columns in Table 10.6. With regard to plant height and leaf length, both heritability and gain are higher in the former character; though the gain is less in plant height than would have been anticipated from the relative heritabilities. Some possible explanations for this latter result could be that the selection differential for plant height was lower than for leaf length, that there was a relatively more rapid reduction in heritability, or that an approach to a physiological limit for tallness was made.

The gain in node number is disproportionately high in relation to its heritability. Some possible explanations for this result could be that the selection differential was higher, that there was a genetic correlation with plant height, or that the selected character was determined by a preponderance of recessive genes (see F_1 result), and individual plants selected for high node number were largely homozygous for recessive+genes.

DISCUSSION

The experimental results have shown that first generation crosses among different varieties of *Nicotiana rustica* exhibit different degrees of character expression ranging from the smaller parent value to above the larger parent. By selection and inbreeding it was possible to develop an essentially true-breeding improved line which exceeded the best P_1 or F_1 in most characteristics measured.

This same type of result has also been obtained in our experience with the commercial species, *N. tabacum*, and it may be generally characteristic of self-fertilized plants, as, e.g., *Phaseolus vulgaris* (Malinowski, 1928), soybeans (Veatch, 1930), and Galeopsis (Müntzing, 1930).

Crossbreeding

There have been relatively few fundamental changes in the standard domestic varieties of *N. tabacum* over a long period of years, except for recent development of types resistant to destructive diseases (Garner, 1946).

Houser (1911) originally suggested the use of first generation intervarietal tobacco hybrids on a commercial scale to increase yields. He presented breeding results on cigar filler types, dating back to 1903, in which the hybrids outyielded the parent types by as much as 57 per cent. Plant breeders in various tobacco-growing areas of the world have observed hybrid vigor among first generation hybrids of commercial varieties (Ashton, 1946), and have suggested its use in practice to increase production. Currently, consideration is being given to improving the yield of flue-cured varieties by this method (Patel et al., 1949).

The results of Hayes (1912), Hayes, East, and Beinhart (1913), and East and Hayes (1912) showed that by intervarietal hybridization, selection, and inbreeding the number of leaves, an important factor in yield of tobacco, could be fixed at a level exceeding the parents or F_1. Regarding the use of F_1 hybrids on a commercial scale, they stated (Hayes, East, and Beinhart, 1913),

> While it is doubtless true that by this method the yield could be somewhat increased, the yield factor, for cigar wrapper types at least, is only of secondary importance compared with quality. Because of the great importance of quality it seems much more reasonable to suppose that further advance can be made by the production of fixed types which in themselves contain desirable growth factors, such as size, shape, position, uniformity, venation, and number of leaves, together with that complex of conditions which goes to make up quality, than by any other method.

The problem of producing higher yielding varieties of *N. tabacum* with acceptable quality characteristics of the cured leaf remains today. Kosmodemjjanskii (1941) bred four families from the cross Dubec 44×Trebizond 1272, two Russian varieties of *N. tabacum*, which, he reported, were uniform for morphological characters and flavor and maintained transgression in plant height and number of leaves to the F_7 generation.

While first generation hybrids between selected parents may be of use as a temporary measure to improve self-fertilizing crop plants, it would appear, in so far as can be generalized from the results on Nicotiana, that production of fixed types with favorable transgressive characteristics offers a better long-time solution. Within any one type of tobacco, such as flue-cured, there are currently available a number of high quality inbred varieties which, though of similar phenotype, may be expected to differ by genes of a multifactorial system affecting size characteristics (Emerson and Smith, 1950). Selections from intervarietal crosses may be expected, therefore, to yield fixed types of increased size without presenting undue difficulties to the breeder attempting to maintain quality.

In order to discuss the hereditary basis for experimental results on heterosis and inbreeding, current concepts of the genetic and evolutionary mechanisms involved are briefly presented. In the evolution of naturally crossbred organisms, mutation and selection result in the accumulation of dominant favorable genes, hidden deleterious recessives, and alleles or complexes of linked polygenes which give heterotic effects as heterozygotes. Heterosis is explained genetically as due to the accumulated effect of the favorable dominants and/or coadapted heterozygous combinations. It is an adaptive evolutionary phenomenon (Dobzhansky, 1950).

Selfing

In naturally selfed populations there are accumulated, for the most part, favorable genes that are either dominant, recessive, or lacking in strong allelic interactions. Dominance is of little evolutionary significance, and hence a preponderance of favorable dominant genes is not to be expected. Furthermore, there would ordinarily be no adaptive significance to favorable heterozygous combinations. One possible exception is suggested by Brieger's (1950) demonstration that "if survival values for both homozygotes should be below 0.5 (compared to the heterozygote value of 1.0) in selfed populations, a final equilibrium is reached with all three genotypes remaining in the population." Such a condition might have adaptive value in maintaining variability in selfed organisms. Hybrid vigor in self-pollinated plants, in view of the above considerations, is a chance manifestation, an "evolutionary accident" causing luxuriant growth (Dobzhansky, 1950), and not an adaptive product of mutation and selection.

However, from published data on crosses within selfed species of cultivated plants, it appears that hybrid vigor is of frequent rather than chance occurrence. Reported results with flax (Carnahan, 1947), wheat (Harrington, 1944), barley (Immer, 1941), tomatoes (Larson and Currance, 1944), eggplants (Odland and Noll, 1948), and soybeans (Weiss, Weber, and Kalton, 1947) all demonstrated that hybrid vigor is characteristic of F_1's. If these data constitute a representative sample, then, although hybrid vigor is an *evolutionary accident* in naturally selfed species, it is not a *genetical accident*.

The result may be interpreted genetically as follows: Selfed species are purged of deleterious genes by selection. Different varieties within the species have accumulated different alleles all of which control "non-defective," slightly different physiological reactions. The combination of divergent alleles in heterozygous condition may, more frequently than not, act as East has suggested in a complementary manner to produce a more efficient physiological condition. This is expressed phenotypically by the hybrid manifesting more vigorous growth than midway between the homozygotes. Subsequent selection and inbreeding, however, would permit an accumulation of the most favorable alleles or gene complexes in the homozygous condition.

As a simplified schematic example, let us assume that two varieties, P_1 and P_2, differ by three alleles or linked polygene complexes: X^1 is dominant and favorable for vigorous growth, Y^1 is a favorable recessive, and at the Z locus the product of the heterozygous condition is above the mean of the homozygotes. The composition of parents, F_1, and selected inbred is shown below with arbitrary "size" values assigned to each.

$$P_1 = X^1X^1\,(4) + Y^1Y^1\,(4) + Z^1Z^1\,(2) = 10$$

$$P_2 = X^2X^2\,(2) + Y^2Y^2\,(2) + Z^2Z^2\,(6) = 10$$

$$F_1 = X^1X^2\,(4) + Y^1Y^2\,(2) + Z^1Z^2\,(5) = 11$$

$$\text{sel.} = X^1X^1\,(4) + Y^1Y^1\,(4) + Z^2Z^2\,(6) = 14$$

Although the difficulty in selecting superior inbreds would become greater with increasing numbers of effective segregating units, the following advantages of selfed over crossbred systems would enhance the opportunity for success: (1) lack of deleterious recessives, (2) less preponderance of dominant favorable alleles, (3) homozygous pairs of alleles are superior, as a result of an adaptive evolutionary process, to heterozygous combinations. Naturally inbred organisms are products of historical evolutionary processes in which harmonious systems of homozygous loci have been selected to attain optimum adaptation. These considerations favor the expectancy and practicability of obtaining maximum advance through selection and inbreeding with self-fertilized organisms.

SUMMARY

There were two general purposes in conducting these experiments: First, to demonstrate that by selection following intervarietal hybridization in a self-fertilized organism, inbreds could be produced which transgressed the character expression in parents and F_1; secondly, to investigate the relation between estimated heritability and the actual results of selection.

An inbred selection of *Nicotiana rustica* which transgressed the P_1 and F_1 characteristics in plant height, node number, and leaf length was obtained. The heritabilities for these three characters were calculated to be 54.9 per cent, 12.4 per cent, and 11.2 per cent, respectively. The gains (in terms of standard deviations) due to selection were 1.74, 2.42, and 0.91, respectively. Some possible explanations for the lack of direct proportionality between heritability and gain were discussed.

The number of effective segregating factors for each of the three characters studied was estimated to be of the same order of magnitude and relatively few. Non-isodirectional distribution of $+$ and $-$ genes in the parent varieties contributed to an underestimation of this number.

Non-allelic interactions were apparently not an important source of variation, as indicated by scaling tests and evidence from double cross means.

Reasons for expecting greater advances by selection and inbreeding, as contrasted to the use of first generation hybrids, in naturally self-fertilizing genetic systems were reviewed.

PAUL C. MANGELSDORF
Harvard University

Chapter 11

Hybridization in
the Evolution of Maize

All varieties and races of maize so far studied prove upon inbreeding to contain numerous heterozygous loci, and all respond to inbreeding with a marked decline in vigor and productiveness. Since contemporary maize is both heterozygous and heterotic, it is probable that the factors which have been responsible for bringing about the present conditions are also factors which have played an important, if not the principal role, in the evolution of maize.

All of the steps involved in the evolution of maize are not yet known. Archaeological remains have told us something of the early stages of maize under domestication, and we can draw additional inferences about its original nature from its present-day characteristics. Our knowledge of the nature and extent of its present variation, although far from complete, is already substantial and is growing rapidly. By extrapolating forward from ancient maize, and backward from present-day maize, we can make reasonably valid guesses about some of the intermediate stages and about some of the evolutionary steps which have occurred in its history.

The earliest known archaeological remains of maize, as well as the best evidence of an evolutionary sequence in this species, occur in the archaeological vegetal remains found in Bat Cave in New Mexico in 1948. This material which covers a period of approximately three thousand years (from about 2000 B.C. to A.D. 1000) has been described by Mangelsdorf and Smith (1949). It reveals three important things: (1) that primitive maize was both a small-eared pop corn and a form of pod corn; (2) that there was an introgression of teosinte into maize about midway in the sequence; (3) that there was an enormous increase in the range of variation during the period of approximately three thousand years resulting from teosinte introgression and interracial hybridization.

INTERRACIAL HYBRIDIZATION IN MAIZE

For additional evidence on interracial hybridization in maize we may turn to existing races of maize. Among these the Mexican races are of particular interest and significance, not because maize necessarily originated in Mexico, since there is considerable evidence that it did not, but because Mexico is a country where primitive races, which in other places are to be found primarily as archaeological remains, still exist as living entities. It is possible in Mexico to find all stages between ancient primitive races and modern highly-developed agricultural races. One has only to place these racial entities in their proper sequence in order to have at least the outline of an evolutionary history.

Wellhausen *et al.* (1951) have recently made a comprehensive study of the races of maize of Mexico. They recognize twenty-five distinct races as well as several additional entities which are still somewhat poorly defined, but some of which may later be described as races. They divide the known races into four major groups as follows:

Group	No. Races
1. Ancient Indigenous	4
2. Pre-Columbian Exotic	4
3. Prehistoric Mestizos	13
4. Modern Incipient	4

Origin of Mexican Races of Maize

Ancient Indigenous races are those which are believed to have arisen in Mexico from the primitive pod-pop corn similar to that whose remains were found in Bat Cave in New Mexico. The races in this group are called indigenous not because they necessarily had their primary origin in Mexico, but because they are thought to be the product of indigenous differentiation from a remote common ancestor. The differentiation is assumed to have resulted from independent development in different localities and environments with hybridization playing little if any part.

Four races of the Ancient Indigenous group—Palomero Toluqueño, Arrocillo Amarillo, Chapalote, and Nal-tel—are recognized. All of these, like their primitive ancestor, are pop corn. Two of the four—Chapalote and Nal-tel—are forms of pod corn. All have small ears, and all are relatively early in maturity.

Pre-Columbian Exotic races are those which are believed to have been introduced into Mexico from Central or South America before 1492. Four of these races—Cacahuazintle, Harinoso de Ocho, Oloton, and Maíz Dulce—are recognized. The evidence for their antiquity and exoticism derives principally from two sources: all have South American counterparts; all except Maíz Dulce have been parents of hybrid races, some of which are themselves relatively ancient.

Prehistoric Mestizos,[1] thirteen in number, are races which are believed to have arisen through hybridization between Ancient Indigenous races and Pre-Columbian races and hybridization of both with a new entity, teosinte. The term prehistoric rather than pre-Columbian is used for this group because, although all are prehistoric in the sense that there is no historical evidence of their origin, it is not certain that all are pre-Columbian.

Modern Incipient races are those which have come into existence in the post-Columbian period. These races, of which four are recognized, have not yet reached a state of genetic equilibrium. They are recognizable entities but are still changing.

The seventeen races comprising the two last groups all appear to be products of hybridization, either between races in the first two groups, or between these races and teosinte. In several cases, secondary and even tertiary hybridization seems to have occurred.

That a race is the product of previous hybridization seems highly probable when the following four kinds of evidence are available.

1. The race is intermediate between the two putative parents in a large number of characteristics.

2. The putative parents still exist and have geographical distributions which make such hybridization possible and plausible.

3. Inbreeding of the suspected hybrid race yields segregates which approach in their characteristics one or the other of the two putative parents—in some cases both.

4. A population quite similar to the race in question can be synthesized by hybridizing the two putative parents.

Wellhausen et al. (1951) have presented all four kinds of evidence for the hybrid origin of a number of the present-day Mexican races. They have presented similar but less complete evidence for the remainder.

The variety Conico, for example, which is the most common race in the Valley of Mexico, is clearly the product of hybridizing the ancient Palomero Toluqueño with the exotic Cacahuazintle. Conico is intermediate between these two races in many characteristics. The two putative ancestral races still are found in isolated localities in the Valley of Mexico. The race is intermediate in its characteristics between the two suspected parents. Inbreeding yields segregates which almost duplicate in their characteristics one of the parents—Palomero Toluqueño. Segregates approaching the other suspected parent, Cacahuazintle, also result from inbreeding but this parent is never exactly duplicated. Obviously the race has become something more complex than a mixture of equal parts of two earlier races. Nevertheless the crossing of Palomero Toluqueño and Cacahuazintle still produces a hybrid which in many respects is scarcely distinguishable from the suspected hybrid race. The data in Table 11.1 show that Conico is intermediate between Palo-

1. Mestizo is the Latin-American term for a racial hybrid.

mero Toluqueño and Cacahuazintle in a large number of characteristics. They also show how closely a recently-made hybrid of these two ancient races resembles the suspected hybrid race, Conico. Ears of the three races and the hybrid are illustrated in Figure 11.1.

The hybrid race, Conico, has in turn been the ancestor of still more complex hybrid races. A Modern Incipient race, Chalqueño, which has originated in historical times in the vicinity of the village of Chalco in the Valley of Mexico,

TABLE 11.1

COMPARISON OF CONICO WITH ITS PUTATIVE PARENTS*

CHARACTERS	RACES			
	Palomero Toluqueño	F₁ Hybrid	Conico	Cacahua-zintle
Ears and plants:				
Ear diameter, mm.	37.1	45.2	45.1	53.2
No. rows grain.	21.8	18.6	15.7	16.2
Width kernels, mm.	4.6	6.8	7.4	9.8
Thickness kernels, mm.	2.8	3.6	3.9	5.3
Diameter peduncle, mm.	8.0	9.2	9.8	10.6
Length ear, cm.	9.8	11.8	12.6	14.7
Height plant, cm.	175	200	193	210
Tillering index.	.26	.35	.22	.39
Pilosity score.	3	4	3–4	4
Internal ear characters:				
Ear diameter, mm.	34.0	. . . .	42.4	47.0
Cob diameter, mm.	19.5	. . . .	19.0	27.7
Rachis diameter, mm.	10.4	. . . .	9.6	11.7
Length kernels, mm.	11.4	. . . .	14.8	14.0
Estimated rachilla length, mm.	.4	. . . .	1.6	3.6
Cob/rachis index.	1.88	. . . .	1.98	2.37
Glume/kernel index.	.40	. . . .	.32	.57
Rachilla/kernel index.	.04	. . . .	.11	.26
Pedicel hairs score.	0	. . . .	2–4	4
Rachis flap score.	0	. . . .	2–3	3

* After Wellhausen *et al.*

is undoubtedly the product of hybridizing Conico with Tuxpeño, a productive lowland race of the Prehistoric Mestizo group. Since Tuxpeño is itself a hybrid, the postulated pedigree for Chalqueño, which is shown in Figure 11.2, becomes quite complex.

In the pedigree of Tuxpeño a distinction has been made (by employing different styles of type) between the facts which are well-established and those which are largely based upon inference. There is little doubt that Conico is a hybrid of Palomero Toluqueño and Cacahuazintle, or that Chalqueño is a hybrid of Conico and Tuxpeño. There is little doubt that Tuxpeño is a hybrid derivative of Tepecintle, but it is not certain that the other parent is Olotillo, although this is the best guess which can be made with the

Fig. 11.1—Ears of the Mexican maize races Palomero Toluqueño, Conico, and Cacahuacintle. Conico is intermediate between the two other races and is thought to be the product of their hybridization.

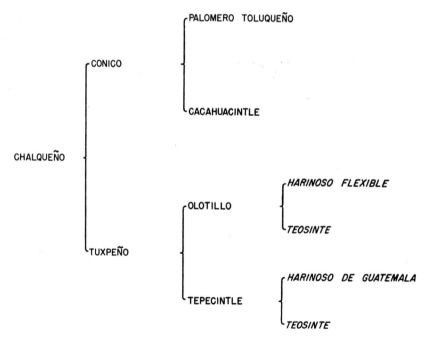

Fig. 11.2—The postulated geneology of the Mexican race Chalqueño. Parts of the genealogy not well established by experimental evidence are shown in italics.

evidence now at hand. That Olotillo and Tepecintle are both hybrid races involving teosinte is even more difficult to prove, although data on chromosome knobs presented by Wellhausen *et al.* tend to substantiate such a conclusion.

There is at least no doubt that interracial hybridization has been an important factor in the evolution of maize in Mexico. Has this hybridization produced heterosis, or has it merely resulted in Mendelian recombination? The extent to which the suspected hybrid races remain intermediate between the two putative parents suggests that natural selection (operating in a man-made environment) has tended to preserve the heterozygote and to eliminate the segregates which approach homozygosity. It is at least certain that the hybrid races are intermediate between their putative parents in their characteristics to a remarkable degree and that they are highly heterozygous. Even in the absence of natural selection favoring the more heterozygous individuals, there would seem to be a tendency for repeated interracial hybridization to create an ever-increasing degree of heterosis. This is the consequence of the fact that maize is a highly cross-pollinated plant, and that heterozygosity does not diminish after the F_2 in cross-fertilized populations in which mating is random.

Wright (1922) has suggested that the vigor and productiveness of an F_2 population falls below that of the F_1 by an amount equal to $1/n$ of the difference between the production of the F_1 and the average production of the parental stock, where n is the number of inbred strains which enter into the ancestry of a hybrid. The formula is also applicable to hybrids in which the parental stocks are not inbred lines, but are stable open-pollinated varieties in which random mating does not diminish vigor. It is, of course, not applicable to hybrids of single crosses which are themselves subject to diminished vigor as the result of random mating.

Hybrid Vigor in Advanced Generations

The rate at which hybrid vigor diminishes in a population after the F_2 generation is related to the proportion of outcrossing. This is true whether hybrid vigor depends upon heterozygosity or upon the cumulative action of dominant genes, and irrespective of the number of genes involved and the degree of linkage. With complete selfing the amount of hybrid vigor retained is halved in each succeeding generation. With complete outcrossing the amount of hybrid vigor falls to one-half in the F_2 and thereafter remains constant. With a mixture of selfing and outcrossing an intermediate result is to be expected. This can be calculated from the following formula presented by Stephens (1950):

$$h = \tfrac{1}{2}\,[\,(1 - k)\,h' + k\,]\,.$$

In this formula h is the proportion of F_1 vigor retained in the current generation, h' is the proportion retained in the preceding generation, and k is the proportion of outcrossing. The formula is based upon the assumption that gene action is, on the average, additive.

It is obvious (according to this formula) that the percentage of hybrid vigor retained in later generations of a cross will approach but never fall below $k/2$. Since the value of k in the case of maize lies usually between .9 and 1.0, it is apparent that the amount of hybrid vigor retained in later generations of maize crosses will (with random mating) seldom fall below the one-half, which is characteristic of the F_2.

There are experimental data which tend to show that advanced generations of maize crosses behave approximately as would be expected from the formulae of Wright and Stephens.

Kiesselbach (1930) compared the $F_1, F_2,$ and F_3 of 21 single crosses with the parental inbred lines. The average yield of the inbreds was 24.0 bushels. The average yield of the F_1 was 57.0 bushels. The theoretical yield of the F_2 is 40.5 bushels. The actual yield was 38.4 bushels which does not differ significantly from the theoretical. The yield of the F_3 was 37.8 bushels which is almost identical to the F_2 yield.

Neal (1935) compared the yield in F_1 and F_2 of 10 single crosses, 4 three-way crosses, and 2 double crosses. The theoretical reduction in yield between the F_1 and F_2 in these three groups (based upon Wright's formula) should have been 31.1 per cent, 21.0 per cent, and 15.2 per cent respectively. The actual reduction was 29.5 per cent, 23.4 per cent, and 15.8 per cent. The agreement could scarcely have been closer.

There is abundant evidence from maize crosses to show that equilibrium is reached in F_2, and that in the absence of selection there is no further reduction in yield in the F_3. Data from the experiments of Kiesselbach (1930), Neal (1935), and Sprague and Jenkins (1943) are summarized in Table 11.2.

The data so far presented are concerned with crosses of inbred strains. Do hybrids of open-pollinated varieties behave in the same way? Since open-pollinated varieties, although not homogeneous, are stable in productiveness they should behave in crosses in the same way as inbred strains. Data from advanced generations of topcrosses presented by Wellhausen and Roberts (1949) indicate that they do. The theoretical yields of the F_2 of a topcross can be computed from a formula suggested by Mangelsdorf (1939).

Wellhausen and Roberts compared the F_1 and F_2 generations of 31 different topcrosses each including the open-pollinated variety Urquiza and two inbred lines of unrelated varieties. The latter were in all cases first-generation selfs. The mean yield of the 31 F_1 hybrids (in terms of percentage of Urquiza) was 132 per cent. The mean yield of the corresponding 31 F_2 hybrids was 126 per cent. Since the yields of the first-generation selfed lines entering into the cross is not known, it is impossible to calculate with precision the theoretical yield of the F_2. However, it is known that good homozygous inbreds yield approximately half as much as open-pollinated varieties

(Jones and Mangelsdorf, 1925; Neal, 1935) which means that inbreds, selfed once and having lost half of their heterozygosity, should yield 75 per cent as much as the open-pollinated varieties from which they were derived. Assuming that the single-cross combinations involved are at least equal to the top-cross combinations—132 per cent—we compute the theoretical F_2 yield of the topcrosses at 117 per cent, which is considerably less than the 126 per cent actually obtained in the experiments. From the results it can be concluded that hybrid combinations including open-pollinated varieties of maize retain a considerable proportion of their vigor in advanced generations.

There is also some evidence to indicate that the amount of heterosis which occurs when open-pollinated varieties are used in hybrid combinations may be

TABLE 11.2

SUMMARY OF EXPERIMENTS DEMONSTRATING EQUILIBRIUM
REACHED IN F_2 AND NO ADDITIONAL YIELD REDUC-
TION IN F_3 OF MAIZE CROSSES

INVESTIGATORS	CLASS OF HYBRIDS	No. HYBRIDS TESTED	YIELD IN PER CENT OF F_1		
			F_1	F_2	F_3
Kiesselbach, 1930	Single crosses	21	100	68.0	66.0
Neal, 1935	Single crosses	10	100	70.5	75.7
Neal, 1935	3-way crosses	4	100	76.6	75.8
Sprague and Jenkins, 1943	Synthetics	5	100	94.3	95.4
Total and averages		40	100	76.9	78.2

considerably higher with Latin-American varieties than with varieties commonly grown in the United States. Wellhausen and Roberts report single topcrosses yielding up to 173 per cent of the open-pollinated variety and double topcrosses up to 150 per cent. A recent report from the Ministry of Agriculture of El Salvador (1949) shows four different hybrids between open-pollinated varieties yielding about 50 per cent more than the average of the parents. Such increases are not surprising, since the varieties used in the experiments are quite diverse, much more so than Corn Belt varieties.

All of the data which are available on the yields of advanced generations of maize crosses, whether the parents be inbred strains or open-pollinated varieties, tend to show that a substantial part of the hybrid vigor characteristic of the F_1 is retained in subsequent generations. Thus maize under domestication is potentially and no doubt actually a self-improving plant. Distinct more-or-less stable varieties or races evolve in the isolation of separated regions. Man brings these varieties or races together under conditions where cross-fertilization is inevitable, and a new hybrid race is born. Repeated cycles of this series of events inevitably lead to the development, without any direct intervention of man, of more productive races. If, in addition, natural selection favors the heterozygous combinations as it does in Drosophila (Dobzhansky, 1949), then the retention of hybrid vigor in advanced generations of maize crosses will be even greater than that indicated by the experimental results.

INTER-SPECIFIC HYBRIDIZATION OF MAIZE AND TEOSINTE

Superimposed upon these evolutionary mechanisms, at least in Mexico and Central America, is a second kind of hybridization which involves the introgression of teosinte into maize. The importance of this evolutionary factor would be difficult to overemphasize, for as Wellhausen *et al.* have shown all of the more productive races of maize of Mexico show evidence of past teosinte introgression.

The genetic nature of teosinte need not enter into the present discussion. Dr. R. G. Reeves and I concluded some years ago that teosinte is not, as many botanists have supposed, the ancestor of maize, but is instead the progeny of a cross of maize and Tripsacum. This conclusion has not yet been experimentally proven, and although there is much evidence to support it, it is by no means universally accepted by other students of corn's ancestry. For the purpose of this discussion we need not debate this particular point, since we need only to recognize that there is a well-defined entity known as teosinte which occurs as a weed in the corn fields of central Mexico and as a wild plant in Southwestern Mexico, Guatemala, and Honduras.

Teosinte is far more common than formerly supposed. Twenty-five years ago its occurrence was known in only three or four localities in Mexico. Since then, numerous additional sites have been described in Mexico and Guatemala, and recently a locality in Honduras has been added (Standley, 1950).

Teosinte is the closest relative of maize. It has the same chromosome number (ten) as maize, and hybridizes easily with it to produce hybrids which are completely fertile, or almost so. The chromosomes of corn and teosinte are homologous to the extent that they pair almost completely. Crossing over between teosinte and corn chromosomes is of the same order as crossing over in pure corn (Emerson and Beadle, 1932).

Present-Day Hybridization

Since both teosinte and maize are wind-pollinated plants and since they hybridize easily, it is almost inevitable that hybridization between the two species should occur in any region where both are growing. There is no doubt that such hybridization is constantly occurring, and that it has been going on for many centuries. F_1 hybrids of corn and teosinte have been collected in both Mexico and Guatemala. They are especially common in Central Mexico where teosinte grows as a weed. In 1943, I obtained some data on the extent to which hybridization occurs near the village of Chalco where teosinte is a common weed in and around the corn fields. In a field where teosinte occurred abundantly as a weed permission was obtained from the owner to tag and harvest 500 consecutive plants. Of the 500 plants tagged, 288 proved to be maize, 219 were teosinte plants, and 3 were F_1 hybrids. Of the 288 ears classified as maize, 4 showed definite evidence of contamination with teosinte in earlier generations. In addition, one ear was found in an adjacent row (not part of the sample of 500 plants) which was identical in its characteristics with a first backcross to teosinte.

The plants in this field therefore furnished unmistakable evidence of hybridization, both present and during the recent past, between maize and teosinte. One plant out of every 167 plants in the field was a vigorous F_1 hybrid shedding abundant pollen which became part of the general pollen mixture in the field. The F_1 hybrids themselves, in spite of their vigor, have a low survival value. The Mexican farmer makes no distinction between teosinte and the F_1 hybrids. Both are left standing in the field when the corn is harvested. The pure teosinte disperses its seeds which are enclosed in hard bony shells, and a new crop of teosinte plants appears the following spring. But the F_1 hybrids have no effective means of seed dispersal, and their seeds, only partially covered, are quite vulnerable to the ravages of insects and rodents.

Both maize and teosinte are quite successful in occupying distinct niches in Mexican corn fields. The one, a cultivated plant, depends for its survival upon its usefulness to man. The other, a weed, depends for survival upon its well-protected kernels and its efficient method of dispersal. There is no such niche for the F_1 hybrid. It is discarded by man as a cultivated plant, and it cannot compete with teosinte as a weed. "Finding no friend in either nature or man" (to use Weatherwax's apt description) the F_1 hybrids would be of no evolutionary significance were it not for the fact that they hybridize with both parents. Thus there is a constant introgression of teosinte into maize and of maize into teosinte. In the vicinity of Chalco, in Mexico, this process has gone on so long and the teosinte has become so maize-like in all of its characters, that maize and teosinte plants can no longer be distinguished until after the pistillate inflorescences have developed. The teosinte of Chalco has "absorbed" the genes for hairy leaf sheaths and red color characteristic of the maize of the region. Individual plants of teosinte have been found which have the yellow endosperm color of corn, although teosinte is normally white-seeded.

The introgression of teosinte into maize in Mexico today is an established fact. The question is how long this process has been going on and whether it is strictly a local phenomenon or whether it has affected the maize varieties of America.

Practically all students of maize and its relatives recognize that teosinte varieties differ in the degree to which they have become maize-like. Longley (1941), for example, considers the teosinte of Southern Guatemala to be the least maize-like and that of Mexico the most maize-like.

Rogers (1950) has shown that teosinte varieties differ quite markedly in their genes governing the characteristics in which maize and teosinte differ, especially characters of the pistillate inflorescence, tillering habit, and response to length of day. He attributes these differences to varieties in the type and amount of maize germplasm which has become incorporated into teosinte.

If teosinte varieties differ in the amount and kind of maize contamination which they now contain, it is difficult to escape the conclusion that maize varieties must likewise differ in the amount of teosinte contamination. There is little doubt that maize varieties do differ in this respect.

Ancient Hybridization

The prehistoric maize from Bat Cave has already been briefly mentioned. The earliest Bat Cave corn, dated at approximately 2000 B.C., shows no evidence whatever of teosinte introgression. Beginning about midway in the series (which would be about 500 B.C. if the sequence were strictly linear but which, according to unpublished radio-carbon determinations made by Libby, is probably somewhat later) cobs make their appearance which are scarcely distinguishable from the cobs which we have produced experimentally by crossing corn and teosinte. Weatherwax (1950) regards this evidence of teosinte introgression as far from conclusive, and it is, of course, quite impossible to prove that a cob a thousand years or more old is the product of hybridization of maize and teosinte. Nevertheless, it is true that teosinte introgression produces certain definite effects upon the cob, as some of us who have studied the derivatives of teosinte-maize crosses on an extensive scale are well aware.

When it is possible to duplicate almost exactly in experimental cultures specimens found in nature, the odds are at least somewhat better than even that the resemblance between the two specimens is more than coincidence. There is little doubt in my mind that the later Bat Cave corn is the product of contamination with teosinte. Certainly it differs from the earlier Bat Cave corn quite strikingly, and it is exactly the way in which it would be expected to differ if it is the product of teosinte introgression.

Significance of Chromosome Knobs

Mangelsdorf and Reeves (1939) suggested some years ago that the deeply staining heterochromatic knobs, characteristic of the chromosomes of many varieties of maize, are the result of the previous hybridization of maize and teosinte, or more remotely of maize and Tripsacum. There has been much indirect evidence in support of this hypothesis (especially Mangelsdorf and Cameron, 1942; Reeves, 1944), and the recent studies of Wellhausen *et al.* on Mexican races of maize provide additional evidence of this nature. Chromosome knob number in Mexican races is closely correlated with the characteristics of the races. The four Ancient Indigenous races, assumed to be relatively pure corn, have an average chromosome knob number of 4.2.

The four Pre-Columbian Exotic races, also believed to be relatively free from contamination, have an average chromosome knob number of 4.3. The thirteen Prehistoric Mestizos and the four Modern Incipient races (all except one of which are assumed to involve teosinte introgression) have chromosome knob numbers of 7.1 and 8.0, respectively.

It is interesting to note that in races for which hybridization is postulated the hybrid race, although usually intermediate in chromosome knob number between its two putative parents, resembles most closely the parent with a high knob number. For the eleven hybrid races for which chromosome knob numbers are available, not only for the hybrid races but for the two suspected parent races, the data (Table 11.3) are as follows: the average of the lower-

TABLE 11.3

CHROMOSOME KNOB NUMBERS OF MEXICAN HY-
BRID RACES OF MAIZE AND OF THEIR
PUTATIVE PARENTS*

HYBRID RACE	RACE	PARENTS	
		Lower	Higher
Tabloncillo..............	7.6	low	8.0
Comiteco................	5.6	5.0	7.0
Jala....................	7.5	5.6	7.6
Zapalote Chico..........	11.7	5.5	9.0
Zapalote Grande.........	7.4	7.0	11.7
Tuxpeño................	6.1	6.3	9.0
Vandeño................	8.1	6.1	7.4
Chalqueño..............	6.8	1.0	6.1
Celaya.................	8.5	6.1	7.6
Conico Norteño.........	8.0	1.0	8.5
Bolita.................	8.6	7.6	11.7
Averages............	7.8	5.1	8.5

* Data from Wellhausen *et al.*

numbered parent was 5.1 knobs, of the higher-numbered parent, 8.5 knobs, of the hybrid, 7.8 knobs. The fact that the average knob number in the hybrid races approaches the average knob number of the higher parents suggests, perhaps, that natural selection has tended to retain the maximum amount of teosinte introgression and hence the maximum number of knobs.

The Effects of Hybridizing Maize and Teosinte

There is no doubt that maize and teosinte are hybridizing in Mexico and Central America today, and there is at least a strong indication that they have done so in the past. What have been the effects of that hybridization?

One valid way of determining what happens when teosinte introgresses into maize is to produce such introgression experimentally. This has been done on an extensive scale by crossing an inbred strain of maize, Texas 4R-3, with four varieties of teosinte, and by repeatedly backcrossing (three times in most instances) the hybrids to the inbred strain, retaining various amounts of teosinte germplasm through selection. The end result is a series of modified inbred strains approximately like the original 4R-3—all relatively isogenic except that parts of one or more chromosome segments from teosinte have been substituted for homologous parts from maize.

That the substitution involves chromosome segments or blocks of genes and not single genes is strongly indicated by the fact that the units have multiple effects and that there is breakage within the units in some cases, although in general they are transmitted intact. Their mode of inheritance and their linkage relations can be determined as though they were single genes. Yet each of the units affects many if not all of the characters in which maize and teosinte differ. The block of genes on chromosome 3, for example, although inherited intact as a single hereditary unit, affects number of ears, size of ear, number of seeds, size of seeds, number of rows of grain, staminate spikelets on the ear, and induration of the rachis. In addition it has a concealed effect, discussed later, upon such characters as response to length of day and the development of single spikelets. The block of genes on chromosome 4 has practically the same effects in somewhat greater degree, but this block shows definite evidence of breakage or crossing over which is of the order of 30 per cent.

These blocks of genes are not random samples of teosinte germplasm, but represent definite genic entities which are transmitted from teosinte to maize in the process of repeated backcrossing. Different varieties of teosinte yield comparable if not identical blocks of genes, and the same variety of teosinte in different crosses does likewise. Regardless of the amount of introgression of maize which teosinte has undergone in its past history, and regardless of the differentiation which has occurred between varieties of teosinte, there are still regions in all varieties of teosinte, perhaps near the centromeres, which have remained "pure" for the original genes.

Effects in Heterozygous Condition

When these blocks of genes are introduced into maize they have profound effects which differ greatly in the heterozygous and homozygous condition. Since maize and teosinte represent completely different morphological and physiological systems (especially from the standpoint of their pistillate inflorescences and their response to length of day), this substitution, of segments of chromatin from one species for homologous segments from the other, represents a drastic interchange of parts comparable, perhaps, to installing a carburetor or other essential part from one make of car into another. In the F_1 hybrid of corn and teosinte where the blocks of genes are heterozygous, there is no particular functional difficulty. Here the two complete systems are operating simultaneously and the result is a vigorous hybrid, vegetatively luxuriant, potentially capable of producing great numbers of seed. Measured solely by total grain yield, the F_1 hybrid does not exhibit heterosis since its grain yield is considerably less than that of corn, but measured in terms of number of seeds, or number of stalks, or total fodder, the hybrid certainly exhibits heterosis.

In the modified inbred in which a block of genes from teosinte has been substituted for a block of genes from maize, the situation is quite different. There are no functional aberrations so long as the block of genes from teosinte is heterozygous. Under these circumstances it has very little discernible

Fig. 11.3—Ears of a teosinte-modified inbred strain 4R-3 which are isogenic except for an introduced block of genes from chromosome 3 of Florida teosinte. The ear at the left lacks the block of teosinte genes, the center ear is heterozygous for it, the ear at the right is homozygous for it. Note the high degree of dominance or potence of the maize genes.

effect. Figures 11.3, 11.4, and 11.5 show ears of corn heterozygous for blocks of genes from chromosomes 3 and 4 respectively, compared to "pure" corn in the same progeny. The blocks of genes from corn are much more "potent" (a term proposed by Wigan, 1944, to describe the integrated dominance effects of all genes) than the block of genes from teosinte, at least in the striking characteristics which differentiate the two species. This is in itself a noteworthy phenomenon since corn is not strongly "dominant" or more potent than teosinte in the F_1 hybrid, where both species contribute more or less equally.

FIG. 11.4—These ears are the exact counterparts of those in Figure 11.3 except that the block of teosinte genes was derived from chromosome 4 of Florida teosinte.

Fig. 11.5—When the inbred 4R-3 is crossed with No. 701 the hybrid ear illustrated above (*left*) is produced. When a modified strain of 4R-3 (*right*) which has had three blocks of genes from Durango teosinte substituted for corresponding maize genes is crossed with No. 701, the hybrid (*center*) is much more maize-like than teosinte-like. The hybrid, being multiple-eared, bears a substantially greater number of seeds than either parent and in one experiment was appreciably more productive.

The reason for the strong potence of maize over teosinte in blocks of genes introduced from teosinte into maize, is to be found in a phenomenon termed "antithetical dominance" which has been postulated by Anderson and Erickson (1941) on theoretical grounds. These writers assumed that in species hybrids such as that between maize and Tripsacum, the F_1 would be intermediate but that backcrosses to either parent would strongly resemble the recurrent parent. The basis for this assumption is that the possibilities for successful recombination of two such different systems is remote.

The conception of antithetical dominance has some relationship to Richey's opinion (1946) that dominance in some cases is no more than a condition where one allele is capable of doing the entire job, or most of it, while the other allele merely stands by. According to this interpretation, genes are not favorable because they are dominant, but are dominant because they are favorable. They reveal their presence by doing something.

There is, in any case, little doubt that something of the general nature of antithetical dominance or the kind of dominance postulated by Richey is involved in the teosinte-maize derivatives. Both teosinte and maize are about equally potent in the F_1 hybrid, but a small amount of teosinte germplasm incorporated into maize in the heterozygous condition is definitely lacking in potence.

Effects in Homozygous Condition

Since a block of teosinte genes introduced into maize is largely recessive in its effects when heterozygous, its effects should become much more apparent in the homozygous condition. This is indeed the case. The ear on the right in Figures 11.3, 11.4, and 11.5 illustrates the effects of one or more blocks of teosinte genes incorporated in a homozygous condition in the inbred strain 4R-3.

The combination of traits from corn and teosinte which occurs in these homozygous teosinte derivatives is characterized by a distinct lack of harmony in the development of the pistillate inflorescence. The husks are too short for the ears, the glumes are too small for the kernels and tend to constrict the growing caryopses producing misshapen kernels. The vascular system is inadequate for the number of kernels borne on the ear, and there are many shrunken kernels as well as numerous gaps where no kernels have developed. Germination of the seeds is often poor, and viability of short duration. Homozygous combinations of this kind obviously have a low survival value. Indeed it has been difficult to maintain some of them in artificial cultures.

These unfavorable effects of teosinte introgression in the homozygous condition may be nothing more than the result of substituting parts of one well-integrated system for corresponding parts of another. They may, however, also involve "cryptic structural differentiation" of the kind suggested by

Stephens (1950) for species of Gossypium, although the extent of this cannot be great, otherwise some combinations would be lethal. But whatever the cause, there is little doubt about the reality of the unfavorable effects. Therefore, if the repeated hybridization of corn and teosinte which has occurred in the past has had any permanent effect, one of two things or both must have happened: (1) The undesirable effects of teosinte have become recessive as the result of natural selection for modifying factors. (2) The regions of the chromatin involving teosinte genes have been kept heterozygous. There is some evidence that both may have occurred.

There is some evidence, by no means conclusive, that maize varieties of today have *absorbed* teosinte germplasm in the past and are now *buffered* against the effects of teosinte genes. There is at least no doubt that when the same variety of teosinte is crossed on a series of maize varieties, considerable variation is displayed by the F_1 hybrids in the potence of the maize parents.

In general, varieties which show some evidence of previous contamination with teosinte are more likely to produce maize-like F_1 hybrids than those which do not show evidence of such contamination. Corn Belt inbreds as a class produce the most maize-like F_1 of any of stocks tested. Figure 11.6 illustrates a case where a South American stock (an inbred strain derived from the Guarany corn of Paraguay) is less potent in crosses with two varieties of teosinte than is a North American stock (a genetic tester). I also have observed that blocks of teosinte genes introduced into an inbred strain of Guarany by repeated backcrossing have a greater effect than these same blocks introduced into Texas 4R-3 or Minn. A158, both of which seem already to contain appreciable amounts of teosinte.

If the increased potency of teosinte-contaminated maize proves to be generally true, then the reason for it is that there has been a selection of modifying factors which have tended to suppress the most unfavorable conspicuous effects of the teosinte introgression. Otherwise, varieties of maize containing teosinte germplasm should produce hybrids which are more teosinte-like, rather than more maize-like, than the average. This is convincingly demonstrated experimentally by crossing the original inbred 4R-3 and one of its modified derivatives with the same variety of teosinte (Florida type). The results are illustrated in Figure 11.7.

The F_1 of 4R-3 × teosinte is a typical F_1 hybrid, intermediate between its parents. It has both single and double spikelets and, although the fact is not revealed by the illustration, it has approximately the same type of response to length of day as does maize. In marked contrast, when a derived strain of 4R-3 (in which a block of teosinte genes on chromosome 3 has been substituted for a corresponding block of maize genes) is crossed with the same teosinte, the F_1 hybrid is scarcely distinguishable in its pistillate spike from pure teosinte. Furthermore, it has teosinte's response to length of day. Plants of this hybrid started in the greenhouse in February did not flower until the following October and November. This derivative of a maize-teosinte hybrid, therefore, carries at least two concealed characteristics of teosinte: single spikelets and response to length of day. Genes for these two characters do not express themselves in the derivative itself, but their presence becomes immediately apparent when the derivative is crossed with teosinte. The situation is comparable to the concealed genes for hair color and texture

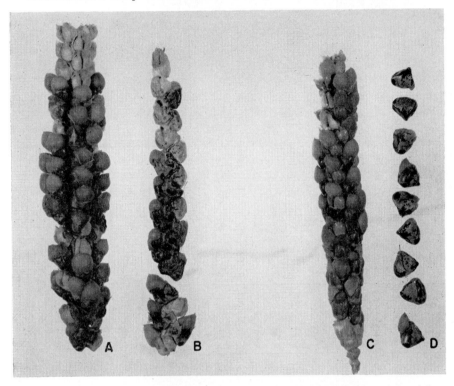

FIG. 11.6—A North American stock is more potent in crosses with Nobogame teosinte (A) and Durango teosinte (C) than the Guarany corn from Paraguay (B and D). This is attributed to previous introgression of teosinte accompanied by the evolution of modifier complexes in North American varieties.

in persons who are completely bald. The genes are there but have no opportunity to express themselves.

Since varieties of maize which appear to be the product of previous teosinte contamination, such as those of the Corn Belt, behave quite differently in crosses from stocks known to be contaminated, there is at least an indication that such contamination has become modified through selection acting upon the modifier complex. More data are obviously needed on this problem.

A second question which arises in considering the effects of the natural hybridization of corn and teosinte is whether there is any mechanism which tends to maintain the maize-teosinte loci in a perpetual state of heterozygosity. It already has been shown that homozygous teosinte genes in the maize complex are decidedly deleterious. Therefore, if the teosinte genes are

FIG. 11.7—When the inbred 4R-3 (*A*) is crossed with Florida teosinte (*C*), the F₁ hybrid ears (*B*) are maize-like in having four-ranked ears, some double spikelets, and partially naked seeds. When a teosinte-modified strain of 4R-3 (*D*) is crossed with Florida teosinte (*F*), the F₁ hybrid (*E*) is much more teosinte-like. The spikes are two-ranked, single, and the seeds are completely enclosed. The teosinte derivative obviously carries "concealed" genes for these teosinte characteristics.

to survive their deleterious effects, they must be modified through selection or the genes must be maintained in a more or less heterozygous state. It may be assumed that the latter mechanism would operate only if heterozygosity for a group of maize-teosinte genes confers a distinct selective advantage making the heterozygous combination superior, not only to the homozygous teosinte genes (as it obviously is) but also to the corresponding homozygous maize genes.

Data are available both from my experiments and those of R. G. Reeves (1950), conducted independently, to indicate that heterozygosity for a block of teosinte genes does sometimes confer a selective advantage. In 1944, in my experiments, five Corn Belt inbred strains were crossed with the Texas in- bred 4R-3, as well as with four modified strains of 4R-3 in which teosinte genes had been substituted for maize genes. The four modified strains may be briefly described as follows:

Strain	No. Blocks Genes	Teosinte Variety
Modified 4R-3 Strain A......... 2		Florida
Modified 4R-3 Strain B........ 2		Florida
Modified 4R-3 Strain C......... 3		Durango
Modified 4R-3 Strain D......... 3		Durango

The F_1 hybrids were grown in 1945 in two replications in a modified Latin- Square yield test. Several hybrids were omitted for lack of sufficient seed. The results are shown in Table 11.4.

TABLE 11.4

AVERAGE YIELDS IN BUSHELS PER ACRE OF HYBRIDS OF CORN BELT INBREDS WITH TEXAS 4R-3 AND ITS TEOSINTE-MODIFIED DERIVATIVES

4R-3 OR DERIVATIVE	CORN BELT INBREDS				
	K155	38–11	L317	701	CC24
4R-3 (check)...........	108.6	85.2	99.0	100.2	100.2
Modified Strain A......	102.6	....	....	87.0	88.8
Modified Strain B......	126.6*	82.8	109.8	....	78.6
Modified Strain C......	94.2	75.6	66.0	97.8	92.4
Modified Strain D......	93.0	57.0	71.4	146.4*	79.8

* Difference probably significant.

Of the 17 hybrids tested, only 3 proved to be better than the correspond- ing checks in total yield, and in only 2 of these is the difference significant. Although the data are not extensive, there is some indication that the Corn Belt inbred strains used in these experiments differ in their ability to "com- bine" with the teosinte derivatives.

Perhaps more important than total yield, from the standpoint of selective reproductive advantage, is total number of seeds per plant (Table 11.5). Here 6 of the 15 hybrids for which data are available were superior to the checks, 4 of these significantly so.

These results, so far as they go, are in agreement with the recently pub- lished results of Reeves (1950). Reeves tested 49 modified 4R-3 lines in hy- brids with a common tester. He found none significantly better than the check in yield, although several were superior in heat-tolerance. Reeves found, however, that when teosinte germplasm was introduced into another inbred strain, 127C, the results obtained in the hybrids were somewhat different. In 1946, 6 hybrids out of 25 were better than the check, 3 of them significantly so. In 1947, 15 hybrids out of 49 were better than the check, 6 of them significantly so. Reeves suggested that the difference between 4R-3 and 127C in their response to teosinte introgression lies in the fact that 4R-3 already contained considerable amounts of teosinte germplasm while 127C does not. The suggestion is supported by differences in the morphological characteristics of the two lines.

There was also an indication in Reeves' experiments that the entries with

TABLE 11.5

AVERAGE NUMBERS OF SEEDS PER PLANT IN HYBRIDS OF
CORN BELT INBREDS WITH TEXAS 4R-3 AND ITS
TEOSINTE-MODIFIED DERIVATIVES

4R-3 OR DERIVATIVE	CORN BELT INBREDS				
	K155	38–11	L317	701	CC24
4R-3 (check).............	849	636	925	1132	1179
Modified Strain A.........	756	....	....	1095	807
Modified Strain B.........	937	....	1107*	....	....
Modified Strain C.........	1419*	809	746	1696*	885
Modified Strain D.........	770	573	843	1811*	864

* Difference probably significant.

teosinte genes made their best showing in 1947, a season of severe drought.

Considering all of the results together it may be concluded that: (a) blocks of teosinte genes in the heterozygous condition do in some instances improve the total yield of the plants which contain them; (b) even more frequently do such blocks of genes increase the total number of seeds produced; (c) there is some evidence that the teosinte derivatives impart resistance to heat and drought to their hybrids.

In those crosses in which the heterozygous combination is superior to either of the homozygous combinations, a block of maize genes or a block of teosinte genes, natural selection would undoubtedly favor, at least initially, the heterozygous combination. If the block of genes were one involving the region of the centromere where crossing-over is reduced, it is quite possible that the block of genes would be retained more or less intact for a considerable number of generations. The maintenance of heterozygosity through natural selection also would be promoted if, as in the case of Drosophila studied by Dobzhansky, one set of genes is superior in adapting the organism to one kind of environment while the other set contributes to adaptation to a wholly different environment which the organism also encounters periodically.

It cannot be proved that such a situation exists in the case of maize which has become contaminated with teosinte, but it is quite possible that it does. For example, human selection when practiced would tend to favor the larger-seeded, larger-eared individuals with a minimum of teosinte contamination. Natural selection would favor the individuals with the larger number of seeds, hence those with an appreciable amount of teosinte contamination. These two forces operating simultaneously or alternately would tend to perpetuate the heterozygote. Similarly, if maize germplasm were superior in seasons of excessive moisture and teosinte germplasm in seasons of drought (for which there is some evidence), there would be a tendency for natural selection to perpetuate heterozygous combinations. It cannot be demonstrated that any of these hypothetical situations actually exist. There is no doubt, however, that present-day maize is highly heterozygous, and there is more than a suspicion that repeated hybridization with teosinte has been responsible for part of the heterozygosity.

DISCUSSION

The present-day heterozygosity of maize may involve a variety of different factors and forces which have operated during its past history. Two of these are now reasonably clear: interracial hybridization, and introgression of teosinte into maize.

When interracial hybridization occurs, hybrid vigor not only manifests itself in the first generation, but also persists in part through an indefinite number of subsequent generations. Maize under domestication is, therefore, potentially a self-improving plant. The evidence from Mexican races of maize indicates that repeated interracial hybridization has been an extremely important factor in the evolution of maize in Mexico. There is every reason to believe that the situation in Mexico, so far as interracial hybridization is concerned, is typical of other parts of America.

The second factor, introgression of teosinte, which is believed to have played an important role in the evolution of maize, is not so easily demonstrated. There is no doubt, however, that teosinte is hybridizing with maize in Guatemala and Mexico today, or that this hybridization has occurred in the past. It would be surprising indeed if such hybridization had no effect upon the evolution of maize. There is every indication that it has had a profound effect. All of the most productive modern agricultural races of maize in Mexico show evidence of contamination with teosinte, not only in their external characters, but also in their internal cytological characteristics.

It can be shown experimentally that teosinte germplasm, when introduced into maize, may sometimes have a beneficial effect when heterozygous, but is always deleterious when homozygous. Therefore it follows that after maize and teosinte have hybridized, and after there has been an introgression of teosinte into maize: (1) the teosinte genes must be eliminated or, (2) their effects must be changed through the accumulation of a new modifier complex, or (3) they must be kept in a heterozygous state. There is evidence, but not final proof, that both of the two last-named factors have operated during the evolution of maize. Interracial and interspecific hybridization accompanied by sustained heterosis are therefore regarded as two important factors in the evolution of maize.

SUMMARY

1. Evidence is presented to show that both interracial and interspecific hybridization, accompanied by heterosis, have been factors in the evolution of maize.

2. The races of maize of Mexico are cited as an example of interracial hybridization. Of the 25 Mexican races described by Wellhausen *et al.*, 14 are considered to be the products of interracial hybridization.

3. The hybrid vigor, which occurs when races of maize are crossed, is capable of persisting in part in subsequent generations. Maize under domestication is therefore potentially a self-improving plant.

4. Interspecific hybridization of maize and teosinte is occurring in Guatemala and Mexico today, and there is evidence—archaeological, morphological, and cytological—that it has occurred in the past.

5. Introgression of teosinte into maize in experimental cultures is sometimes beneficial when the teosinte genes are heterozygous, but is always deleterious when they are homozygous.

6. It, therefore, seems probable that the persistence of teosinte germplasm in races of maize has been accompanied either by development of modifier complexes which have made the teosinte genes recessive in their action, or by the maintenance of a continued state of heterozygosity.

7. The possibility that heterozygosity in maize has been preserved by natural selection as it has been in Drosophila is discussed.

STERLING EMERSON
California Institute of Technology

Chapter 12

Biochemical Models
of Heterosis in Neurospora

Some of the things that have been learned about gene controlled reactions in Neurospora can be used in forming a picture of how individual genes contribute to heterosis. I wish to consider especially those examples which indicate that heterozygosity at a single locus may influence the growth of an organism to a considerable extent.

It should be noted at the beginning, however, that one is not justified in assuming that the situations found in Neurospora are necessarily similar to those occurring in the higher organisms in which heterosis is ordinarily studied. It may be unwise to assume that any two organisms are essentially similar. There are special reasons for caution in making comparisons between Neurospora and higher plants and animals, since the nuclear and chromosomal basis for the expression of heterosis is so dissimilar. On the other hand, there is a considerable accumulation of information about the parts played in the physiology and biochemistry of Neurospora by individual genes (Beadle, 1948; Horowitz, 1950) and, with proper caution, we may assume that some of this information may have rather broad application.

In any haploid organism, such as the ascomycetous fungus Neurospora, in which there is a single set of genes in each nucleus, such phenomena as dominance, heterozygosis, and heterosis cannot occur. There is, however, a condition known as heterocaryosis which permits a loose approximation to each.

CHARACTERISTICS OF HETEROCARYONS

The plant body of Neurospora can be said to be made up of cells, but they are very different from the cells of higher plants. In the first place, the cells contain a large and variable number of nuclei in a common cytoplasm. The so-called cells themselves are not as discrete as cells are generally supposed to be. The walls between them have perforations which permit both cyto-plasm and nuclei to move from cell to cell. If all nuclei are identical, their movement and distribution is probably of minor importance, but if they are not identical there may be effects of considerable consequence arising from irregularities in nuclear distribution.

There are two ways in which a mixture of different kinds of nuclei within a single cell may come about. In the growth resulting from a sexually pro-duced ascospore, or from a uninucleate asexual microconidium, all nuclei are directly descended from a single haploid nucleus. Barring mutation, they should all have the same genetic constitution. After the growth has become

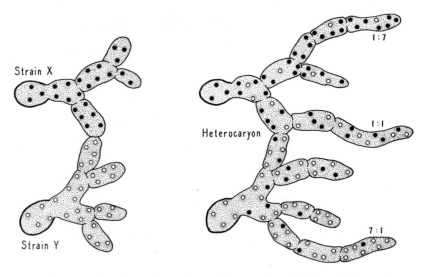

F??. 12.1—Heterocaryon formation resulting from hyphal fusion (a diagram).

multinucleate, if a mutation should occur in one nucleus, the descendants of that nucleus would then have a different genetic constitution from the re-maining nuclei in the common cytoplasm, and a condition of heterocaryosis would exist. The second way in which heterocaryons arise is from the direct fusion of branches or hyphae of different strains, with the subsequent in-termingling of their nuclei. By the latter method, heterocaryons of pre-determined genetic constitution can be made at will.

The controlled production of heterocaryons is shown diagrammatically in Figure 12.1. Strain X is represented as having black nuclei to distinguish them from the nuclei of strain Y, which are pictured as being white. After fusion between hyphae, nuclei of strain Y may migrate into cells of strain X, and those of X into Y. It is possible that different hyphal tips, growing from this common mass of cells, will have different relative numbers of the two sorts of nuclei, as illustrated by the ratios 1:7, 1:1, and 7:1 in three of the hyphal tips. To prove that two kinds of nuclei were present in the same cells of such heterocaryons, Beadle and Coonradt (1944) cut off single hyphal tips, transferred them to fresh medium, and then identified two kinds of nuclei in the resulting growth by genetic test.

Where there is freely branching filamentous growth, as in Neurospora, it is possible for the two types of nuclei in a heterocaryon to become sorted out

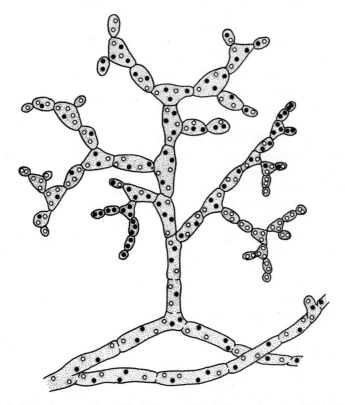

F⟨ɪɢ⟩. 12.2—Somatic segregation of dissimilar nuclei in the formation of conidia (a diagram).

purely as a matter of chance, as illustrated in a schematic way in Figure 12.2. This diagram actually represents an erect fruiting branch, or conidiophore, on which the asexual spores are born. The conidia of Neurospora have variable numbers of nuclei, but generally more than one. Dodge (1942) proved that two kinds of nuclei were present in the same cell of a heterocaryon by growing cultures from single conidia, and then showing by genetic test that some of these cultures had both types of nuclei. In some instances he was able to distinguish the heterocaryotic and both homocaryotic types in culture derived from single conidia by their morphological characteristics.

The essential differences between Neurospora and higher organisms with respect to heterosis result from the points just noted. In a diploid which is heterozygous for a single gene pair, both alleles are present in the same nucleus and in equal dosage. Whereas in the corresponding haploid heterocaryon, the two alleles are present in different nuclei, and the relative proportions of the two alleles vary with the frequencies of the two types of nuclei. All cells of a diploid heterozygote have the same genetic constitution, but there can be a considerable variation in genetic constitution in different parts of a heterocaryotic individual. Interactions between alleles, by which I mean such things as the expression of dominance, must result from the ability of genes to act at some distance in heterocaryons, in which there is no possibility of an intimate association of alleles within a nucleus (Lewis, 1950). It is considerations such as these that show that dominance and heterosis-like effects in Neurospora are only approximations to the phenomena as known in diploid organisms.

HETEROSIS IN HETEROCARYONS

An enhancement of growth, closely simulating heterosis, in heterocaryons of *Neurospora tetrasperma* was reported by Dodge in 1942. In this paper he distinguished between heterocaryotic vigor and the hybrid vigor of diploid organisms along much the same lines as I have just done. He suggested that the heterocaryotic vigor observed might be the result of complementing growth factors whose production was controlled by the two types of nuclei (Robbins, 1950). It was later (Dodge, Schmitt, and Appel, 1945) demonstrated that genes responsible for enhanced growth segregated and recombined in a normal fashion. These studies showed that genes residing in different nuclei, but in a common cytoplasm, can cooperate in establishing conditions favoring rapid growth, and that a condition resembling hybrid vigor occurs.

Meantime, Beadle and Coonradt (1944) had reported on heterocaryons between pairs of mutant strains of *Neurospora crassa*, each of which is unable to synthesize a particular vitamin or amino acid. Each mutant strain by itself is unable to grow unless supplied with its specific growth requirement, but nine heterocaryons involving different combinations of seven mutant strains grew at rates approximating that of wild type without the addition of growth factors. The authors conclude that the wild type allele is dominant to the mutant allele in each of the examples studied.

Beadle and Coonradt note further that in such heterocaryons, in which there is the opportunity for great diversity in the relative numbers of the two types of nuclei in different hyphal tips, those tips having the most favorable proportions of nuclei should grow most rapidly. Conversely, rapidly growing hyphae should have the two sorts of nuclei in roughly optimal proportions. In heterocaryons involving pairs of mutant strains, Beadle and Coonradt found nuclear ratios varying between approximately 1:1 and almost 20:1. They interpreted these results to mean that the wild type alleles of different mutant genes have different degrees of dominance. A strongly dominant wild type allele will need to be present in relatively few nuclei—say one in twenty.

A heterocaryon between two mutant strains could grow at the maximum rate over a large range of nuclear proportions, provided the wild type alleles concerned were both strongly dominant. A weakly dominant wild type allele, on the other hand, must be present in a large proportion of the nuclei— say nineteen of twenty—to ensure vigorous growth. Heterocaryons in which the wild type alleles concerned are both weakly dominant could never result in vigorous growth, since the two wild type alleles cannot both be present in excess, one being in one type of nucleus and the other in the remaining nuclei.

HETEROSIS DUE TO HETEROZYGOSITY AT ONE LOCUS

The heterosis effect in heterocaryons studied by Beadle and Coonradt results from the mutually complementary nature of the nuclei involved. For each deleterious mutant allele in one nucleus there is the corresponding favorable and dominant wild type allele in another. In contrast to these there are other heterocaryons (briefly reported in Emerson, 1947) in which the nuclei differ in only one gene, yet which still show the heterosis effect. Heterocaryons in which some nuclei carry the dominant allele and some the recessive are superior to homocaryons, all of whose nuclei have the dominant allele, or all the recessive.

Heterocaryotic Suppression of the Sulfonamide-requiring Character

Most of the heterocaryons of this sort that have been found so far have involved the so-called sulfonamide-requiring mutant strain. At 35° on minimal medium, this strain makes extremely poor growth, but it does keep creeping along. After varying lengths of time, it frequently happens that the growth will change to a rapid vigorous type. Growth curves of six cultures which have reverted to something approaching wild type growth are shown in Figure 12.3. When the mycelium had reached the end of the growth tubes, inocula from the newest growth were introduced into fresh tubes containing minimal medium, resulting in the growth curves shown in the upper part of the figure.

From these curves it can be seen that the reverted type of growth usually persists through a conidial transfer. After the mycelium had reached the end of the second tube, conidia were removed and used in outcrosses to wild type to determine the genetic constitution of their nuclei. These tests showed that each of the six cultures represented in Figure 12.3 was a heterocaryon. One type of nucleus present in each heterocaryon was identical to those in the original sulfonamide-requiring strain. The second type of nucleus in each also carried the sulfonamide-requiring gene, *sfo* (in one instance, that derived from culture number 1 in Figure 12.3, the *sfo* gene itself was somewhat

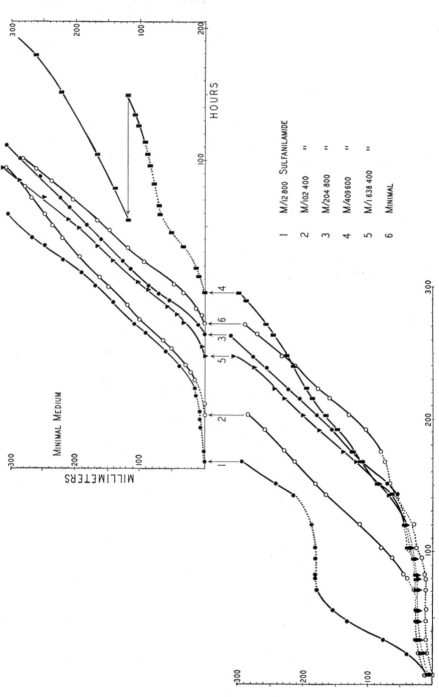

FIG. 12.3 —Growth curves of the sulfonamide-requiring strain of Neurospora showing the development of *reverted* type of growth. Solid lines represent vigorous growth; dotted lines, poor growth. Cultures grown by the tube method (Ryan, Beadle, and Tatum, 1943) at 36.4°.

modified), and in addition a second mutant gene, S, which was presumably responsible for the change in growth (Table 12.1).

The new mutants appearing in the heterocaryons have been called suppressors because they overcome the deleterious effect of the sulfonamide-requiring gene in heterocaryons. Actually they are not like the usual suppressors, because in homocaryotic strains which also carry the sulfonamide-requiring gene they do not result in wild type growth.

Growth characteristics of strains homocaryotic for four of these suppressors, with and without the sulfonamide-requiring gene, are represented in

TABLE 12.1

DISTRIBUTION OF NUCLEI IN
THE HETEROCARYONS REPRE-
SENTED IN FIGURE 12.3

FROM CULTURE TUBE NUMBER	NUCLEI	
	sfo, +	sfo, S
1...............	3	5
2...............	6	5
3...............	15	2
4...............	8	1
5...............	8	1
6...............	1	14

Figure 12.4. From these growth curves it can be seen that wild type $(+, +)$ is neither inhibited by sulfanilamide in a concentration of 2×10^{-4} M, nor stimulated by p-aminobenzoic acid in a concentration of 10^{-4} M when grown at 35°, and is only slightly inhibited by sulfanilamide at 25°. At 35° growth of the sulfonamide-requiring strain $(sfo, +)$ is stimulated by sulfanilamide and inhibited by p-aminobenzoic acid, though neither substance has an appreciable effect at 25° in the concentrations used.

The suppressor from tube 1 $(+, S\text{-}1)$ does not grow at 35°, and grows slowly on all media at 25°. The suppressor from tube 2 $(+, S\text{-}2)$ differs from wild type principally in taking longer to attain its maximum growth rate, though there is also some stimulation by sulfanilamide at 35°. When combined as a double mutant with the sulfonamide-requiring gene $(sfo, S\text{-}2)$, it almost approximates the growth of wild type. The suppressor from tube 4 $(+, S\text{-}4)$ differs from wild type in being stimulated by p-aminobenzoic acid and inhibited by sulfanilamide, the inhibition being stronger at 25°. In combination with the sulfonamide-requiring gene $(sfo, S\text{-}4)$ it resembles the sulfonamide-requiring strain itself except that there is a long lag phase on sulfanilamide at 35°, and inhibition at 25°. The suppressor from tube 6, either alone

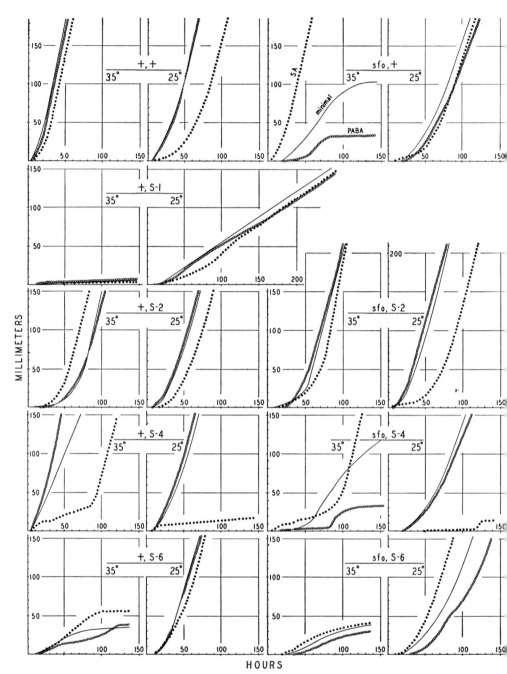

FIG. 12.4—Growth curves of suppressor strains in absence and presence of the sulfonamide-requiring gene (*sf*
at 35° and 25° on minimal medium (light line), 10^{-4} *M* *p*-aminobenzoic acid (line of open circles −PABA), an
2×10^{-4} M sulfanilamide (dotted line −SA).

$(+, S\text{-}6)$ or in combination with the sulfonamide-requiring gene $(sfo, S\text{-}6)$, grows very poorly at $35°$.

Of those illustrated, suppressors numbered 4 and 6 are perhaps the most significant to the present discussion. When combined with the sulfonamide-requiring gene $(sfo, S\text{-}4$ and $sfo, S\text{-}6)$, neither grows well on minimal medium at $35°$. Yet heterocaryons between either of these double mutants and the sulfonamide-requiring strain are enabled to grow quite well under those conditions. In these heterocaryons the sulfonamide-requiring gene is present in all nuclei, in some of which it is combined with a suppressor. The suppressor is not capable of overcoming the ill effects of the sulfonamide-requiring gene when present in all nuclei, but is effective when present in only some of them.

Biochemical Basis for the Sulfonamide-requiring Character

This seeming paradox becomes less important once the nature of the reaction controlled by the sulfonamide-requiring gene is understood (Zalokar, 1948, 1950; Emerson, 1950). The diagrams in Figure 12.5 illustrate some of the important reactions involved. There are a large number of amino acids, vitamins, components of nucleic acid, and so on, that are essential to growth. But we shall consider only two amino acids, methionine and threonine, and the vitamin p-aminobenzoic acid. Para-aminobenzoic acid is involved in a number of reactions essential to growth, one of which is the final step in the synthesis of methionine from homocysteine. Wild type carries out all essential reactions and produces all essential growth factors, with the exception of biotin which must be supplied to all strains.

The reaction governed by the sulfonamide-requiring gene has not yet been identified, but we know quite a little about it. It requires the presence of both homocysteine and p-aminobenzoic acid. Presumably homocysteine is used as a substrate in this reaction, and p-aminobenzoic acid, or a derivative, is needed as a catalyst. The reaction either results in the destruction of threonine or else interferes with its normal utilization, so that the sulfonamide-requiring strain has too little threonine for growth. We also know that more homocysteine is required for this deleterious reaction than for the synthesis of methionine, and that in the presence of limiting amounts of homocysteine, the synthesis of methionine goes on without any interference with the utilization of threonine.

Furthermore, the deleterious reaction requires larger amounts of p-aminobenzoic acid than are needed for all essential reactions combined. Only about half as much is needed in the synthesis of methionine, about a quarter as much in the production of purines, and very much less still for other essential, but still unidentified factors. Both wild type and the sulfonamide-requiring strain produce about one hundred times as much p-aminobenzoic acid as is needed for all essential reactions.

We know of three ways in which the deleterious reaction leading to threo-

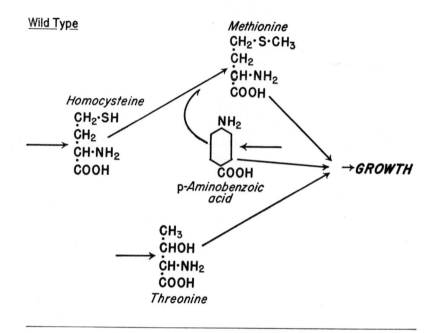

Wild Type

Methionine
$$CH_2 \cdot S \cdot CH_3$$
$$CH_2$$
$$CH \cdot NH_2$$
$$COOH$$

Homocysteine
$$CH_2 \cdot SH$$
$$CH_2$$
$$CH \cdot NH_2$$
$$COOH$$

$$NH_2$$

$$COOH$$
p-Aminobenzoic
acid

→ GROWTH

$$CH_3$$
$$CHOH$$
$$CH \cdot NH_2$$
$$COOH$$
Threonine

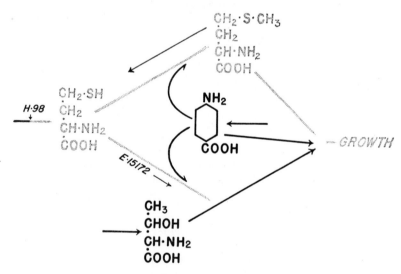

Sulfonamide Requiring, Homocysteineless

$$CH_2 \cdot S \cdot CH_3$$
$$CH_2$$
$$CH \cdot NH_2$$
$$COOH$$

H-98

$$CH_2 \cdot SH$$
$$CH_2$$
$$CH \cdot NH_2$$
$$COOH$$

E-15172

$$NH_2$$

$$COOH$$

→ GROWTH

$$CH_3$$
$$CHOH$$
$$CH \cdot NH_2$$
$$COOH$$

FIG. 12.5—Certain biochemical reactions essential to growth in Neurospora as influenced by genes of the sulfonamide-requiring strain (E-15172), the homocysteineless strain (H-98), and the aminobenzoicless strain (1633).

Sulfonamide Requiring

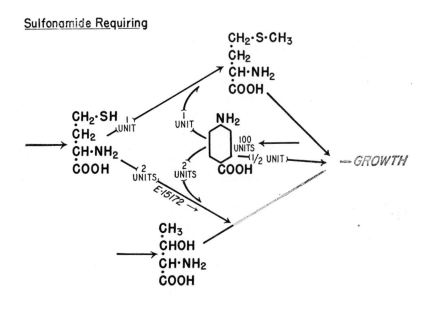

Sulfonamide Requiring, Aminobenzoicless

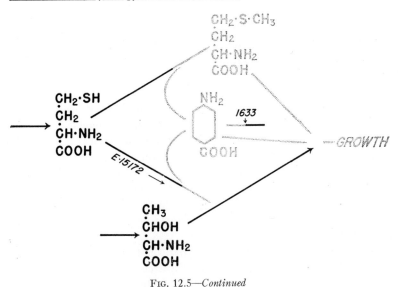

FIG. 12.5—*Continued*

nine deficiency can be prevented by genetic means. The simplest is of course by introducing the wild type allele of the sulfonamide-requiring gene, but the other two are of more interest. One of these is by introducing a genetic block to the synthesis of homocysteine. Mutant strain H-98 blocks the terminal step in the synthesis of homocysteine. In the double mutant—sulfonamide-requiring, homocysteineless—there is no interference with the availability of threonine for growth, since the deleterious reaction does not take place in the absence of homocysteine. In the absence of homocysteine, however, there can be no synthesis of methionine, so that the double mutant fails to grow because of a methionine deficiency. The double mutant will grow if supplied with exactly the right amount of methionine—more inhibits growth, because methionine is degraded to homocysteine which then supports the deleterious reaction (Zalokar, 1950).

The remaining method is to introduce a genetic block to the synthesis of p-aminobenzoic acid. In the double mutant—sulfonamide-requiring, amino-benzoicless—there is again no interference with the utilization of threonine since there is no p-aminobenzoic acid to catalyse the deleterious reaction. There is again a deficiency for methionine, because p-aminobenzoic acid is needed in its synthesis. There is also a deficiency of p-aminobenzoic acid for other essential processes. The double mutant will grow if supplied just the right amount of p-aminobenzoic acid to satisfy the essential requirements, but not enough to stimulate the deleterious reaction (Zalokar, 1948).

Model Heterocaryons

It can be seen that the simple sulfonamide-requiring mutant on the one hand, and the two double mutants on the other, have different deficiencies. One produces methionine and p-aminobenzoic acid, but not enough threonine. The others produce sufficient threonine, but no methionine, and in one case, no p-aminobenzoic acid. In heterocaryons between the simple and double mutants, the two types of nuclei should complement each other in the production of essential growth substances. If the nuclear ratios can be so adjusted that the different substances are produced in appropriate amounts, vigorous growth should result. Heterocaryons involving the simple sulfona-mide-requiring mutant and the double mutant sulfonamide-requiring, amino-benzoicless have resulted in vigorous growth (Emerson, 1948) in every test so far made. Growth curves of some of these heterocaryons are illustrated in Figure 12.6.

Growth of these heterocaryons is usually not maintained at a constant rate. Growth may stop completely after a time, or it may nearly stop and then start again. This is believed to be due to fluctuations in the ratio of the two kinds of nuclei in the advancing hyphal tips. Apparently there must be many times as many double mutant nuclei as simple sulfonamide-requiring nuclei to result in a favorable combination. This is not surprising since the

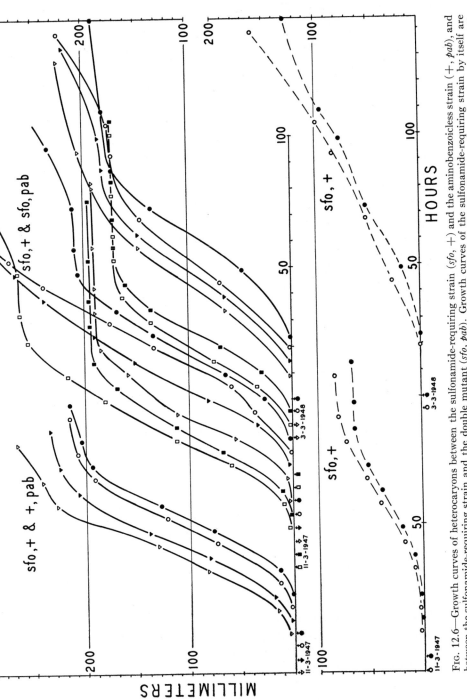

FIG. 12.6—Growth curves of heterocaryons between the sulfonamide-requiring strain (*sfo*, +) and the aminobenzoicless strain (+, *pab*), and between the sulfonamide-requiring strain and the double mutant (*sfo*, *pab*). Growth curves of the sulfonamide-requiring strain by itself are shown at the bottom of the figure, the aminobenzoicless and double mutant controls grew not at all. All cultures on minimal medium at 35°.

sulfonamide-requiring strain produces something in the order of one hundred times as much p-aminobenzoic acid as is required for essential reactions, or about fifty times as much as is required for the reaction which makes threonine unavailable for growth.

Limited direct tests of nuclear frequencies in such heterocaryons indicate that nuclei carrying only the sulfonamide-requiring gene are much less frequent than those carrying the aminobenzoicless gene as well. In one test of about one hundred nuclei, all proved to be double mutants. In another test, conidia from heterocaryons were transferred to fresh growth tubes which contained a concentration of sulfanilamide sufficient to inhibit growth of the double mutant very strongly and still be favorable to the growth of the simple sulfonamide-requiring mutant. Only one of five such transfers grew—again suggesting that simple sulfonamide-requiring nuclei were infrequent.

If in order to have rapid growth there must be many double mutant nuclei and few simple mutants, it is not surprising that vigorous growth should cease rather suddenly. Ryan, Beadle, and Tatum (1943) have shown that growth substances can be transported for a distance of about one centimeter in the mycelium of Neurospora. One sulfonamide-requiring nucleus at a distance of about a centimeter from the tip might supply enough p-aminobenzoic acid for the growth of that tip. But as the tip grows, that nucleus might easily be left behind. A deficiency of p-aminobenzoic acid would then develop in the tip, and growth would be arrested unless a nucleus of the proper constitution happened to migrate into the tip.

Attempts to obtain rapidly growing heterocaryons involving the sulfonamide-requiring mutant and the sulfonamide-requiring, homocysteineless double mutant were unsuccessful. It may be that it is impossible to have a nuclear ratio which will produce sufficient, but not too much methionine, and at the same time sufficient threonine for the requirement of the heterocaryon.

Interpreting Suppressor Heterocaryosis Based on Model Experiments

The heterocaryons between the sulfonamide-requiring mutant and its double mutants with aminobenzoicless and homocysteineless were set up as models which should duplicate the behavior observed in the sulfonamide-requiring strain when suppressor mutations occurred, provided the interpretation placed on them was correct. For this purpose, the results obtained were gratifying. We should like to know just where each of the suppressor mutations studied fits into the biochemical scheme, but at present it can be shown only that they fit in a general way.

Four suppressors in the first lot of six (those illustrated in Fig. 12.4), which are the only ones that have been studied in any detail at all, apparently represent mutation at four different loci, though almost no direct tests for allelism are available. The inference that they are distinct genes is based on the data summarized in Table 12.2.

The reactions controlled by the suppressor genes have not been identified. Suppressor S-4 is stimulated in growth by additional p-aminobenzoic acid, and is inhibited considerably by sulfanilamide at concentrations twenty times less than that required to inhibit wild type. It is possible that a deficient amount of p-aminobenzoic acid is produced by this mutant, which would make it approximate the condition in one of the model heterocaryons. Growth of suppressor S-2 is somewhat stimulated by sulfanilamide (Fig. 12.4) and by threonine, in this respect resembling the sulfonamide-requiring mutant which it "suppresses." It is even more stimulated by the purine,

TABLE 12.2

EVIDENCE SUGGESTING THAT SUP-
PRESSORS S_1, S_2, S_4, AND S_6 ARE
DIFFERENT GENES

Suppressor	Second Division Segregation	Relation to 1633	Genetically Independent of
S_1	25%	none	....
S_2	50%	allele ?	....
S_4	0%	none	S_6
S_6	60%	none	S_4

adenine, as shown by the growth curves in Figure 12.7. It was previously known that in the presence of methionine, adenine reduces the normal requirement for p-aminobenzoic acid to about one-tenth its usual value. This suggested that the production of adenine also requires p-aminobenzoic acid. The reaction controlled by this suppressor may thus be closely related to that controlled by the sulfonamide-requiring gene. No clues have turned up to indicate how the reactions governed by the remaining suppressor mutations may be related to these.

In the living cell of Neurospora the reactions which are influenced in one way or another by the amount of available p-aminobenzoic acid must be fairly numerous. The production of adenine and methionine requires the presence of this vitamin as does the reaction in the sulfonamide-requiring mutant which makes threonine unavailable.

Strauss (1950) has studied a mutant strain (44602) which requires pyridoxine unless grown at high pH with ammonia as nitrogen source. He found that under the latter conditions it is inhibited by methionine, and that this inhibition is reversed by sulfanilamide, as if p-aminobenzoic acid were required for the inhibition. Still another interrelationship has been found by Shen (1950) in studies of a mutant strain (84605) which requires sulfur in a form at least as reduced as thiosulfate. At 35° it has no other requirement, but at 25° it needs reduced sulfur, generally supplied as the amino acid cysteine, and also tyrosine. When methionine is supplied as the source of sulfur at 25°, growth is strongly inhibited by choline. Under these conditions, choline does not inhibit at 35°, but there is an unexpected stimulation in growth by p-aminobenzoic acid at that temperature.

Mutant strains have been reported on two occasions which require either choline or p-aminobenzoic acid—choline may be the source of the methyl

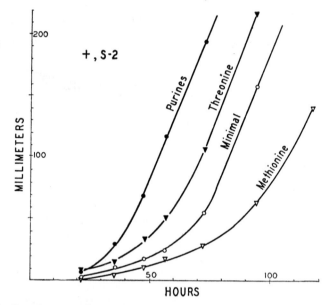

Fig. 12.7—Growth curves of suppressor mutant strain S-2 on minimal medium, on threonine (5 mg/100 ml), on methionine, and on purines (5 mg/100 ml each adenine sulfate and guanine hydrochloride) at 35°.

group of methionine. Strehler (1950) has reported a strain which requires either methionine or p-aminobenzoic acid. There is also a suggestion that p-aminobenzoic acid may be involved in the metabolism of lysine. In Neurospora this is suggested only because the double mutants between the sulfonamide-requiring strain and two different mutants which are unable to synthesize lysine do not grow on any combination of growth factors we have tried. In bacteria a strain has been found which requires either lysine or p-aminobenzoic acid as a growth factor (Koft et al., 1950), strengthening the supposition of a similar interrelationship in Neurospora.

These observations are referred to at this time because they indicate that there are a large number of metabolic reactions that are in one way or another related to the availability of p-aminobenzoic acid. These reactions must themselves be interrelated in the sense that an upset in one of them may have a strong effect on one or more of the others, possibly through changing the availability of p-aminobenzoic acid or a derivative. The model heterocaryon experiments described earlier show that it is possible for one mutation to cause an upset in one reaction and thus be detrimental to growth, and for a second mutation to restore conditions favorable to growth by actually interfering with a different reaction which is itself essential to growth, but which is interrelated with the first reaction. In the reactions related to the metabolism of p-aminobenzoic acid, there is sufficient complexity to account for the occurrence of a large number of different suppressors of the sulfonamide-requiring character.

DISCUSSION

It has been shown that increased vigor can result from heterocaryosis in which the two kinds of nuclei differ by only one pair of alleles. This may be true only under very special conditions such as have been present in the examples discussed. On the other hand, it is possible that the necessary conditions may be met with rather frequently in Neurospora, as suggested by the following examples.

In mutant strains which have specific requirements for particular amino acids, it is commonly found that their growth is inhibited by the presence of other amino acids which do not ordinarily interfere with growth. Some mutants which require an outside source of threonine are strongly inhibited by methionine, (Teas, Horowitz, and Fling, 1948). Mutants specifically requiring lysine are inhibited by arginine (Doermann, 1944), and so on. In each of these instances, the inhibition by a particular amino acid is competitively antagonized by the specific amino acid required by the strain in question. The growth of these mutants should be favored by a reduction in the amount of the inhibiting amino acid, as would occur if some of the nuclei carried a genetic block to its synthesis.

In extreme cases, the specific requirement for an amino acid may not result from a failure in its synthesis, but from an oversensitivity to the inhibiting amino acid. Thus, the sulfonamide-requiring strain can be said to be oversensitive to homocysteine in a way that leads to a requirement for threonine. One of the lysineless mutants (33933) seems to be oversensitive to arginine in much the same way. Heterocaryons having the lysineless gene in all nuclei, some of which also carry a genetic block to the synthesis of arginine (from strain 36703), make considerable growth on minimal medium, whereas neither the lysineless nor the double mutant does (Fig. 12.8).

Mary B. Mitchell (personal communication) recently observed that the stock cultures of certain lysineless mutants (4545, 15069, and 33933) had become less sensitive to inhibition by arginine. Tests of these showed that they were heterocaryons, some of whose nuclei were unchanged. Some carried mutant genes which lowered the sensitivity to arginine inhibition while leaving the requirement for lysine. These heterocaryons were more vigorous than the original lysineless strain, but no more vigorous than the pure double mutant strains extracted from the heterocaryons.

In studies on reverse mutation in a leucineless strain (33757), Ryan and Lederberg (1946) found that heterocaryons, whose nuclei differed only in

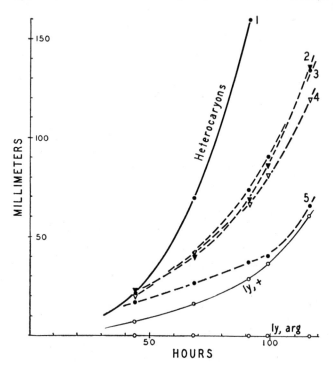

FIG. 12.8—Growth curves of heterocaryons between lysineless (*ly*, +) and lysineless, arginineless (*ly*, *arg*) strains of Neurospora at 35° on minimal medium. Curve 1: heterocaryon in which both nuclear types were of mating type A; curves 2 to 5: heterocaryons made up of nuclei of different mating types (*ly*, +, *A* and *ly*, *arg*, *a*)—*cf*. Beadle and Coonradt (1944).

that some carried the wild type allele and some the mutant allele of the leucineless gene, almost invariably reverted to the homocaryotic condition. By the time growth had reached the end of a tube containing minimal medium, nothing but wild type nuclei remained. In tubes containing limiting concentrations of leucine, nothing but leucineless nuclei were present after a short period of growth. This was under conditions where the growth rate of the leucineless strain is considerably less than that of wild type. Under both of these conditions, the heterocaryon is at a strong disadvantage compared to its components. It is not known whether or not there is a particular concentration of leucine which would favor the heterocaryon.

Houlahan and Mitchell (1948) have studied the interactions of mutant strains involved in the metabolism of pyrimidines and lysine. A pyrimidine-less mutant (37301) has a specific requirement for pyrimidine. There is a suppressor of this mutant which enables it to grow without added pyrimidine, unless arginine is also added, whereupon the pyrimidine requirement is restored. One lysineless strain (33933) can utilize α-amino adipic acid in place of lysine. As a double mutant with the pyrimidine suppressor, it can still use α-amino adipic acid, but requires four times as much as the simple lysine-less strain unless small amounts of arginine, or an arginine precursor, are added. The double mutant combining this lysineless with the pyrimidineless mutant is unable to use α-amino adipic acid unless a small amount of lysine is added—arginine is ineffective in this instance. A second lysineless mutant (4545), which has a specific requirement for lysine and which secretes pyrimidines into the medium, behaves in a predictable fashion as a double mutant with pyrimidineless, or its suppressor, but not as the triple mutant lysineless, pyrimidineless, suppressor of pyrimidineless. Instead of requiring only lysine for growth, this triple mutant also requires pyrimidines and arginine. This example is cited as another in which metabolic interactions may be as complex as in those discussed earlier which depend in one way or another on *p*-aminobenzoic acid.

Applicability to Classical Heterosis

Observations relating to one-gene heterosis in higher plants are discussed in other papers in this series (Crow, Hull, Jones, and Whaley). Studies of Neurospora heterocaryons have shown that a very similar phenomenon occurs under certain special physiological conditions. In a particular genetic background, the amount of an essential metabolite normally produced has deleterious consequences which are removed by reducing the dosage of a gene responsible for the production of that metabolite. This reduction was brought about through heterocaryosis in the studies reported, but it should also result from heterozygosis under similar physiological conditions. There is nothing in the studies of heterocaryosis in Neurospora to suggest that one-gene heterosis is of general occurrence and importance, or that other examples should have similar biochemical backgrounds.

TH. DOBZHANSKY
Columbia University

Chapter 13

Nature and Origin of Heterosis

Exploitation of heterosis in cultivated plants and animals is to date by far the most important application of the science of genetics in agricultural practice. It is therefore unfortunate that few of the studies so far made on heterosis go beyond crudely empirical observations and descriptions and that little effort is being made to understand the underlying causes of the phenomena involved. Such an understanding is needed particularly because the advances of general genetics make it evident that several quite distinct, and even scarcely related, phenomena are confused under the common label of *heterosis* or *hybrid vigor*.

In what follows, an attempt is made to indicate briefly what seem, to the writer, promising lines of approach to a classification and study of the various kinds of heterosis. The tentative nature of the classification here suggested is fully realized. But it is believed that this classification may nevertheless serve a useful function if it directs the attention of the students of heterosis to factors which are only too often overlooked.

MUTATIONAL EUHETEROSIS

Perhaps the simplest kind of true heterosis—*euheterosis*—is that which results from sheltering of deleterious recessive mutants by their adaptively superior dominant alleles in populations of sexually reproducing and cross-fertilizing organisms.

Although only a small fraction of the existing species of organisms have been investigated genetically, it is reasonable to assume that mutational changes arise from time to time in all species, albeit at different rates. Furthermore, a great majority of the mutations that arise are deleterious, and lower the fitness of their carriers to survive or to reproduce in some or in all

218

environments. This deleterious character of most mutations seems surprising, especially because in modern biology the process of mutation is regarded as the source of the raw materials from which evolutionary changes are constructed.

A little consideration shows, however, that the adaptively negative character of most mutations is by no means unexpected. Indeed, since every mutation has a finite probability to occur in any generation, the mutants which we observe in our fields and laboratories must have arisen many times in the history of the species. The rare mutants which confer adaptive advantages on their possessors in the environments in which the species normally lives have had the chance to become established in the species populations as components of the *normal* species genotype. In a more or less static environment, the genotypes of most species are close to the upper attainable level of adaptedness.

The above argument may seem to prove too much. In the absence of useful mutants, evolution would come to a standstill. The paradox is resolved if we recall that the environment is rarely static for any considerable periods of time. Furthermore, most living species occur not in a single but in several related environments. Genotypes which are adaptively valuable in a certain environment may be ill adapted in other environments, and vice versa. It should be possible then to observe the occurrence of useful mutations if we place the experimental organisms in environments in which their ancestors did not live.

Progressive improvement of domesticated animals and plants in the hands of breeders constitutes evidence that useful mutations do occur. The genetic variants which are being made use of by breeders have arisen ultimately through mutation. These mutations have been arising from time to time, before as well as after the domestication. But while they were deleterious in the wild state, some of them happened to be suitable from the standpoint of the breeders. They were useful in the man-made environment or they were useful to man. Favorable mutations can be observed also in wild species, provided that the latter are placed in unusual external or genetic environments. This has been demonstrated in experiments of Spassky and the writer on *Drosophila pseudoobscura*. Several laboratory strains of this fly were subjected to intense selection for fifty consecutive generations, and improvements of the viability have been observed in most of them.

Many, perhaps most, deleterious mutants are nearly or completely recessive. Others are more or less dominant to the "normal," or ancestral, state. The fate of the dominant deleterious mutants in populations of sexually reproducing and cross-fertilizing species is different from that of the recessives. By definition, deleterious mutants in wild species lower the fitness of their carriers to survive or to reproduce, and in cultivated species impair the qualities considered desirable by the breeders. Natural and artificial selection will consequently tend to lower the frequency, or to eliminate deleterious mutants.

Selection against a dominant deleterious mutant is, however, a far more efficient process than that against a recessive mutant. This is because deleterious recessive mutant genes are sheltered from selection by normal dominant alleles in heterozygotes. Deleterious dominants are eliminated by selection within relatively few generations after their origin. Deleterious recessives accumulate in heterozygotes until their frequencies become so high that recessive homozygotes are produced. Dominant alleles are not intrinsically beneficial, and recessives are not necessarily deleterious. But at any one time, we find in cross-fertilizing populations more deleterious recessives than deleterious dominants, because the former are not eliminated by selection as promptly as the latter.

Analysis of wild populations of several species of Drosophila has revealed extensive infestation of the germ plasm by deleterious recessive mutant genes. According to the unpublished data of Payan and collaborators, 41 per cent of the second chromosomes in Brazilian populations of *Drosophila willistoni* are lethal or semilethal when homozygous. Among the remainder, 57 per cent are sublethal when homozygous. Furthermore, 31 per cent of the second chromosomes make the homozygotes completely sterile in at least one sex, 32 per cent retard the development, and 16 per cent cause various visible abnormalities. Comparable figures for the third chromosomes are 32 per cent of lethals and semilethals, 49 per cent subvitals, 28 per cent steriles, 36 per cent retarded, and 16 per cent containing visible mutants. Since every fly has two second and two third chromosomes, it is easily seen that a great majority of individuals in Brazilian populations carry several deleterious variants in heterozygous condition.

The mass of deleterious recessives carried in normally breeding natural populations has no disastrous effects on the average fitness of members of such populations. This is because the frequency of recessive homozygotes found in a population at equilibrium is equal to the number of the corresponding recessive mutants that arise in every generation. The loss of fitness caused in a normally breeding population by dominant and by recessive mutants is thus proportional to the frequency of the origin of these mutants by mutation.

The situation changes completely if a normally crossbred population is subjected to inbreeding. For inbreeding renders homozygous many recessives that would remain sheltered in heterozygotes under normal crossbreeding. These recessives become suddenly exposed to natural, or to artificial, selection. The loss of fitness in inbred lines of normally cross-fertilized species is the consequence. Conversely, the heterosis observed in the progeny of intercrossed inbred lines is the outcome of restoring the normal reproductive biology and the normal population structure of the species.

BALANCED EUHETEROSIS

Balanced heterosis is due to the occurrence of a rather special class of mutations and gene combinations, which confer on heterozygotes a higher adaptive value, or a higher agricultural usefulness than is found in the corresponding homozygotes.

The conditions most frequently found in heterozygotes are either dominance and recessiveness, when the heterozygote is more or less similar to one of the homozygotes, or phenotypical intermediacy between the homozygotes. A heterozygote may, however, be in some respects phenotypically more extreme than either homozygote. Thus, a heterozygote may be more viable, more productive, or otherwise exceed both homozygotes in some positive or negative quality. This condition is sometimes spoken of as overdominance (Hull).

Although overdominance is, by and large, an exceptional situation, it is of particular interest to a student of population genetics, and especially to a student of heterosis. Suppose that a certain gene is represented in a population by a series of alleles, A^1, A^2, A^3 . . . which are deleterious in homozygous condition, A^1A^1, A^2A^2, A^3A^3 . . . , but which show a relatively higher fitness in heterozygotes A^1A^2, A^1A^3, A^2A^3 . . . , etc. Natural or artificial selection would preserve in the population all the variants A^1, A^2, A^3 . . . , regardless of how poorly adapted the homozygotes may be. In fact, one or all homozygotes may be semilethal or even lethal, and yet selection will establish an equilibrium at which every one of the variants will be present with a definite frequency. This equilibrium can easily be calculated if the selective disadvantages of the homozygotes, compared to the heterozygotes, are known. The resulting situation is referred to as balanced polymorphism.

Balanced polymorphism may be produced by mutations in single genes, provided that the heterozygotes exhibit overdominance in fitness in some environments. This has been demonstrated, among others, by Gustafsson and Nybom. They observed several mutations in barley that were deleterious in homozygotes, but produced heterozygotes superior to the ancestral "normal" homozygotes. Ford and others showed that certain color variants in butterflies, which are inherited as though caused by a single genetic change, are maintained in natural populations by the same mechanism.

Detailed data are available on balanced polymorphism in several species of Drosophila, in which natural populations are very often polymorphic for gene arrangements in some chromosomes. These gene arrangements differ in inversions of blocks of genes. Thus, in certain populations of *Drosophila pseudoobscura* from Southern California, at least 70 per cent of the wild individuals are inversion heterozygotes. In populations of *Drosophila willistoni* from central Brazil (Goyaz), an average individual is heterozygous for as many as nine inversions, and very few individuals are homozygous.

Now, it has been shown by observation both on natural and on experimental populations of some Drosophila species, that the heterozygotes for the naturally occurring inversions possess considerable adaptive advantages over the homozygotes. For example, taking the adaptive value of the heterozygotes for ST and CH inversions in *Drosophila pseudoobscura* to be unity, the adaptive values of the ST/ST and CH/CH homozygotes are about 0.8 and 0.4 respectively. Further, it has been shown that the heterosis in the ST/CH heterozygotes occurs only if the constituent chromosomes are derived from the same population, or from populations of nearby localities. Chromosomes with the same gene arrangements, ST and CH, derived from remote localities (such as Central and Southern California, or Southern California and Mexico) exhibit little or no heterosis.

This finding is most compatible with the assumption that the overdominance in fitness observed in the heterozygotes is the property not of a single gene locus, or of a chromosome structure, but rather of integrated systems of polygenes. Such polygenic systems are coadapted by natural selection to other polygene complexes present in the same populations. The role of the chromosomal inversions in the formation of the heterotic state of balanced polymorphism is due to the suppression of crossing over caused by most inversions, at least in Drosophila. Elimination of crossing over prevents the breakup of the adaptively integrated polygene complexes which are carried in the chromosomes involved.

It should be noted that adaptively integrated polygene complexes can be maintained in crossbreeding populations with the aid of genetic mechanisms other than chromosomal inversions. Any factor which restricts or prevents crossing over in chromosomes, or parts of chromosomes, can accomplish the same biological function. Localization of chiasmata may be such a factor. If, for example, chiasmata are found chiefly or exclusively at some definite points in a chromosome, the genes carried in the sections which intervene between these points are inherited in blocks. Such gene blocks may act exactly as gene complexes bound together by inversions.

Balanced heterosis differs profoundly from mutational heterosis. The latter is due simply to the sheltering of deleterious recessive mutants by their dominant alleles. Balanced heterosis is a result of overdominance. Mutational heterosis is a protective device of a sexual species with a certain population structure against the mutation pressure. Balanced heterosis is an evolutionary contrivance that permits maintenance in a population of a multiplicity of genotypes that may be adaptive in different ecological niches which the population occupies.

LUXURIANCE

Mutational and balanced heterosis resemble each other in one important respect—both are normal adaptive states attained in outbred sexual species as a result of an evolutionary history controlled by natural or by artificial selection. The normal heterotic state can be disrupted by sudden inbreeding, which is evidently a disturbance of the reproductive biology to which the species is adjusted. The heterotic state can also be restored by intercrossing the inbred lines. This is true heterosis, or euheterosis. Euheterosis is a form of evolutionary adaptation characteristic of sexually reproducing and cross-fertilizing species.

Numerous instances are known, however, when hybrids between species, neither of which can be regarded as inbred, are larger, faster growing, or otherwise exceeding the parental forms in some quality. Similar *luxuriance* is observed in some hybrids between normally self-fertilizing species, races, or strains. This kind of luxuriance of hybrids cannot be ascribed to sheltering of deleterious recessive mutants, because the latter are sheltered in the parental populations. It is also unlikely to arise from overdominance since, at least in wild species, natural selection would be expected to have induced such balanced heterosis in the parental species or strains.

Luxuriance is, from the evolutionary standpoint, an accidental condition brought about by complementary action of genes found in the parental form crossed. Two sets of facts are important in this connection. First, in cases of luxuriance there is usually no indication whatever that the luxuriant hybrids would prove adaptively superior in competition with the parental forms in the natural habitats of the latter. Second, luxuriance appears to be more frequently encountered in domesticated than in wild species.

It stands to reason that increase in body size, or in growth rate, is by no means always an adaptively superior change. To equate size with vigor, fitness, or adaptive value would be a height of anthropomorphic naïveté. The rate of growth and the size attained by an organism in its normal environments are evidently controlled by natural selection. Excessive as well as deficient sizes are adaptively about equally disadvantageous. The checks upon excessively rapid growth and excessive size are, however, very often relaxed under domestication. In man-controlled environments those qualities often become desirable from the standpoint of the breeder if not from that of the organism. Luxuriance is, really, pseudoheterosis.

DONALD F. JONES

Connecticut Agricultural Experiment Station

Chapter 14

Plasmagenes and Chromogenes in Heterosis

The word *heterosis* is essentially a contraction of the phrase *stimulus of heterozygosis*. It was first used by G. H. Shull (1914). The concept of a stimulation resulting from the genetic union of unlike elements was developed by East (1909). Previous to the Mendelian conception of units of heredity, it was generally considered by plant and animal breeders that the invigorating effect of crossing unlike varieties of plants and breeds of livestock was due to the correction of imperfections that existed in both parental types. This idea is clearly stated by Samuel Johnson in the second edition of his book *How Crops Grow* (1891).

The early recordings of instances of hybrid vigor and the various means of accounting for this phenomenon have been stated and restated so many times that there is no need or useful purpose in repeating them here. Excellent reviews of the literature are readily available (see especially East and Hayes, 1912; Jones, 1918; East and Jones, 1919; East, 1936; and Whaley, 1944).

THE EXPRESSION OF HETEROSIS

At the present time, the term *heterosis* designates the increased growth or other augmented action resulting from crossing, however it is produced. As generally used, it is essentially synonymous with *hybrid vigor*. Heterosis has two general modes of expression. In one, there is an increase in size or number of parts. This is usually the result of a greater number of cells and a faster rate of cell division and cell activities. This results in an improvement in general well-being of the organism similar to the result of being placed in a more favorable environment. Such luxuriance may be accompanied by partial or complete sterility in diverse crosses.

A somewhat different manifestation of heterosis is an increase in biological efficiency, such as reproductive rate and survival ability. This may even be shown with a reduction in productiveness as measured by economic characters. Some confusion has arisen by not distinguishing clearly between these two different manifestations of heterosis.

In addition to these two general types of heterotic effects, there may also be a reduction in both growth and survival ability; in other words, hybrid weakness or a reversed or negative heterosis. This effect is much less common and is seldom found in cultivated plants and domesticated animals.

TYPES OF GENE ACTION

An understanding of the mode of action of heterosis has now resolved into a study of the nature of gene action. The genes usually used to illustrate Mendelism are the loss variations that have a major effect such as the inability to produce some essential substance. This results in a block in the normal chemical processes, finally resulting in an individual of greatly altered appearance, size, or ability to survive. The effect ranges in intensity from a completely lethal condition at some stage of development, up to individuals that differ only slightly in appearance from normal with no appreciable reduction in growth or survival ability. Such genes are illustrated by the long lists of Mendelizing characters now tabulated for maize, Drosophila, mice, and many other animals, plants, and lower organisms.

DOMINANT AND RECESSIVE GENES

In these cases, the normal allele is usually designated by a capital letter, with the mutant, deficient allele denoted by the corresponding lower case letter. In comparison with the normal allele, the recessive mutants are deficient in some respect. In their inability to produce certain specific substances, as shown in the haploid Neurospora by Beadle and his co-workers, they are referred to as A-less, B-less, C-less, etc. In diploid organisms A is usually completely dominant over $a;$ that is, one A allele functions as well or nearly as well as two.

There is no question that the accumulation in a hybrid of the normal alleles of this type results in heterosis. In the simplest example of a cross of A-less by B-less ($aaBB \times AAbb$) the hybrid offspring are all $AaBb$, and essentially normal for whatever effect A and B have. But since the mutant recessive alleles of this type are so drastic in their effect, most of these deficiencies are removed by natural selection in all species whether self-fertilized or cross-fertilized. Therefore they have little part in the heterosis that is shown by these organisms when crossed. Furthermore, genes of this type are eliminated when naturally cross-fertilized species, such as maize, are artificially self-pollinated. Yet such inbred strains show the largest amounts of heterosis.

There is evidence, as will be shown later, that there are many genes of this type having small effects that are not eliminated by natural or artificial selection either in the wild or under domestication, and that these deficiencies or degenerative mutants do have a large part in bringing about reduced growth. Before presenting this evidence, there are other types of gene action that should be considered.

CHROMOSOMAL DELETIONS

In addition to the recessive mutant alleles that are deficient as compared to their normal alleles, there are also chromosomal deletions which result in the complete elimination of the normal locus. Large deletions are usually lethal and are quickly eliminated. Small deletions that cannot be detected cytologically are haplo-viable, and may persist indefinitely if they are closely linked with essential loci. Changes of this type have been demonstrated by McClintock (1931) and by Stadler (1933). They cannot be readily distinguished from recessive mutants of the A-less type. In fact there may be no difference. In practically all cases they show varying amounts of germ cell abortion, and do not mutate back to normal. Deletions of this type are designated Ao.

DOMINANT UNFAVORABLE GENES

In many cases of deletion the heterozygote, or the hemizygote, is visibly and unfavorably altered from normal, in which event the genes involved are listed as dominant, and if partially viable they can bring about negative heterosis or hybrid weakness. It is not known whether all dominant unfavorable genes are deletions of this type, but as far as their effect on heterosis is concerned it makes little difference whether or not they are. An illustration of this type of gene action may be seen in a cross of Ragged and Knotted maize plants. Both of these genes result in a marked reduction in growth in the heterozygous condition. They are not completely lethal in the homozygous dominant condition, but seldom produce seed or pollen. When both dominant genes are present together in the heterozygous condition, there is a marked reduction in size, rate of growth, and reproductive ability as compared with either parental type.

Tunicate, teopod, and corn grass are also dominant genes that reduce grain yields in both the homozygous and heterozygous condition. They are probably reversions to a primitive condition which in suitable genetic combinations may be favorable to survival in the wild. Dunn and Caspari (1945) describe many structural abnormalities in mice that seem to be due to deletions having a dominant effect in the hemizygote. Some of these counteract each other and tend to restore a more normal condition, while others accumulate unfavorable effects. A similar situation has been reported in Drosophila by Stern (1948).

In addition to recessive deletions with a dominant effect in the heterozygote, there are also dominant inhibitors that have no indication of being deletions, but do prevent other genes from having their usual expression. Most of these inhibitors control color characters and are usually not involved in heterosis. If they were, there would be more negative heterosis than actually is found.

GENES WITHOUT DOMINANCE

Unlike the visible Mendelizing genes with their clear-cut dominance and unfavorable action of one or the other allele, there are many genes that differentiate size or number of parts, time of flowering and maturing. These are the genes usually involved in normal variation. They are the ones the plant and animal breeder are mainly concerned with and could expect to have a major effect on heterosis. Since neither member of an allelic pair can be considered abnormal or deficient, both are designated with a capital letter with some prefix to differentiate them, as for example A and A^1.

Genes of this type usually have simple additive effects such as the Y endosperm color gene in maize, in which each allele adds a definite increment in total carotene content. Such additive genes without dominance are used to interpret the inheritance of quantitative characters which have been shown to segregate and recombine in a Mendelian manner.

No clear distinction can be made between the Aa and AA^1 types of genes and this has led to much confusion. The first class shows complete or nearly complete dominance. The second shows no dominance or very little dominance, but one type integrates into the other. The principal question at issue is whether either type shows over-dominance, or in other words, an interaction between alleles such that $Aa > AA$ or aa or $AA^1 > AA$ or A^1A^1. Before considering the evidence for or against over-dominance, two remaining types of genes should be considered.

CHROMOSOMAL REARRANGEMENTS

By chromosomal rearrangements such as inversions and translocations, genes without alteration are placed in different spatial relations with other genes. In their altered position they have different effects. Dobzhansky and his associates have studied many geographical races of Drosophila that differ by chromosomal rearrangements. Crosses between these chromosomal types from the same region exhibit heterosis, whereas the same chromosomal type from different regions do not show such a high degree of heterosis. This seems not to be a position effect, but is the result of an accumulation of gene differences that are protected from random distribution by the prevention of crossing over in hybrids of different chromosomal types.

COMPOUND GENES AND GENES WITH MULTIPLE EFFECTS

In many organisms, loci are known which have different effects on different parts of the organism. In maize the A, P, and R genes have been studied in considerable detail by Stadler and his co-workers. These loci each have a series of alleles that produce characteristic color patterns and intensities of colors in different parts of the plant such as culm, leaf sheath, leaf blade, glumes, anthers, silks, cob and pericarp, and endosperm. They may be considered either as genes located so closely together that they never show crossing over, or compound genes with multiple effects. Without going into the evidence for or against these two hypotheses, it is obvious that compound genes can have an important part in heterosis if they control growth processes. More information is needed on the specific effect of compound genes.

In Godetia a series of multiple alleles has been described by Hiorth (1940) that is often cited as an illustration of an interaction between alleles producing an effect analogous to heterosis. Actually these are color determiners that control pigment production in different parts of the flower quite similar to the A, P, and R loci in maize. Each allele has a different manifestation, and all tend to accumulate color in the heterozygotes.

The familiar notation of a chromosome as a linear arrangement of loci, each of which is the site of a single gene with one effect function, is probably an oversimplification of the actual condition. It is difficult to see how an organism could have originated in this way. It is more likely that a chromosome is an association of primitive organisms of varying types and functions. These primitive organisms found it to be an advantage in the evolutionary process to become associated in some such process as the colonial organisms now exhibit. This association has undergone very great modification and ramifications, but the compound genes may be vestigial structures of such an association, differing greatly in size, arrangement, and function. Many of them still retain some independence, and when removed from their normal position in the chromosome could function as plasmagene or viroid bodies.

These compound genes may undergo mutation and possibly recombination or reorganization within themselves, but crossing over takes place for the most part only between these compound structures. Compound genes also arise by unequal crossing over and duplication of loci are shown by the Bar eye gene in Drosophila and others of similar type.

In addition to compound or multiple genes, there are single genes with multiple effects. Many of these are important in growth processes and are illustrated by chlorophyll production in maize studied by H. L. Everett (1949). One major gene is essential for the production of carotene. In the recessive condition the seeds are pale yellow in color, in a normal, dark yellow seeded variety. The young seedlings grown from these pale yellow seeds are devoid of chlorophyll. The recessive allele is therefore lethal. By using the pale yellow endosperm as a convenient marker and crossing with a number of standard field corn inbreds, it has been found that these inbreds differ widely in their normal chorophyll mechanism. Many of them have genes that can restore normal chorophyll production without restoring the production of carotene in the seed. Other genes restore chlorophyll production only partially (see Table 14.1). Hybrid combinations that bring these genes together are appreciably more efficient in chlorophyll production than combinations that lack some of them. However one of these dominant alleles has a suppressing effect on chlorophyll development. The combination of all of these chlorophyll genes so far studied is not the most productive. There are many genes of this type that block chemical syntheses, that are not lethal in the usual genetic assembly, but which combine to give a cumulative efficiency in most cases.

Lethal genes which show complete dominance of the normal allele would have no effect on heterosis other than to reduce the number of offspring. Such

TABLE 14.1

GENES CONTROLLING CHLOROPHYLL PRO-
DUCTION IN MAIZE*

Cl_1	Cl_2	Cl_3	Seed Color	Chlor. Grade	Viability
−	−	−	Pale	Albino	Lethal
−	+	−	Pale	Virescent	Lethal
−	−	+	Pale	Light green	Normal
−	+	+	Pale	Light green	Normal
+	−	−	Yellow	Light green	Normal
+	+	−	Yellow	Med. green	Normal
+	+	+	Yellow	Dark green	Normal
+	−	+	Yellow	?	Normal

* Data from H. L. Everett.

genes would be just as effective in the homozygous as the heterozygous condition. Genes that have any part in the type of heterosis that is manifested in increased growth must be viable and have some degree of dominance. In other words, Aa must be greater than $\frac{1}{2} AA$. Aa may even be greater in its effect than AA or aa in which case theoretically there is over-dominance, but very little specific evidence is available to show that such a situation actually exists.

I can see no way in which it is possible to separate over-dominance from a stimulus of heterozygosis. They seem to be different ways of saying the same thing. The essential point at issue at the present time is whether or not over-dominance actually occurs, and if so, how important this is in the total amount of heterosis in addition to the known accumulation of favorable dominant effects.

INTERACTION BETWEEN ALLELES

Evidence has been presented from many sources bearing on the problem of over-dominance and interaction between different alleles. Much of the argument is based on mathematical treatment of data that require many assumptions. What is needed is more specific evidence where the effect of multiple genes can be ruled out. Very few specific examples of single gene action are available.

In one case studied by the writer there is clear evidence for an interaction between alleles (Jones, 1921). A mutation in a variety of normally self-fertilized tobacco changed a determinate plant into an indeterminate, non-flowering variation. It was a change in the normal response to the summer day length period. The mutant plants failed to flower in the normal growing season and continued in a vegetative condition. Reciprocal crosses between the mutant and normal types both grew at the same rate as the normal plants showing complete dominance of the normal growth rate. The heterozygous plants continued their vegetative growth longer and produced taller plants with more leaves and flowers than the normal homozygous plants. This result I consider not to be heterosis, since there was no increase in growth rate. It is merely an interaction between alleles to produce a result that is different from either parent. There are undoubtedly many allelic interactions of this type. Whether or not they can be considered to contribute to heterosis is largely a matter of opinion.

Other cases in corn where heterosis resulted from degenerative changes (Jones, 1945) were at first assumed to be single allelic differences, since they originated as mutations in inbred and highly homozygous families. The degenerate alterations were expressed as narrow leaves, dwarf plants, crooked stalks, reduced chlorophyll, and late flowering. All of these mutant variations gave larger amount of growth in a shorter period of time and clearly showed heterosis.

The further study of this material has not been completed, but the results to date indicate that the differences involved are not single genes. Both the extracted homozygous recessives and the extracted homozygous dominants from these crosses are larger than the corresponding plants that originally went into the crosses.

This indicates quite clearly that the visible changes were accompanied or preceded by other changes with no noticeable effects, but which are expressed in growth rates. A more complete summary of these results will have to wait until all of the evidence is at hand. It is a simple matter to extract the homozygous recessives from these crosses, but it is difficult to extract the homozygous dominants. Many of the self-fertilized plants proved to be heterozygous.

GENES CONTROLLING GROWTH

Additional evidence that there are a large number of genes having small effects on growth without visible morphological changes is becoming clearly apparent from a backcrossing experiment now in progress. Several long inbred lines of corn, one of which is now in the forty-first generation of continuous self-fertilization, were outcrossed to unrelated inbred lines having dominant gene markers which could be easily selected. The markers—red cob, yellow endosperm, and non-glossy seedlings—were chosen because they had little or no effect on growth of the plant.

The first generation outcrosses showed the usual large increases in size of plant, time of flowering, and yield of grain that is expected in crosses of unrelated inbred strains of corn. The hybrid plants were backcrossed as seed parents with pollen from the inbred with the recessive gene marker. In every generation, plants with the dominant gene marker were selected for backcrossing. These plants have now been backcrossed six successive times. Many progenies have been grown. They are all heterozygous for the gene marker plus whatever neighboring regions on the same original chromosome from the non-recurrent parent that have not been lost by crossing over.

The plan is to continue the backcrossing until no measurable differences remain between the backcrossed plants and the recurrent parent, or between the two classes of backcrossed individuals in the same backcrossed progeny, those with the dominant marker and those with the recessive marker. When the point is reached where no differences can be detected, the plan is to compare successive earlier generations from remnant seed to pick up whatever single gene differences there might be that could be measured and detected by their segregation.

So far both classes of backcrossed plants in nearly all progenies are taller and flower earlier, showing that they have not been completely converged to the parental type (see Table 14.2). The differences are small and not statistically significant in the tests so far made, but are nearly all in the direction of a heterotic effect. As yet there are not sufficient data to base final conclusions. It is hoped that the comparison of the two classes of backcrossed progeny with the original recessive parent will permit a distinction between the favorable action of dominant genes and an interaction between heterozygous alleles. Also that it may be possible to show whether or not there is any residual cytoplasmic effect, since some of the outcrossed plants have the same cytoplasm as the dominant gene marker and some do not.

Important facts do stand out clearly from this experiment. Since heterosis still remains after these many generations of backcrossing, it shows clearly that these three chromosome regions selected as samples have an appreciable effect on growth. Since the gene markers themselves have no effect on growth, as far as this can be determined in other material, these three regions are random selections for growth effects. This indicates quite clearly that there are genes in all parts of the chromosomes that contribute to normal growth and development. While the evidence so far available does not permit a clear separation between the effects of an accumulation of favorable genes as contrasted to an interaction between alleles, or between genes and cytoplasm, the results show that there are many loci involved in the heterotic effect in addition to the dominant gene markers.

This follows from the evidence at hand. If the heterosis now remaining were due solely to the interaction between the dominant and recessive markers, there would have been a rapid approach to the level of vigor now remaining. If it were due to a larger number of genes distributed rather evenly along the chromosome, the reduction in heterosis would be gradual, as it has proved to be. Small amounts of heterosis may persist for a long time until all of the genes contributing to it are removed by crossing over.

A recent experiment by Stringfield (1950) shows a difference in productiveness between an F_2 selfed generation and a backcross having the same parentage. The amount of heterozygosis as measured by the number of allelic pairs is the same in both lots. In the backcross there are more individuals in the intermediate classes with respect to the number of dominant

TABLE 14.2

INCREASE IN HEIGHT OF PLANT IN SUCCES-
SIVE BACKCROSSED GENERATIONS HET-
EROZYGOUS FOR A DOMINANT GENE
MARKER

NUMBER OF GENERATIONS BACKCROSSED→	PER CENT INCREASE IN HEIGHT		
	4	5	6
20y×243Y.......	6.7	2.2	1.5
20y×P8 Y.......	1.9	2.3	1.2
20p×243 P......	6.6	3.0	1.1
243gl×20Gl.....	....	....	−1.3

genes. This indicates a complementary action of favorable dominant genes.

Gowen et al. (1946) compared the differences in egg yield in Drosophila between random matings, 47 generations of sib mating, and homozygous matings by outcrossing with marker genes. The differences are significant, and indicate a large number of genes having dominant effects on the reproductive rate.

INTERACTION OF GENES AND CYTOPLASM

The suggestion has been made many times that heterosis may result from an interaction between genes and cytoplasm. Within the species, differences in reciprocal crosses are rare. In commercial corn hybrids, reciprocal differences are so small that they can usually be ignored. Evidence is accumulating that there are transmissible differences associated with the cytoplasm, and that these must be considered in a study of heterosis. Small maternal effects are difficult to distinguish from nutritional and other influences determined by the genotype of the mother and carried over to the next generation.

The cross of the two different flowering types of tobacco previously cited shows a maternal effect. The first generation cross of the indeterminate or non-flowering type as seed parent grows taller than the reciprocal combination, and flowers later. These differences are statistically significant.

Reciprocal crosses between inbred California Rice pop, having the smallest seeds known in corn, with inbred Indiana Wf9 having large embryos and endospersms, show differences in early seedling growth and in tillering. Inbred Wf9 produces no tillers. California Rice, also inbred, produces an average of 4.1 tillers per plant. The first generation cross of Rice pop×Wf9 averages 1.0 tillers, while the reciprocal combination under the same conditions produced 2.2 tillers per stalk. In this case the non-tillering variety, when used as the seed parent, produces more than twice as many tillers. This seems to be a carry-over effect of the large seed. Tillering is largely determined by early seedling vigor. Anything that induces rapid development in the early stages of growth tends to promote tillering.

PLASMAGENES AND CHROMOGENES

In addition to these transitory effects there are many cases of cytoplasmic inheritance. Caspari (1948) has reviewed the evidence from fungi, mosses, the higher plants, and from Paramecium, insects, and mammals to show that many differences do occur in reciprocal crosses and that they persist into later backcrossed generations. Reciprocal differences in the amount of heterosis have been demonstrated in Epilobium (Michaelis, 1939) and in mice (Marshak, 1936).

Cytoplasmic pollen sterility has been found in Oenothera, Streptocarpus, Epilobium, flax, maize, onions, sugar beets, and carrots. In every case that has been adequately studied, the basic sterility remains the same in repeated generations of backcrossing, but the amount of pollen produced varies in different genotypes. There is an interrelation between plasmagenes and chromogenes determining the final result (Jones, 1950).

In maize the amount of pollen produced ranges from 0 to 100 per cent. Only by suitable tests can these cases of full fertility be recognized as having any cytoplasmic basis. Interest in this problem now centers on the effect of these cytoplasmic differences on heterosis.

A series of standard inbreds have been converted by crossing these onto suitable sterilizer stocks, and backcrossing a sufficient number of generations to re-establish completely the inbred, and maintaining the inbred in a sterile condition by continuous backcrossing. It has been found necessary to select both the cytoplasmic sterile seed parent individuals and the individual fertile pollen parents for their ability to maintain complete sterility both in inbreds and in crosses. In some lines it has proved to be impossible to establish complete sterility, but the majority are easily sterilized and maintained in that condition.

A comparison of fertile and sterile progenies in inbreds, in single crosses of two inbreds, and multiple crosses of three and four inbreds, shows that this cytoplasmic difference has no appreciable effect on size of plant as measured by height at the end of the season, in days to silking, or in yield of grain. The results are given in Table 14.3. With respect to pollen sterility-fertility, the cytoplasm has no effect on heterosis.

In the conversion of standard inbreds to the cytoplasmic sterile pollen condition, it has been found that many of these long inbred strains, presumably highly homozygous, are segregating for chromogenes that have the ability to restore pollen fertility. In normally fertile plants these genes have no way of expressing themselves. They are not selected for or against unless they contribute in some way to normal pollen production. It is one more

TABLE 14.3

A COMPARISON OF FERTILE AND STERILE MAIZE PLANTS

	Fertile	Sterile	
5 Inbreds...............	72.3	70.1	Height of stalk
7 Crosses of two inbreds...	102.6	97.7	Height of stalk
7 Crosses of two inbreds...	58.5	58.3	Days to first silk
3 Crosses of three inbreds.	111.7	108.9	Yield, bushels per acre
1 Cross of three inbreds. . .	99.1	103.3	Yield, bushels per acre
3 Crosses of four inbreds	123.9	119.0	Yield, bushels per acre
5 Crosses of four inbreds..	61.1	64.5	Yield, bushels per acre
2 Crosses of four inbreds ..	115.8	117.3	Yield, bushels per acre
14 Crosses, average yield....	102.8	102.6	Yield, bushels per acre

source of evidence to show that there is a considerable amount of enforced heterozygosity in maize. Even highly inbred families remain heterozygous. This has been shown to be true for other species of plants and animals.

SUMMARY

Specific evidence from a study of chlorophyll production in maize and from similar studies in Neurospora, Drosophila, and other plant and animal species proves conclusively that there are numerous mutant genes that reduce the ability of the organism to grow and to survive. Such genes exist in naturally self-fertilized and cross-fertilized organisms and in artificially inbred families such as maize. The normal alleles of these mutant genes show either complete or partial dominance, and any crossbred individual contains a larger number of these dominant, favorable alleles than any inbred individual.

Evidence from Nicotiana shows that there is an interaction between divergent alleles at the same locus such that the heterozygote produces a larger amount of growth and a higher reproductive rate than either homozygote. There is no increase in growth rate and this instance is considered not to be heterosis. The assumption of an increased growth rate, or true heterosis, in such allelic interactions is not supported by specific evidence that cannot be interpreted in other ways. The experimental evidence to date does not distinguish clearly between a general physiological interaction and a specific contribution from favorable dominant effects. More evidence on this point is needed.

Backcrossing experiments in maize, where dominant gene markers are maintained in a heterozygous condition, show heterosis continuing to the sixth generation. The approach to the level of growth activity of the recurrent inbred parent is so slow as to indicate that every region of the chromosomes, divisible by crossing over, has an effect on growth.

The growth rate in these backcrossed generations is maintained at a level appreciably above the proportional number of heterozygous allelic pairs. This effect can be interpreted in a number of ways other than a general physiological interaction, such as enforced heterozygosity, and the complementary action of dominant genes at different loci.

There is no way known at the present time to distinguish clearly between the accumulation of favorable dominant effects of compound or multiple genes at the same loci and a general physiological interaction or over-dominance.

Reciprocal crosses differ in many species, resulting in appreciable divergence in the amount of growth, and these differences have a cytoplasmic basis. The evidence from maize, however, shows clearly that cytoplasmic pollen sterility has no effect on size of plant, time of flowering, or productiveness.

M. R. IRWIN
University of Wisconsin

Chapter 15

Specificity
of Gene Effects[*]

If an attempt were made to survey all the possible ramifications suggested
by the title of this paper, it should include much of the published work in
genetics. It is of course a truism to all students of genetics to state that some
sort of differential specificity towards the end product must exist between
allelic genes or their effects could not be studied. It would be very interesting
as a part of this discussion to attempt to trace the change in concepts held by
various workers during these past fifty years concerning the nature and paths
of action of the gene. However, beyond a few remarks, such considerations
are hardly within the scope of this chapter.

Since the effects of genes can be recognized only if there are differences in
the end product, it is quite natural that the differences in the experimental
material first subjected to genetic analyses should have been those which
were visible, as differences in form, color, etc. Although the pendulum has
swung somewhat away from intensive investigations of such hereditary characteristics, it should be emphasized that by their use the underlying mechanisms of heredity have been elucidated.

Major attention was given by most of the investigators during the first
quarter of this century to the effects of respective genes upon individual
hereditary characters. In some quarters there was an oversimplification in
the interpretation of the relation of the gene to the character affected by it.
Gradually, however, the concept has become clearer that the majority of
hereditary characters—even many of those which had previously appeared
to be most simply inherited—are affected by many genes.

An early observation of gene specificity, too long neglected by all but a few
geneticists, was that made by Garrod in 1909 (see 1923 edition of *Inborn*

[*] Paper No. 433 from the Department of Genetics, University of Wisconsin.

Errors of Metabolism) on the inability of some humans to break down homo-gentisic acid (2,5-dihydroxyphenylacetic acid), resulting in the disease known as alcaptonuria. Observations reported by Gross (1914) indicated that this affliction was due to the lack of a ferment (enzyme) in the serum of alcapto-nurics, whereas the enzyme capable of catalyzing the breakdown of homo-gentisic acid was demonstrable in the serum of normal individuals. As Beadle (1945) has stated, no clearer example exists today that "a single gene substitution results in the absence or inactivity of a specific enzyme and that this in turn leads to the failure of a particular biochemical reaction." (The writer distinctly remembers that, while he was a student in a class in physio-logical chemistry, the instructor paid considerable attention to the chemical explanation of alcaptonuria, but none at all to its hereditary nature.)

Another example of gene specificity and also of gene dosage is that of yel-low endosperm in corn and the content of vitamin A reported by Mangelsdorf and Fraps (1931). Their study showed that the amount of vitamin A in the endosperm of white corn was almost negligible, but that the presence in the endosperm of one, two, or three genes for yellow pigmentation was accom-panied by corresponding increases in the amounts of the vitamin.

GENE EFFECTS IN A SERIES OF REACTIONS

There are numerous examples which have shown that many genes con-tribute to the development of a heritable character. Thus, in corn there are many genes which affect the development of chlorophyll. Each recessive allele, when homozygous, allows the formation of only partial pigmentation, or in extreme cases no pigmentation at all, and the seedlings are albino. It is generally believed that the majority, if not all, of these different genes for albinism affect different steps in the process of chlorophyll development. A breakdown of the process at any one of these steps results in albinism of the seedling. Haldane (1942) has likened the complexity of such a synthetic proc-ess to the activity of an equal number of students as there are genes, "en-gaged on different stages of a complicated synthesis under the direction of a professor, except that attempts to locate the professor have so far failed. Or we may compare them to modern workers on a conveyor belt, rather than skilled craftsmen each of whom produces a finished article."

One of the earliest examples of the physiological bases of the specificities which are the final gene products is that of the chemical analyses of genetic variations in flower color. These studies were carried out in England by sev-eral workers. See reviews by Beadle (1945), Beale (1941), Haldane (1942), Lawrence and Price (1940) for the general results and references to specific papers.

Mention will be made here of only one of the many investigations which have defined in chemical terms the hereditary differences in pigmentation. Anthocyanin is one of the five types of pigments concerned in flower color, and its presence or absence in several species is genetically determined. One way in which anthocyanin may be modified is by the degree of oxidation of the prime ring. According to Beale (1941) in the two genera Lathyrus and Streptocarpus, the hydroxyl group is at position 4′ in the pelargonidin type, at positions 3′ and 4′ in the cyanidin types, and at 3′, 4′, and 5′ in the delphinidin types. The more oxidized pigments are usually dominant to the less oxidized types. Thus flowers with genes AB and Ab will be of the delphinidin type of pigment, those with aB of the cyanidin type, and those with ab of the pelargonidin type.

These and other extensive chemical studies on the anthocyanin pigments genetically modified in various ways are dramatic examples of the specificities of gene effects. The analogy drawn above between the various genes and students working on a complicated synthesis becomes a little more clear in relation to flower pigments, since considerable information is available as to what some of the genes accomplish.

A further example of the effect of many genes upon a character is that of eye color in *Drosophila melanogaster*. Between twenty-five and thirty genes are known to modify the brownish-red color of the wild-type eye. There appear to be two independent pigments, brown and red, concerned in the development of the wild-type eye, each of these being affected by specific genes. Certain components of the brown pigment are diffusible from one part of the body to another, and hence are more readily subjected than others to chemical analyses.

The details of these analyses are presented in other review articles (Beadle, 1945; Ephrussi, 1942a, 1942b). Briefly, dietary tryptophan is converted to alpha-oxytryptophan by a reaction controlled by the wild-type allele of the vermilion gene (v). This substance is oxidized further to kynurenine (the so-called v^+ substance). By virtue of the activity of the normal allele of the cinnabar gene, kynurenine is further oxidized to the cn^+ substance, which may be the chromogen of the brown pigment (Kikkawa, 1941). The production of either brown or red eye pigment can be blocked by genes at the white eye locus, thus indicating that such genes act on a common precursor of the red and brown pigments.

Mention should be made of the relation between the original designation of certain of the genes for eye color and their presently known effects. Thus, the eyes of flies with the mutant alleles $bw\ bw$ are brown. But it is now known that this pair of alleles, instead of being concerned with the production of brown pigment, restricts the development of red pigment and thus we see only the brown color. Similarly, the four gene pairs whose mutants modify the red coloration do so by virtue of their effect on the brown pigment, not upon the red.

Wheldale (1910) proposed four decades ago that genetic characters were the resultant of a series of reactions, and that if a break in the chain occurred, the series of steps would have proceeded only to that point. Following the initial work in Neurospora by Beadle and Tatum (1941) on mutants which blocked certain metabolic processes, this type of approach has expanded enormously and profitably. Attention can be called here to but one very significant example of this kind of experimental study in microorganisms. A report by Srb and Horowitz (1944) shows clearly how many genes act in the synthesis of arginine. Of fifteen mutant strains studied, there were seven different steps represented in the synthesis of arginine. One of the forms grew only if arginine was supplied. Two others required either arginine or citrulline, and these two strains were genetically different. Four other strains, genetically different from the first three strains and from each other, would grow if arginine, citrulline, or ornithine were provided. For a diagrammatic representation of these steps, see Beadle (1945).

DIRECT EFFECTS OF GENES

The preceding examples are but a few of the many which could be cited to illustrate the gene specificities in the development of a genetic character which involves the successive activities of many genes. Are there any genetic characters which may be the immediate products of the causative genes? An example almost unique in higher plants is that of the waxy gene in corn (Collins, 1909) in its effects upon the starch of the pollen grain and the endosperm reserves. As is well known, the starch granules in the pollen grains bearing the waxy gene are stained reddish-brown with iodine, as are the endosperm reserves of waxy seeds, in contrast to the typical blue reaction of the starch granules of non-waxy pollen and of the endosperm reserves of non-waxy seeds. Following studies of the physiological effects of the waxy gene, Brink (1929) proposed that this gene has its effect on the enzyme amylase which functions directly in the synthesis of starch.

Another class of hereditary characters which in some respects appears to satisfy some of the criteria for a direct effect of the causative genes is that of the antigenic characters of the red blood cells of animals. With only rare exceptions, to be considered later in more detail, each of the known antigenic substances has appeared in the cells of an individual only if one or both parents also possessed it. If there is but a single pair of contrasting characters, each is expressed in the heterozygote. Further, the cells which give rise to the hematopoietic tissue from which the red blood corpuscles are derived are laid down shortly after the first division of the fertilized egg. The possibility cannot be excluded, of course, that there is a chain of reactions within each cell leading to the formation of the antigen, but no block in such a chain of reactions has yet been observed. There are two statements concerning the cellular antigens which are of interest: (1) the antigenic substance must be located at or near the surface of the cell in order to be detectable, and (2) there is no known effect of the environment upon them.

We should avoid misunderstanding about the meaning of the terms commonly used in immunological literature. For example, the word antigen was originally defined as any substance which, when introduced parenterally into an animal, would invoke the production of antibodies. This definition would now be extended to include any substance which will react visibly with an antibody. And an antibody would be defined as a constituent of the serum which reacts with an antigen in any of several ways. The circle of reasoning here is obvious. However, insofar as chemical studies of various antigens have contributed to an understanding of their specificities, the specificities have always been associated with structural differences of the antigenic substances. On the other hand, the reasons underlying the specificities in reactivity of the antibodies are almost completely unknown, although it is known that the antibodies are intimately associated with the globulins of the serum, and in fact may constitute the gamma globulins of the serum.

CELLULAR ANTIGENS IN HUMANS

As our first example of these antigenic substances, let us consider the well known and extensively studied O, A, B, and AB antigenic characters, or blood groups, of human cells. Following their discovery by Landsteiner (1900, 1901), it soon became clear that these substances were gene controlled. At the present time, the theory of three allelic genes, as postulated by Bernstein (1924) on statistical grounds, is generally accepted. The two other theories proposed for their inheritance—independent and linked genes, respectively—are fully discussed by Wiener (1943). Landsteiner noted that the serum of certain individuals would agglutinate (clump) the cells of other individuals, and from this observation the reciprocal relationship between the presence and absence of each antigen and its specific antibody has been elucidated.

Group	A or B Antigen on the Cells	Antibody of the Serum
O	None	Anti-A, Anti-B
A	A	Anti-B
B	B	Anti-A
AB	AB	None

It may readily be seen that the presence of an antigen, as A, on the cells is accompanied by the presence of the antibody (anti-B) for the contrasting antigen, as B, in the serum, and vice versa. If both antigenic characters are found on the cells, as in AB individuals, the serum contains no antibodies. While if neither A nor B is present on the cells, the serum contains both anti-A and anti-B.

These phenomena pose the question whether the genes producing the cellular substances also have an effect on the antibodies of the serum. That is, does the gene which is responsible for the O antigen (which is definitely an entity but is less reactive than A and B) also effect both anti-A and anti-B in the serum—while in individuals with substance A, only anti-B is found; in those with B, only anti-A is present; and in AB individuals the effects of the respective genes on the antibodies are somehow neutralized?

Before attempting to answer this question, it will be advisable to review the present knowledge of the chemistry of the A and B substances of human cells. See Kabat (1949).

These antigens (blood groups, cellular characters, antigenic factors, etc.) are found in nearly all the fluids and tissues of the human body. They also are widely distributed throughout the animal kingdom. The A substance or an A-like substance has been found, for example, in hog gastric mucosa, in the fourth stomach (abomasum) of the cow, and in swine pepsin, while both A and B substances have been noted in the saliva and stomachs of horses. Following chemical fractionations, principally of horse saliva and hog gastric mucosa, various investigators have obtained preparations with activity related to the A substance. These preparations have been largely polysaccharide in nature. In addition to the polysaccharides, even in the purest preparations, some workers have noted traces of amino acids.

At present, while it appears that both the A and B substances of human cells may be classed as nitrogenous polysaccharides, no information is available as to the structural differences between them. Our knowledge of such specificities rests entirely upon the technics of immunology, that is, by the interaction of either naturally occurring antibodies (as anti-A and anti-B), or immune antibodies, with the respective substances A and B.

The antigenic substances A and B of human cells are complex polysaccharides, while the antibodies are modified globulins, or are found in serum protein very closely related to the globulin fraction. If the gene which effects antigen A is responsible also for the B antibody, and that for antigen B for the A antibody, it would seem that here is a clear-cut case of pleiotropic effects of the respective genes. This explanation runs into difficulties in AB individuals which, on this proposal, should have both kinds of antibodies but actually have none. In contrast, a current explanation of the reciprocal presence of the antigenic substance of the cells and the antibody for the contrasting substances is that the antibodies for both substances (A and B) are normal constituents of human serum. Production of the antibodies would then be controlled by a gene or genes at another locus than that having to do with the cellular substances, if genes were involved in their production. If an individual carries the gene for A, and hence has A substances widely distributed throughout his body, the A antibodies are presumed to be absorbed from the serum, and of course the B antibodies are left. Also, an individual with the B substance would absorb the B antibodies, and the antibodies to A would remain, while both anti-A and anti-B would be absorbed in an AB individual. Other hypotheses are given by Wiener (1943). Unfortunately, no experimental test of the correctness of this or other hypotheses is likely.

Landsteiner and Levine (1927) announced the discovery in human cells of a new pair of contrasting antigens, called M and N. These were detectable only by the use of immune sera produced in rabbits, as was another antigenic factor called P. The heritability of the M and N substances is adequately explained by the assumption of a single pair of allelic genes, and the substance P appears to be dominant to its absence.

Another antigenic factor in human blood which has aroused wide interest is the recently discovered Rh substance, or complex, as it might be termed. In 1940, Landsteiner and Wiener (1940) reported that a new antibody, derived from a rabbit immunized with the erythrocytes of a rhesus monkey, was reactive with the cells of about 85 per cent of the white population of New York. They gave the name Rh (a contraction of rhesus) to this agglutinable property of human cells. As Boyd (1945) aptly states:

The technic of testing for the new factor was difficult, the best available serums were weak, and had it not been for a remarkable series of discoveries which followed in the next few months, the Rh factor might have aroused no more interest than its practically stillborn brethren. . . .

The Rh factor was shown to be involved in previously unexplained complications following transfusions (Wiener and Peters, 1940), but is most widely known for its role as the etiologic agent in the majority of cases of hemolytic disease of the newborn. The proposal was first made by Levine and Stetson (1939) that an antigen in the fetus, foreign to the mother and presumably transmitted by the father, could pass through the placenta and immunize the mother. Later studies implicated the Rh factor as the foreign antigen, and showed that the antibodies developed in the mother may pass back through the placenta and affect the red blood cells of the fetus, before or following birth. Although the majority of cases of hemolytic disease of the newborn may be justly ascribed to Rh incompatibility between the father and mother, there is no satisfactory explanation as to why only about one in forty of such potentially dangerous combinations leads to morbidity.

There exist several subgroups, or subtypes, of the Rh complex, and investigations as to their respective specificities occupy the center of interest of many workers at the present writing. There are two schools of thought as to the mode of inheritance of these subgroups, which also involves the terminology to be used in their identification (see Strandskov, 1948, 1949, for leading references). One explanation is that the various subtypes are manifestations of a series of multiple allelic genes, the other that they are the result of the action of respective genes at three different but closely linked loci. It is not within the province of this chapter to discuss the arguments for and against these two proposals. However, it should be stated that the genetic results under either explanation are essentially the same.

One of the most pertinent statements which can be made about these various antigenic substances of the erythrocytes is that they are detectable no matter in what gene complex they may occur. That is, other genes than the causative ones have no measurable influence upon their expression. A possible exception to this statement might be proposed for the A and N characters, respectively, since each is somewhat less readily agglutinated when in the heterozygote, AB and MN, than when either occurs singly.

THE HYBRID SUBSTANCE IN SPECIES HYBRIDS

Until the early part of this century, most of the workers in immunology had reached the conclusion that the specificities obtained in immunological reactions were primarily if not entirely concerned with proteins. Therefore, the finding by Heidelberger and Avery (1923, 1924) that the immunological specificities of the pneumococcal types were dependent upon polysaccharides was indeed a forward step in our understanding of the chemical nature of biological specificity. It is a pleasure to acknowledge that this work of Heidelberger and Avery convinced the writer that immunological technics should be a useful tool in studying genetic phenomena. Also, although at that time pollen differing in gene content seemed (and still does) to be promising experimental material, the species and species hybrids in pigeons and doves produced by the late L. J. Cole were tailor-made for further studies.

Pigeon-Dove Hybrids

The first step was to determine whether the cells of one species could be distinguished from those of the other. In brief, all the comparisons by immunological technics, between any pair of species of pigeons and doves, have resulted in the ability to distinguish the cells of any species from those of another, and to show that each species possessed antigenic substances in common with another species, as well as those peculiar to itself—those species specific. A dozen or more kinds of species hybrids have been obtained in the laboratory, and in general, each kind of hybrid has contained in its cells all or nearly all of the cellular substances of both parental species. One such species hybrid is that obtained from a mating between males of an Asiatic species, the Pearlneck (*Streptopelia chinensis*) and the domesticated Ring dove females (*St. risoria*). The corpuscles of these hybrids contained all the substances common to each parental species, but did not contain quite all the specific substances of either parental species. Further, the cells of these hybrids did possess a complex of antigenic substances not found in the cells of the parents. These relationships are presented in Table 15.1 and are given in diagrammatic form in Figure 15.1. This new antigen has been called the "hybrid substance," and it has been present in every hybrid produced between these two species.

Upon repeatedly backcrossing these species hybrids and selected backcross hybrids to Ring dove, ten antigenic substances which differentiate Pearlneck from Ring dove have been isolated as probable units. That is, a backcross bird carrying any one of these unit substances, when mated to a Ring dove, has produced approximately equal proportions of progeny with, and without, the particular substance in their blood cells. These substances peculiar to Pearlneck, as compared with Ring dove, have been called d-1, d-2, d-3, d-4, d-5, d-6, d-7, d-8, d-11, and d-12. Each of these is distinct from the others (Irwin, 1939) both genetically and immunologically. Thus it appears that a gene or genes on each of ten of the thirty-odd pairs of chromo-

TABLE 15.1

ANTIGENIC RELATIONSHIPS OF THE BLOOD CELLS
OF PEARLNECK, RING DOVES, AND
THEIR HYBRIDS

Immune Serum	Absorbed by Cells of	Agglutination Titers with Cells of		
		Pearlneck	Ring Dove	F₁
Pearlneck		23040	23040	23040
Pearlneck	Ring dove	11520	0	11520
Pearlneck	F₁	90	0	0
Ring dove		15360	15360	15360
Ring dove	Pearlneck	0	3840+	3840+
Ring dove	F₁	0	180	0
F₁		15360	15360	15360
F₁	Pearlneck	0	3840+	3840+
F₁	Ring dove	7680	0	7680
F₁	Pearlneck and Ring dove	0	0	360+

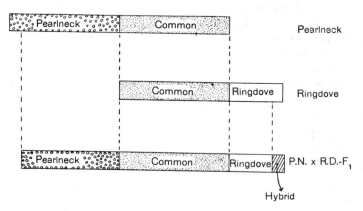

FIG. 15.1—Diagrammatic representation of the antigenic relationships of the Pearlneck, Ring dove, and their hybrids.

somes of Pearlneck produce effects on cellular antigens which differentiate Pearlneck from Ring dove. Although the cellular substances particular to Ring dove, in contrast to Pearlneck, have not been obtained as units, the available evidence indicates strongly that a gene or genes on nine or ten chromosomes of Ring dove produce antigenic effects which differentiate that species from Pearlneck.

The question may well be raised as to what this recital of antigenic characters in man and doves, which in general illustrates gene specificity in the production of cellular antigens, has to do with the general topic of heterosis. The so-called *hybrid substance* has one word (hybrid) in common with the term hybrid vigor, and suggests a possible relationship of the two terms.

The hybrid substance seemingly represents a departure from the hypothesized direct action of a gene on the antigenic substance, in that it appears to result from the interaction of two or more genes in the species hybrids to produce some antigenic substance different from any detectable in either parent. With but one exception proposed by Thomsen (1936) in chickens, and for which another explanation will be considered shortly, a hybrid substance has thus far been found only in species hybrids.

Mention should be made of the technics required for the detection of the hybrid substance. Briefly, if an antiserum prepared against the cells of an individual, whether a species hybrid or not, would be absorbed by the cells of both its parents and would then react with the cells of the individual, but not with the cells of either parent, there would be evidence of a different antigenic substance in the homologous cells—those used in the immunization. (If an antigen were recessive, it would be present in the heterozygote, and presumably could absorb its specific antibody.)

Domestic Fowl Hybrids

As stated above, Thomsen (1936) reported that within each of two families of chickens there was a different antigenic substance present than was found in the parents. Attempts in our laboratory by Mrs. Ruth Briles to duplicate this finding were without success, but a very interesting and quite unexpected observation was made which may be the explanation of Thomsen's finding. If an antigenic substance were present in an individual different from that possessed by either parent, immunization of either parent (as #1) with the cells of this individual might engender antibodies against the new substance. Absorption of such an antiserum by the cells of the other parent (as #2) should remove all antibodies except those formed against the new or hybrid substance, and such a reagent should be reactive only with the cells containing the new substance. This was the procedure followed by Thomsen, except that his tables do not show that the cells of the two parents were used as negative controls in the tests made after the various absorptions.

Immunizations of each of the parents of a family of chickens against the cells of one of the offspring, or the pooled cells of two or more, were made by Mrs. Briles. Following the absorption of the antiserum obtained from either parent by the cells of the other, it was noted that the absorbed antiserum was at least weakly reactive with the cells of the individual from which the antiserum was obtained. That is, such an antiserum would not react (agglutinate) with its own cells before absorption with the cells of the mate, but after such absorption it definitely would agglutinate the cells of the individual from which it was derived.

To use a concrete example, bird R614 (containing B_1 antigen) was immunized with the washed cells of R2043, to produce B_3 antibodies (Briles, McGibbon, and Irwin, 1951). After this antiserum from R614 was mixed for absorption with the washed cells of R622 (having B_3 antigen in its cells and having been immunized to produce B_1 antibodies), all cells containing the B_1 antigen were reactive with it, including those of R614 itself. Thus it appears that the antibodies to B_1 which were circulating in the serum of R622 were also attached to the surface of the red blood cells and were transferred to the antiserum from R614 during the absorption process. It was possible to demonstrate that, after washing the cells of R622 in saline, the saline contained antibodies, even after nine successive washings. Hence, unless the cells of both parents were used as controls in comparable tests for the presence of a hybrid substance, agglutination of any cells could be explained as due to a transfer of antibody from the blood cells to an antiserum. Unfortunately, such controls are not given in Thomsen's paper, and the possibility cannot be eliminated that the reactions obtained by him were due simply to segregation within the various families of an antigenic character of one of the parents. This possibility was mentioned by Thomsen (1936), but was not considered applicable to his experiments.

Hybrid Substances

Returning to the hybrid substance for which there is definite evidence, it should first be stated that such a substance has not been found in all kinds of species hybrids, as may be seen from the data given in Table 15.2. It has been reported from our laboratory in hybrids between Pearlneck and Ring dove, the pigeon (*Columba livia*) and Ring dove, the Mallard (*Anas platyrhynchos*) and Muscovy duck (*Cairina moschata*), but not in the hybrids between the triangular spotted pigeon (*C. guinea*) and *livia*. Irwin (1947) gives the specific references to pertinent articles.

A hybrid substance has been detected but not previously reported in hybrids from matings between the Philippine turtle dove (*St. dussumieri*) and Ring dove, the dwarf turtle dove (*St. humilis*) and Ring dove, the Oriental turtle dove (*St. orientalis*) and Ring dove, and the band tail pigeon (*C. fasciata*) and *livia*. No such substance has been observed in the hybrids between the Senegal dove (*St. senegalensis*) and Ring dove, an African dove

(*St. semitorquata*) and Ring dove, the Senegal dove and the Cape turtle dove (*St. capicola*), the spot wing pigeon (*C. maculosa*) and *livia*, and between the Grayson dove (*Zenaidura graysoni*) and the common mourning dove (*Zen. macroura*). It is possible that a hybrid substance does exist in these latter species hybrids, but the same technics by which it was observed in the other species hybrids failed to demonstrate its presence in them.

Three different fractions of the hybrid substance have been demonstrated in the hybrids between Pearlneck and Ring dove (Irwin and Cumley, 1945), by virtue of a frequent association of each fraction with one or more antigens

TABLE 15.2

TESTS FOR HYBRID SUBSTANCES IN THE CELLS OF
VARIOUS SPECIES HYBRIDS

ANTISERUM TO	ABSORBED BY CELLS OF		REACTIONS OF PARENTAL AND HYBRID CELLS WITH THE RESPECTIVE REAGENTS		
	Parent 1	Parent 2	Parent 1	Parent 2	Hybrid
F₁—Pearlneck × Ring dove.........	Pearlneck	Ring dove	0	0	++
F₁—*C. livia* × Ring dove..........	*livia*	Ring dove	0	0	++
F₁—*St. dussumieri* × Ring dove....	*dussumieri*	Ring dove	0	0	+
F₁—*St. humilis* × Ring dove.......	*humilis*	Ring dove	0	0	+
F₁—*St. orientalis* × Ring dove......	*orientalis*	Ring dove	0	0	+
F₁—*C. fasciata* × *livia*............	*C. fasciata*	*livia*	0	0	+
F₁—Mallard × Muscovy...........	Mallard	Muscovy	0	0	++
F₁—*St. senegalensis* × Ring dove....	*St. senegalensis*	Ring dove	0	0	0
F₁—*St. semitorquata* × Ring dove...	*St. semitorquata*	Ring dove	0	0	0
F₁—Senegal × *St. capicola*.........	Senegal	*St. capicola*	0	0	0
F₁—*C. maculosa* × *livia*...........	*C. maculosa*	*livia*	0	0	0
F₁—*C. guinea* × *livia*.............	*C. guinea*	*livia*	0	0	0
F₁—*Zenaidura graysoni* × *Zen. macroura*......................	*Zen. graysoni*	*Zen. macroura*	0	0	0

peculiar to Pearlneck. Thus one fraction called dx-A was always associated in the backcross hybrids with the d-11 substance, dx-B seemingly was loosely linked with the d-1 character and with certain others as well—thereby providing strong evidence that on several chromosomes of Pearlneck there are duplicate or repeat genes—and dx-C was always associated with the d-4 antigen. The pertinent reactions which show these specificities are given in Table 15.3 and are represented diagrammatically in Figure 15.2.

Because of the constant association of the dx-A and dx-C fractions with the d-11 and d-4 substances, respectively, one cannot be certain that these two fractions, although antigenically distinct from the d-1 and d-11 specific characters, are not simply a new specificity conferred upon the specific characters by some sort of rearrangement of the specific substances following the interaction of the causative genes. This question cannot be completely answered until either a genetic separation has been observed, as between the dx-A and d-11, or the chemical separation into two distinct substances has been done. On the other hand, the dx-B fraction has been separated from each of the species specific characters to which it presumably is loosely linked, thereby showing that this fraction of the hybrid substance is an antigenic entity.

The reagent which interacts with the hybrid substance (hybrid antiserum

TABLE 15.3

TESTS FOR SIMILARITIES AND DIFFERENCES OF THE COMPONENTS OF THE "HYBRID SUBSTANCE" OF THE SPECIES HYBRID BETWEEN PEARLNECK AND RING DOVE

	REACTIONS OF DIFFERENT CELLS WITH ANTI-F_1 SERUM							
Cells	Absorbed by Cells of Both Pearlneck and Ring Dove	Absorbed by the Cells of Both Pearlneck and Ring Dove, in Combination with Others as Listed						
		d-1 (dx-B)	d-4 (dx-C)	d-11 (dx-A)	$F_1 \frac{P.N.}{R.D.}$	$F_1 \frac{Pgn}{R.D.}$	Sen.	Aus. cstd.
Pearlneck..........	0	0	0	0	0	0	0	0
Ring dove.........	0	0	0	0	0	0	0	0
F_1—P.N./R.D.....	++	++	++	+	0	++	++	++
d-1 (dx-B)....	+	0	+	+	0	+	+	±
d-4 (dx-C)....	+	?	0	±	0	±	±	±
d-11 (dx-A)...	++	++	++	0	0	+	++	++
F_1—Pgn/R.D......	+	+	+	0	0	0	+	+
Senegal..........	+	0	0	0	0	0	0	±
Australian crested.	±	±	±	0	0	0	±	0
Column..........	2	3	4	5	6	7	8	9

Symbols: ++ = marked agglutination; + = agglutination; ± = definite but weak agglutination; ? = doubtful reaction; 0 = no agglutination—at the first dilution of the serum cell mixture.

absorbed by the cells of both Pearlneck and Ring dove) will also agglutinate the cells of various species. Thus in the genus Streptopelia, there were five species (*capicola, dussumieri, humilis, orientalis,* and *senegalensis*) other than Pearlneck and Ring dove whose cells were reactive, and one (*semitorquata*) with nonreactive cells. Within the genus Columba, the cells of one species (*rufina*) likewise reacted with this reagent, but those of seven other species (*fasciata, flavirostris, guinea, livia, maculosa, palumbus,* and *picazura*) did not. And of twelve species tested in other genera within the Columbidae, only three species from Australia (Australian crested dove, or *Ocyphaps lophotes,* the bronze wing dove or *Phaps chalcoptera,* and the brush bronze wing dove, or *Phaps elegans*) possessed reactive cells. In Table 15.3, the Senegal cells are representative of the parallel reactions of the five species of the Streptopelia, as are those of the Australian crested of the equivalent reactivities of the three Australian species.

Although the reagent for the hybrid substance did not agglutinate the cells of *livia*, it invariably clumped those of the hybrids between pigeon (*livia*) and Ring dove. As previously reported (Irwin and Cole, 1936), these hybrids also contain a hybrid substance. Because of the cross reactions existing between these two hybrid substances, a certain degree of similarity can be assumed. That the fraction in the hybrid substance of the F_1-Pearlneck $\times$

DIAGRAMMATIC REPRESENTATION OF THE "HYBRID SUBSTANCE" OF THE HYBRID BETWEEN PEARLNECK AND RINGDOVE

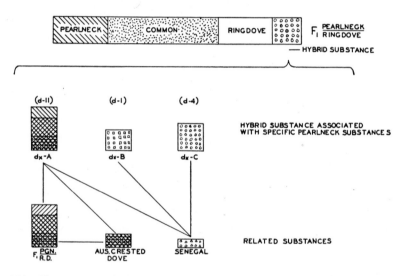

FIG. 15.2 —The separation into constituent parts of the *hybrid substance* of the species hybrid between Pearlneck and Ring dove.

Ring dove, which is primarily if not entirely responsible for the cross reactions, is dx-A may be deduced from Table 15.3, in that this fraction (associated with d-11) is the only one which will exhaust the antibodies from the reagent for the cells of the pigeon-Ring dove hybrid (column 5). Also, in unpublished tests the reagent for the hybrid substance of the pigeon-Ring dove hybrid (anti-hybrid serum absorbed by the cells of pigeon and Ring dove) did not react with Pearlneck cells, but reacted strongly with d-11 cells, presumably by virtue of their content of the dx-A fraction, and not definitely with cells carrying dx-B or dx-C. If the dx-A hybrid substance of the species hybrids between Pearlneck and Ring dove were partially or largely a rearrangement of an antigenic substance, in this case d-11, which is species specific to Pearlneck—since the Ring dove is a common parent of the two kinds of species hybrids—that specific substance (d-11) should be detectable in the cells of *livia*.

To date, reasonably extensive tests (unpublished) have not shown that the cells of *livia* contain more than a trace of an antigenic substance related to the d-11 of Pearlneck. Whatever the relationship of the genes in Pearlneck (associated with those on a chromosome effecting the d-11 specific substance) and *livia*, respectively, which presumably by interaction with a gene or genes from Ring dove in the two species hybrids effect a common fraction of the two hybrid substances, they are not associated with genes which produce similar antigenic patterns in the two species. On these grounds, it would seem unlikely that the hybrid substances in these two kinds of species hybrids are merely a different arrangement of a species specific antigen.

The question is pertinent as to whether such reactivities in the cells of these other species, as Senegal and Australian crested, are themselves an indication of antigenic response to gene interaction within each species, or the more direct product of a gene. This cannot be answered directly. But, as given in Table 15.3, the fact that absorption of the reagent for the hybrid substance by fractions dx-A, dx-B, or dx-C removes the antibodies for the cells of Senegal indicates that there is some common constituent of these three fractions related to, if not identical with, a reactive substance in Senegal cells. However, only the dx-A fraction removes the antibodies for the cells of the Australian crested dove. Further, absorption by the cells of the pigeon-Ring dove hybrid also removes the antibodies from this reagent for the cells of the Australian crested dove.

The hypothetical explanations could be advanced, (1) that the antigenic substances in Senegal and the Australian crested dove, themselves being distinct, but both related to the hybrid substance in Pearlneck-Ring dove hybrids, are the result of a genic interaction. But there is no evidence for such an assumption. Also, (2) the argument could be advanced that the relationship between these substances in Senegal and Australian crested, and in the respective species hybrids, is fortuitous, simulating the occurrence of the Forssman antigen in many species of animals and plants, including bacteria (Boyd, 1943). That is, the antigenic substances involved (related in some manner to the hybrid substance) may be gene controlled in each of the related species, since indistinguishable substances to those of Senegal were found in four other species of *Streptopelia*, *capicola*, *dussumieri*, *humilis*, and *orientalis*, and to those of the Australian crested dove in two species of another genus, *Phaps chalcoptera* and *Phaps elegans*, but the antigenic similarity to the hybrid substance is by virtue of some related antigenic component. Various ramifications of these and other explanations would be purely speculative.

The hybrid substance, as it has been observed in the cells of various species hybrids in birds, simulates for cellular antigens the expression of heterosis in plants and animals. That is, it appears as the resultant of an interaction between genes. One may well ask if there is any other manifestation of heterosis in these species hybrids and backcross hybrids. Extensive measurements of eight body characteristics, as over-all length, extent, width of tarsus, width of band, length of wing, beak, middle toe, and tail, were made over a period of years under the supervision of L. J. Cole. The differences in the averages of these various characteristics between the parental Pearlneck and Ring dove species, as yet unpublished, were statistically significant, and the averages of the measurements of these characteristics in the species hybrids showed them to be in general intermediate between those of the parental species. Thus there was no evidence of heterosis in any external characteristic of the species hybrids, and no correlation with the hybrid substance of the blood cells.

CELLULAR CHARACTERS WITHIN A SPECIES

The finding that one or more genes on each of nine or ten pairs of chromosomes of Pearlneck had effects on the species specific antigens of the blood cells of this species made plausible the belief that many more genes than commonly believed would have effects within a species making for individuality of the cellular patterns. Acting on this assumption, a series of exploratory tests were made in experimental animals, principally in cattle and chickens. For example, following the transfusion of the blood of a young cow into her dam, an antibody was obtained from the serum of the recipient which reacted (produced lysis of the reacting cells upon the addition of complement to the serum-cell mixture) with the cells of some individuals, but not with those of others. The reactive substance was called A.

The objective was to be able to detect each antigenic factor separately, according to the following criterion. The reactive cells from any individual should remove the antibodies from the reagent specific for those cells, when added in excess to the reagent. However, if there were antibodies in the reagent which recognized two or more distinct blood factors, any such absorption with cells containing only one such substance would remove only a part of the antibodies. Those remaining would still be reactive with all cells containing the substance corresponding to the unabsorbed antibody.

To this criterion was added that of genetics for a single character, using the gene-frequency method since controlled matings were not possible. A typical example of the analysis is that for substance A, as follows:

Type of Mating	Number of Offspring	
	With Antigen A	Lacking Antigen A
A×A..........	217	23
A×−..........	76	51
−×−..........	0	41

These results illustrate the observation that an individual has any cellular character recognized to date only if one or both parents possessed it. Also, each behaved as if it were a dominant to its absence.

From further isoimmunizations in cattle, and from immunizations of rabbits, various antisera have been obtained which detect other antigenic factors of cattle cells. Each of these has been subjected to the criteria of both genetics and immunology for a single character, as described in reports by Ferguson (1941), Ferguson *et al.* (1942), and Stormont (1950). At present, about forty different reagents are regularly used in typing cattle cells.

Other Antigens in Cattle

As stated above, the first substance detected in cattle cells was named A. The next was called B, the next C, . . . Z. That called A' implies no relationship to A, nor B' to B, etc. Each of these antigenic factors is therefore recognized independently, and when subjected to an analysis of gene frequency, each has behaved as expected if effected by a single gene in comparison to its absence.

However, some definite associations have been noted among them. For example, Ferguson (1941) reported that the C and E factors were not independent, for only C occurred alone, whereas E was present always with C, and such cells therefore had CE. It was postulated that there were three allelic genes involved, one for the components C and E together, one for C alone, and a third for the absence of both C and E.

It was later noted by Stormont that certain additional antigenic factors appeared only if one or more other components also were present. For example, the substance B occurs alone, as does that called G. But a third factor called K has never been observed unless both B and G were also present. (A possible exception to this rule was noted shortly after these factors were first demonstrable, and a weak reaction at that test with the reagent for the G substance was probably incorrectly recorded.) This association of K with B and G has been noted in over eighteen hundred animals of more than six thousand tested. Hence the combination of the BGK factors has always occurred as a unit, and it has also behaved as a unit in the progeny of individuals possessing it. A compilation of some unpublished data has yielded the following information:

TYPE OF MATING	NUMBER OF OFFSPRING	
	With BGK	Without BGK
BGK×BGK......	151	44
BGK×−.........	185	137
−×−..........	0	160

Notwithstanding the fact that B, G, and K are recognized separately by respective reagents, these data, and the observation that K has occurred only with both B and G, are strong evidence for the conclusion that B, G, and K in the cells behave as a unit.

Further, offspring of some individuals possessing B and G (BG) in their cells have given only two classes of offspring, those with B and those with G, as would be expected if the causative genes were alleles. But another type of BG individual has produced offspring of two quite different types—those with both B and G (BG) and those with neither, as if a gene producing B and

TABLE 15.4

THE DISTRIBUTION OF THE CONSTITUENTS OF
THE "B" COMPLEXES IN THE OFFSPRING
OF SELECTED SIRES

Sire	Antigenic Complex	Number of Off-spring	Antigenic Complex	Number of Off-spring
H-1	$B_{BGIO_1T_2A'}$	25	$B_{O_1Y_2A'}$	23
H-4	$B_{BO_2A'E_3'}$	35	$B_{O_3J'K'}$	31
H-5	$B_{BO_1Y_2D'}$	26	$B_{O_3J'K'}$	24
H-6	B_{BO_1}	15	$B_{GY_2E_1'}$	23
H-7	$B_{BGKE_2'}$	14	$B_{GY_2E_1'}$	15
H-11	$B_{O_1A'}$	31	$B_{O_3J'K'}$	23
H-19	$B_{GY_2E_1'}$	19	B_b	13
G-19	$B_{IE_1'}$	8	B_b	7

G together was allelic to one not effecting either B or G. These combinations of antigenic substances, as BG and BGK, have been called *antigenic complexes*.

There are two series of such complexes, called the B and C series, respectively. In the B series there are twenty-one of the forty-odd antigenic characters which are associated in various conbinations. At least seven of these may appear singly, as was described for B and G. The other fourteen have been found only in various antigenic complexes, each of which may be made up of from two to eight of the twenty-one characters. The majority of these twenty-one characters do not occur at random in a complex with each of the others. As was stated above, the character K has always been found with B and G, but it has never occurred with I, with which it appears as a contrasting substance. In contrast, either B or G may be present in a complex with I. No separation of the antigenic characters of a complex has ever been observed in the cells of the offspring of an individual possessing it. A few examples are listed in Table 15.4 from more complete data given in a paper by Stormont, Owen, and Irwin (1951). All present evidence makes it seem somewhat more reasonable to assume that each antigenic complex is produced by a single gene than by linked genes. The various antigenic complexes in each of the two systems, or series, would then be produced by a series of multiple alleles. The possibility of pseudo-alleles cannot be eliminated, but for the present may be assumed not to be a complicating factor.

If the assumption be granted that a single gene controls an antigenic complex, as BGK, what explanation or explanations can be proposed for the different antigenic specificities of this and other complexes, and, in turn, what can be inferred from such an explanation as to the action of the causative gene?

Antigens of Pneumococci

By virtue of the ability to attach simple chemical compounds to proteins, thereby preparing conjugated antigens with specifically reacting components of known constitution, there has emerged from such studies the realization that a so-called single antigenic substance may engender a multiplicity of antibodies of varying specificities (see Landsteiner, 1945, for a critical review and references). A pertinent example of this sort may be found in the antigenic relationship existing between type III and type VIII pneumococci. Cross reactions between the respective antisera (produced in horses) and the two types of pneumococci have been observed, implying to them some sort of antigenic similarity.

As is well known, the specificities of the pneumococcal types depend upon the carbohydrates of the capsules (Heidelberger and Avery, 1923, 1924). Thus, the carbohydrate of type III has been found to be a polyaldobionic acid (Reeves and Goebel, 1941). The understanding of the structure of the polysaccharide of type VIII is not as complete as for type III, but about 60 per cent of the molecule of the carbohydrate of type VIII appears to be aldobionic acid. Cross reactivity may therefore be expected between the soluble specific substances of types III (S III) and VIII (S VIII), by virtue of the presence in each of multiples of the same aldobionic acid as a structural unit. It is probable that the serologically reactive unit in each of these two types is a larger portion of the polysaccharide molecule than a single chemical structural unit. Type S VIII also contains approximately two glucose molecules for every aldobionic acid residue, thereby presumably accounting for at least a part of the specificity of type VIII in contrast to type III. Thus it may be seen that serological cross reactions may be expected when the antigenic substances under comparison are closely related chemically. Also to be expected is the ability to distinguish between such substances, as was actually possible in the case of types III and VIII (Heidelberger, Kabat, and Meyer, 1942).

Genetic Significance

The above example may be combined with other findings in the field of immunochemistry to allow the statement that antigenic substances of related but not identical chemical constitution may—but sometimes do not—incite the production of cross reacting antibodies. From the serological point of view, a pertinent question concerning these antigenic complexes in cattle is whether the cells which react with the B reagent, or with any other specific reagent, do so by virtue of the presence of a specific reacting substance in a single antigenic molecule, or otherwise? Does the complex BGK, for example, represent (1) three different and separate antigenic substances? Or does it represent (2) a single antigenic substance with (a) a possible common base and three more or less different reactive groups accounting for B, G, and K, respectively, or (b) a single substance capable of inciting many specificities of antibodies, of which those for B, G, and K represent only a part of the re-activities of the spectrum of antibodies which may be produced? A combina-tion of (a) and (b) also may be a possibility.

At present, very little experimental evidence is available concerning the adequacy of any one or combination of the above possibilities to explain the antigenic relationships of the components of the antigenic complexes of cattle cells. Tests are under way to determine whether the reactive substance called B, for example, is the same in all cells in which it appears, whether singly or in an antigenic complex.

In terms of the action of the causative genes, apart from the possibilities of linkage and pseudo-allelism, the question seems to resolve itself around two main aspects: (1) Do the genes controlling an antigenic complex, as a single gene for BGK, have separate specificities for B, G, and K, or (2) does this gene produce a single substance with no such separate specificities, and the similarities between such a complex as BGK and BGIY, are due primarily if not entirely to the general similarities in their chemical structure. The writer is inclined to adopt a combination of these two possibilities as a current work-ing hypothesis. No matter what may eventually prove to be the correct in-terpretation of antigenic structure of the complexes, and the action of the controlling genes, it appears that these studies have given some insight into the complexities of the gene products and perhaps also of the causative genes.

The studies of the specificities of the gene products—the antigens of the blood cells of cattle—and the resulting inferences of the structure of the genes themselves, may not be directly related to the over-all heterosis problem. Nevertheless the writer is convinced that somewhat comparable specificities might well be obtained in plants, in which attempts are currently in progress to measure various aspects of the genetic bases for heterosis. Just how useful an additional tool of this sort would be is only a guess.

CARL C. LINDEGREN
Southern Illinois University

Chapter 16

Genetics and Cytology
of Saccharomyces

In the middle of the last century, Buchner ground up yeast cells and proved that the cell-free filtrate contained a substance capable of fermenting sugar. This experiment settled a heated controversy between Liebig and Pasteur concerning whether or not living structures were essential to fermentation. The substance responsible for the fermentation was called an enzyme, the word being derived from the Greek and meaning "in yeast." Since that time, yeast has been the organism of choice for experimenting in enzyme chemistry because of the abundant supply obtainable from breweries and from factories producing bakers' yeast. The biochemistry of fermentation has provided the foundation for our present understanding of the biochemistry of respiration and of muscular contraction—two of the fundamental problems which have intrigued biologists. It has led to an understanding of vitamins and through them to an understanding of chemotherapy.

BIOCHEMICAL DEFECTS AS GENE MARKERS

The work of Beadle and Tatum has popularized the generally accepted view that enzymes are derived somehow or other from genes. Their work initiated a new interest in biochemical genetics. They showed that the inactivation of a specific gene caused a deficiency which could be met by supplying a specific chemical. Vitamins, amino acids, purines, and pyrimidines were the substances chosen in this analysis. They used the fungus, Neurospora, because its life cycle had been thoroughly worked out by B. O. Dodge and because the Lindegrens had shown by genetical analysis that it contained conventional chromosomes on which genes, arranged in linear order, could be mapped by the standard procedures used in studying corn and the fruit fly.

256

YEAST GENETICS

Until 1935, yeasts were considered to be devoid of sex and, therefore, unsuitable for genetical analysis. At that time, Winge showed that the standard yeast cell carried two sets of chromosomes—one contributed from each parent—and was, therefore, a typical hybrid. The hybrid yeast cell produces four spores, each with a single set of chromosomes. Each of these spores is a sex cell. By fusing in pairs they can produce the standard (hybrid) yeast cell and complete the life cycle. In this laboratory it was shown that the spores are of two mating types, and that each spore can produce a culture each cell of which can act as a sex cell, like the original spore. Mass matings between two such spore-cultures result in the production of fusion cells, from which new hybrids are produced by budding.

This work made it possible to study the inheritance of biochemical deficiencies in the organism on which classical enzyme study is based, and to attack the problem of the relation of genes to enzymes in this fruitful material. We have related specific genes to several of the most thoroughly studied classical enzymes: sucrase, maltase, alpha methyl glucosidase, melibiase, and galactase.

The principal advantages of yeasts for biochemical genetics are:

(1) Yeast enzymes have been the subject of intensive biochemical study.

(2) Techniques for studying respiration and fermentation are based principally on work with yeast and thus especially adapted to this organism. Yeasts grow as free cells rather than as mycelial matts and, therefore, can be subdivided any number of times without injury, thus simplifying weighing and dilution of the cells.

(3) Large quantities of cells are available from industrial sources or can be grown cheaply and quickly and are easily stored in living condition.

(4) A variety of genes concerned with the differential utilization of numerous monoses as well as di- and poly-saccharides are available.

(5) A polyploid series of yeast cultures is now available: (a) haploid cells, each containing a single set of chromosomes, (b) diploid yeast cells, each containing the double number of chromosomes, (c) triploid, and (d) tetraploid cells (made available by our recent discovery of diploid gametes [Lindegren and Lindegren, 1951]).

(6) With free cells it is possible to study competition between genotypes and to observe the advantages or disadvantages in controlled environments. The populations involved are enormous and the life cycles short, so it is possible to simulate natural selection in the laboratory. Experiments of this type have enjoyed an enormous vogue with bacteria, but it has not been possible to distinguish gene-controlled variation from differentiation. For this reason, experiments with bacteria cannot be interpreted in terms of the comparison between gene-controlled and other types of inherited characteristics.

CHROMOSOMAL INHERITANCE

In our selected breeding stocks of Saccharomyces, irregular segregations do not occur very frequently. In maize or Drosophila a similar frequency of irregularity would not be detectable since tetrad analysis is not possible in these forms. Using regularly segregating stocks of Saccharomyces we have mapped four and possibly five chromosomes for genes controlling the fermentation of carbohydrates and the synthesis of various nutrilites (Fig. 16.1).

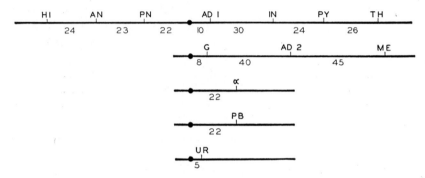

FIG. 16.1   Chromosome maps of Saccharomyces.

Chromosome I, PN (pantothenate), centromere, AD1 (adenine), IN (inositol), PY (pyridoxine), and TH (thiamin).

Chromosome II, centromere, G (galactose), AD2 (adenine), ME (melibiose).

Chromosome III, centromere, α (mating type).

Chromosome IV, centromere, PB (paraminobenzoic acid).

Chromosome V, centromere, UR (uracil).

Chromosomes IV and V may or may not be different; UR and PB have not been used in the same hybrid.

HI (histidine) and AN (anthranilic acid) are linked to each other (24 morgans) but have not yet been located on a chromosome.

DIRECT TETRAD ANALYSIS

The focal point in the life cycle is the reduction division, at which the chromosomes of a diploid cell are sorted out, and the haploid sex cells (such as sperm, eggs, pollen, or yeast spores) are produced. Each diploid parent cell divides twice to produce a tetrad of four haploid sexual nuclei. This process is substantially the same whether a single yeast cell produces four spores or a cell in the testis produces four sperm. In yeast, however, each of the four spores of a single tetrad can produce clones which are available for individual study, and the reduction division can be analyzed directly instead of by inference.

Many yeast hybrids have been produced by mating sex cells carrying chromosomes marked with biochemical mutant genes. The tetrads from these hybrids have been analyzed by growing clones from each of the four spores of a single ascus and classifying each of the spore-cultures. These experiments are *direct tests of the Mendelian theory.* They have shown that exceptions to the Mendelian theory occur more frequently than was hitherto supposed.

CURRENT STATUS OF IRREGULAR MENDELIAN SEGREGATION

Tetrad analysis of triploid and tetraploid yeasts has revealed that some of the irregular (not 2:2) segregations in hybrid asci arise from the fact that one or both of the parents is diploid (Lindegren and Lindegren, 1951; Roman, Hawthorne, and Douglas, 1951). Roman, Hawthorne, and Douglas have concluded that all irregular segregations in Saccharomyces arise from the segregation of triploid or tetraploid zygotes. We have recently completed the analysis of segregation in diploid hybrids heterozygous for both MA/ma and MG/mg. This analysis revealed that in many asci in which segregation of MA/ma was 2:2 ($MA\ MA\ ma\ ma$), segregation of MG/mg was 1:3 ($MG\ mg$ $mg\ mg$). This finding excludes the possibility that the hybrid was either triploid or tetraploid since segregation of both genes would have been equally affected. The phenomenon has been explained as conversion of the MG gene to mg in the zygote. This conclusion is further supported by evidence indicating that both genes are in the same linkage group.

One hypothesis of the nature of the gene developed during the study of irregular segregation seems to have some merit. This is the proposal that the gene is a complex of many more or less loosely connected molecules rather than a single macromolecule. In this view, the gene is composed of a series of identical sites around the periphery of a more or less cylindrical chromosome. These sites may be extremely numerous since they are of molecular dimensions around the periphery of a thread easily visible under the microscope. At these sites identical agents responsible for the action of the gene are located.

GENE DIVISION

The concept of the gene as a *bracelet* of catalysts arranged on the outside of the chromosome simplifies the concept of gene reproduction. When one conceived of genes as macromolecules arranged like *beads on a string*, it was difficult to understand how all the genes on a chromosome could divide simultaneously. If, however, there are thousands of loci and chromogenes at the site of a single gene on the *outside* of an otherwise inert chromosome which is composed principally of *skeletal* material, any longitudinal splitting of the chromosome will partition two qualitatively equivalent parts which may or may not be quantitatively equivalent. The restoration of balance by *interdependence* of the autonomous organelles may make precise division unnecessary.

EXTRACHROMOSOMAL INHERITANCE

When a pure haplophase culture of red yeast (adenine dependent) is planted on an agar plate, both red and white colonies appear. When the white colonies are subcultured, only white colonies appear. The red cells when planted on a second plate continue to produce both red and white colonies. The white colonies are stable variants derived from red. Bacterial variations of this type are ordinarily called gene mutations, but bacteriologists have been unable to test their so-called mutations by breeding experiments except

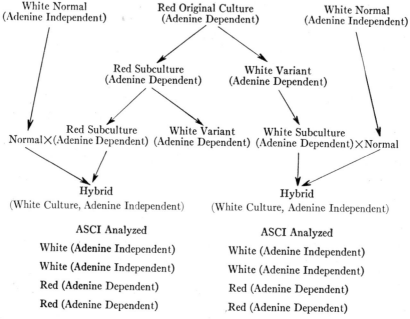

Fig. 16.2—Inheritance of pink versus white colony in Saccharomyces. The white mutants derived from pink produce pink offspring and are indistinguishable from the original pink genetically.

in a few cases. The white cultures have lost their color but they are still characteristically adenine dependent like their red progenitor. Breeding experiments (Fig. 16.2) have been carried out with the white yeast cultures derived from the red. When the derived white cultures were used as parents, they produced precisely the same kind of offspring as the original red culture from which they arose. This proves that the change from red to white did not affect a gene. The change from red to white may, therefore, be called a *differentiation* since it occurs without gene change.

The phenomenon of Dauermodifikation which was first described by Jollos (1934) has thus been confirmed in yeast genetics. The stable change from red to white resembles the discontinuous variations which occur in the vegetative cycles of bacteria. Hybridization experiments have revealed that the origin of white cultures does not involve gene change. This phenomenon in yeast, called *depletion mutation,* is identical with Dauermodifikation in Paramecia. Since neither involves gene change, both are equivalent to differentiation.

It is not possible to study Dauermodifikationen using the classical objects of genetical research, maize and Drosophila, since each generation of these higher organisms is produced sexually—a process during which Dauermodifikationen revert to normal. The stable variants in vegetative cultures of yeast, which revert to normal (produce only normal offspring by sexual reproduction) have no parallel in maize and Drosophila. This points up a striking disadvantage of maize and Drosophila—that they cannot be propagated vegetatively. One cannot be certain that the characteristic variations in flies, which occur when they hatch on wet medium or are subjected to shock treatment, would be lost on vegetative cultures unless one were able to propagate the bent wings or other peculiarities asexually, possibly in tissue culture.

THE AUTONOMOUS ORGANELLES OF THE YEAST CELL

In addition to the chromosomes (Lindegren, 1949) there are other permanent structures in the yeast cell which never originate *de novo* (Lindegren, 1951). They have the same type of continuity in time as chromosomes but are less precisely partitioned than the latter.

The Cytoplasm

The cytoplasm is a limpid fluid which is transmitted to each daughter cell. It is rich in RNA but varies in basophily and contains the mitochondria, usually adhering to the surface of the centrosome or the nuclear vacuole.

The Mitochondria

The state of the mitochondria varies from highly refractile lipoidal structures, sharply defined from the cytoplasm to less refractile organelles with somewhat irregular boundaries.

The Centrosome

The centrosome is a solid and rigid structure which stains with acid fuchsin but does not stain with basic dyes. This highly basic organelle may contain some of the basic proteins which Caspersson and Mirsky have found in chromosomes. The centrosome is always attached to the nuclear vacuole and is the most rigid structure in the cell as revealed by its behavior following shrinkage of the cell. It never originates *de novo* and plays a leading part in budding, copulation, and meiosis.

The Centrochromatin

The centrochromatin is a basophilic, Feulgen-positive substance closely attached to the basic centrosome (probably by an acid-base reaction). Some portion of it is usually in contact with the nuclear vacuole. It is partitioned between the cells following budding by a direct division controlled by two tiny centrioles. In the resting cell it may assume a spherical form and cover most of the centrosome. In division it is usually present in the form of a long strand. The centrosome and centrochromatin have been identified with the nucleus by several workers, but this view has been criticized by Lindegren (1949), Lindegren and Rafalko (1950), and Rafalko and Lindegren (1951). The filament often bends on itself to assume a V- or U-shape. In some preparations it appears to be composed of numerous small particles, but this is due to poor fixation and is especially prevalent in preparations fixed with alkali. The view that the centrochromatin is a single filament external to the centrosome is supported by a multitude of observations on well-fixed cells. Centrochromatin is probably homologous to the heterochromatin of higher forms differing only in being carried on the centrosome rather than the chromosome.

The Nuclear Membrane and the Chromosomes

The nuclear vacuole contains the chromosomes and the nucleolus. The chromosomes are partitioned between mother and bud vacuole in a precise orderly manner without recourse to a spindle. The wall of the nuclear vacuole does not break down at any time in the life cycle; it is a permanent cellular structure.

The Cell Membrane and the Cell Wall

The cell membrane is a permanent cell structure. The cell wall appears to be formed *de novo* in the spores, but it may depend on the cell wall surrounding the ascus for its origin.

BUDDING

Figure 16.3–1 shows a cell in which the acidophilic centrosome attached to the nuclear vacuole is surrounded by the darkly staining cytoplasm. A band of basophilic centrochromatin is securely applied to the side of the centrosome and is also in contact with the nuclear vacuole. Greater differentiation often reveals a small centriole at each end of this band. The nuclear contents are unstained.

Figure 16.3–2 shows the first step in the process of budding. The centrosome produces a small conical process which forces its way through the cytoplasm and erupts into the new bud shown in Figure 16.3–3.

Figure 16.3–4. The nuclear vacuole sends out a long, slender process which follows the centrosome into the bud. Although the cell wall is not visible in these preparations it must be assumed that the cell wall never ruptures but is

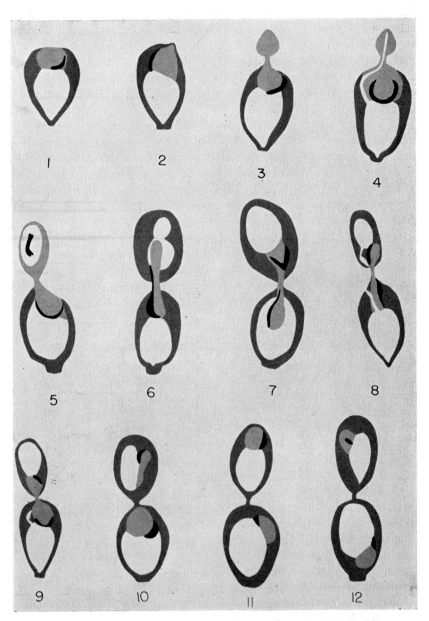

FIG. 16.3—Behavior of the centrosome and centrochromatin during budding.

extended to enclose the bud at all times. The vacuolar process follows the external surface of the centrosome into the bud, lying between the cell wall and the centrosome.

Figure 16.3–5 shows a cell in which the bud vacuole has received its two-stranded chromosome complex. This is an exception to the rule that the chromosomes usually are completely destained in the differentiation by iron alum.

In Figure 16.3–6 the bud vacuole is lobed. This is a rather common phenomenon. The cytoplasm has passed into the bud and completely surrounds the centrosome and the bud vacuole. The extension of the centrochromatin along the surface of the acidophilic centrosome has begun.

Figures 16.3–7, 16.3–8, and 16.3–9 show cells in which the separation of the centrochromatin has been completed with mother and bud held together by the centrosome.

In Figure 16.3–10 the division of the centrosome is complete, but both centrosomes are near the point of budding. In Figure 16.3–11 the bud centrosome has reached the distal end of the bud while the mother cell centrosome still lies in the neighborhood of the point of budding. In Figure 16.3–12 both centrosomes have reached the distal ends of the cells and are prepared for the formation of the next bud.

CONCLUSIONS CONCERNING EXTRACHROMOSOMAL INHERITANCE

Cytological examination of the yeast cell shows that many of its organelles may have the same integrity and continuity in time that characterize the chromosomes—they cannot arise *de novo*. In the yeast cell there are seven or eight such "continuous" organelles. The cell membrane, the nuclear membrane, the centrosome, the centrochromatin, the cytoplasm, the mitochondria, and the chromosomes are permanent cell structures. Because they apparently divide in a manner which does not provide for precise transmission of specific portions to each daughter cell, it appears that the other components differ from the chromosomes in a significant manner—they are probably homogeneous, or their heterogeneity is simple, possibly a few different types of dipolar molecules held together in a specific manner.

There is no reason to assume that any one of these components is of more importance, or directs the "activities" of any one of the other components. The cell can function only if all its component parts are present in proper structural correlation and in adequate amounts. There is no reason to assume that any one of these components is unique in the manner in which it reproduces itself. The present hypothesis proposes that they all reproduce by the simple accretion of molecules like those which they contain, and it is their association with each other in an adequate milieu which provides the molecules necessary for their increase in size. Each of the different organelles is rate limiting in growth. When any one is present in less than the minimal amount, the other organelles cannot obtain the supply of molecules necessary for maintenance and increase until the amount of the deficient organelle has increased.

The chromosomes differ from the other permanent organelles in their high degree of linear heterogeneity. It is this characteristic which has given them the spurious appearance of "controlling" other cellular activities. Mutations with which we are familiar in the laboratory constitute defects or deletions in the extraordinarily heterogeneous chromosomes. The deficiency in the organism caused by the defect—the deletion of the contribution ordinarily made by the intact region of the chromosome—becomes apparent only because the rest of the chromosome produces sufficient materials to enable the defective cell to continue to grow in its absence, although in a manner different from that which was previously characteristic.

Any transmissible defect in a homogeneous structure like the cell wall, the cell membrane, the nuclear membrane, the centrosome, or the centro-chromatin would result in total failure of the organism to survive and bring all vital activity to a halt. The survival of the defective mutants in their altered condition due to the defect in the chromosome (which has been called a mutant gene) has led to the view that genes are different from other cellular components since they can *reproduce variations in themselves*. This is an incorrect point of view. It is more proper to say that when a defect or deletion occurs in a small segment of a chromosome, the rest of the organism can carry on, albeit in a changed condition due to the absence of the contribution previously made by that region, now called the gene. This denies the importance of the ordinary mutations encountered in the laboratory as factors for progressive evolution, and implies that progress in evolution must occur in some other way.

It may be that progressive evolution occurs more frequently as the result of changes in the chromosomes than of other organelles. But the present hypothesis does not exclude the possibility that advances in evolution can occur by "progressive" changes in the composition of any one of the *eternal* organelles such as the nuclear membrane or the centrosome. The condition for the perpetuation of any change would be that the mutated organelle could be provided with the materials necessary for its continuance by the cell as a whole in its surrounding environment *at the time of its occurrence*. On this hypothesis, progressive changes in evolution are not confined to any single cellular component, but constitute a potential of every component of the cell. Although progressive changes of the different substances comprising the chromosome may not occur significantly more frequently than changes in the substances making up the other organelles, more changes may occur in the chromosomes *in toto* because a change in each individual component of the extraordinarily heterogeneous chromosome registers as a separate change.

In many types of organisms the chromosomes are always separated by the nuclear membrane from the cytoplasm. The mitochondria (like the chromosomes) are relatively non-homogeneous, but apparently the balance of their activities is not so critical since no specific devices appear to be required to limit their reproduction or activity. The cytoplasm is probably heterogeneous also, with every separate eternal component having the same continuity in time as the chromosomes. However, it comprises substances transmitted to the daughter cells in a manner which is apparently subject to control by the environment, and this may constitute the basis for differentiation. In the germ line, the *entire* cytoplasmic potential must be maintained. In fact, the main function of the germ line under this hypothesis would be to maintain an intact cytoplasm. The integrity of the chromosomes is usually provided for in either the somatic or the germinal tract. Defects in the extra chromosomal apparati are reconstituted in an outcross, thus differentiating so-called *cytoplasmic* from *genic* inheritance.

H. H. PLOUGH
Amherst College

Chapter 17

Genetic Implications of Mutations in S. Typhimurium*

The contribution that an account of studies in bacterial genetics can make to the problem of heterosis must be indirect, since actual sexual or other fusion in bacteria has not been observed and the weight of evidence is against the view. Even the very interesting genetic evidence of recombination discovered by Tatum and Lederberg (1947) in the K12 strain of the colon bacillus, and now being developed by the capable studies of Lederberg (1947, 1949) and others, is still susceptible of other interpretations. Diploid strains, if they occur at all, are certainly so rare as to be unimportant in the production of hybrid vigor in bacterial populations.

The applications of bacterial genetics to the problem of heterosis must be rather in the information they make available concerning the kinds and frequencies of gene mutations, and the ways in which they interact with each other within populations. It has been generally recognized by geneticists only recently that the bacteria are excellent material for studies of these problems, though bacterial mutation was first mentioned by Massini in 1907, and distinctive and precise food requirements for bacterial strains have been known since 1913 (Hinselwood, 1946). Studies in the genetics of bacteria have, of course, been greatly stimulated by the pioneer work on mutations in fungi by Thom and Steinberg (1939), and particularly on Neurospora by Dodge, by Lindegren, and by Beadle (1949) and his associates, as well as by the important work on yeast as presented in Dr. Lindegren's chapter. Long before the currently enlarging wave of interest in bacteria as objects of genetic study, Gowen had shown that mutations of the same order of frequency as in higher plants or animals were induced by radiation in Phyto-

* This research was supported by a grant from the Atomic Energy Commission, Division of Biology and Medicine #AT(30-1)-930.

monas (1945). He and Zelle had indicated the genetic basis of virulence in Salmonella (Zelle, 1942).

ADVANTAGES OF SALMONELLA FOR GENETIC STUDIES

I became acquainted with the Enterobacteriaceae and particularly with the pathogenic forms in Zinsser's laboratory at the Columbia Medical School. My own realization that Salmonella offered excellent material for studies in microbial genetics was heightened when, as an Army bacteriologist in the Philippines, I had to diagnose enteric infections. I found most of the Salmonellas which Flexner first described from Manila still present in the islands. More than 140 strains or species of Salmonella are recognized which are distinguishable by a common pattern of fermentation reactions (dextrose and maltose-AG, lactose and sucrose-negative, citrate and H_2S positive). Each one has been shown by the serological studies of White (1929), Kaufmann (1944), or Edwards and Bruner (1942) to have a very precise and readily separable antigenic constitution.

The antigens are determined by agglutination studies using serums from different rabbits immunized to one or another of the major strains. They fall into two distinct groups: the somatic (O) antigens associated with the surface protein layers, and the flagellar (H) antigens determined by proteins of the flagella. Each of these groups is known to be compound, with some twenty separate O antigens—each strain may carry three or four (O) antigens—and eight or ten different specific (H) antigens as well as certain alternative and non-specific phases of the latter. Thus each strain can be shown to have a distinctive and readily determinable antigenic constitution (S. typhimurium is I, IV, V, XII—i, 1, 2, 3). The whole group naturally falls into a tree-like pattern very like the evolutionary trees made for families of animals or plants on the basis of structure.

Tatum's (1946) discovery that mutagenic agents (including radiation and nitrogen mustards) could induce mutants of colon bacteria having constant growth factor requirements more limited than the parental organism, just as with Neurospora, has re-emphasized the one gene–one enzyme hypothesis. It has strengthened the idea of bacterial evolution developed by Lwoff (1943) that the parasitic forms have been derived from the less exacting heterotrophic organisms by successive losses of synthetic abilities. Thus it gives added meaning to the tree-like interrelationships suggested by the antigenic analyses.

Soon after the war our Amherst group entered on an intensive study of induced biochemical and antigenic mutations in the food poisoning organism, *Salmonella typhimurium*. It was our hope that this organism would prove more favorable for genetic studies than *E. coli*, not only for the analysis of the mode of action of genes, but for evidence on the genetic nature of type specificity, virulence, and their bearing on evolutionary relationships.

METHODS OF INDUCING AUXOTROPHIC MUTATIONS

The strains of *Salmonella typhimurium* which we have used are two: 519 received from the New York Salmonella center at Beth Israel Hospital, and 533 (11c) from Gowen.

Our method for isolating mutations to specific food or growth factor requirements by penicillin screening is that of Lederberg and Zinder (1948) and of Davis (1949) with some additions of our own. *S. typhimurium* is a heterotrophic organism of the least exacting sort. Cultures will grow on a basic medium containing ammonium sulphate, sodium chloride, potassium phosphate buffers, with traces of other metallic ions, and glucose added as an energy source. Better growth is obtained with a supplementary nitrogen source, such as asparagin, and a further energy source, citrate, but these are not essential. Thus the organism synthesizes all its own food components, coenzymes, and growth factors, as well as the enzymes necessary for food and energy tranformations.

Suspensions are subjected to radiation by X-rays (up to 100,000 roentgens) or ultraviolet light (up to 3,600 ergs per mm.^{2}), and are then transferred to an enriched nutrient broth for 24 hours. The broth stimulates active division of all organisms. These are centrifuged off, washed, and reinoculated for 24 hours into the basic or minimal medium containing 100 units per ml. of penicillin. This stops the divisions, and progressively kills the organisms which divide actively.

These organisms which penicillin screens out are called *prototrophic* (Lederberg), and they are, of course, the unchanged originals. Any mutated organisms which now require some specific nutrilite will not divide on the basic medium, and so they are not affected by penicillin. These are now *auxotrophic* organisms (Davis), and they are isolated by plating on complete agar, and identified by paper disc inoculations on successive plates of basic medium with single nutrilites added—amino acids, nucleic acid fractions, or vitamins, as shown in Figures 17.1 and 17.2. These methods are described in more detail by Plough, Young, and Grimm (1950).

AUXOTROPHIC MUTATIONS FROM RADIATED LINES

I shall cite only one set of isolations from such a radiation experiment, the data for which are given in Table 17.1. Suspensions from an unradiated control and from seven successively increased X-radiation dosages were run through the penicillin screening, and 500 auxotrophic mutants isolated. Of these a total of 459 were recovered and their specific requirements determined. Although the control had been derived from successive single colony isolations within 3 days of the tests, still 5 per cent of the isolated strains were mutants—indicating that spontaneous mutation occurs and accumulates in stock strains.

From the major strain used (#533), 234 strains out of the 459 isolated

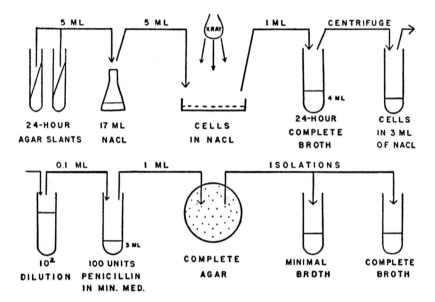

FIG. 17.1—Diagram showing methods for the production of radiation-induced auxotrophic mutations in Salmonella and for their isolation by screening through minimal medium containing penicillin.

PAPER DISC METHOD FOR TESTING BIOCHEMICAL MUTANTS

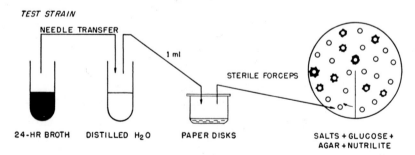

FIG. 17.2—Diagram showing method for determining the particular nutrilite required by the auxotrophs isolated as in Figure 17.1. A series of Petri plates is used, each containing a different test substance.

were auxotrophic mutants, among which 17 different auxotrophic mutants occur according to tests of the specific nutrilite required. A summary of these requirements with the numbers of each is given in Table 17.2. The most frequent auxotroph is the one requiring cysteine. The next most frequent is the histidine auxotroph, and so on down the list to one which has a double requirement of both valine and isoleucine for growth. Only two auxotrophic mutants require substances other than amino acids. One must be supplied

TABLE 17.1

FREQUENCIES OF AUXOTROPHIC MUTATIONS IN *S. TYPHIMURIUM* AFTER X-RADIATION AND PENICILLIN SCREENING

1 X-Ray Dosage and Time	2 % Bacteria Surviving	3 Total No. Tests	4 Total No. Mutants	5 % Mutants	6 No. Different Mutants	7 % Different Mutants
Strain 533						
I Controls...............	100	135	7	5.1	3	2.2
II 11,400 R 4 min........	40	62	16	25.9	4	6.4
III 17,100 R 6 min........	25	86	18	20.9	4	4.7
IV 22,800 R 8 min........	14	41	11	26.8	3	7.3
V 28,500 R 10 min........	6	25	19	76.0	6	24.0
VI 34,300 R 12 min........	1.5	94	64	68.1	8	8.4
VII 45,600 R 16 min........	0.9	99	72	72.6	17	17.2
VIII 57,000 R 20 min........	1	50	34	68.0	12	24.0
Totals.................	....	459	234	....	....	....
IX II+III+IV.............	....	189	45	23.8	11	5.8
X V+VI+VII+VIII.....	....	268	189	70.5	43	16.0
Strain 519						
XI 45,600 R 16 min........	25	100	22	22.0	9	9.0

with adenine, and others (not found in this experiment) must have either guanine or thiamin in the medium.

In our published report of these data (Plough, Young, and Grimm, 1950, Table 3) we listed a number of additional strains showing alternative requirements. Davis (personal communication) retested a number of these and found them to be mixtures of single autotrophs. We have just completed an extensive recheck of all strains listed originally as alternates, and now confirm his results except for the three types of alternates listed in Table 17.2 (Plough, Miller, and Berry, 1951).

MUTATION FREQUENCY AND X-RAY DOSAGE

One of the most interesting results of this experiment is the clear relation between the frequency of auxotrophic mutants and the X-ray dosage. This is shown in Table 17.1, column 5, lines II–VIII, and I could add to the data from other experiments. The numbers of tests vary for the different radiation dosages, and some of the values are less significant statistically, but the percentage of mutants is significantly higher at the higher dosages. This is emphasized by lines IX and X where the sums of the first three and the last four values are compared. The same conclusion is evident from inspection of column 7 in the table, where the numbers of different mutants at the successive dosages are shown. Nearly three times as many were isolated from the upper group as from the lower.

TABLE 17.2

KINDS OF AUXOTROPHIC MUTATIONS IN *S. TYPHIMURIUM*

No.	Strain 533 Single Amino Acids	No.	Strain 519 Single Amino Acids
105.....	Cysteine	8......	Histidine
55.....	Histidine	3......	Cysteine
15.....	Leucine	3......	Methionine
14.....	Proline	3......	Proline
5.....	Tyrosine	1......	Leucine
5.....	Threonine	1......	Tryptophane
4.....	Methionine	1......	Phenylalanine
2.....	Valine		
1.....	Arginine		
	Nucleic Acid Fraction		
5.....	Adenine		
	Multiple Amino Acids		
1.....	Valine and isoleucine		
4.....	Unanalyzed		
	Alternative Amino Acids		*Alternative Amino Acids*
21.....	Cysteine or methionine	1......	Cysteine or Methionine
1.....	Tyrosine or tryptophane		
1.....	Tyrosine or phenylalanine		

Line XI in the table shows the result of one radiated series made on a different initial strain, #519. Comparison of the column 5 and column 7 totals with line VII above, shows that this strain is much more resistant to radiation than is strain #533. It is clear that comparisons of the mutagenic effects of radiation dosage must always be made between samples from the same strain.

The data in Table 17.1, column 5, are graphed in Figure 17.3. Comparison of the percentages of mutants at successive dosages shows a positive correlation, though rather far from a straight line curve. As the penicillin screening method involves a 24 hour growth in complete broth, and another 24 hours in minimal medium with penicillin, it might be expected that the final percentage of mutant strains would not bear the direct relation to dosage shown in tests of mutations produced in germ cells in sexually reproducing organisms. Indeed Davis, in his account of the penicillin screening method as used in *E. coli,* stated ". . . the method as developed so far does not appear to yield quantitative survival of mutants." Such a statement assumes that the penicillin screening may be expected to be complete, which in fact is not true. Rather penicillin acts, as do all antibiotics, in a progressive fashion according to a typical logarithmic killing curve. If two or more mutant cells

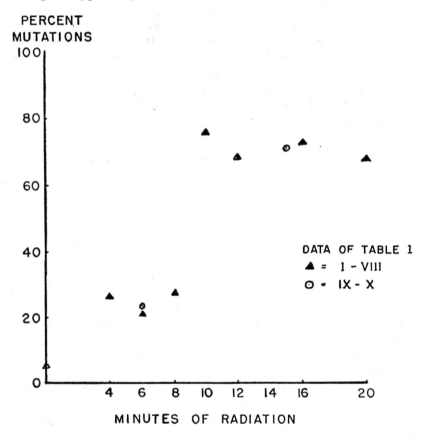

FIG. 17.3—Graph showing the relation between percentage of mutations isolated and X-ray dosage in minutes (2850 R per minute).

appear in a growing wild type population, they will increase logarithmically and form smaller less numerous clones. As the penicillin acts, the far more numerous parent clones will be logarithmically reduced in numbers, while the mutant clones exposed will have reached a level which may be maintained during the 24 hour period of penicillin action. It is clear that if a sample is taken, and plated at any point short of the complete killing off of the wild type, we may expect frequencies showing the same order as in the original population, although the mutant percentages are greatly magnified.

An actual test of artificially made mixtures of the parent strain and one cysteine requiring mutant as screened by the media is shown in Table 17.3. The data show that a mixture of 90 per cent wild and 10 per cent mutant still gives a greater number of wild survivors after penicillin screening than does a mixture having 10 per cent wild and 90 per cent mutant. For the actual experiments reported in Table 17.1 the proportion of mutants to unmutated wild type even after 24 hours of growth in complete broth is one in many thousands, rather than 10 per cent to 90 per cent. So it seems justified to consider the percentage of mutants and wild type as an index of muta-

TABLE 17.3

EFFECT OF GROWTH IN COMPLETE MEDIUM FOLLOWED BY PENICILLIN SCREENING ON ARTIFICIAL MIXTURES OF CONTROL (533) AND A CYSTEINE AUXOTROPH (533-169)

MIXTURE	PERCENTAGES ORIGINAL MIXTURE		PERCENTAGES AFTER 24 HRS. IN BROTH		PERCENTAGES AFTER SUBSEQUENT SCREENING	
	533	533-169	533	533-169	533	533-169
A........	90	10	70	30	8	92
B........	50	50	33	67	2	98
C........	10	90	5	95	2	98

tion frequency in comparing X-ray dosages. The trend in Figure 17.3 suggests a sigmoid curve rather than a straight line as Hollaender (1948) has shown for ultraviolet induced visible mutations in fungi. Essentially the same interpretation can be drawn from a comparison of the number of different mutations found at the successive X-ray dosages. Much more extensive data are now available showing the relation between mutation frequency and both X-radiation and ultraviolet dosages and they will appear in another publication. In general they all bear out the conclusion that the frequency of auxotrophic mutations is directly correlated with radiation dosage as is true for gene mutation in other organisms.

A rather interesting result of comparison of these percentages of mutants present after penicillin screening is that the most frequent class changes from the lower to the higher dosages. Thus after 11,000 roentgens, a cysteine auxotroph is the most frequent, while after 57,000 r it is a histidine requirer. Perhaps we are dealing with a specific effect of dosage or conceivably with a differential effect of wave length, but until the complex nature of the cysteine mutants are more fully understood it is unwise to attempt too definite an interpretation.

RECOMBINATION TESTS IN SALMONELLA

Much interest has been excited among geneticists as well as bacteriologists by Lederberg's proof that mixtures of multiple mutant stocks of the K12 strain of *E. coli* give rise to new strains having the auxotrophic mutants in new combinations. These initial observations have been repeated in different combinations and amply confirmed by the observations of many other investigators. As Lederberg has suggested, these results are most reasonably interpreted as due to bacterial union like a sexual fusion of gametes, followed by an immediate reduction process involving segregation and genetic recombination, suggesting linkage in a single chromosome system. More recently Lederberg (1949) has found evidence of what appears to be a diploid strain which gives highly aberrant segregation ratios. These require assumptions of such an extremely complex and involved type of chromosome interchange that it becomes questionable whether some other explanation is not after all more probable.

In *S. typhimurium* we now have more mutant strains carrying single auxotrophic genes or multiple combinations of these than in any other bacterial species except *E. coli*. This makes it especially important to test the theory with our strains. Accordingly Miss Marie McCarthy has been mixing these in varying combinations, and then plating out in heavy suspensions on base medium supplemented so as to show up the transfer of one or more requirements from one to the other original combination.

Although more than a hundred such tests have been made and carefully checked, the results have been unequivocally negative until very recently. This work will be reported in detail in a later publication, but I will describe it briefly here. Multiple strain #519-38-94-41 requiring tryptophane, methionine, and histidine was mixed with #533-486-96-85 requiring leucine, threonine, and arginine. On plating in appropriate media it was found that in addition to the original parental combinations several colonies each gave strains requiring two new sets of requirements. Recombination No. 1 required tryptophane, leucine, and threonine. Recombination No. 2 needed all six amino acids: tryptophane, methionine, histidine, leucine, threonine, and arginine. These new stocks have been retested, and there can be no question of the fact that we have here two recombinations of the original stocks used. Other recombinations have now appeared but reciprocal classes are never found. Thus we have in Salmonella confirmation of the recombination results found by Lederberg in the K12 strain of *E. coli*. In view of the irregularity of such results both in *E. coli* and in Salmonella, it would seem wise to suggest that some alternative explanation may yet prove to be more satisfactory than recombination or chromosomal crossing-over.

BIOCHEMICAL STUDIES OF AUXOTROPHIC MUTANTS

The Neurospora studies of Beadle and his associates as well as those of Lindegren (1949) on yeast have made it evident that in studying the action of auxotrophic mutants we are many steps closer to the initial determinative activities of the genes themselves than is ordinarily true for characters in the higher plants and animals. When a series of auxotrophic genes can be shown to block successive steps in the syntheses of particular amino acids or vitamins or more complex products, the one gene–one enzyme hypothesis offers the most satisfactory preliminary explanation, even though the presence of the particular enzyme as a gene product has not been demonstrated. Each set of auxotrophic mutants offers data on the chain of synthetic processes to some essential substance, and thus becomes a challenging biochemical problem. It is significant that many of those already studied in the fungi have also been uncovered in *E. coli*, but every organism shows individual differences. So far in Salmonella we have investigated the biochemical steps in only two such series of auxotrophs, but many others await study especially as new mutants are added.

TABLE 17.4

UTILIZATION OF SULPHUR COMPOUNDS BY VARIOUS
AUXOTROPHS OF *S. TYPHIMURIUM*

Strain	Na_2SO_4	$Na_2S_2O_3$	Na_2S	Cysteine	Cysta-thionine	Methio-nine	Block in Fig. 17.4
1. Original 533.....	+	+	+	+	+	+	None
2. 533-575.........	−	+	+	+	+	−	7+2
3. 533-526.........	−	+	+	+	+	+	7
4. 533-452.........	−	−	−	+	+	−	5+2
5. 533-P249........	−	−	−	−	+	+	4
6. 533-535.........	−	−	−	−	−	+	2

The first of these sets of interacting synthetic steps which we have studied is the cysteine-methionine auxotroph series. These mutants fall into many of the same gradations described by Lampen, Roepke, and Jones (1947) for *E. coli*, by Emerson (1950) for Neurospora, and by Teas (1950) for *B. subtilis*. We have tested all of the apparent cysteine or methionine requirers for their ability to reduce inorganic sulfur compounds as well as to utilize organic precursors of methionine. The wild type strains can reduce sulphate, sulphite, or sulfide, and can grow with no other source of S. It has been shown, however, that none of the apparent cysteine requirers can reduce sulphate, but some can reduce sulphite and some sulfide. Many, however, must have cysteine or cystathionine (kindly supplied by Dr. Cowie) and others require methionine as such.

A summary of representative mutants isolated as cysteine or methionine requirers and their abilities to grow on various compounds as the sole source of S is given in Table 17.4. This can be visualized as in Figure 17.4 in terms of a succession of steps, each catalyzed by an enzyme controlled by a gene which is inactivated by the mutation numbered in parentheses. Such a straight line series appears to run in the direction of the arrows from sulphate to protein. When a mutation occurs, as at (5), it must be assumed that growth requirements will be satisfied by any compound succeeding the break in the synthetic chain, unless a second mutation has occurred. This does not hold for methionine which cannot be utilized in mutants #2 and 4 (Table 17.4). Such a result suggests that cysteine is enzyme controlled through a gene which is inactivated by the mutation numbered in parentheses. Cysteine is ordinarily made from methionine (as has been shown for the mammal) and so the reverse dotted arrow marked (1) is shown in the figure. It is hardly likely that a second mutation is indicated for the mutants cited as showing two blocks, but rather that certain mutations cause inhibition of more than one enzyme system. A more comprehensive scheme for the cysteine-methionine synthesis based on the Neurospora work has been given by Emerson (1950).

It is certain that more is involved in the series of reactions shown in Figure 17.4 than the furnishing of essential sulphur for cysteine and methionine.

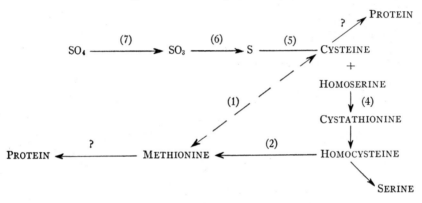

FIG. 17.4—Possible chain of reactions involving sulphur-containing compounds. (Mutant blocks indicated by numbers in parenthesis.)

Sulphate, sulphite, and sulfide, as well as cysteine itself, may act as H acceptors, cooperating with dehydrogenases involved in the respiratory or energy producing activities of the organism. That the organism reduces more sulphate than is necessary for the S required in the amino acids is indicated by the fact that Salmonella forms a readily testable excess of H_2S. We are attempting to trace the course of the sulphur by the use of the radioactive isotope S^{35}. Last summer Dr. T. P. Ting and the writer were able to show that $(NH_4)_2S^*O_4$ is taken up by the wild type 533 organisms and not at all by a cysteine requiring mutant, thus confirming our growth tests (see also Cowie, Bolton, and Sands, 1950).

We hope to continue this work using labeled sulphur in sodium sulfide or barium sulfide, which should be utilized by wild and mutants number (7), (6), (5) (Fig. 17.4). Finally it should be possible to determine by quantitative tests how much S^{35} is combined into bacterial protein and how much passed out in H_2S. Comparisons between different strains in oxygen utilization are being made with the Warburg respirometer. As already shown in

Table 17.3, some cysteine requiring strains will overgrow the parent and this may be due to differences in energy requirements.

The second set of steps in synthesis being studied concerns the adenine requirer. Here we appear to have rather more definite information than was described by Guthrie (1949) for the purine auxotrophs of *E. coli*. It has been shown that the Salmonella auxotroph utilizes adenine and hypoxanthine, but not guanine and xanthine. Of the nucleosides and nucleotides only adenosine and adenylic acid are used, and much more of the latter is required for comparable growth than of adenine. Thus it appears that in purine metabolism, Salmonella and an animal like Tetrahymena (Kidder and Dewey, 1948) show almost opposite requirements, for the bacteria do not convert adenine to guanine. Preliminary studies by Mrs. Helen Y. Miller demonstrate a sparing action for adenine utilization by the amino acid histidine. This suggests

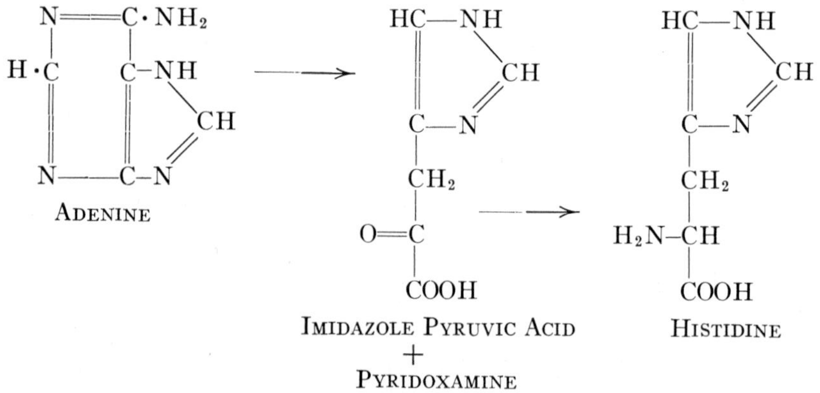

FIG. 17.5—A Possible relation of Adenine to Histidine synthesis (after Broquist and Snell).

that for this organism as with Lactobacillus (Broquist and Snell, 1949) the purine is a precursor of histidine, probably by the utilization of the imidazole ring through pyruvic acid, and the transaminating action of pyridoxamine (Figure 17.5). While these facts have been revealed by a study of the adenine mutant alone, further gene changes and their reactions with the histidine auxotrophs already available should help clarify some of the interactions of purines and amino acids in the bacterial cell.

ALTERATION OF ANTIGENIC SPECIFICITY

The auxotrophic mutations reveal a series of biochemical steps or transformations common to whole groups of organisms. Antigenic analysis, on the other hand, has revealed precise specific or strain differences which are as distinctive as the form or structural differences of complex animals and plants. This has been clearly demonstrated by the blood group analysis presented in the studies of Irwin and his colleagues. The specificity is no less sharp in the antigenic analyses of Salmonella. The tree-like relationship which they suggest was our chief stimulus to a study of bacterial genetics in this organism.

Preliminary tests of all of the auxotrophic mutants made by Miss Dorothy Farley show that they are unchanged antigenically. Not only the specific antigens, but the agglutination titers are the same as the original strains. This has been confirmed by reciprocal absorption tests, as well as by precipitation, and inhibition of agglutination using supernatants from boiled cultures. Thus it appears that the loss of ability to synthesize a particular amino acid in no way alters the antigenic configuration. Apparently if proteins are formed at all they take on the antigenic configuration of the cytoplasm already there. The auxotrophic mutants and the antigenic patterns fall into two quite independent systems so far as present evidence goes. This seems to be true also for variations in or loss of virulence. The relation of the auxotrophic mutants to virulence for mice is being studied in detail by Gowen and his associates and will be reported separately, but so far at least it appears that there is no relation between virulence and the biochemical requirements of the strain.

It was originally and is still our hope to be able to induce antigenic variants by radiation, but so far such attempts have given negative results. We have inoculated radiated suspensions into one end of U tubes of semisolid agar containing low concentrations of O serum from a rabbit immunized against the specific strain, and the organisms grow through the medium. When agar containing specific H serum is used, however, the organisms grow only at the site of inoculation. If antigenic mutants had occurred we would expect that the homologous serum would act as a screen to block off the original and let the mutants through, just as the penicillin does for the auxotrophs. The result simply means that we have not found any antigenic mutants following radiation. Perhaps we should not expect any.

Antigenic mutants have been induced in several bacteria by other methods, especially by McCarty (1946) in the pneumococcus, by Bruner and Edwards (1947) in Salmonella, and by Boivin (1947) in *E. coli*. The pneumococcus method is not applicable to Salmonella, and the Boivin method involving exposure of the organism to autolysates of rough variants of other strains gives negative results. Tests using similar culture filtrates have been unsuccessful in altering the antigenic constitution of our organism. On the other hand, Miss Farley has made use of the Edwards technique of growing an auxotrophic mutant in a semi-solid medium containing homologous O serum previously absorbed with a related organism which lacked one of the major antigens, XII (and in another case lacked V but carried an additional antigen XXVII). By this method two successful transformations of type have been secured out of several tried. Both of these transformations were performed on an auxotrophic mutant (519–P10) requiring histidine.

Preliminary tests showed that these strains were antigenically similar and gave the same agglutination titer with homologous serum as the parental wild types—(I) IV, V, XII, for the O antigens. The parentheses indicate that (I) is very weak or absent. The first case is typical. Specific serum from animals immunized by #519 was absorbed with a suspension of organisms of #527, an unnamed strain known to have O antigens IV, V only. After it was passed through semisolid agar containing the absorbed serum now carrying XII antibodies only, 519–P10 was retested and shown now to give agglutination at a very low titer (1/320 instead of 1/10,000) compared with the original. Further testing has demonstrated that this strain retains the two major O antigens (IV and V), but has lost XII. Thus it has been transformed to IV, V like strain #527. Further tests on differential media prove that the strain is unchanged as an auxotrophic mutant, and still cannot grow unless the medium contains histidine (519–10).

In the other case 519 O serum was absorbed by *S. schleissheim* (V, XII, XXVII). The mutant after growing through the absorbed serum failed to agglutinate in XII serum, and had a higher titer in XXVII than *S. schleissheim*. Thus the changed mutant has lost XII and taken on antigen XXVII. It still retains its histidine requirement.

Thus we have two independent cases of the alteration of antigenic specificity by the Edwards method of passage through specific serum. Here again the evidence indicated no relation between antigenic configuration and the biochemical requirements. We are now exposing these antigenically altered strains to further radiation with the idea of building up multiple auxotrophic stocks combining the two major systems of mutations. These can then be used for more conclusive tests of possible fusion and recombination. However, this demonstration that antigenic mutants can be induced by specific serum adds to the possibility that mutual interaction of genes or gene products between organisms in mixtures may give a more acceptable explanation of the recorded cases of recombination in bacteria, than does one based on genetic analogies with higher forms.

SUMMARY

An account has been given of the results of X-radiation of suspensions of the two strains of *Salmonella typhimurium*, and the isolation of strains with specific nutrilite requirements (auxotrophic mutants). These strains are isolated by the Davis-Lederberg method of growth for twenty-four hours in enriched broth, followed by twenty-four hours in minimal broth containing 100 units per ml. of penicillin. The method screens out the unmutated organisms according to a logarithmic survival curve, and preserves the mutant bacteria.

Successive tests show a relation between X-ray dosage and the percentage of recovered auxotrophic mutants, and also between dosage and the number of different mutants.

In all, 249 separate auxotrophic mutants, of which 20 are different, were isolated out of 459 tests. Most of these showed requirements for single amino acids, but a few required the purine base adenine, and others showed alternative, and a small number, multiple requirements.

A large number of tests involving growth of multiple mutant stocks in mixtures followed by re-isolations have been made to test for possible fusion and recombination as reported by Lederberg and others in the K 12 strain of *E. coli*. Recombination has been found but it is unlike that in sexually reproducing organisms.

Detailed studies of the different auxotrophs requiring cysteine or methionine show a step-like series beginning with loss of ability to reduce inorganic sulphate, and continuing to the loss of ability to form methionine. Many of these mutational steps are explainable as due to the inactivation of a specific enzyme, but several require a complex pattern of chemical interactions.

Similar studies of the adenine auxotroph suggest that adenine may be a source of histidine.

Tests have been made to determine if antigenic specificity can be altered by radiation, with negative results. However, an auxotrophic mutant has been antigenically altered in two different cases by the Edwards technique of passing through absorbed immune serum. In each case, one of the O antigens was removed, and in one case another O antigen was added. In both cases the biochemical requirement of histidine was retained.

It appears that the auxotrophic and antigenic series represent two quite different and unrelated sets of mutations.

JAMES F. CROW
University of Wisconsin

Chapter 18

Dominance
and Overdominance*

Since the first attempts to explain hybrid vigor and the deleterious effects of inbreeding in Mendelian terms, there have been two principal hypotheses. Both were advanced early, and though each has had its ups and downs in popularity, both have persisted to the present time. The first hypothesis is based on the observed correlation between dominance and beneficial effect (or recessiveness and detrimental effect). Inbreeding uncovers deleterious recessives, and typically results in deterioration.

With hybridization, some of the detrimental recessives brought into the hybrid zygote by one parent are rendered ineffective by their dominant alleles from the other, and an increase in vigor is the result. If the number of factors is large, or if there is linkage, the probability becomes exceedingly small of a single inbred line becoming homozygous for only the dominant beneficial factors. Consequently, there should be a consistent decrease in vigor with inbreeding, and recovery with hybridization. This idea has been called the *dominance* or the *dominance of linked genes* hypothesis.

The alternative theory assumes that there is something about hybridity *per se* that contributes to vigor. In Mendelian terms this means that there are loci at which the heterozygote is superior to either homozygote, and that there is increased vigor in proportion to the amount of heterozygosis. This idea has been called *stimulation of heterozygosis, super-dominance, over-dominance, single gene heterosis, cumulative action of divergent alleles,* and simply *heterosis*.

In accordance with the title of this discussion I shall use the words *dominance* and *overdominance* for the two hypotheses. This leaves the word *heterosis* free for more general use as a synonym for *hybrid vigor* (Shull, 1948).

* Paper No. 434 from the Department of Genetics, University of Wisconsin.

In most situations, the hypotheses of dominance and overdominance lead to the same expectations. In either case there is a decrease of vigor on inbreeding and a gain on outcrossing. Wright (1922c) has shown that with the dominance hypothesis the decline in vigor is proportional to the decrease in heterozygosis, regardless of the relative number of dominant and recessive genes and of the degree of dominance. The same decline in vigor with decreasing heterozygosity is true with overdominance.

It is usually impossible in a breeding experiment to differentiate between true overdominance in a pair of alleles, and pseudo-overdominance due to the effects of two pairs of alleles closely linked in the repulsion phase. Only in special circumstances, such as when a mutation has recently occurred in an isogenic stock, can the experimenter be reasonably certain that the effect is due to a single allelic difference. Furthermore, there is the possibility of heterosis due to borderline situations, such as might arise in pseudoalleles with a position effect, which could not even theoretically be classified as due to dominance of linked genes or overdominance. Finally, it should be noted that the various hypotheses may not be equally important in all situations. For example, it is reasonable to expect that overdominance would be more important in determining differences between inbred lines of corn previously selected for general combining ability than in lines not so selected.

If the two hypotheses are not mutually exclusive, neither are they collectively exhaustive. There is no reason to think that multiple factors are any less complex in their interactions than factors concerned with qualitative differences. With the number of genes involved in heterosis, and with the complexity of interactions known to exist in cases where individual gene effects have been isolated and studied, there must surely be all sorts of complex interactions in heterosis. Therefore no single theory can be expected to account for the entire effects of heterosis. Although it is difficult to separate by statistical methods the effects of dominance and epistasis, it may be possible to construct simple models which are of some utility.

DOMINANCE

Davenport (1908) was the first to point out the now well-recognized fact that in most cases the dominant character is beneficial to the organism possessing it, while the recessive has a weakening effect. He noted that this could help explain the degeneration that usually follows inbreeding. Davenport was thinking of relatively few factors with individually large effects, whereas at present, more emphasis is given to multiple factors. But he was close to the ideas now held.

Keeble and Pellew (1910) found that hybrids between two pure varieties of peas were taller than either parent. In this case, two different dominant factors were involved—one resulting in longer internodes and the other increasing their number. Here only two gene pairs were involved, but it was mentioned that similar systems might hold for more complex cases.

A more general development of the dominance hypothesis was given during the same year by Bruce (1910). He designated the frequencies of dominant and recessive alleles as p and q in one breed and P and Q in the other. The array of individuals in the two groups will then be $(p^2DD + 2pqDR + q^2RR)^n$ and $(P^2DD + 2PQDR + Q^2RR)^n$, where D and R are the dominant and recessive alleles and n is the number of factor pairs involved.[1] If these two populations are crossed, the mean number of homozygous recessive loci is nqQ, whereas the average number for the two parent populations is $n(q^2 + Q^2)/2$. The former is the geometric mean of the two parental recessive genotype frequencies while the latter is the arithmetic mean. Since the geometric mean is always less than the arithmetic, the number of homozygous recessive loci will always be less in the hybrid population than the mean number in the two parent populations. If either or both the parent populations are inbred the decrease will be greater.

Bruce then said:

> If, now, it be assumed that dominance is positively correlated with vigor, we have the final result that the crossing of two pure breeds produces a mean vigor greater than the collective mean vigor of the parent breeds. . . . I am aware that there is no experimental evidence to justify the assumption that dominance is correlated with a "blending" character like vigor; but the hypothesis is not an extravagant one, and may pass until a better takes the field.

The average proportion of recessive homozygotes in the parents, which is $(q^2 + Q^2)/2$, may be rewritten as $qQ + (q - Q)^2/2$. This is always larger than qQ, the proportion in the hybrid, unless q and Q are equal. Although Bruce didn't mention this, after one generation of random mating the proportion of recessives in the hybrid population becomes $(q + Q)^2/4 = qQ + (q - Q)^2/4$, which shows that half the gain in vigor is lost as soon as random mating begins.

Bruce concentrated his attention on the decrease of homozygous recessive loci in the hybrid, and postulated a correlation between recessiveness and deleterious effect. He could have used the same algebraic procedures to show that crossing produces an increase in heterozygous loci, and thus based a theory of hybrid vigor on overdominance. He showed remarkable foresight in choosing the former, at a time when he had no evidence of a correlation between dominance and beneficial effect.

1. The notation used by Bruce implies equal frequency of dominant and recessive alleles at all loci. This assumption is not at all necessary for the argument, and I think that what Bruce really meant was

$$\prod_{i=1}^{n} (p_i^2 DD + 2p_i q_i DR + q_i^2 RR).$$

Objections to the dominance hypothesis were made largely on two grounds. First, if vigor is not a product of heterozygosity as such, it should be possible by selection to obtain individuals which are homozygous for all the beneficial dominant factors, and hence have the same vigor as hybrids. Secondly, in the F_2 of a cross between two inbred strains there should be a skew distribution of the trait being measured—since the dominant and recessive loci would be distributed according to the expansion of $(3/4 + 1/4)^n$, where n is the number of factors.

These objections were largely removed when Jones (1917) pointed out that, with linkage, the consequences of the dominance hypothesis were much closer to those postulating superior heterozygotes. If a detrimental recessive were linked with a favorable dominant, the heterozygous chromosome would be superior to both homozygotes, and the linked combination might not break up readily. Later, Collins (1921) showed that with a large number of factors, regardless of linkage, the skew distribution disappears. The probability of getting all the beneficial dominants into one homozygous strain becomes vanishingly small, so the objections hold only if a small number of factors is assumed.

Most of the mutations known in Drosophila and elsewhere are recessive, and practically all are in some way deleterious. Even if dominant and recessive mutations were occurring with equal frequency, the deleterious mutations in a population at any time would be mostly recessive, since the dominants would be rapidly eliminated. It is to be expected—and it has been often observed—that at most unfixed loci the recessive is deleterious in comparison with its dominant allele.[2]

Almost thirty years ago Sewall Wright (1922c) wrote:

> Given the Mendelian mechanism of heredity, and this more or less perfect correlation between recessiveness and detrimental effect, and all the long-known effects of inbreeding—the frequent appearance of abnormalities, the usual deterioration in size, fertility, and constitutional vigor in the early generations, the absence of such decline in any one or all of these respects in particular cases, and the fixation of type and prepotency attained in later generations—are the consequences to be expected.

It has been shown many times that populations actually contain a large number of detrimental recessives—sufficient to account for a large decline in vigor on inbreeding. In *Drosophila pseudoobscura*, Dobzhansky *et al.* (1942) found that almost every fly examined had at least one concealed lethal. Further evidence that at least some heterosis is due to dominant favorable genes is provided by the experiments of Richey and Sprague (1931) on convergent improvement in corn.

2. I consider the statement that a dominant is beneficial and the statement that a recessive is deleterious as meaning the same thing. Since a geneticist ordinarily can study gene effects only by substituting one allele for the other, he cannot distinguish what each factor is doing individually or whether it is harmful or beneficial except relative to its allele. That is, he can only tell what the effect of the substitution is.

OVERDOMINANCE

The concept of a stimulating effect of hybridization began independently with Shull (1908, 1911b) and East (1908). It was assumed that there was a physiological stimulus to development which increased with the diversity of the uniting gametes—with increasing heterozygosis. East (1936) elaborated the idea further by postulating a series of alleles each having positive action functions, and with these functions to some extent cumulative. As the alleles became more and more divergent in function, the action was postulated to become more nearly additive in the heterozygote.

At the time when East and Shull first formulated the hypothesis, there was no direct evidence of any locus at which the heterozygote exceeded either homozygote. For a number of years, overdominance as an explanation of heterosis largely was given up because of the failure to find such loci.

Stadler (1939) pointed out that in certain of the R alleles in corn a situation obtains in which certain heterozygotes have more areas pigmented than either homozygote. He suggested that genes acting in this manner could result in overdominance for such characters as size and yield. Other such loci are known in corn.

There are now several cases in the literature of single genes with heterotic effects. In most of these it is not possible to rule out the possibility of close linkages giving pseudo-overdominant effects. In particular, many cases may turn out to be pseudoallelism, but the consequences for the animal or plant breeder would not be changed.

Several workers (Teissier, 1942a; Robertson, unpublished) have found persistent lethals in Drosophila population cage experiments. If these are not due to individually heterotic loci, extremely close linkage must be postulated. Also certain recessive genes, such as *ebony*, come to an equilibrium with their normal alleles in population cages. One of the most convincing cases is that of the eye color mutant described by Buzzati-Traverso in this volume. This mutant persists in the population, and was found in three independent stocks. It is quite improbable that in each of these cases the gene happened to be linked in the repulsion phase with another harmful recessive.

The idea of superior heterozygotes has been upheld by Hull (1945) who suggested the word overdominance. Hull's original argument for overdominance is a simple one. He noted that in most cases the hybrid between two inbred maize lines has a greater yield than the sum of the two inbreds. This would not be possible with dominant genes acting in a completely additive manner—unless it were assumed that a plant with no favorable dominants had a negative yield.

The validity of this argument depends on the unimportance of epistasis in corn yields. Evidence on this point is very incomplete and somewhat contradictory. Neal (1935) reported that the F_2 yields were almost exactly intermediate between the F_1 and the average of the parents. This would suggest that epistatis is not important or else that there is some sort of cancelling out of various effects. On the other hand, Stringfield (1950) found that in many cases backcrosses showed consistently higher yields than the F_2. This suggests some sort of interaction, as if some of the gene combinations selected for during the inbreeding process were active in the backcross, but were broken in the F_2. None of these data give any evidence as to the importance of epistasis in determining the difference between an inbred line and a hypothetical line with none of the favorable dominants, since the data do not extend into this range. It is in this range where non-additivity might be expected to be most pronounced.

Hull's second argument is based on results obtained by the technique of constant parent regression. The regression of F_1 on one parent, with the other parent held constant, has different expectations when there is overdominance than when there is dominance. With overdominance the regression may be negative when the constant parent is high-yielding, so the regression surface is different from that expected with dominance. In this volume Hull gives data which conform with this expectation.

Overdominance is not the only possible explanation of such results, as Hull has pointed out. In addition, the constant parent regression technique, or any technique making use of yield data on inbred lines, is complicated by the difficulty of obtaining consistent results with inbreds. Another possibility is that the factors responsible for yield in inbreds are largely different genes from those determining the yield in the hybrids. This possibility will be considered later.

For these reasons it is still not possible to be sure of the importance of overdominance from Hull's methods. They are at least strongly suggestive, and recent data from Robinson et al. (1949), obtained by an entirely different procedure, also gave evidence of overdominance.

MAXIMUM HETEROSIS WITH THE DOMINANCE HYPOTHESIS

In this discussion several assumptions are made. Most of these have been implicit in most discussions of heterosis, but it is best that they be clearly set forth at the outset. The assumptions are:

1. Genes concerned with vigor are dominant, and in each case the dominant allele is beneficial and the recessive deleterious. This is an assumption of convenience which does not alter the essential nature of the hypothesis. The conclusions still hold if dominance is not complete. Also there are loci in which the recessive is advantageous or in which the heterozygote is intermediate; but these are of no consequence for heterosis and therefore can be omitted from the discussion.

2. There is complete additivity of effects between loci—no epistasis.

3. There are no barriers to recombination that prevent each gene from reaching its own equilibrium frequency independently of other loci.

4. The gene and phenotype frequencies of the parent population are at their equilibrium values.

5. Increased vigor results in, and can be measured in terms of, increased selective advantage, though the selection may be natural or artificial. This assumption restricts the discussion to those cases in which heterosis results in changes in the same direction as selection had previously been acting. Such an assumption appears to be valid for yield characters in field crops, and for viability and fertility as is measured in Drosophila population studies. It is highly questionable for such things as increase in size of hybrids between wild varieties or species, where natural selection pressure may well have been toward an intermediate size.

Under this assumption the increase of vigor on hybridization depends directly on the number of loci which are homozygous recessives in the parent, but which become heterozygous in the hybrid. The individual or population of maximum vigor is one in which every allelic pair contains at least one dominant. The actual attainable heterosis would be less than this in any particular case.

Consider the case of complete dominance. The recessive phenotype is assumed to have a selective disadvantage of s. That is, the dominant and recessive phenotypes are surviving and reproducing in the ratio of 1 to $1 - s$. The rate of mutation from A to a is u per gene per generation. Reverse mutation will be ignored as it can be shown to have a negligible effect on the equilibrium gene frequency attained.

Genotype	$A\,A$	$A\,a$	$a\,a$
Frequency	P	$2Q$	R
Selective value	1	1	$1 - s$

$$P + 2Q + R = 1$$

Under these assumptions, the frequency of gene A will be $P + Q$, while the frequency of a will be $Q + R$. With mutation from A to a at rate u, the frequency of A will be reduced in one generation by $u(P + Q)$ and the frequency of a increased by the same amount. Likewise, due to the effect of selection, the frequency of a will be decreased by sR. Therefore the gene ratio, $(P + Q)/(Q + R)$, will change in one generation due to the effects of mutation and selection to

$$\frac{(P+Q)(1-u)}{(P+Q)u+Q+R-sR}.$$

When equilibrium is reached the gene frequency will no longer change from generation to generation which, stated algebraically, is

$$\frac{P+Q}{Q+R} = \frac{(P+Q)(1-u)}{(P+Q)u+Q+R-sR}.$$

This has the solution, $R = u/s$. (For a more pedantic demonstration of this, see Crow, 1948.)

The average reduction in selective value of the population due to a detrimental factor will be the product of the selective disadvantage of the factor and the proportion of individuals possessing the factor. This amounts to (s) (u/s), or, simply, u, the mutation rate. Hence, the effect of a detrimental gene on the selective value of the population is equal to the mutation rate to that gene, and is independent of the selective disadvantage which that factor causes, as was first pointed out by Haldane (1937). This fact, which at first appears paradoxical, is readily understandable when one notes that a mildly deleterious mutant persists much longer in the population, and hence affects many more individuals than one which has a greater harmful effect.

The total effect on the population of all the loci capable of mutating to deleterious recessives is simply the sum of the individual mutation rates as long as the gene effects are additive. If there are n such loci with an average mutation rate of $\bar{u}$, the net reduction in selective value due to all homozygous detrimental recessives at all loci in which they occur is $n\bar{u}$. This is also approximately correct if the factors are multiplicative, provided the individual effects are small.

The product $n\bar{u}$ is probably in the vicinity of .05 (Crow, 1948). This means that if all the deleterious recessives were replaced by their dominant alleles, the selective advantage of an equilibrium population would be increased by about this amount. This could be considered as the maximum average improvement in vigor, as measured in terms of selective advantage, that could occur due to hybridization. This means that the dominance hypothesis cannot, under the conditions postulated, account for average increases of more than a few per cent in vigor.

There are several reasons why the 5 per cent figure given above may be too large. One is that many deleterious factors considered to be recessive may not be completely recessive. Stern and Novitski (1948) and Muller (1950) have shown that the majority of lethals and detrimentals that occur in laboratory cultures of Drosophila are not completely recessive. Even if the detrimental effect of the heterozygote is much less than that of the homozygote, the greatest selection effect will still be on heterozygotes because of their much greater frequency in the population. Thus, from the population standpoint, these factors would be acting more like dominants than recessives. This means that each locus would have a detrimental effect of $2u$ instead of u (since a dominant gene would be responsible for twice as many "genetic deaths" as a recessive), but the locus would be unimportant for heterosis. Since the n in the formula refers only to the number of loci which are capable of mutating to a completely recessive allele, its value may be smaller than previously assumed and the product $n\bar{u}$ proportionately less.

It has been assumed that the parent populations are at equilibrium between selection and mutation pressures. This assumption probably is not strictly correct for any population. Any equilibrium involving occurrences as rare as mutations must be slow of attainment. Hence many if not most populations must not be at equilibrium. Probably the most common way in which a population gets out of equilibrium is by an alteration of the breeding structure or population number so that the effective amount of inbreeding is changed. If the change in population structure is such as to increase the amount of homozygosity, a new equilibrium is reached comparatively rapidly through the elimination by selection of the recessives which have been made homozygous. On the other hand, if the change in population is such as to decrease the amount of homozygosity a new equilibrium is attained only through the accumulation of new mutations. This is an extremely slow process.

Since the return to equilibrium is much slower when the population changes in the direction of less inbreeding, it follows that most populations which are out of equilibrium will be out in the direction of having too few detrimental recessives. Therefore the effect of fluctuations in population size and breeding structure will be on the average such as to increase the fitness of the population. For this reason, the average loss of fitness per locus is probably less than the mutation rate. Fisher (1949) has pointed out that if the yield of a crop is near a "ceiling," the relative effect of each factor conditioning yield becomes less. There will be a similar tendency for the population to be out of equilibrium because of the slowness of occurrence of the mutations required to bring the population to the new equilibrium level.

Another factor also pointed out by Fisher is that complete lethals and highly deleterious factors contribute to the mutation rate but, at least in grain crops, have no appreciable effect on yield since they are crowded out by other plants.

All of these factors make the 5 per cent figure an overestimate, so it should be regarded as a maximum. The true value may be much less. In this connection Fisher (1949) said:

> . . . it would appear that the total elimination of deleterious recessives would make less difference to the yield of cross-bred commercial crops than the total mutation rate would suggest. Perhaps no more than a 1 per cent improvement could be looked for from this cause. Differences of the order of 20 per cent remain to be explained.

These considerations make it difficult to explain, in terms of the dominance hypothesis, cases in which two equilibrium populations produce hybrids with considerable heterosis, or in which crosses between inbred lines average appreciably more than the randomly mating populations from which they were derived.

This discussion is relevant only when the character is measurable in terms of selective value. For yield characters subject to any high degree of artificial selection an increase in yield is probably accompanied by a greater proportional increase in selective value. Thus any conclusions about maximum proportional increase in selective value would hold *a fortiori* for yield. Fisher (1949) reaches a similar conclusion when he says: "If the chance of survival is equated to the yield, as is reasonable with grain crops."

Another assumption is that the hybrids are compared with equilibrium populations. There is room for question, particularly with domestic plants and animals, as to whether selection has been occurring long enough and its direction has been consistent enough for a gene frequency equilibrium to have been attained. Another point that must be remembered in discussions of maize is that commercial hybrids are not random combinations of inbred lines, but highly select combinations. An *average* hybrid may have a yield very close to that of a randomly mating population. Thus the argument of this section may not be relevant for corn. But it can hardly be true that the high yield of certain corn hybrids is due to the elimination of deleterious recessives during inbreeding.

The quantitative limit placed on average improvement on hybridization with the dominance hypothesis does not hold for overdominant loci. A locus at which the homozygote AA has a selective disadvantage of s with respect to the heterozygote, and the homozygote $A'A'$ has a disadvantage of t, will come to equilibrium with gene frequency of A equal to $t/(s + t)$, and the frequency of A' equal to $s/(s + t)$ (Wright, 1931b; Crow, 1948). The average reduction in selective advantage of the population due to the two homozygous genotypes comes out to be $st/(s + t)$. The loss in fitness of the population is of the order of magnitude of the selection coefficients, as Haldane (1937) has first shown, whereas with a detrimental recessive, the loss is of the order of the mutation rate. Hence a single overdominant locus has a tremendously greater effect on the population fitness than a single locus with dominance or intermediate heterozygote. If such loci are at all frequent they must be important. The question is: how frequent are they?

Even with overdominance it is difficult to understand large average increases in selective advantage of hybrids between equilibrium populations. Such populations should be somewhere near their optimum gene frequencies, which means that the hybrids would be about the same as the parents. It may be that, on the average, hybrids do not greatly exceed their parents in selective advantage, and that the cases of increased size observed in variety crosses and occasionally in species crosses are nothing but *luxuriance*. If so, they are much less difficult to explain.

As Bruce showed in 1910, if the parents differ at all in gene frequencies, the hybrids will be more heterozygous. If both parents are at equilibrium they should have, for additive genes, approximately the same frequencies. But what differences there are—due to chance, for example—will amount to much more in an overdominant than in a dominant locus because the former has a gene frequency much nearer .5.

POPULATION VARIANCE

The same considerations which show that an overdominant locus has a much greater effect on average population fitness than a dominant locus also show that an overdominant locus has a much greater effect on the population variance. If the selective values of the three genotypes, AA, Aa, and aa are 1, 1, and $1 - s$ respectively, the frequency of aa genotypes is u/s and the average selective value $1 - u$. The variance in fitness will be su. On the other hand, with an overdominant locus where the fitnesses of the three genotypes are $1 - s$, 1, and $1 - s$, the mean fitness is $1 - s/2$. The variance in fitness is $s^2/4$.

The ratio of these variances is $s/4u$, which means that an overdominant locus causes a population variance $s/4u$ times as great as that resulting from a recessive locus of the same selective disadvantage. If $4u$ is 10^{-5}, this amounts to 100 for $s = .001$, or is 1000 for $s = .01$. This makes an overdominant locus with these selective values equivalent to 100 or 1000 ordinary loci in its effect on the population variance. Haldane (1950) has emphasized the importance of loci with adaptively superior heterozygotes in increasing the variance of natural populations.

From this we must conclude that there doesn't have to be a very high proportion of overdominant loci for overdominance to be the most important factor in the genetic variance of the population. If much of the genetic variance of a population is due to overdominance, this would explain the great slowness of selection. Characters with high genetic determination but low parent-offspring correlation might be due to this cause.

The facts of hybrid corn also are consistent with this. Ordinary selection has not been effective. Yet there is a great deal of variation in an open-pollinated variety. It has been relatively easy to find combinations of inbred lines that have yields well above the open-pollinated averages. There appears to be a relatively high degree of genetic determination of yield, but relatively low heritability. These results are not impossible with dominant genes, especially with epistasis, but are precisely what would be expected if some of the variance were due to overdominant loci.

A population with many overdominant loci is always well below its maximum possible fitness. It is expected that such factors could eventually be replaced in long evolutionary periods. This might occur by an appropriate mutation, by duplication, or by modifiers. Or a population with too many overdominant loci might disappear due to inter-population competition. But at any particular time, a population may have a small proportion of such loci, and it does not require many for these to be the major source of variation.

DO THE SAME GENES DETERMINE VARIATION IN INBREDS AND HYBRIDS?

The rarer a recessive phenotype is in a population, the greater will be its relative increase in frequency on inbreeding. If the frequency of the recessive gene is q, the frequency of recessive homozygotes in a randomly mating population is q^2. With increasing amounts of inbreeding, the frequency changes from q^2 to q. The smaller the value of q, the greater is the ratio of q to q^2. If a gene is highly deleterious it will be very rare in the population. Hence the genotypes which are most deleterious are those which have the greatest relative increase in frequency on inbreeding.

These relationships are brought out in the following figures, based on a mutation rate of 10^{-6}. The ratio given is the ratio of homozygous recessives in a homozygous population as compared with one which is mating at random.

Selective disadvantage (s)	.0001	.001	.01	.1	lethal
Gene frequency (q)	.1	.032	.01	.003	.001
Ratio (q/q^2)	10	32	100	316	1000

This means that highly deleterious recessives, which ordinarily have an effect on the population only of the order of the mutation rate, become much more important with inbreeding and may become the major factors in determining the fitness of an inbred population. This might to some extent be offset by selection during the inbreeding process, but such selection would be directed against factors which are of no consequence in a more heterozygous population.

The detrimental recessive factors referred to here include the lethals and semilethals (such as chlorophyll deficiencies) that show up during inbreeding. But more important are the larger number of factors, not individually detectable, which collectively result in the loss of vigor with inbreeding despite rigorous selection.

On the other hand, the major part of the variance of a non-inbred population may well be determined by genes of intermediate frequencies, from .1 to .9. The effect of such factors in determining the population variance in fitness would change only slightly with inbreeding.

As an example, consider a hypothetical population mating at random whose variance is made up of two components. Ninety per cent of the variance is due to relatively common loci with gene frequencies of the order of .5. The other 10 per cent is due to loci with recessive gene frequencies of the order of .01 or less. Now when this population is inbred without selection, the variance due to the common genes will not change greatly but the variance due to the recessive loci will increase by a hundred fold or more. Thus the factors which originally contributed only 10 per cent to the variance may now contribute over 90 per cent of the variance between the various inbred lines derived from the population.

Gene frequencies of the order of .5 might result from several causes. They might be genes which are advantageous in one geographical location and disadvantageous in another so as to form a cline. Or there might be seasonal differences in selective value. They may be due to complex interactions with other loci or be of extremely small selective advantage or disadvantage. But another explanation is selective superiority of heterozygotes (Haldane, 1950), at least for those factors of importance in heterosis.

If yield is determined entirely by dominant factors, the correlation between inbreds and their hybrids should be positive. If it is due to overdominant loci, the correlation should be generally positive, though there would be negative correlations between yield of hybrids and inbreds when the other inbred is constant and high yielding. If both factors are involved and overdominant loci are relatively important in hybrids while dominants are important in inbreds, the correlation would approach zero. The experience of corn breeders has been that selection for yield during inbreeding is relatively ineffective, and that the correlation of hybrid with inbred yield, though positive, is small.

With overdominant loci the effect of a certain percentage increase in heterozygosity is to cause the vigor to increase by a certain amount. Decreasing the heterozygosity by the same percentage would cause a decrease of approximately the same amount. On the other hand, with dominant loci, making the original equilibrium population more heterozygous would cause a very slight increase, whereas making the population more homozygous would have a decreasing effect of a much greater amount. Therefore it is easier to account for inbreeding depression by dominant loci than to account for increase in vigor on hybridization above the level of a random mating population.

I should like to suggest the following interpretation of the effects of inbreeding and hybridization: The deleterious effects of inbreeding and the recovery on hybridization are mainly due to loci where the dominant is favorable and the recessive allele so rare as to be of negligible importance in a noninbred population. Variance of a non-inbred population, and hybrid vigor when measured as an increase over an equilibrium population, are determined largely by genes of intermediate frequency, probably mostly overdominants.

OVERDOMINANCE AND GENE ACTION

In order to have overdominance it is not necessary that the immediate gene products of the heterozygote exceed in quantity or variety those of either homozygote. At the level of the immediate gene product, or any intermediate state, the effect of the heterozygote may be intermediate between the two homozygotes and still result in a greater final result. Any kind of situation in which something is produced for which an intermediate amount is optimum could be such that the heterozygote is nearer this optimum than either homozygote.

A model for such cases is found in the sulfanilamide-requiring strain of Neurospora reported by Emerson (1948). When this mutant is present the heterokaryotic state of the suppressor gene results in more nearly the optimum amount of para-amino benzoic acid than either homokaryon. Other cases, less known biochemically, may be similar.

I think that it is doubtful whether such a system would persist for long evolutionary periods. Alleles of intermediate productivity could arise and replace the originals. Also modifiers altering the expression of the homozygotes would have considerable selection pressure. Or if the alleles were antimorphic, the situation might be resolved by duplication, as Haldane (1937) has suggested. It is significant that the system reported by Emerson is not one which is ordinarily of importance, but acts only in the presence of the sulfanilamide-requiring mutant.

A form of gene action that appears more likely to account for instances of overdominance is one in which the two alleles differ qualitatively or each does something that the other fails to do. Instances of mosaic dominance provide excellent examples. This has been demonstrated for the *scute* series of bristle characters in Drosophila and for color pattern in beetles (Tan, 1946). Other examples are provided by the A and R loci in maize.

Similar examples of *physiological mosaic dominance* are found where the heterozygote apparently produces something approximating—at least qualitatively—the total effect of the two homozygotes. An example is rust resistance in flax, where each strain is resistant to a certain rust but the hybrid is resistant to both (Flor, 1947). By the usual tests for allelism, the two resistance factors are alleles. Another series of examples is found in the blood group antigens in man, cattle, and elsewhere. In almost every instance the heterozygote has all the antigenic properties of both homozygotes (Irwin, 1947). The presence of both the normal and abnormal types of hemoglobin in humans heterozygous for the gene for sicklemia provides another example (Pauling, 1950).

Many instances of overdominance may have a similar explanation. This is the kind of action that East (1936) postulated in his discussion of heterosis due to cumulative action of divergent alleles. It is not necessary that the effects be completely cumulative; only that the net effect on the phenotype be greater in the heterozygote than in the homozygote. Any system in which the alleles act on different substrates to produce the same or different products, or convert the same substrate into different products—neomorphs, in Muller's terminology—could result in overdominance.

Any of the examples listed above may turn out to be closely linked genes (pseudoalleles) rather than alleles. In most cases it is impossible to distinguish between these alternatives. If the overdominance effect is due to linked genes, eventually a crossover should result in a situation where the desirable effects could be obtained in a homozygous individual. If there are position effects, it may be that no homozygous arrangement is as advantageous as one which is heterozygous. Unless there are position effects, it does not seem likely that heterosis due to pseudoallelism would persist for any great length of time, but in any particular population such factors might be important.

IS INCREASED SIZE ADAPTIVE?

The foregoing arguments are based on the assumption that heterosis is measurable in terms of increased selective advantage. The selection may be natural or man-imposed. This assumption would appear to be reasonable for such factors as fertility and resistance to disease. It also would apply to increase in size or yield, if the direction of selection in the past were in this direction, as in corn. However, it is questionable whether the increase in size that is sometimes observed in variety hybrids is really adaptive.

Mather (1943) and especially Dobzhansky (1950) have emphasized that increased size does not necessarily result in increased fitness in natural populations. Dobzhansky proposed the words *euheterosis* and *luxuriance*, respectively, for increased selective advantage and for mere non-adaptive increase in size. In these terms this discussion has dealt entirely with euheterosis.

If euheterosis occurs in species or variety crosses, it is very difficult to explain. It raises the troublesome question: How can the hybrid between two well adapted strains be better adapted than its parents when there has been no selection in the past for its adaptation? It may be that euheterosis is developed only under some form of selection, as in the inversion heterozygotes studied by Dobzhansky, or in the series of hybrids between inbred lines of corn selected for combining ability.

If large size is not advantageous, luxuriance may be due to the covering of recessive factors which were acting as size bottlenecks and had been selected into the population because of this. Each of the parents might have its growth limited by or held in check by a series of factors, and if some of these were recessive, increased size would be found in the hybrids.

SUMMARY

Since the earliest attempts to explain hybrid vigor in Mendelian terms there have been two principal hypotheses. The first of these is the dominance hypothesis. This notes the observed correlation between recessiveness and detrimental effect and attributes the increased vigor of heterozygosity to the covering of deleterious recessive factors by their dominant alleles. The alternative hypothesis, the overdominance hypothesis, assumes that heterozygosity *per se* is important—that there exist loci at which the heterozygote is superior to either homozygote.

It is clear that the dominance hypothesis is adequate to explain the deterioration that results from inbreeding and the recovery of vigor on outcrossing, but it is difficult to explain how the hybrids could greatly exceed in fitness the equilibrium populations from which their parents were derived. The overdominance hypothesis demands the assumption of a kind of gene action known to be rare, but it is pointed out that if only a small proportion of the loci are of this type, these may nevertheless be the major factor in the population variance.

The following interpretation is suggested: Inbreeding depression and recovery on crossing are mainly the result of loci at which the favorable allele is dominant and the recessives are at low frequency. On the other hand the variance of heterozygous populations and the differences between different hybrids are due mainly to loci with intermediate gene frequencies. It appears likely that such loci are due to selectively superior heterozygotes, but there are several other possibilities.

LEROY POWERS
USDA, Bureau of Plant Industry

Chapter 19

Gene Recombination
and Heterosis

This article will be confined primarily to the tomato (*Lycopersicon*) genetic work which has a bearing on gene recombination and heterosis. The barley (*Hordeum*) genetic research which is discussed briefly was conducted at the University of Minnesota. The tomato genetic research which constitutes the bulk of the material discussed was conducted at the United States Horticultural Field Station, Cheyenne, Wyoming.

With the present available methods of analysis it is difficult in quantitative inheritance studies to distinguish between blocks of fairly closely linked genes and individual pairs of genes. This has been shown by the work of Jones (1917), Warren (1924), Mather (1942, 1949), and Straus and Gowen (1943). Consequently, in this article where the two genetic systems are not distinguishable the term pairs of genes will be employed. Mather (1949) has used the term *effective factor* to depict such a genetic situation.

MARKER GENES AND LINKAGE IN BARLEY

Powers (1936) has shown that in a cross between B1 (*Hordeum deficiens*) and Brachytic (*Hordeum vulgare*) the F_1, which is a two-row barley, gave a greater yield of seed per plant than either the two-row or six-row parents. Then, weight of seed per plant shows heterosis. The data on marker genes and linkage in barley presented have some bearing upon whether any of the advantages of the F_1 hybrid attributable to heterosis can be recovered in inbred lines through gene recombinations.

The deficiens (two-row) character was found to be differentiated from the vulgare (six-row) character by one pair of genes designated as Vv, and the brachytic character from the normal character by one pair of genes designated as *Brbr*. Using these symbols, the genotype of the F₁ is *VvBrbr*. The *Vv* gene pair is carried on chromosome 1 and the *Brbr* gene pair on chromosome 7.

Table 19.1 gives the comparative effect upon four quantitative characters of genes associated in inheritance with *Vv* and *vv* and *VV* and *vv*, as deter-

TABLE 19.1

COMPARATIVE EFFECT UPON FOUR QUANTITATIVE CHARACTERS OF GENES ASSOCIATED IN INHERITANCE WITH *Vv* AND *vv*, AND *VV* AND *vv*; F₂ GENOTYPES OF A BARLEY HYBRID

GENOTYPE	WEIGHT OF SEED*		SPIKES PER PLANT*		HEIGHT OF PLANT*		LENGTH OF AWN*	
	Vv-vv	*VV-vv*	*Vv-vv*	*VV-vv*	*Vv-vv*	*VV-vv*	*Vv-vv*	*VV-vv*
BrBr	−2.22	−3.44	1.72	0.21	1.54	0.64	16.58	7.50
Brbr	−2.98	−3.74	0.94	0.39	2.08	1.41	16.42	9.20
brbr	−1.88	−2.74	0.13	−0.94	1.03	−0.68	1.95	−6.68

* Weight of seed per plant is expressed in grams, spikes per plant in number, height of plant in inches, and length of awn in millimeters.

TABLE 19.2

COMPARATIVE EFFECT UPON FOUR QUANTITATIVE CHARACTERS OF GENES ASSOCIATED IN INHERITANCE WITH *Vv* AND *VV*, AND *VV* AND *vv*; F₂ GENOTYPES OF A BARLEY HYBRID

GENOTYPE	WEIGHT OF SEED*		SPIKES PER PLANT*		HEIGHT OF PLANT*		LENGTH OF AWN*	
	Vv-VV	*VV-vv*	*Vv-VV*	*VV-vv*	*Vv-VV*	*VV-vv*	*Vv-VV*	*VV-vv*
BrBr	1.22	−3.44	1.51	0.21	0.90	0.64	9.08	7.50
Brbr	0.76	−3.74	0.55	0.39	0.67	1.41	7.22	9.20
brbr	0.86	−2.74	1.07	−0.94	1.71	−0.68	8.63	−6.68

* Weight of seed per plant is expressed in grams, spikes per plant in number, height of plant in inches, and length of awn in millimeters.

mined by differences between means of F₂ plants. In every case, the differences between *Vv* and *vv* are greater than the differences between *VV* and *vv* for spikes per plant, height of plant, and length of awn. With the exception of the comparison between *VV* and *vv* within the *brbr* genotype, the differences are in favor of the two-row (*Vv* and *VV*) segregates as compared with the six-row (*vv*) segregates. Within the *brbr* genotype, *vv* plants exceed the *VV* plants for all three characters. As regards weight of seed per plant in every case the six-row plants outyielded the two-row plants whether heterozygous deficiens or homozygous deficiens. However, the differences between *vv* and *Vv* were less than those between *vv* and *VV*.

The data of Table 19.2 show that for all characters the *Vv* plants give an increase over the VV plants, and with the exception of the $Brbr$ genotype for height of plant and length of awn, the differences of Vv-VV are greater than the differences for VV-vv.

These facts concerning the data reveal that Vv is associated with an increase in all four quantitative characters. For spikes per plant, height of plant, and length of awn this increase results in heterosis.

Hypotheses for Difference in Vigor

If the increase noted is due solely to an interaction between V and v such as is depicted by East's physiological hypothesis, then it would not be possible to obtain homozygous lines possessing any of this increase. However, if the heterosis noted is due to a combination of favorable and unfavorable genes linked with V and v, it should be possible to obtain lines in which some of the favorable genes are recombined. These lines should show some increase in the four quantitative characters studied. In the event that linkage of genes favorable and unfavorable to an increase in the quantitative characters was found to furnish the most logical explanation, an intraallelic interaction such as depicted by East's physiological hypothesis still may be having some influence as the two systems are not mutually exclusive.

Tables 19.1 and 19.2 show that Vv results in an increase of all four characters: weight of seed per plant, number of spikes per plant, height of plant, and length of awn. This fact is most simply explained by assuming the production of a favorable growth-promoting substance which influences all of them. Then such being the case, on the basis of East's (1936) physiological hypothesis, V and v supplement each other, resulting in greater development. Next consider the development of the lateral florets which determines the number of rows of kernels per spike (two-row or six-row spikes). The Vv segregates are two-row types, whereas the vv segregates are six-row types. Hence, as regards the character number of rows of kernels per spike, the interaction between V and v is such as to prohibit the development of the lateral florets, resulting in a two-row barley spike rather than a six. Summing up, on the basis of the physiological hypothesis, in the case of four quantitative characters the interaction between V and v is such as to stimulate development. In the case of number of rows of kernels per spike the interaction is such as to prohibit development of the lateral florets. From physiological genetic considerations such a pleiotropic effect seems rather improbable.

Explaining the heterosis associated with Vv plants on the basis of linkage, a simple interpretation would be that the favorable linked genes and their alleles interact according to Jones's (1917) hypothesis to produce a substance favorable to growth processes, resulting in the heterosis noted; and that V is dominant to v resulting in Vv (F_1) plants having two-row barley spikes. This explanation does not require the assumption that V and v stimulate growth in one character and inhibit it in another, and hence is more in accord with modern physiological genetic concepts.

The article by Powers (1936) furnishes additional information pertaining to gene recombination and heterosis. If genes other than Vv are responsible for the heterosis noted, then F_2 plants having a genotype identical to the F_1 generation should give a somewhat lower yield than the F_1. Since the F_1 plants were not grown in a randomized experiment with the F_2 plants, the comparison must be made through the B1 parent. As compared through the B1 parent an actual reduction of one gram in yield of seed per plant was found (Powers, 1936). This reduction could be due to genes carried on chromosome 1, as are V and v, or to genes carried on other chromosomes. In either event, theoretically some of the genes favorable to increased weight

TABLE 19.3

COMPARISON BETWEEN PARENTS AND F_2 PAREN-
TAL GENOTYPES FOR WEIGHT OF SEED
PER PLANT IN A BARLEY HYBRID

TOTAL NUMBER OF PLANTS	WEIGHT OF SEED PER PLANT IN GRAMS			
	F_2	Parent	Difference	t
78 and 266*........	3.9	1.9	2.0	28.189
64 and 63†.........	4.5	4.0	0.5	0.761
Interaction........	....	....	1.5	5.807

* $VVBrBr$, genotype of B1 parent, two-row normal.
† $vvbrbr$, genotype of Brachytic parent, six-row Brachytic.

of seed per plant that resulted in the heterosis noted in the F_1 population must be capable of recombination.

Even though some of the genes favorable to increased growth can be recombined, the yield of the lines in which the favorable genes have been combined depends upon the nature of the interaction of the genes. The weights of seed per plant of parents and F_2 plants of the parental genotypes are given in Table 19.3. From this table it can be seen that the F_2 plants of the $VVBrBr$ genotype gave an increased yield of 2.0 grams per plant over the B1 parental plants having the same genotype. However, the F_2 plants of the same genotype as the Brachytic parent gave an increase over this parent of only 0.5 grams per plant, which is not statistically significant. The interaction of 1.5 grams (Table 19.3) is statistically significant. This means that a preponderance of the genes favorable to increased weight of seed per plant must have entered the cross from the Brachytic parent. The balance of the unfavorable genes that entered the cross from the B1 parent did not cause a corresponding decrease in weight of seed per plant of the F_2 plants possessing the $vvbrbr$ genotype.

In this same study (Powers, 1936) found that the greater the number of genes in the genotype tending to increase a character the greater is the effect of any given gene. It is apparent that it is not possible to definitely predict the yield of seed per plant resulting from recombining genes favorable to growth because of the interactions noted. Either a greater or smaller increase than expected may be obtained. Such interactions of genes would affect the yield of plants in which the favorable genes were recombined, and hence the feasibility of obtaining inbred lines equaling or excelling the F_1 hybrid. In some cases the probability of getting the desired results would be increased and in other cases decreased; depending on the type of interallelic and intra-allelic interactions of the genes.

GENE RECOMBINATIONS DIFFERENTIATING WEIGHT PER LOCULE WHICH EXCEED HETEROSIS OF F_1 POPULATION

The data for weight per locule of fruit for the Porter $\times$ Ponderosa tomato hybrid and parental populations grown at Woodward, Oklahoma, in

TABLE 19.4

ARITHMETIC AND LOGARITHMIC MEANS FOR WEIGHT PER LOCULE OF PORTER $\times$ PONDEROSA TOMATO HYBRID AND PARENTAL POPULATIONS*

	MEAN	
POPULATION	Arithmetic	Logarithmic
Porter..............	10.2	1.018253 ± 0.012325
B_1 to Porter.........	11.8	1.070936 ± 0.009939
F_1.................	14.4	1.168729 ± 0.010134
F_2.................	13.5	1.128481 ± 0.011879
B_1 to Ponderosa.....	13.7	1.124941 ± 0.012651
Ponderosa..........	9.8	0.982054 ± 0.011845

* Grown at Woodward, Oklahoma, in 1941; original data taken in grams and transformed to logarithms to obtain the means and standard errors of the logarithms.

1941 (Powers, Locke, and Garrett, 1950) will be analyzed to determine whether in F_2 and backcross populations gene recombinations are occurring which exceed the heterosis of the F_1 population.

The means for weight per locule calculated on both the arithmetic and logarithmic scales are given in Table 19.4. Weight per locule is greatest for the F_1 population, and the means of the B_1 to Porter, F_2, and B_1 to Ponderosa populations are larger than the means of the Ponderosa and Porter parents, but smaller than the mean of the F_1 population. The only means not showing significant differences are the means of Porter and Ponderosa, and the means of the F_2 and B_1 to Ponderosa populations. Hence, in these hybrid populations weight per locule definitely shows heterosis on either scale.

The frequency distributions for weight per locule for the Porter × Ponderosa hybrid and parental populations are given in Table 19.5. This table shows that the F_2 and B_1 to Ponderosa populations have plants falling into classes of greater value than 1.511883, the last class in which F_1 or Ponderosa plants occur. There are nine such F_2 plants and three such B_1 to Ponderosa plants. If no recombination of genes to produce plants with weight per locule greater than the F_1 plants is possible, these plants with values greater than any individual of the F_1 population must be chance deviates. Moreover, the chance deviates must be those plants in the F_2 population having the F_1

TABLE 19.5

OBTAINED FREQUENCY DISTRIBUTIONS FOR WEIGHT PER LOCULE
OF TOMATO FRUITS FOR PORTER × PONDEROSA HY-
BRID AND PARENTAL POPULATIONS*

POPULA-TION	UPPER LIMIT OF CLASS IN LOGARITHMS OF GRAMS																					TOTAL PLANTS
	0.397940	0.653212	0.812913	0.929419	1.021189	1.096910	1.161368	1.217484	1.267172	1.311754	1.352182	1.389166	1.423246	1.454845	1.484300	1.511883	1.537819	1.562293	1.585461	1.607455	1.795880	
Porter....	1	..	4	27	80	98	20	2	...	...	...	...	...	...	...	...	...	...	...	...	...	232
B_1 to Porter.....	1	3	13	54	81	102	80	49	35	16	11	1	..	1	..	1	...	...	...	...	...	448
F_1........	..	..	1	6	22	35	49	37	34	23	13	4	2	3	4	...	...	...	...	...	...	233
F_2........	..	..	13	31	68	82	81	63	42	24	17	11	8	3	1	..	4	2	..	2	1	453
B_1 to Ponderosa..	1	6	17	29	45	71	72	62	52	26	19	18	1	4	4	4	1	1	1	..	..	434
Pondero-sa.....	..	10	21	28	25	16	18	9	4	6	2	3	1	..	1	1	...	...	...	...	...	145

* Grown at Woodward, Oklahoma, in 1941; original data taken in grams and transformed to logarithms to obtain the means and standard errors of the logarithms.

genotype or a very similar genotype. The probability of their being chance deviates possessing the F_1 or similar genotypes can be determined.

The mean of the logarithms of the F_1 population is 1.168729, and the standard error of a single determination is 0.123426. Calculations (for method see Powers, Locke, and Garrett, 1950) show that only 0.3 per cent of such a genotypic population would be expected to have a value greater than 1.511883. The following tabulation shows the theoretical number of gene pairs differentiating the parents, the theoretical percentage of the population of the F_2 or B_1 to Ponderosa populations possessing the same genotype as the F_1, the theoretical number of plants of the F_1 genotype in a population of 453 F_2 plants and in a population of 434 B_1 to Ponderosa plants, and the theoretical number of plants of the F_1 genotype in the F_2 population and in the B_1 to Ponderosa population expected to exceed a value of 1.511883.

An examination of the data opposite one pair of genes in the tabulation below shows that only 0.68 F_2 plants would be expected to exceed a value of

1.511883, whereas 9 plants did so (see Table 19.5). The same comparison for the B_1 to Ponderosa population is 0.65 expected and 3 obtained. Also, a study of the tabulation below reveals that with an increased number of gene pairs differentiating the parents the odds become even greater against those plants which exceed 1.511883 being chance deviates.

It remains to be seen whether plants of the F_1 genotype plus plants of genotypes which might have similar effects, but do not possess recombination of favorable genes in excess of the total number of favorable genes car-

Number Pairs of Genes	Per Cent Population of F_1 Genotype	Number of Plants of F_1 Genotype		Number of Plants Expected To Exceed a Value of 1.511883	
		F_2	B_1	F_2	B_1
1..........	50.00	226.50	217.00	0.68	0.65
2..........	25.00	113.25	108.50	0.34	0.33
3..........	12.50	56.62	54.25	0.17	0.16
4..........	6.25	28.31	27.12	0.08	0.08
5..........	3.12	14.17	13.56	0.04	0.04

ried by the F_1, could be responsible for the results noted. The result would be to increase the proportion of the F_2 and B_1 to Ponderosa populations fluctuating around means very similar in magnitude to that of the F_1 population. The extreme case (but highly improbable) would be to have all of these two populations made up of such plants. On this basis and on the basis that the parents are differentiated by one pair of genes, the number of plants of the F_2 population expected to exceed 1.511883 is 1.36, and for the B_1 to Ponderosa population is 1.30. The number of plants obtained (Table 19.5) is 9 for the F_2 population and 3 for the B_1 to Ponderosa population. Furthermore, the B_1 to Porter population had 1 plant in a class beyond that in which any F_1 plants occurred.

The analysis can be carried further. For the F_2 population the number of plants expected to exceed 1.562293 is 0.3223 and the number obtained is 3. Whereas the values for the B_1 to Ponderosa population are 0.3087 and 1, respectively. Also, the frequency distributions (Table 19.5) in general do not support the supposition that over one half of the plants of the F_2 and B_1 to Ponderosa populations are fluctuating around a mean as great as that of the F_1 generation. Again with an increase in number of gene pairs differentiating the parents, the odds against the plants exceeding 1.562293 being chance deviates become even greater. It is evident that the data are not in accord with the assumption that plants of the F_1 genotype have the greatest weight per locule. This is true regardless of the number of gene pairs differentiating the parents. Therefore, some of the plants falling in classes having values greater than 1.511883 must have genotypes composed of more favorable genes than the F_1, and therefore recombinations of genes to produce plants having a greater weight per locule than the F_1 plants have occurred.

Whether inbred lines retaining this increased weight per locule can be established is dependent upon the number of gene pairs differentiating the parents and linkage relations (Jones, 1917). Close linkage of genes favorable to increase in weight per locule would favor recombination. Whereas close linkage of genes favorable to increase in weight per locule with those not favorable would hinder recombination and hence reduce the chances of obtaining inbred lines retaining some or all of the advantages attributable to heterosis.

The data furnish evidence concerning the number of gene pairs differentiating weight per locule. From Table 19.5 it can be seen that the plants of the F_2 generation falling beyond the value 1.511883 are distributed over four different classes, and those of the B_1 to Ponderosa population falling beyond this same value occur in three different classes. The behavior of these plants cannot be explained on the basis of five or more independently inherited pairs of genes, as there are too many of these plants falling beyond the 1.511883 class. In addition, the weights per locule of those falling in these classes are greater than can be explained on the basis of chance deviation.

Further, to account for the plants of the F_2 and B_1 to Ponderosa populations falling in those classes beyond 1.511883, on the basis of five or more pairs of independently inherited genes differentiating the parents, it would be necessary to assume that 50 per cent or more of the plants were fluctuating around a mean greater than that of the F_1 generation. Since the means (Table 19.4) of the F_2 and B_1 to Ponderosa populations are less than the mean of the F_1, these populations cannot have a greater majority of the plants fluctuating around a mean larger in magnitude than that of the F_1 plants. This deduction is confirmed by the frequency distributions of Table 19.5, as both of these populations have a greater percentage of their plants in lower classes of the frequency distributions than does the F_1 population. Powers, Locke, and Garrett (1950) have shown that the data give a good fit to frequency distributions calculated on the assumption that the parents are differentiated by three pairs of genes.

Here, proof of recombination of genes to produce plants in the F_2 and B_1 to Ponderosa populations with greater weight per locule than F_1 plants is fairly conclusive. Also, since the number of gene pairs or closely linked blocks of genes is few, it should be possible by selection to establish inbred lines retaining this advantage.

MAIN AND COMPONENT CHARACTERS

The data from the parental and hybrid populations of tomatoes on the main and component characters provide information concerning the relations between gene recombination, dominance, and heterosis.

Weight of Fruit and Its Component Characters

The data on weight per locule, number of locules, and weight per fruit for the Porter × Ponderosa hybrid and parental populations are given in Tables 19.4 and 19.6. On the arithmetic scale, smaller numbers of locules show partial dominance. On the logarithmic scale the means of the F_1 and F_2 populations are not significantly different from the average of the means of the Porter and Ponderosa populations. The mean of the B_1 to Porter population is not significantly different from the average of the means of the Porter and F_1 populations. The mean of the B_1 to Ponderosa population is not sig-

TABLE 19.6

THE ARITHMETIC AND LOGARITHMIC MEANS FOR NUMBER OF LOCULES AND WEIGHT PER FRUIT OF PORTER × PONDEROSA TOMATO HYBRID AND PARENTAL POPULATIONS*

| POPULATION | NUMBER OF LOCULES | | WEIGHT PER FRUIT | |
	Arithmetic	Logarithmic	Arithmetic	Logarithmic
Porter..........	2.1	0.307072 ± 0.002151	21.5	1.326101 ± 0.012358
B_1 to Porter......	3.1	0.468411 ± 0.008158	36.6	1.539833 ± 0.010394
F_1.............	4.5	0.637265 ± 0.007663	65.0	1.806845 ± 0.009416
F_2.............	4.7	0.628793 ± 0.012522	63.5	1.762614 ± 0.013078
B_1 to Ponderosa..	7.1	0.829404 ± 0.007738	97.3	1.954430 ± 0.013269
Ponderosa.......	10.0	0.983292 ± 0.017094	97.7	1.965097 ± 0.008750

* Grown at Woodward, Oklahoma, in 1941; original data taken in numbers and grams and transformed to logarithms to obtain the means and standard errors of the logarithms.

nificantly different from the average of the means of the F_1 and Ponderosa populations. Hence, on the logarithmic scale there is no dominance, and the data indicate that the genetic variability follows the logarithmic scale. In other words, the effects of the genes differentiating weight per locule are multiplicative. This is true of both the intraallelic and interallelic interactions.

Thus on the logarithmic scale number of locules shows no dominance, weight per locule shows heterosis (Table 19.4) and the two combine additively to give weight per fruit. For weight per fruit the F_1 indicates partial dominance of greater weight per fruit, the B_1 to Ponderosa complete dominance, and the B_1 to Porter no dominance. On the arithmetic scale the two component characters unite multiplicatively, and the F_1 indicates partial dominance of greater weight per fruit, the B_1 to Ponderosa complete dominance, and the B_1 to Porter partial dominance of smaller weight per fruit. Then it is clear that regardless of scale, one of the component characters shows some degree of dominance, the other heterosis. They combine to produce the main character which in turn shows some degree of dominance.

Powers, Locke, and Garrett (1950) found the number of major gene pairs differentiating number of locules to be 3. Since weight per locule was found to be differentiated by 3 pairs of major genes, a comparatively few (probably 6) pairs of major genes differentiate weight per fruit. Hence, the number of major gene pairs responsible for heterosis of weight per locule is no greater than the number of major gene pairs responsible for no dominance of number of locules and partial or complete dominance of weight per fruit on the logarithmic scale. Then, in this study the number of pairs of major genes differentiating the character has no bearing on whether the hybrid populations will show no dominance, partial dominance, complete dominance, or heterosis.

From these results it follows that in this material recombination of genes to retain the advantages of heterosis is no different than recombination of genes to combine desirable characters. Furthermore, these data furnish rather convincing evidence that dominance and heterosis are different degrees of expression of the same physiological genetic phenomena, as was postulated by Powers (1941, 1944).

Main and Component Characters of 45 Hybrids Produced by Crossing 10 Inbred Lines of Tomatoes

Table 19.7 summarizes the dominance relations of the main and component characters of 45 hybrids produced by crossing 10 inbred lines of tomatoes.

The percentage values given in Table 19.7 were calculated from data presented in a previous article (Powers, 1945). The reader is referred to this article for the experimental design, a description of the material, and methods. Here, only the method of compiling the data need be given. All of the values of this table with the exception of those listed under heterosis were calculated from the formula $100[2\bar{F}_1/(\bar{P}_1 + \bar{P}_2)]$. The percentages listed under the column headings "heterosis" were calculated from the formula $100(\bar{F}_1/\bar{P}_1)$ and $100(\bar{F}_1/\bar{P}_2)$, respectively. $\bar{F}_1$ is the mean of the F_1 population, $\bar{P}_1$ the mean of the parent with the smaller value, and $\bar{P}_2$ the mean of the parent with the larger value. The 11 characters listed in Table 19.7 were originally expressed in the following units of measurement: Spread of plant in inches, yield per plant in grams, number of fruit that ripened per plant, height per plant in inches, weight per locule of the fruit in grams, number of days from first fruit set to first fruit ripe, number of days from first bloom to first fruit set, weight of fruit in grams, number of days from seeding to first bloom, number of locules per fruit, and number of days from seeding to first fruit ripe.

The odds against any value belonging in an adjacent classification (column) are greater than 19:1 with the exception of the two values designated with an asterisk. Even for these two values the odds against their deviating more than one class are greater than 19:1. When interpreting the data it is necessary to have in mind that parental percentage values would have fallen into the complete dominance columns, the P_1 value into the first such column, and the P_2 into the second such column. Also, it should be kept in mind that the values listed in Table 19.7 are for the different F_1 hybrids, and with the exception of the values listed under the columns headed "heterosis" are percentages based on the means of the two respective parents. The percentages listed under the heterosis columns are based on the mean of the parent that fell into the adjacent complete dominance columns.

TABLE 19.7

PERCENTAGE RANGE IN EXPRESSION OF DOMINANCE FOR DIFFERENT CHARACTERS OF F_1 TOMATO HYBRIDS*

CHARACTER	DOMINANCE						
	Heterosis	Complete	Partial	None	Partial	Complete	Heterosis
Spread of plant..........						114	122
Yield, ripe fruit per plant...				106	117	166	171
Number, ripe fruit per plant.			78	99	142	172	155
Height of plant...........			96	100	104	112	121
Weight per locule.........			70	98		109	119
Period, first fruit set to first fruit ripe.............		90	93	99	103		
Period, first bloom to first fruit set...............	75	80				125*	
Weight per fruit..........	95		53	102			
Period, seeding to first bloom.	89	95	99	100*			
Number of locules per fruit..	73	69	79	96			
Period, seeding to first fruit ripe...................	95	93	96				

* As measured by percentages of averages of values of parents and percentages of parental values.

If dominance and heterosis are different degrees of expression of the same physiological genetic phenomena, then the different genotypes, as represented by the different F_1 hybrids, might be expected to show ranges in expression of a given character from different degrees of dominance to heterosis.

Every character listed in Table 19.7 except number of days from first fruit set to first fruit ripe, in the different hybrids, ranges from some degree of dominance to heterosis. Yield in grams of ripe fruit per plant, depending upon the genotype (F_1 hybrid), varied from no dominance through all classes to heterosis for increased yield. Number of ripe fruit per plant and height of plant varied through all classes from partial dominance of a decrease in magnitude of these two characters to heterosis for an increase. Weight of fruit in grams, number of days from seeding to first bloom, and number of locules per fruit varied from no dominance to heterosis for a decrease of these characters. Considering all of the characters there is a continuous array of values (that is values in all classes) from heterosis for decrease of a character to heterosis for increase of a character, depending upon the character and genotype (F_1 hybrid).

The most logical conclusion from these figures is that dominance and hetosis to a considerable extent are different degrees of expression of the same physiological genetic phenomena. This hypothesis is greatly strengthened by findings of Powers (1941) that whether a character shows dominance or heterosis in some cases is dependent upon the environment and in other cases upon the genotype. As pointed out previously, gene recombination in relation to heterosis is no different from combining any two desirable characters by recombination of genes. A study of the component characters of the main characters given in Table 19.7 offers further evidence in support of this contention.

Yield of ripe fruit as determined by weight of fruit in grams is dependent upon number of fruits that ripen and weight per fruit. The first of these component characters, depending upon the F_1 hybrid being considered, varies from partial dominance of fewer number of ripe fruits to heterosis for an increased number of ripe fruits. The second component character varies from no dominance to heterosis for smaller weight per fruit. They combine multiplicatively, and in many cases result in heterosis for yield of fruit (Table 19.7 and Powers, 1944). Here again, then, is a case involving combination of characters to produce heterosis. To retain some of the benefits of heterosis in inbred lines would involve recombination of the genes differentiating the two component characters.

In turn the number of fruit that ripens is dependent to a large extent at Cheyenne, Wyoming, on earliness of maturity, number of days from seeding to first fruit ripe (Powers, 1945). Earliness of maturity varies from partial dominance of fewer days from seeding to first fruit ripe to heterosis for the shorter period. The component characters of earliness of maturity are period from seeding to first bloom, period from first bloom to first fruit set, and period from first fruit set to first fruit ripe. Number of days from seeding to first bloom varies from no dominance to heterosis for the shorter period. Number of days from first bloom to first fruit set varies from complete dominance of the longer period to heterosis of the shorter period. Number of days from first fruit set to first fruit ripe varies from partial dominance of the longer period to complete dominance of the shorter period.

Weight per fruit is dependent upon weight per locule and number of locules per fruit. Weight per locule varies from partial dominance for less weight per locule to heterosis for greater weight per locule. Number of locules varies from no dominance to heterosis for fewer locules. On the arithmetic scale these two component characters combine multiplicatively so that weight per fruit varies from no dominance to heterosis for less weight per fruit.

From the above, as was found true for yield per plant, the heterosis noted for earliness of maturity results from the combination of component characters which in certain F_1 hybrids may themselves exhibit heterosis. The same is true for weight per fruit. In other words, the study of genetics of heterosis has been somewhat simplified by breaking the main characters down into their component characters. Also, as before, the study shows that gene recombination to retain some or all of the increase of the F_1 hybrid over the parents is dependent upon the same physiological genetic phenomena as are involved in attempting to combine two or more desirable characters into a single inbred line.

RECOVERING INBRED LINES RETAINING ADVANTAGES ATTRIBUTABLE TO HETEROSIS

The physiological genetic phenomena that hinder or aid, by the recombination of genes, the recovery of inbred lines retaining some or all of the advantages attributable to heterosis are the same as those emphasized by Jones (1917) and East (1936). These are the number of gene pairs differentiating the parents, linkage relations of the genes, pleiotropy, and the interaction of the genes as determined by the measurement of end products, both interallelic and intraallelic. This genetic information can be obtained only by rather detailed genetic studies. With the quantitative characters such studies are expensive and time consuming. Hence, very few such studies have been made with tomato hybrids. Powers, Locke, and Garrett (1950) and Powers (1950b) have made a gene analysis for some of the main characters and their more obvious components. Even though the gene analysis for number of days from seeding to first fruit ripe has been completed for only one of the four crosses to be considered, this character and weight per locule will be treated as component characters of yield of ripe fruit per plant in the section dealing with number of pairs of genes differentiating the parents.

Number of Gene Pairs Differentiating Parents

In considering the bearing that number of gene pairs differentiating the parents has upon gene recombination and heterosis, just two characters will be considered: weight per locule and number of days from seeding to first fruit ripe. That both of these characters have an effect upon yield of ripe fruit should be kept in mind during the analyses and discussions which follow. Also, other component characters listed in Table 19.7 could be studied. However, the additional information gained would not justify the time and space required, as the fundamental principles involved can be brought out from an analysis and discussion of the data for the two characters chosen. The number of gene pairs (effective factors; Mather, 1949) differentiating weight per locule has been determined for all the hybrid populations listed in Table 19.8. For days from seeding to first fruit ripe the number of gene pairs (effective factors) differentiating the parents has been determined for the Porter × Ponderosa hybrid populations only.

In discussing the bearing the number of gene pairs differentiating the two parents has upon gene recombination and heterosis, information concerning phenotypic dominance of the characters for the hybrid populations is necessary and will be derived by studying the means of the parental and hybrid

TABLE 19.8

MEANS FOR WEIGHT PER LOCULE AND NUMBER OF DAYS FROM SEEDING TO FIRST FRUIT RIPE WITH TYPE AND NUMBER OF GENE PAIRS DIFFERENTIATING THE PARENTS FOR WEIGHT PER LOCULE*

POPULATION	DANMARK × RED CURRANT		DANMARK × JOHANNISFEUER		JOHANNISFEUER × RED CURRANT		PORTER × PONDEROSA	
	Weight per Locule (Gm.)	No. of Days From Seeding to Fruit Ripe	Weight per Locule (Gm.)	No. of Days From Seeding to Fruit Ripe	Weight per Locule (Gm.)	No. of Days From Seeding to Fruit Ripe	Weight per Locule (Gm.)	No. of Days From Seeding to Fruit Ripe
P_1†	0.45	156.9	4.61	164.9	0.44	126.0	10.2	147.7
B_1 to P_1	0.97	155.0	6.72	165.0	1.04	123.1	11.8	152.0
F_1	2.33	153.8	7.96	165.6	2.70	118.9	14.4	149.6
F_2	2.12	156.6	8.35	166.4	2.12	125.5	13.5	155.0
B_1 to P_2	4.82	159.7	8.32	167.6	4.48	124.7	13.7	168.8
P_2‡	10.36	169.8	9.92	170.0	6.20	136.1	9.8	204.8
Type and number of pairs of genes	Minor 40+	....	Major 2 or 3	....	Minor 40+ Major 2 or 3	....	Major 3	Major 8

* For the hybrid populations of Danmark × Red Currant, Danmark × Johannisfeuer, Johannisfeuer × Red Currant, and Porter × Ponderosa.

† P_1 is Red Currant, Johannisfeuer, Red Currant, and Porter, respectively.

‡ P_2 is Danmark, Danmark, Johannisfeuer, and Ponderosa, respectively.

populations given in Table 19.8. The means for weight per locule of tomato fruits and number of days from seeding to first fruit ripe together with the type and number of gene pairs differentiating the parents for weight per locule for the hybrid populations of Danmark × Red Currant, Danmark × Johannisfeuer, Johannisfeuer × Red Currant, and Porter × Ponderosa are given in Table 19.8.

The first two hybrid populations were grown at Cheyenne, Wyoming, in 1938, the third hybrid population at the same location in 1939, and the last hybrid whose means are listed in the extreme right hand column of Table 19.8 was grown at Woodward, Oklahoma, in 1941. The means of this table were taken from the following publications: Powers and Lyon (1941), Powers, Locke, and Garrett (1950), and Powers (1950a). The data will be analyzed to obtain information concerning the recombination of the genes differentiating weight per locule and number of days from seeding to first fruit ripe. Also, the data will be studied to ascertain the probable bearing this information has upon the production of inbred lines, by gene recombination, that retain some or all of the advantages attributable to heterosis of yield of ripe fruit per plant which the hybrid populations would be expected to exhibit.

On the arithmetic scale the Danmark × Red Currant populations show partial phenotypic dominance for smaller weight per locule. The parents of the Danmark × Red Currant hybrid were found to be differentiated by a large number of gene pairs (probably more than 40) which individually had minor effects. From these results it is evident that, if somewhere near one-half of the genes for smaller weight per locule in the Danmark × Red Currant hybrid populations had entered the cross from one parent and the balance from the other parent, smaller weight per locule would have shown heterosis. Some of the genes must be linked because the parents have a haploid chromosome number of 12. In fact, since 40 or more pairs of genes are differentiating the parents, it seems highly probable that a system of linked polygenes is involved. With 40 pairs of genes differentiating the parents in the F_2, to recover an individual possessing all of the genes for increased weight per locule (without linkage) would require a population of 10^{24} individuals. The size of such a population can be appreciated by considering the fact that 10^{11} is 100 billion. The bearing this has upon the feasibility of recovering from segregating populations inbred lines retaining much of the advantage that might be exhibited by F_1 hybrids is apparent.

The Red Currant parent which possesses small weight per locule also possesses earliness of maturity. Hence, some of the genes tending to increase weight per locule are almost certain to be located on the same chromosomes with a non-beneficial gene or genes tending to increase the time required for maturity. However, due solely to the large number of gene pairs differentiating weight per locule, with no close linkage, pleiotropy, or unfavorable interallelic and intraallelic interactions of the genes, only a comparatively small amount of the increased weight per locule of the Danmark parent could be combined with the earliness of maturity of the Red Currant parent by selection in the F_2 or backcross populations.

Weight per locule and earliness of maturity have a material influence on yield of ripe fruit per plant (Powers, 1945). In some crosses (see Tables 19.7 and 19.8) greater weight per locule is at least partially dominant. Since the shorter period for days from seeding to first fruit ripe for the Danmark × Red Currant cross shows heterosis (Table 19.8) the hybrid populations would be expected to show heterosis for yield of ripe fruit per plant in crosses having such a polygenic system conditioning weight per locule, provided greater weight per locule was at least partially dominant, and provided the genes for increased weight per locule and shorter period from seeding to first fruit ripe were divided between the two parents. The analyses and discussions in the immediately preceding paragraphs show that in such an event it would be almost impossible to obtain inbred lines which through gene recombination would retain any appreciable amount of the yield of the F_1 hybrid.

On the arithmetic scale the Johannisfeuer $\times$ Red Currant populations show partial phenotypic dominance of smaller weight per locule with the exception of the B_1 to P_2 which indicates no dominance. The parents of the Johannisfeuer $\times$ Red Currant hybrid populations were found to be differentiated by a large number of gene pairs (probably more than 40) each of which individually had minor effects and in addition by a few gene pairs (probably 2 or 3) having major effects. In these hybrid populations the total effect of the minor genes was greater than the total effect of the major genes. Again the shorter period from seeding to first fruit ripe showed heterosis.

With the number and type of gene pairs conditioning weight per locule found for the Johannisfeuer $\times$ Red Currant hybrid, and provided the genes differentiating weight per locule exhibited at least partial dominance, as is indicated for the Danmark $\times$ Johannisfeuer populations, certain parental combinations of the genes would result in the hybrid populations showing heterosis for increased yield of fruit per plant. Since comparatively few major gene pairs differentiate weight per locule, it should be possible by recombination of genes through selection in F_2 and backcross populations of such a cross to combine into inbred lines some of the increased yield attributable to heterosis.

The Danmark $\times$ Johannisfeuer hybrid populations show partial phenotypic dominance for greater weight per locule, and complete dominance for shorter period from seeding to first fruit ripe. Two or three major gene pairs were found to be differentiating weight per locule. For weight per locule and number of days from seeding to first fruit ripe, dominance is such that had the genes tending to increase each of these two characters been divided between the two parents, the hybrid populations would have shown heterosis for both component characters. Likewise, if the above conditions had been fulfilled, yield of ripe fruit per plant would have shown heterosis in the hybrid populations.

The Porter $\times$ Ponderosa hybrid populations showed at least partial genic dominance for weight per locule (Powers, Locke, and Garrett, 1950). The parents were found to be differentiated by three pairs of genes and the genes tending to increase weight per locule were distributed between the two parents. As was to be expected, the hybrid populations showed heterosis for increased weight per locule. Period from seeding to first fruit ripe showed almost if not complete dominance for the shorter period from seeding to first fruit ripe. The number of major gene pairs found to be differentiating the parents was eight. Due to the magnitude of the work involved it was not possible to measure yield of fruit, but in all probability the hybrid populations of this cross would have shown heterosis for yield of ripe fruit per plant. In such an event it seems highly probable that some and perhaps a considerable amount of the increase in yield attributable to heterosis could be obtained in inbred lines through recombination of genes.

Considering the data for all the crosses listed in Table 19.8 the information may be summarized as follows: In the Danmark × Red Currant cross a large number of gene pairs differentiates the parents and individually the genes have minor effects. The same is true of the Johannisfeuer × Red Currant cross with the exception that two or three pairs of genes have major effects. In both the Danmark × Johannisfeuer and the Porter × Ponderosa crosses weight per locule is differentiated by a comparatively few pairs of genes having major effects. It is apparent that in the Porter × Ponderosa cross it should be possible by selection in the segregating populations to obtain by recombination of genes inbred lines equaling if not excelling the F_1 fruits in weight per locule.

The discussions treating weight per locule and number of days from seeding to first fruit ripe as component characters of yield of ripe fruit per plant reveal that the recombination of genes to retain some or all of the advantages of the F_1 hybrid is analogous to recombination of genes for the purpose of combining desirable characters.

Linkage Relations

Linkage may be an aid or a hindrance to gene recombination. The data in Table 19.9 were computed to facilitate a consideration of the manner in which different linkage relations may affect recombination of genes.

Certain assumptions were essential to a calculation of the data. First, it was assumed that the coefficient of coincidence is 1. Since in most cases there is interference, to assume a coefficient of coincidence of 1 is to err on the conservative side. For example, all the values given in the second row heading (with the exception of the first and last) would increase as the coefficient of coincidence became smaller. The reverse is true of the figures in the third and fourth columns. The frequencies listed in the second, third, and fourth columns of Table 19.9 are the theoretical number of individuals in the F_2 population carrying the 12 plus genes in the homozygous condition. The crossover values expressed as decimal fractions are assumed to be equal for the different sections of the chromosomes delimited by any two adjacent genes.

The conclusions to be drawn from the theoretical data of Table 19.9 are not invalidated by these assumptions. They merely serve the purpose of allowing the calculation of theoretical values for illustrative purposes. Other assumptions such as different values of crossing over for the various sections of the chromosomes and different numbers of genes, combinations of genes in the parents, and number of linkage groups would not alter the conclusions to be drawn. In the illustration chosen only two linkage groups are shown and each has three pairs of genes. Also, the top row of genes represents the gamete from one parent and the lower row of genes the gamete from the other parent. In all three assumed cases, 3 plus and 3 minus genes entered the cross from each parent.

It is evident that innumerable plausible cases could be assumed, but the fundamental principles derived from a consideration of the theoretical values given in the table would not be altered. One further assumption should be

TABLE 19.9

THEORETICAL NUMBER OF INDIVIDUALS IN THE F_2 POPU-
LATION THAT CARRY 12 PLUS (+) GENES WHEN THE PAR-
ENTS ARE DIFFERENTIATED BY 6 PAIRS OF GENES, EACH
OF 2 CHROMOSOME PAIRS CARRYING 3 PAIRS OF GENES*

CROSS-OVER VALUE	LINKAGE RELATIONS IN F_1 (NUMBER PER MILLION)		
	$\left(\begin{array}{ccc}+&+&+\\-&-&-\end{array}\right)\left(\begin{array}{ccc}-&-&-\\+&+&+\end{array}\right)$	$\left(\begin{array}{ccc}+&+&-\\-&-&+\end{array}\right)\left(\begin{array}{ccc}-&-&+\\+&+&-\end{array}\right)$	$\left(\begin{array}{ccc}+&-&+\\-&+&-\end{array}\right)\left(\begin{array}{ccc}-&+&-\\+&-&+\end{array}\right)$
0.000...	62,500	0.000	0.000000
0.075...	33,498	1.448	0.000063
0.225...	8,134	57.787	0.410526
0.375...	1,455	188.596	24.441630
0.450...	523	234.520	105.094534
0.500...	244	244.141	244.140625

* The crossover values for each section of the chromosome being equal and of the magnitude shown.

mentioned. In every case the plus genes are assumed to give an increase in some desirable quantitative character and, comparatively, the minus genes a decrease. Finally, in the table two extreme situations are shown, namely that in which there is no crossing over and that in which the two sections of the chromosome between adjacent genes show 50 per cent of crossing over.

The data in the second column apply to that situation in which all of the plus genes occur in one member of the homologous chromosomes in each of the two pairs of chromosomes depicted. In the case of 50 per cent of crossing over or independent inheritance, only 244 individuals in a million of the F_2 population possess all twelve plus genes. The number of such individuals among a million F_2 individuals increases with a decrease in the percentage of crossing over until with no crossing over 62,500 individuals in a million possess all six pairs of the plus genes in the homozygous condition.

The data in the third column apply to that situation in which two plus genes are linked with one minus gene in one member of a chromosome pair and two minus genes with one plus gene in the other member of the same chromosome pair. In this column the situation is reversed as compared to column two. Again 50 per cent of crossing over gives 244 individuals among a million in the F_2 possessing all twelve plus genes. This decreases with a decrease in the percentage of crossing over until with no crossing over no individuals in the infinite F_2 population contain more than eight plus genes. However, since two of the plus genes are carried on the same chromosome in each of the two linkage groups, an increase in the linkage intensity results in an increased number of individuals in the F_2 population possessing all eight plus genes in the homozygous condition.

Here, then, is a case in which close linkage facilitates recombination of desired genes up to a certain number, and from a practical standpoint further advances by selection in that generation are impossible. Also, it would be difficult to make further advances by continued selection in later generations. In the F_2 population with a crossover value of 0.075 the frequency of the $\left(\begin{smallmatrix} + & + & - \\ + & + & - \end{smallmatrix}\right)\left(\begin{smallmatrix} + & + & - \\ + & + & - \end{smallmatrix}\right)$ genotype expressed as a decimal fraction is 0.183024 and of the $\left(\begin{smallmatrix} + & + & - \\ + & + & + \end{smallmatrix}\right)\left(\begin{smallmatrix} + & + & - \\ + & + & - \end{smallmatrix}\right)$ genotype is 0.014840.

To obtain some F_3 families derived from F_2 plants of the latter genotype would require growing at least 300 selections in the F_3 generation. To separate the F_3 families derived from the F_2 plants of the former genotype from those derived from the latter genotype would require an adequately replicated, well designed experiment. Anyone who has worked with the quantitative characters either in genetics or plant breeding realizes the difficulties besetting such a task. After such F_3 families had been determined, only 25 per cent of the individuals would be of the $\left(\begin{smallmatrix} + & + & + \\ + & + & + \end{smallmatrix}\right)\left(\begin{smallmatrix} + & + & - \\ + & + & - \end{smallmatrix}\right)$ genotype. These would have to be tested in the F_4 to separate them from F_4 families derived from F_3 plants of the $\left(\begin{smallmatrix} + & + & - \\ + & + & + \end{smallmatrix}\right)\left(\begin{smallmatrix} + & + & - \\ + & + & - \end{smallmatrix}\right)$ and the $\left(\begin{smallmatrix} + & + & - \\ + & + & - \end{smallmatrix}\right)\left(\begin{smallmatrix} + & + & - \\ + & + & - \end{smallmatrix}\right)$ genotypes. Even with the small number of genes assumed in the above example, it would not be a simple matter to make progress by continued selection in later generations. The addition of a few more genes having the plus and minus genes alternating on the same chromosome would make further progress by continued selection in generations later than the F_2 practically impossible. From the above it is apparent that any series of plus genes being adjacent without minus genes intervening would facilitate recombination of desirable genes in the F_2 generation. It seems that in actual genetic and plant breeding materials many such combinations do exist.

The figures in the fourth column of Table 19.9 are the theoretical frequency distributions for that situation in which the plus and minus genes alternate on the chromosome. Again the number of individuals expected in the F_2 generations possessing all twelve plus genes decreases rather rapidly with a decrease in the percentage of crossing over. Even in the case of 50 per cent of crossing over it is doubtful whether it is possible for the plant breeder or geneticist to isolate individuals from the F_2 population carrying twelve plus genes.

The data in Table 19.9 emphasize that even with the probably over-simplified genetic situation depicted it is not possible to recover in a single individual all of the genes favorable to the production of a desirable character for which the F_2 population is segregating, unless the favorable genes are located on the same chromosome and immediately adjacent to each other without unfavorable genes intervening. If any of the favorable genes are adjacent to each other without unfavorable genes intervening, then decided advances can be made by selection in the F_2 populations up to a certain point. Beyond that point further selection in the F_2 will have no effect, and selection in advanced generations does not offer much promise. The most difficult situation is that in which the linkage relation is such that the favorable and unfavorable genes alternate on the chromosome and the number of such linkage groups is at a minimum for the number of gene pairs involved.

For the sake of clarity of illustration only three linkage relations were shown. However, it is apparent that undoubtedly in the material available to plant breeders and geneticists, the possible different kinds of linkage relations are almost innumerable. Some will aid the investigator in obtaining the desired recombination of genes and others will be a decided hindrance. In the cases of undesirable linkage relations it will be almost impossible for the breeder to obtain individuals possessing recombinations of genes making that individual equal to or superior to the F_1 for the character exhibiting heterosis. On the other hand, desirable linkage relations may make it possible to obtain the recombination of genes sought even though a large number of gene pairs differentiates the parents used in hybridization.

Pleiotropy, and Interallelic and Intraallelic Interactions

Powers, Locke, and Garrett (1950) have made a rather detailed genetic study of eight quantitative characters in hybrid and parental populations involving the Porter and Ponderosa varieties of *Lycopersicon esculentum* Mill. The characters studied and the indicated number of major gene pairs differentiating the parents are as listed immediately below.

Character	Gene Symbols
Percentage of flowers that set fruit..............	$F_1 f_1 F_2 f_2 F_3 f_3 F_4 f_4$
Period from seeding to first fruit ripe:	
Seeding to first bloom......................	$B_1 b_1 B_2 b_2 B_3 b_3$
First bloom to first fruit set.................	$S_1 s_1 S_2 s_2 S_3 s_3$
First fruit set to first fruit ripe...............	$R_1 r_1 R_2 r_2$
Weight per fruit:	
Number of locules.........................	$Lc_1 lc_1 Lc_2 lc_2 Lc_3 lc_3$
Weight per locule.........................	$W_1 w_1 W_2 w_2 W_3 w_3$

With most quantitative characters it is difficult to distinguish between pleiotropy and linkage. It seems highly probable that linkage instead of pleiotropy produced the relations noted by the above authors between the four series of genes Ff, Ss, Rr, and $Lclc$ with the exception of the Ff and Ss relation, because all the associations noted are those expected on the basis of linkage. If pleiotropy were involved, such relations would be coincidental, which for all these gene series is highly improbable. However, as pointed out by Powers, Locke, and Garrett (1950) some of the genes of the Ff and Ss series must be identical, as percentage of flowers that set fruit has an effect on period from first bloom to first fruit set. The $Lclc$ and Ww series of genes, differentiating number of locules and weight per locule, respectively, were independent as regards linkage and pleiotropy. In these studies pleiotropy was not of major importance.

Phenotypic and genic dominance furnish some information concerning the interallelic and intraallelic interactions of the genes. That genic dominance is dependent upon the genotypic milieu was pointed out by Fisher (1931) and many others (Dobzhansky, 1941). Hence both interallelic and intraallelic interactions as measured by end products are second order interactions, genes $\times$ genes $\times$ the environment.

Any of the interactions of genes noted as affecting any of the component characters dealt with in the study by Powers, Locke, and Garrett (1950) were interactions of genes differentiating yield of ripe fruit per plant. With this fact in mind, it is interesting to note the interactions of the genes differentiating the component characters. The intraallelic and interallelic interactions of the Ff gene series were such that genic dominance was intermediate. The intraallelic and interallelic interactions of the Bb series of genes were such that one of the six dominant genes shortened the period from seeding to first bloom as much as all six, which shows that both dominance and epistasis were complete. For the Ss series and Rr series of genes, genic dominance was complete. Also, the effects of the gene pairs were cumulative.

Had the dominant genes of the Ss series entered the cross from one parent and the dominant genes from the Rr series entered the cross from the other parent, the F_1 hybrid would have shown heterosis for earliness of maturity. Porter would then represent an inbred line which by recombination of genes retained the earliness of maturity of the F_1 hybrid. Genic dominance was partial for genes (Lc_1Lc_2) tending to produce fewer locules per fruit and for the (Lc_3) tending to produce more locules per fruit. A series of genes such as Lc_1 and Lc_2, some entering the cross from one parent and some from the other, would produce an F_1 hybrid showing heterosis for fewer locules per fruit. On the other hand a series of genes such as (Lc_3), some entering the cross from one parent and some from the other, would produce heterosis for more locules per fruit.

Finally, for the Ww series of genes, genic dominance was partial for increased weight per locule and the effects of the gene pairs were cumulative. As regards this character, both parents did contribute genes for increased weight per locule, and the F_1 hybrid did show heterosis for increased weight. Also, as has been shown in the F_2 and B_1 and P_2 populations some individuals were obtained having greater weight per locule than the F_1 plants and this greater weight per locule proved to be due to recombination of favorable genes.

Also, the interallelic interactions of the genes as determined by the interrelations of the component characters are of interest because of the information they provide concerning recombination of genes and heterosis. The effects of the Bb series of genes, the Ss series, and the Rr series, respectively, were found to be cumulative. On an average the S genes would be expected to shorten the period from first bloom to first fruit set less in the presence of the R genes than in the presence of the r genes—if the physiological reactions affecting these two component characters that were instigated by the environment were the same as those instigated by the Ss and Rr gene series. That such was the case seems probable from the results of Goldschmidt's work (1938) with phenocopies. In fact it seems almost axiomatic that this was the case, because the second order interaction (Ss gene series $\times$ Rr gene series $\times$ environment) was such that, on an average, when the Ss series responded to a given environment by shortening the period from first bloom to first fruit set the Rr series in the same plant tended to produce a longer period from first fruit set to first fruit ripe. Then the effects of these two series of genes were less than additive as regards the dependent character period from seeding to first fruit ripe

About the same situation existed in respect to the $Lclc$ series and the Ww series of genes in that greater number of locules, on an average, was accompanied by less weight per locule. This type of interallelic interaction would tend to decrease the possibility of obtaining inbred lines combining desirable characters. This would be particularly true of the interallelic interaction between the Ss and Rr gene series, because a shorter period from first bloom to first fruit set tended to be accompanied by a longer period from first fruit set to first fruit ripe.

The data do not furnish any evidence concerning that type of intraallelic interaction postulated by East's (1936) physiological hypothesis, other than to say that no cases of overdominance were found. This would indicate that probably overdominance does not play a predominant part in the production of heterosis in the tomato hybrids studied.

A. J. MANGELSDORF

Experiment Station, Hawaiian Sugar Planters Association, Honolulu, T.H.

Chapter 20

Gene Interaction in Heterosis

Sugar cane behaves very much like corn in its reaction toward inbreeding and outcrossing. Although the sugar cane flower is normally provided with both male and female organs, male sterility is not uncommon. Among the varieties that produce an abundance of pollen, many are partially or highly self-sterile. As a consequence, cross-fertilization by wind-borne pollen is the rule in sugar cane, as in corn. When sugar cane is subjected to self-pollination, the usual result is a reduction in seed setting and a marked reduction in the vigor of the offspring.

The sugar cane breeder enjoys one great advantage over the corn breeder: sugar cane can be propagated asexually. Each node on the stalk is provided with a bud and with a number of root primordia. In field practice, stalks of the selected variety of sugar cane are sectioned into cuttings of two or more internodes each. These cuttings are then placed horizontally in furrows and covered lightly with soil. In due course the cutting sends out its roots, the buds develop into shoots, and a new plant is established.

Were it possible to apply this procedure to corn, and thus to perpetuate outstanding individuals from whatever source, it is unlikely that the corn breeder would have felt obliged to resort to the laborious procedures now employed.

When sugar cane varieties are propagated by cuttings, the traits by which we are able to distinguish one variety from another maintain their integrity through many cycles of clonal propagation. This is true not only of morphological traits, but also of physiological traits.

Sugar cane has a number of relatives growing in the wild, some of which may be ancestral to the original cultivated forms. Wild *Saccharums* are widely distributed in the tropical and sub-tropical regions of the Old World, from central Africa through Asia and Malaya, to and including the Indonesian and many of the more westerly Pacific islands. This heterogeneous array of

wild forms has been somewhat arbitrarily classified into two great groups—
the *S. spontaneum* group and the *S. robustum* group. Each of these groups
comprises a diversity of types which differ among themselves in morphology
and in chromosome number. The members of the *spontaneum* group have
slender stalks; they are often strongly stoloniferous. The members of the
robustum group have hard, woody stalks, sometimes of good diameter; sto-
lons, if present, are not strongly developed.

The original cultivated varieties likewise may be classified into two great
groups. The first of these comprises a number of slender varieties which appear to be indigenous to India, and which have been lumped together under
the name *S. Barberi*. Certain of the *Barberi* varieties bear a striking resemblance to the wild *spontaneums* of that region.

The New Guinea region is the home of a group of large-stalked tropical
cultivated varieties of the type which Linnaeus named *S. officinarum*. The
wild form most closely resembling *S. officinarum* and possibly ancestral to
it is *S. robustum*, which is indigenous to that region.

In the closely related genus *Sorghum*, the difference between varieties
having pithy stalks containing but little sugar, and varieties with sweet
juicy stalks, has been shown to be determined by a single major gene. In
Saccharum the change from the dry, pithy, low-sucrose stalks of the wild
forms to the juicy, high-sucrose stalks of the cultivated varieties appears to
have been brought about by several, but perhaps by no more than three or
four major gene changes.

The cultivated and wild forms also differ in genes for stalk size. In crosses
between the two, the genes responsible for the slenderness of the wild forms
show a high degree of dominance.

A striking feature of this multiform genus is the prevalence of inter-
fertility among its members. Widely divergent forms can be crossed without
undue difficulty. The resulting hybrids are rarely completely sterile; they
are often highly fertile. The explanation is presumably to be sought in the
polyploidy which is characteristic of both the wild and the cultivated forms.
They range in chromosome number from 24 to 80 or more pairs. It appears
that once the minimum chromosomal complement needed to produce a functional zygote has been supplied, there is considerable latitude in the number
and in the assortment of chromosomes that can be added without impairing
the viability, or even the fertility of the hybrids.

Since the breeder is as yet unable to create superior genes at will, he is
obliged to content himself with developing new combinations of the genes
available in whatever breeding material he may be able to assemble. The
sugar cane breeder is fortunate in having in the wild relatives of sugar cane a
reservoir of genes for disease-resistance and hardiness. Those are traits that
had to some degree been lost in the course of domestication. Considerable

use has already been made of the wild forms. The important varieties today are almost without exception complex hybrids that include in their ancestry representatives of both the *S. officinarum* and the *S. Barberi* groups of cultivated varieties, together with representatives of one or both of the wild species.

Thus the sugar cane breeder has been exploiting, to the best of his ability, the advantages that heterosis has to offer. He is, however, acutely aware that a better understanding of the genetic basis of heterosis is prerequisite to its more effective utilization. Since he suffers the disadvantage of isolation from the centers of research, he cherishes such rare opportunities as he may have to peer over the shoulder of the research worker, to whom he must look for new facts that may lead to a better understanding of the mechanism of gene action and thus, of heterosis.

Recently some of us who are engaged in sugar cane breeding in Hawaii formulated a number of postulates with the object of providing a basis for discussing heterosis and related matters. These postulates have been excerpted or inferred from the published literature and from correspondence with workers engaged in genetic research, whose helpful suggestions are gratefully acknowledged.

Although the evidence supporting these postulates is sometimes meager, and sometimes capable of other interpretations, we have deliberately phrased them in a categorical vein in the belief that they might thus better serve their primary purpose—that of provoking a free exchange of ideas.

POSTULATES RELATING TO INCIDENCE OF LESS FAVORABLE ALLELES

1. Naturally self-fertilized populations tend to keep their chromosomes purged of all alleles other than those which in the homozygous condition interact to best advantage with the remainder of the genotype and with the existing environment[1] to promote the result favored by natural selection (or by human selection). This does not imply that any single population will contain all of the best alleles existing in the species. Selection can make a choice only between the alleles present in the population.

2. In addition to their prevailing (normal, plus, or wild type) alleles, cross-fertilized organisms such as corn and sugar cane carry in the heterozygous condition, at many loci, recessive alleles which in the homozygous condition would be inferior in their action to that of their normal or prevailing partners.

3. These less favorable alleles may be thought of as belonging to one of two classes, which, although differing in their past history, may have similar physiological consequences: (*a*) fortuitous, resulting from sporadic mutation, and representing the errors in the "trial and error" of the evolutionary process; or (*b*) relic, representing the residue of what were once the prevailing

---

1. The term *environment* is here used in a broad sense to mean the sum-total of the external influences acting upon the organism, including its nutrition.

alleles but which, in the course of evolution or under a changed environment, have been displaced, to a greater or lesser degree, by still better alleles.

4. The prevailing allele at a given locus has reached its pre-eminent position through the sifting action of natural selection over many generations. Given a stable environment, further improvement, through mutation, at that locus would long since have materialized if the chances for such improvement were high. It is not strange that random mutation should only rarely be able to produce a superior new allele. Nevertheless, once the possibilities for improvement through recombination of existing genes have been exhausted, further evolutionary progress will be contingent upon just such an event, however rare its occurrence may be.

5. Whether dominant or recessive, and whether in a naturally self-fertilized or naturally cross-fertilized population, a substantially superior mutant, once established in the population, is destined to increase in frequency and to become the prevailing allele in the population.

6. A deleterious dominant is doomed to eventual extinction. In a cross-breeding population of sufficient size a deleterious recessive may persist indefinitely, its incidence, except for random drift, being determined by the balance between its elimination by selection and the rate at which it recurs by mutation.

7. The best allele for one environment may not be best for another environment. The burden of less favorable alleles which cross-fertilized organisms carry along generation after generation is not an unmitigated liability. It serves as a form of insurance by providing a reservoir of adaptability to changing conditions.

ROLE OF LESS FAVORABLE ALLELES

Turning now to the role of these less favorable alleles in the heterosis phenomenon as manifested in naturally cross-fertilized organisms we may formulate a second group of postulates:

1. At many and perhaps at most loci, Aa is as good or nearly as good as AA, and both AA and Aa are better than aa.

2. There may be a few loci where aa is better than AA or Aa. This is particularly likely to be the case for loci affecting traits which are advantageous under domestication, but disadvantageous in the wild under natural selection.

3. There may, for all we know, be occasional loci where AA' is better than AA or $A'A'$ (overdominance).

4. There may be many regions in the chromosomes which *behave as though* AA' were better than AA or $A'A'$. With deleterious recessive alleles in the heterozygous condition at many loci, it seems almost inevitable that some of these will be closely linked in the repulsion phase, as for example Ab/aB, which in the absence of crossing over would behave as a single locus, the

heterozygous condition of which is superior to either homozygote. It is to be expected that such a linkage will eventually be broken. However, there may be regions in the chromosomes, such as the centromere region, for example, where crossing over is reduced, and where a group of genes may act indefinitely as a single gene. We may for convenience designate the effect of such reciprocal apposition of favorable dominants to their less favorable recessives as a pseudo-overdominance effect. It will be noted that such a *balanced defective* situation conforms with the dominance and linkage hypothesis advanced by Jones as an explanation of the heterosis phenomenon.

5. Even in the absence of linkage, an overdominance type of reaction (but resulting from pseudo-overdominance) must assert itself whenever each of the two members of a pair of gametes is able to supply the favorable dominant alleles required to counteract the less favorable recessives carried by the other member of the pair. The likelihood of success in retaining, in successive generations of selfing, all of the favorable dominants heterozygous in F_1, and eliminating all of the less favorable recessives, diminishes exponentially with increasing numbers of loci heterozygous in F_1. It would seem that naturally cross-fertilized organisms which carry, at many loci, deleterious recessives of low per locus frequency in the population could hardly fail to manifest a pseudo-overdominance type of response to inbreeding and outcrossing.

6. From an evolutionary standpoint, it may be important to distinguish between the consequences of (a) true overdominance (heterozygosis at the locus level) and (b) pseudo-overdominance (heterozygosis at the zygote level resulting from the reciprocal masking of deleterious recessives by their dominant alleles). From the standpoint of the breeder who is of necessity working against time, this distinction may have little practical importance if many loci are involved in the pseudo-overdominance effect. A breeding plan designed to deal efficiently with one of these alternatives should be effective also in dealing with the other.

7. Whether due to true overdominance or to pseudo-overdominance, the widespread if not universal occurrence among naturally cross-fertilized organisms of an overdominance type of response to inbreeding and outcrossing poses a problem which the breeder cannot afford to disregard.

8. Neither overdominance nor pseudo-overdominance can be called upon to explain the differences in vigor between different varieties of wheat, beans, sorghums, and other self-fertilized forms. Such differences are determined by genes in the homozygous state, as are also the differences between homozygous inbred lines of corn.

ROLE OF LIMITING FACTORS

A consideration of the role of limiting factors in quantitative inheritance leads us to a third group of postulates:

1. The adequacy of a diet is determined not by those constituents which are present in ample amounts, but by those which are deficient to the point of acting as limiting factors. Similarly the excellence of a genotype is determined not by its strongest but by its weakest links. The term *weak link* as here employed refers to a gene pair at a particular locus which at some moment in the life of the organism proves so inadequate in performing the task required of that locus as to act as a limiting factor—a bottleneck in an essential physiological process. A bottleneck effect may result from a deficiency of an essential gene product or from an excess of a gene product.

2. At each moment throughout its life the physiological processes of even the most vigorous organism are held down to their prevailing rates by bottlenecks or limiting factors. We are merely rephrasing a genetic axiom when we say that a bottleneck in the physiological reaction system is neither purely genetic nor purely environmental. The physiological bottleneck at any given moment results from the interaction of a particular locus (which we may for convenience refer to as the bottleneck locus) with the remainder of the genotype and with the environment of that moment. When we speak of an environmental bottleneck, we are merely focusing attention upon the environmental component of the genetic-environmental bottleneck. When we speak of a bottleneck gene, we are referring to the genetic component of the genetic-environmental bottleneck.

3. The value of an otherwise perfect diet would be seriously impaired by the omission of a single essential element. Similarly an otherwise superior genotype could be rendered mediocre or worse by a single bottleneck. A potentially superior genotype is unable to manifest its potentialities so long as it is being throttled by a genetic-environmental bottleneck. A breeder looks at the bottleneck and sees the need of a better allele at the bottleneck locus. An agriculturist looks at the same bottleneck and sees the need for correcting its environmental component. Bottlenecks relating to climatic limitations usually can be most economically dealt with by breeding.[2] On the other hand, bottlenecks resulting from nutritional deficiencies can often be advantageously dealt with by correcting the environment.

4. The substitution, at a bottleneck locus, of a better combination of alleles[3] will result in an improvement in yield providing that no other limiting factor, genetic or environmental, asserts itself before an appreciable gain has been realized.

5. The substitution of potentially better alleles at loci *other* than bottleneck loci cannot substantially improve yields any more than the addition of calcium to the diet of a plant or an animal can relieve the effect of a phosphorus deficiency in that diet. We take it for granted that each essential

2. This rule is not without exceptions. For example, a bottleneck resulting from a deficiency of rainfall can sometimes be economically eliminated by irrigation.

3. As already indicated, the best combination of alleles may be AA, Aa, or aa depending upon the particular locus.

chemical element has its specific role to perform in the physiological reaction system. Similarly we accept as well established the thesis that gene action is likewise specific—that a particular gene can perform its particular function, and that function only. Nevertheless we sometimes engage in speculations which ignore these convictions and which appear to assume that genes affecting quantitative characters such as yield are freely interchangeable, one with another, and that one *yield* gene can serve as well as another, regardless of its locus or function.

6. A bottleneck locus may act as such throughout the life of the individual or it may act as a limiting factor only for a short period and under specific conditions, such as drought, nitrogen deficiency, or excessively high or low temperatures. Under a varying environment the bottleneck of one moment may be superseded by a different bottleneck at the next moment.

7. The physiological bottleneck may be ameliorated or removed by correcting the particular feature of the environment contributing to the bottleneck. In the examples cited above this would entail supplying moisture, or nitrogen, or lowering or raising the temperature. Or the bottleneck may be ameliorated or removed by substituting a more effective allele at the bottleneck locus, providing that such an allele is available.

8. As already indicated, the amelioration or removal of a bottleneck, either by improving the environment or by substituting a better allele at the bottleneck locus, will permit a rise in the rate of the essential physiological processes. This rise may be small or it may be large, depending upon the point at which the next ensuing bottleneck begins to make itself felt. The substitution of a more efficient allele at a bottleneck locus in a certain genotype, under a particular environment, may result in a large gain. The substitution of the same allele in a different genotype or under another environment may result in little or no gain. It is not strange that difficulty should be encountered in analyzing the inheritance of genes affecting yield and other quantitative characters which are subject to the influence of a varied and fluctuating array of genetic-environmental bottlenecks.

9. A diet that is low in calcium may supply calcium at an adequate rate so long as growth is being retarded by a lack of phosphorus. But once phosphorus is supplied at an adequate rate, calcium deficiency becomes a bottleneck which limits the rate of growth. Similarly a mediocre gene m at one locus may be adequate (not a bottleneck) so long as the rate of physiological activity of the organism is being throttled by environmental limitations or by a bottleneck gene at some other locus. But once the other genetic-environmental limiting factors have been removed, the mediocre gene m is unable to handle the increased load and becomes the bottleneck in the reaction system.

10. The maximum vigor or yield possible under a given environment will be attained when the organism is endowed with the best available allele or

combination of alleles at each bottleneck locus. There are presumably many loci that never act as bottlenecks in any part of the reaction system affecting vigor or yield, no matter which allele or combination of alleles happens to occupy such a locus.

11. The difference between the weakest inbred and the most vigorous hybrid is merely one of degree. Each represents an integration of the many genetic-environmental bottleneck effects under which it has labored. The weak inbred has been throttled down by one or more bottlenecks to a low level. The superior hybrid is able to go much further, even attaining what we might concede to be extreme vigor. But both the weak inbred and the vigorous hybrid have throughout their lives been held down to their respective levels by their genetic-environmental bottlenecks.[4]

MISCELLANEA

The fourth and last group of postulates comprise a heterogeneous population randomly listed as separate topics for discussion.

1. If each step in a complex physiological process such as photosynthesis is conditioned by the action of a specific gene, and if each successive step in the chain of reactions is contingent upon the successful completion of the preceding steps, it follows that in attempting a biomathematical analysis of the inheritance of quantitative characters such as yield we may not be justified in assuming, as a basis for our calculations, that each of the genes concerned is independent in its action.

2. Since our efforts to "improve" the genotype are constantly being thwarted by bottleneck genes, we may be tempted to damn all such genes as inventions of the Devil. No doubt there are many defective genes that would have to be classed as liabilities under any normal environment. But certainly there are many bottleneck genes that are indispensable to survival—genes that act as governors in regulating physiological reactions and in fitting the organism to its particular ecological niche. A mouse or a moss can survive and reproduce where larger organisms would perish. And a mouse which, as a result of changes in certain of its adaptive bottleneck genes attained the size of a rat, might find itself at a disadvantage in a community of normal mice.

3. If we are correct in assuming that even a single major bottleneck locus can act as a limiting factor in the development of an otherwise superior geno-

---

[4] Certain of the foregoing postulates pertaining to the role of bottleneck genes in quantitative inheritance may be guilty of gross over-simplification. So complex is the physiological reaction system of even the simplest organism that we are only now beginning to gain an inkling of the extent of its complexity. These postulates may also be guilty of exaggeration. Because we believe that the action of limiting factors in quantitative inheritance has not received the attention that it deserves, we have intentionally stressed the importance of the bottleneck locus, even at the risk of over-emphasis. Furthermore, we have pictured the limiting factor at a given moment as pertaining to a single bottleneck locus. This may or may not be the rule. It would not be difficult to imagine a bottleneck which pertains to several loci and which could be relieved or eliminated by substituting a more effective allele at any one of these loci.

type, it is hardly to be expected that the phenotype of an inbred line will afford a wholly reliable indication of its breeding potentialities in hybrid combinations.

4. We need to keep in mind the limitations that pertain to a rating for general combining ability. The best "general" combiner thus far discovered in corn is not so general in its combining ability as to be able to combine to advantage with itself or with any other genotype that happens to be afflicted with the same bottleneck genes. At best, a rating for general combining ability can represent nothing more than an average arrived at by lumping a given population of specific combinations. An average derived from a different population of specific combinations could result in quite another rating.

5. If a series of inbreds A, B, etc., be crossed with a tester inbred T, we obtain the hybrids AT, BT, etc. The yield of AT will be determined by the bottleneck genes in the AT genotype. The yield of BT will be determined by the bottleneck genes in the BT genotype. The test cross can tell us which lines combine to best advantage with the tester line, but it cannot reasonably be expected to tell us more than that. It cannot, for example, tell us with certainty what we may expect from $A \times B$. Both A and B may combine to advantage with T, but if A and B each happen to be afflicted with one or more of the same bottleneck genes (not present in T) the yield of the cross AB will suffer.

6. The failure of a cross between two convergently improved lines to equal the cross between the two original lines from which they were derived cannot be taken as critical evidence for the existence of an overdominance mechanism. The benefits which convergent improvement seeks to achieve can be vitiated if a recessive bottleneck gene b, present in only one of the original parent lines, should become homozygous in both convergently "improved" lines. Selection exercised with the object of preventing such an occurrence may be ineffective if b becomes a bottleneck only under the enhanced rate of physiological activity of the $A(B) \times B(A)$ hybrid.

7. During recent years several examples of heterosis reported in the literature have been attributed to the effect of heterozygosity at a single locus. When the amount of heterosis is substantial, it should be possible to verify the validity of the hypothesis by breeding tests. If the two parents are really isogenic, except for the heterosis locus H, and if H_1H_2 individuals are more vigorous than either homozygote, then by selfing only the most vigorous individuals in each generation it should be possible to retain in one-half of the population the original vigor of F_1 even after many generations of selfing, and such a line should continue indefinitely to segregate H_1H_1, H_1H_2, and H_2H_2 individuals in a $1:2:1$ ratio.

8. East describes the effect of heterosis as "comparable to the effect on a plant of the addition of a balanced fertilizer to the soil or to the feeding of a more adequate and more chemically complete diet to the animal." The simi-

larities noted by East between the beneficial effects of heterosis and those of improved nutrition are more than coincidental. The first prerequisite for enhanced well-being is the removal of the bottlenecks that stand in the way· This can sometimes be accomplished by improving the nutrition, sometimes by substituting more efficient alleles at the bottleneck loci, and sometimes by both.

9. The term *heterosis* remains ambiguous in spite of the many attempts to define it. It continues to have different meanings for different workers.

10. If heterosis is to be measured by comparing performance of offspring with performance of parents, then the higher the standing of the two parents in the scale of measurement, the lower the degree of heterosis to be expected in their offspring. Conversely the lower the standing of the parents, the greater the heterosis to be expected. (Exceptions to the latter rule will occur when both parents owe their enfeeblement to the same bottleneck genes.)

11. Success in crop and livestock production depends largely upon the skill of the grower in detecting, diagnosing, and correcting the environmental components of the bottlenecks affecting yield. Success in developing higher yielding genotypes depends largely upon the ability of the breeder to substitute more effective alleles at the bottleneck loci, and to accomplish this without establishing new and equally serious bottlenecks at other loci.

GORDON E. DICKERSON
University of Missouri

Chapter 21

Inbred Lines for Heterosis Tests?

The justification for considering heterosis tests in breeding work rests on the mode of action and interaction of the genes responsible for genetic variability in the material available to the geneticist. The nature of this genetic variability may vary widely between species or populations in response to differences in the degree of inbreeding and kind of selection, natural or imposed, that has characterized the population over an extended period. For any given trait or combination thereof, structure of genetic variation will depend upon how consistent, intense, and prolonged selection has been.

It follows that choice of the system of mating and selection appropriate for most rapid improvement in economic attributes of any given plant or animal population should be guided by as complete knowledge of the kind of genetic variation in the population as analysis of all available data affords. The discussion which follows is an attempt (1) to interpret the evidence presently available concerning the sort of genetic system which underlies important economic traits, using swine as the example; and (2) to compare expected effectiveness of several alternative breeding methods.

NATURE OF GENETIC VARIATION IN ECONOMIC TRAITS

Types of association between the genotype and its phenotypic expression have been classified logically as intra-allelic and inter-allelic. The former includes all degrees of dominance or levels of expression for the heterozygote relative to the corresponding homozygotes. The concept of heterozygote advantage or overdominance differs from the usual ideas of dominance in that each gene is visualized as exerting certain dominant favorable effects lacking in its allele. Inter-allelic gene action or epistasis includes all effects of a gene in one set of alleles on the expression of genes in other sets of alleles. Complementary, inhibiting, duplicate dominant, and duplicate recessive gene interactions are extreme examples.

By definition, epistasis is universal in the sense that expression of every gene is to some degree dependent on and modified by the effects of genes in other sets of alleles. Epistasis would include fixed multiplicative or proportional effects of each gene on the expression of non-allelic genes. Such epistasis, although unlikely to be important, would be of a highly predictable sort and would disappear if phenotypes were measured in log scale units. A potentially much more important sort of epistasis would be that involved whenever a phenotypic maximum is associated with an optimum genetic intermediate (Wright, 1935). Here a given gene may have either a positive or a negative selective value, depending on whether the individual's average genotype is above or below the optimum genetic intermediate.

Some of the evidence concerning the kind of genetic variability with which we must deal in seeking to improve economic characters of swine has been considered earlier (Dickerson, 1949, 1951) and may be summarized here as follows:

Inbreeding and Crossbreeding Effects

Proportion of heterozygous loci has a major influence on total performance, affecting most the highly important but lowly heritable characters for which selection has been consistently in one direction. Take for example, an intra-season comparison of 538 inbred and 325 linecross litters from the same lines in four projects of the Regional Swine Breeding Laboratory (Dickerson et al., 1947). This showed a decline in performance per 10 per cent increased inbreeding of litter amounting to 2.6 and 7.8 per cent, for litter size at birth and weaning, respectively; 2.6 per cent for pig weight at 154 days of age; and 11.4 per cent for total weight of litters at 154 days. Similar estimates per 10 per cent increased inbreeding of dam, based on sixty-three inbred and fifty linecross dams at the Iowa Station, were 2.1 and 5.0 per cent for litter size at birth and weaning; 1.6 per cent for pig weights at 21 days; and 5 per cent for total weight of litters at 154 days.

Results from studies of regression of performance on inbreeding of dam and litter within line and season (Blunn and Baker, 1949; Stewart, 1945; Comstock and Winters, 1944; and Hetzer et al., 1940) agree quite well with the figures given. Inbreeding of dam and litter together greatly depresses prolificacy, suckling ability, pre- and post-natal viability and growth rate, and particularly their product—total litter weight. Inbreeding effects on carcass composition, body conformation, and efficiency of food utilization were relatively minor (Dickerson et al., 1946).

The results of the earlier crossbreeding experiments have been summarized by Lush (1939) and Winters (1936). When the mean of the two purebred stocks crossed is compared with the crossbred litters, the results of many experiments summarized by Carroll and Roberts (1942) indicate that the average performance of crossbred individuals is increased about as much as it would be by a 10 per cent reduction of inbreeding (see Table 21.1). More recent studies of crossbreeding using inbred strains (Hazel *et al.*, 1948; Sierk, 1948) verify the earlier conclusions.

Some degree of dominance is the most obvious genetic mechanism by which change in heterozygosity from inbreeding or crossbreeding would affect the level of performance. Inbreeding decline due to dominance would be a function of $2q(1 - q)k\ f$, where q is frequency of the dominant allele, f is Wright's inbreeding coefficient, and k is the degree of dominance (Hull, 1945) defined in terms of phenotypic scale as $(2\ Aa\text{-}AA\text{-}aa)/(AA\text{-}aa)$.

TABLE 21.1

RESULTS OF CROSSBREEDING EXPERIMENTS SUM-
MARIZED BY CARROLL AND ROBERTS (1942)

Factors of Production	No. of Expts.	Mean of Two Pure Breeds	Mean of Crossbreds	Relative Performance of Crossbreds with Purebreds = 100
No. pigs per litter........	12	9.74	9.48	97.3
Birth weight of pigs (lbs.).	6	2.77	2.79	100.6
Survival ability (%)......	15	76.3	80.2	105.1
Weaning wt. of pigs (lbs.).	15	32.5	33.12	101.8
Weaning wt. of litters (lbs.)*................	13	235.6	254.1	107.9
Av. daily gain (lbs.)......	9	1.381	1.436	104.0
Feed for 100 lbs. gain (lbs.)	6	374.1	368.6	98.5
Danish pig-testing stations:				
Av. daily gain.........	32	1.359	1.381	101.5
Feed per 100 lbs. gain..	32	345.4	344.3	99.7

* From the original publications of these experiments.

If genetic intermediates in one or more primary functions produce maximum performance, the increased total genetic standard deviation $(\sqrt{1 + f})$ associated with inbreeding would tend to increase the average deviation from optimum genotype and hence depress performance roughly in proportion to $(\sqrt{1 + f} - 1)$. Inbreeding alone would not alter mean level of performance without dominance, if only epistatic factors of the complementary or duplicate sort were involved.

Inbreeding depression and crossbreeding advantage indicate some degree of dominance or of genetic intermediate optimum, but, alone, they fail to distinguish between the two or to indicate the probable degree of dominance.

Effectiveness of Selection within Inbred Lines

Selection within mildly inbred lines has been only slightly effective. Decline in performance with mild inbreeding (2 to 4 per cent per generation) has been much the same as would have been expected from inbreeding without selection. These statements are based largely on a study[1] of time trends

1. To be published in more detail, separately.

in litter size and growth rate in 49 inbred lines from five projects with an average of 9 seasons per line (see also Dickerson, 1951). In Figure 21.1 the average actual linear time trend (*solid line*) is negative for both litter size at weaning and for pig weight at 154 days of age. An estimate of the effectiveness of selection was made by adjusting the time trends for the effect of the increased inbreeding, using corrections derived from the intra-season comparison of inbreds and linecrosses from the same inbred lines involved in the time trends. The adjusted time trend (*dashed line*) indicates that selection

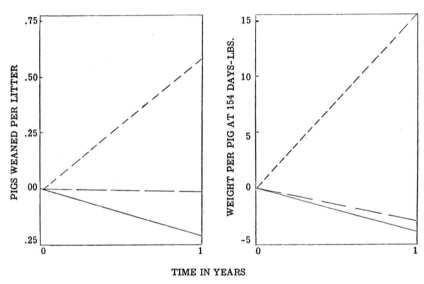

TIME IN YEARS

FIG. 21.1—Linear time trend within mildly inbred strains for pigs weaned per litter and 154-day weight per pig. Solid line is actual trend, dashed line is trend adjusted for effect of inbreeding trend to non-inbred basis, and the top broken line indicates mean superiority of selected parents.

has failed to improve genetic merit for litter size and has allowed growth rate to decline, although selection of parents per year has averaged about .6 pigs for size of litter weaned by the dam and sixteen pounds for pig weight at 154 days (*top broken line*).

These results must be accepted with caution, because time trends can be influenced by trends in nutrition, parasites, disease, management, or other factors. Also, the correction for inbreeding effects may have been underestimated. It seems clear that improvement has been at best only a small fraction of what would have been expected from the heritability of these traits and the amount of selection practiced for each. Evidence from comparison of intra-breed linecrosses with representative purebreds is meager but does not suggest any major improvement. Intra-herd comparisons of viability and growth rate of progeny from inbred and from representative purebred boars

(Hazel *et al.*, 1948) likewise have shown little advantage accruing from selection during development of the inbred lines.

The apparent inability of selection to offset the decline in performance from mild inbreeding casts doubt on the assumption that epistasis or ordinary dominance (between none and complete) can account for the major influence of inbreeding on performance in swine. Unless one assumes a preponderance of tight repulsion phase linkages, selection should have increased the frequency of favorable dominant genes. Similarly, under epistasis in which the genetic intermediate is optimum, selection should have prevented fixation of the more extreme homozygous combinations, particularly if a rather large number of loci determine the genetic range for each primary function.

The type of genetic mechanism that would most surely produce an inbreeding decline relatively unresponsive to selection is heterozygote superiority ($k > 1$). Here selection would maintain gene frequency near some intermediate equilibrium value, rather than move it toward fixation of any one allele (q_A smaller). Linear regression of genotype on phenotype (heritability) would be lower than for lesser degrees of dominance, making selection relatively ineffective. Inbreeding depression for dominance, which is proportional to $2 q_A(1 - q_A) k f$, would increase with k, particularly since q_A would be smaller and $q_A (1 - q)$ larger than under partial or complete dominance.

"Controlled" Selection Experiments

Results have been published from two "controlled" experiments on selection with minimum inbreeding in swine. In both the Illinois study of growth rate (Krider *et al.*, 1946) and the Alabama study of feed efficiency (Dickerson and Grimes, 1947), the high and low selection lines separated appreciably and significantly. However, it is difficult to judge from the time trends whether the difference came partly from improvement in the high line or almost entirely from decline in the low line. Taken at face value, the time trends indicate that the separation was due to decline in growth rate of the low line in the Illinois experiment, but that efficiency increased in both lines in the Alabama study.

In these experiments, the low line involved a reversal in the usual direction of selection. This amounted to assigning new selective values to genes affecting growth and feed utilization, and hence selection might be expected to be unusually effective for the first few generations in moving toward some new equilibrium. In both experiments, selection was most effective in the first generation.

In Goodale's (1938) and in MacArthur's (1949) selection for size in mice, there is no question that a steady increase in size was produced. However, these experiments with adult size in mice are not directly analogous to those with prolificacy, viability, and growth rate in swine, for several reasons. First, the history of selection prior to the beginning of the experiment presumably had not been consistently positive for adult size in mice, as it was for prolificacy, viability, and rate of growth in swine. Second, selection for increased size of the organism may be quite different from selection for a further increase in efficiency within the same adult body size. Adult size is generally highly heritable but not consistently selected for in either direction in farm animals. The steady decline in effectiveness of selection without reduction in variability for size in MacArthur's study suggests approach to an equilibrium similar to that postulated for total performance in swine.

Heritability Estimates

Heritability, the portion of observed variance linearly associated with genotype, ranges from about 10 to 50 per cent for individual characters of economic importance. But heritability is found to be lower for the highly important characters such as prolificacy and viability, for which selection has been appreciable and always in one direction, than for traits such as carcass composition or external dimensions, for which selection has been mild or in opposite directions in different portions of the breed or during different periods of time. Heterozygote superiority is more likely to be important for genetic variability in the highly important characters, since selection would have had greater opportunity to fix those genes whose homozygotes were equal or superior to alternative genotypes at the same locus, leaving at intermediate frequencies (larger $q_A[1 - q_A]$) genes exhibiting heterozygote advantage.

Ineffectiveness of selection for heritable traits suggests that degree of dominance may be higher and heritability lower for total performance than for its individual components. This has been shown for grain yield and its components in corn by Robinson *et al.* (1949) and by Leng *et al.* (1949). In swine, Cummings *et al.* (1947) found heritabilities of 22 per cent for size of litter at birth, 40 per cent for survival from birth to weaning, but only 7 per cent for total litter weight at weaning. Heritability of total weaning weight jumped from 7 to 59 per cent when effects of size of litter at birth and of survival were held constant. These results could have arisen from negative genetic-physiological or from high positive environmental correlations, or both, between numbers per litter and weight per pig at weaning.

Positive estimates of heritability for economic characters may be obtained, even though selection is ineffective due to heterozygote advantage. If $k > 1$ and rates of reproduction were proportional to phenotypic levels, equilibrium frequency for the more favorable allele would be $q_A = (1 + k)/2k$. At this point, the linear regression of genotype on phenotype in an unselected population would be zero, and all intra-allelic genetic variability would be due to dominance deviations (Fig. 21.2). Here both paternal $\frac{1}{2}$-sib correlation and regression of progeny on parent would yield zero estimates of heritability, if only dominance were involved.

Equilibrium gene frequency actually will be determined by degree of dominance expressed in terms of relative selective values or reproductive rates (k') rather than in terms of relative performance levels (k) of the several genotypes. Conceivably, k' could be either larger or smaller than k. If culling is mild, difference in reproduction rates will be smaller between Aa and AA and larger between AA and aa than if proportional to phenotypic levels, and effective k' will be smaller and equilibirium q_A larger. Conversely if phenotypic selection is intense, differences in reproduction rates between

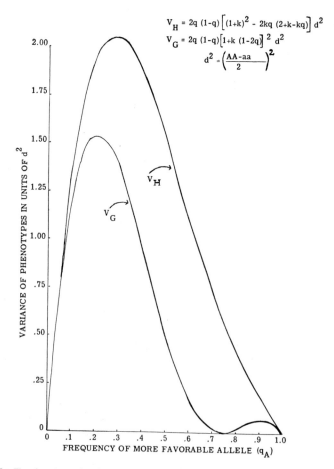

$$V_H = 2q\,(1-q)\left[(1+k)^2 - 2kq\,(2+k-kq)\right]d^2$$

$$V_G = 2q\,(1-q)\left[1+k\,(1-2q)\right]^2 d^2$$

$$d^2 = \left(\frac{AA-aa}{2}\right)^2$$

FIG. 21.2—Total variance in phenotype (V_H) and portion linearly associated with genotype (V_G) in a random breeding population for a single chromosomal unit and heterozygote advantage of $k = 2$, at varying frequencies for the more favorable of two alleles.

Aa and AA will be magnified and those between AA and aa minimized, making k' larger than k and equilibrium q_A smaller than $(1 + k)/2k$. The larger the number of genes controlling genetic variation in the basis of selection, the less difference intensity of culling will introduce between k' and k.

Estimates of heritability from regression of offspring on parent will increase positively as equilibrium q becomes larger than $(1 + k)/2k$, and assume larger negative value as q becomes smaller than $(1 + k)/2k$. Larger positive heritability estimates based on paternal $\frac{1}{2}$-sib correlation will be obtained as q becomes either larger or smaller than $(1 + k)/2k$, since this method estimates fraction of the phenotypic variance linearly associated with genotype regardless of the sign of the regression of offspring on parent (Fig. 21.2).

It seems clear that positive estimates for heritability of individual characters do not rule out the possibilities (1) that heterozygote advantage obtains, especially for net selective advantage or total performance; and (2) that effectiveness of selection may be only a small fraction of that indicated by the estimates of heritability for individual characters. More attention needs to be given estimates of heritability for total performance indices and their components.

Negative Genetic Correlations between Components
of Total Performance

Existence of negative genetic correlations would correspond to heterozygote superiority. This is in the sense that an increase in frequency of genes with partially or completely dominant favorable effects on one character would amount to a decrease in frequency of their alleles having partially or completely dominant favorable effects on one or more other characters. This involves the reasonable assumptions that genes have manifold end effects and that selection maintains at intermediate frequencies—where contribution to genetic variability is larger—only those genes having dominant favorable but recessive unfavorable effects on performance. MacArthur's (1949) experiment provided ample evidence that selection for a single character (adult size) produces many important changes in other characters.

Direct evidence for negative genetic correlations is not plentiful. Much data must be analyzed to estimate genetic correlation with precision, particularly when the traits correlated are of low heritability. Also, it is difficult to avoid bias from environmental correlations. If leaner hog carcasses are considered desirable, the genetic correlations of .3, .7, and −.7 for ratio of fat to lean cuts with 180-day weight, daily gain, and feed requirements per unit of weight gain found in a study of Iowa Record of Performance data (Dickerson, 1947) need to be considered. In the same and in another study (Dickerson and Grimes, 1947) evidence for genetic antagonism between good milking ability and rapid, economical fattening in swine is presented.

Other reasons for expecting negative genetic correlations that might be mentioned are (1) lower heritability for total performance than for its components, as outlined previously, and (2) approach to some physiological maximum, where increase in one function must necessarily reduce others, as in division of nutrient energy available between milk production and fleshing.

Negative genetic correlation, in some degree, is maintained by the process of selection itself and would disappear if selection were relaxed. Animals mediocre in any one respect are retained as breeders only if superior in several other characters. Thus selection leads to a negative correlation between characters among the animals selected as parents. To a much lesser degree, these negative relationships would appear among the progeny, where fresh selection would magnify them again. Such negative character relationships may explain in part the discrepancy between rates of improvement "expected" and obtained, and could exist quite apart from any real heterozygote advantage.

Analogy between Results with Corn and with Swine

In both corn and swine, (1) inbreeding has been slight during domesticated history, until recently at least, (2) degree of heterozygosity exerts a major influence on performance, (3) effectiveness of continued phenotypic selection is questionable in stocks with a long history of selection for the same complex of characters in which further improvement is sought.

Hull (1945) has postulated overdominance or heterozygote superiority, with additive interaction of non-alleles, to explain corn breeding results. He does so on the basis that (1) yields of parental, F_1, F_2, and backcross populations are linearly related to proportion of loci heterozygous (Neal, 1935), (2) yields are usually less than one half as large for homozygous lines as for their F_1 crosses, (3) regression of F_1 yield on parental inbred yield among F_1 crosses having one parent in common often is zero or negative for the higher yield levels of the common parent. Robinson et al. (1949) have obtained estimates indicating heterozygote advantage ($k = 1.64$) for grain yield but only partial to complete dominance for components of yield. Crow (1948) has shown that under complete dominance ($k = 1$) of favorable genes combining additively, average superiority of maximum hybrid over the variety at equilibrium gene frequency would be the product of mutation rate and number of loci, or less than 5 per cent, whereas potential hybrid advantage under some degree of heterozygote advantage ($k > 1$) at even a small proportion of loci could be many times greater, in agreement with results already obtained

The impossibility of accounting for the 15 to 25 per cent advantage of better corn hybrids over open-pollinated varieties through complete dominance of favorable genes combining additively can be demonstrated (Dicker-

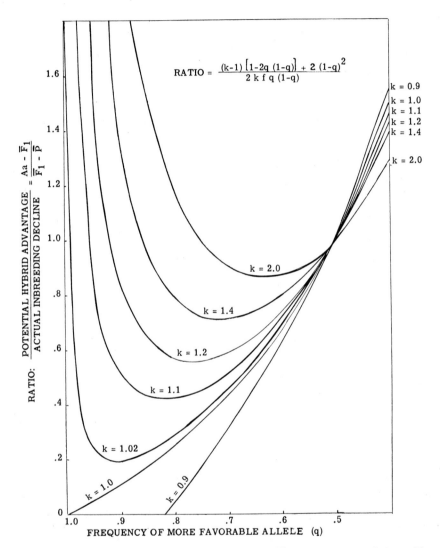

FIG. 21.3—Potential hybrid advantage per locus $(Aa - \overline{F}_1)$ as a proportion of observable inbreeding decline $(\overline{F}_1 - \overline{P})$, for varying degrees of dominance and frequencies of the more favorable allele in a population of homozygous $(f = 1)$ lines and their F_1 crosses.

son, 1949) from the average ratio per locus of maximum potential superiority of hybrid over average of all possible F_1's to the observable mean advantage of the F_1's over the inbred lines themselves (Fig. 21.3). Using $(1 - q)$ for frequency of the less favored allele, f for Wright's inbreeding coefficient, k for degree of dominance, as before, and $d = (AA - aa)/2$:

$$\bar{H} = \text{Maximum heterozygote} = C + (1 + k) \, d$$

$$\bar{F}_1 = \text{Mean of } F_1 \text{ crosses} = C + 2 \, q \, [\, 1 + k \, (1 - q) \,] \, d$$

$$\bar{P} = \text{Mean of inbred lines} = C + 2 \, q \, [\, 1 + k \, (1 - q) \, (1 - f) \,] \, d$$

$$\text{Hence}, \; \frac{(\bar{H} - \bar{F}_1)}{\bar{F}_1 - \bar{P}} = \frac{(k - 1) \, [\, 1 - 2 \, q \, (1 - q) \,] + 2 \, (1 - q)^2}{2 \, k \, f \, q \, (1 - q)}$$

Under partial or complete dominance, equilibrium $(1 - q) = (k - 1)/2k = 0$, except for reverse mutation pressure. When the parental lines are homozygous $(f = 1)$, mean $(1 - q)$ lies between .05 and .1 and mean inbred yield is about 40 per cent of that for F_1 crosses, the maximum increase of hybrid over average F_1 would lie between 3 and 7 per cent. There is little reason to suppose that present better hybrids approach the maximum. The potential maximum increase over open-pollinated varieties increases rapidly with degree of heterozygote advantage (k), approaching $(\bar{F}_1 - \bar{P})$ or about 50 per cent in corn yield.

The evidence thus far obtained in swine suggests that the genetic basis of variation in net productivity is fundamentally quite similar to that in corn. This indicates challenging possibilities for increasing productivity of swine by utilizing potential heterosis.

Heterozygote Advantage for Single Loci and Chromosome Segments in Other Species

Dobzhansky (1949) has shown experimentally that natural selection favors individuals heterozygous for inversion chromosome segments in Drosophila. He also has shown that the resulting equilibrium between frequency of alternative homologous segments fluctuates with locality and season of the year, depending on relative selective advantage of alternative "homozygous" segments. He postulates natural selection for increased *coadaptation* between alternative segments in heterozygotes within each interbreeding population. Demonstration of heterozygote advantage at individual loci would be difficult, since any one locus usually would account for only a small part of the total variability in selective value or in any complex character. However, some cases of presumably single gene mutations exhibiting heterozygote advantage have been reported (Jones, 1945; Gustafsson, 1946, 1947). The "yellow" gene of the agouti series in mice (Danforth, 1927; Dickerson and Gowen, 1947) provides a classic example of manifold effects of genes and of heterozygote superiority in food utilization, if not in selective value.

It seems inevitable that manifold effects of genes and equilibrium between frequencies of alternative alleles are commonplace, with relative selective values shifting with the characters given emphasis in selection at each stage of development from conception through maturity.

EFFECTIVENESS OF METHODS OF SELECTING FOR MAXIMUM HETEROSIS

The evidence presented provides several related assumptions concerning the nature of genetic variability in economic characters of swine as the basis for considering how selection for maximum heterosis can be made most effective. These are: (1) Heterozygote advantage ($k > 1$) is important for total performance when its components are characters that have had consistently positive selective values, although lesser degrees of dominance may obtain for individual characters. (2) Average gene frequency approaches an intermediate equilibrium near $q_A = (1 + k)/2k$, whose value and stability depend on the intensity, consistency, and duration of selection. (3) Performance levels attainable by selection in outbred populations are far below the maximum heterozygote, because more than one-half of the individuals are homozygous at each locus. (4) Inbreeding decline may be considered as due largely to the reduced number of genes useful to the species that can be carried by the more homozygous individuals, rather than to fixation of unfavorable recessive genes.

Under these assumptions, any method of selecting for maximum performance will involve (1) selection for maximum proportion of heterozygous loci in crosses of complementary strains, and (2) selection based on progeny tests of individuals or lines in crosses. These methods are indicated only when individual and family selection become relatively ineffective, because the intensity of selection per unit of time is much lower for selection based on test-cross progeny performance.

Importance of Recurrent Selection to Achieve Maximum Heterosis

Hull (1945) has emphasized the great importance of utilizing cumulative gains from recurrent selection for heterosis in crosses, rather than relying on a single selection among F_1 crosses of a group of homozygous lines. This principle may be illustrated by contrasting the observed distribution for number of heterozygous loci in a population of F_1 crosses among inbred lines with the potential range (Fig. 21.4). It can be shown that the standard deviation in proportion of heterozygous loci is:

$$\sigma_{Hw} = \sqrt{\frac{2q(1-q)(1-f)[1-2q(1-q)(1-f)]}{n}}$$

within linecrosses, and

$$\sigma_{Hb} = \sqrt{\frac{2\,q\,(1-q)\,f\,[\,1-2\,q\,(1-q)\,(2-f)\,]}{n}}$$

among linecrosses, where f is the inbreeding of the population of lines and n is the effective number of segregating chromosomal units.

Range in degree of heterozygosity among all F_1 crosses of a population of lines for likely values of n ($n = 100$ and $f = 1$ in Fig. 21.4) is small rela-

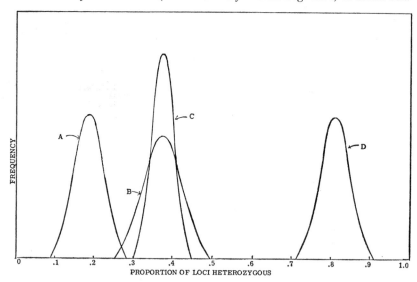

Fig. 21.4—Frequency distribution for proportion of 100 loci heterozygous when $k = 2$ and initial $\bar{q}_A = .75$ within lines 50 per cent inbred (A), between F_1 crosses of homozygous lines or in a non-inbred population (B), between F_1 crosses of lines inbred only 50 per cent (C), and in a cross between complementary strains ($\bar{q}_1 = .95, \bar{q}_2 = .15$) attainable only through recurrent selection for cross performance (D).

tive to the potential range. Hence recovery of F_1 crosses much above the average for all F_1's or for non-inbred stock cannot be expected. Inbreeding provides a means for steadily reducing the proportion of heterozygous loci. What is needed is recurrent selection in complementary strains to make them steadily approach opposite extremes in gene frequency at each locus exhibiting heterozygote advantage. The best F_1 of a population of 100 F_1 crosses would average about 2.6 σ_{Hb} above the mean, whereas the best 1 of 10 would average about 1.54 σ_{Hb} above the mean and cumulative selection of the best 1 of 10 in each of 10 recurrent cycles of selection would amount to choosing F_1's that were 10 (1.54) $\sigma_{Hb} = 15.4$ σ_{Hb} above the original mean.

Homozygous Tester versus Reciprocal Selection

Hull (1945) has proposed recurrent cycles of selection in crossbred material based on progeny test in crosses with a single homozygous line (alternatively, with two related lines or their F_1) as a method of producing highly complementary lines to be used in production of commercial hybrids. Comstock *et al.* (1949) have compared expected effectiveness of Hull's plan with that for reciprocal selection for cross performance between two foundation stocks of divergent origin, avoiding inbreeding in both stocks. They point out that the potential limits of improvement are the same for the two methods, except for loci exhibiting only partial dominance ($k < 1$), where the use of a tester homozygous for any of the less favorable alleles would reduce potential hybrid performance. Existence of important epistatic effects also would tend to make limits lower for use of a homozygous tester.

There is no reason to expect initial cross performance to differ between reciprocal and homozygous tester selection, other than because of the performance of the inbred tester line itself (inbreeding effects on maternal environment of the litter in swine). If anything, it would be easier to find a population differing materially in gene frequency at individual loci from a homozygous tester than to find two similarly complementary non-inbred populations.

Relative rates of improvement expected from the two plans depend on (1) selection pressure applied, and on (2) size of regression of gene frequency in the material under selection on performance of test-cross progeny. Hull's homozygous tester plan limits selection to only one of the parental stocks. Hence selection applied will be only $\frac{1}{2}$ as great as in reciprocal selection. However, as long as frequencies of the more favorable alleles (q) are anywhere near their expected equilibrium of $(1 + k)/2k$, progress toward complementary gene frequencies (toward maximum proportion of heterozygous loci in the cross) per cycle of selection will be far less for reciprocal than for homozygous tester selection.

Comstock (1949) has shown that improvement in performance of random crosses between two segregating populations per generation of selection, at a given locus, is:

$$\Delta P_r = [\Delta q_1 (1 + k - 2 k q_2) + \Delta q_2 (1 + k - 2 k q_1) - 2 k \cdot \Delta q_1 \cdot \Delta q_2] \, d \quad (1)$$

The change in gene frequency at a given locus within each of the two selected populations (Δq_1 and Δq_2, respectively) will be determined by (1) the intensity of selection based on the test-cross progeny means (s = selection differential in σ units), (2) the correlation between q_1 and the mean progeny performance (P), and (3) the size of σ_{q_1} among the tested individuals, as follows:

$$\Delta q_1 = s \, r_{q_1 P} \sigma_{q_1} = s \, \frac{\mathrm{Cov}_{q_1 P}}{\sigma_P} = \frac{s d}{2 \sigma_P} q_1 (1 - q_1) (1 + k - 2 k q_2) \quad (2)$$

Hence, as Comstock indicates, improvement in cross performance from one cycle of reciprocal selection and for any one locus is:

$$\Delta P_r = \frac{s d^2}{2 \sigma_P} [q_1 (1 - q_1) (1 + k - 2 k q_2)^2 + q_2 (1 - q_2) (1 + k - 2 k q_1)^2] \\ - 2 k \cdot \Delta q_1 \cdot \Delta q_2 \quad (3)$$

However, equation (3) is not applicable for evaluating Hull's (1945) plan of recurrent selection for cross performance with a homozygous tester line. Here, cross performance will improve as $q_i \to 0$ for loci at which the more favorable homozygote (AA) is fixed in the tester, and as $q_j \to 1$ for loci at which the tester is homozygous for the less favorable allele (aa). If $\bar{q}_T$ repre-

TABLE 21.2

MEANS, VARIANCES, AND COVARIANCES FOR GENOTYPES OF
SELECTED POPULATION AND PHENOTYPES OF TEST-CROSS
PROGENIES FROM HOMOZYGOUS TESTER

	SELECTED POPULATION GENOTYPES (q_s)		MEAN PHENOTYPES OF PROGENIES FROM HOMOZYGOUS TESTER	
			AA at $\bar{q}_T$ of Loci (G_i)	aa at $(1-\bar{q}_T)$ of Loci (G_j)
AA	Means	1.0	$2d$	$(1+k)d$
	Dev.	$1-q_s$	$(1-q_i)(1-k)d$	$(1-q_j)(1+k)d$
	Freq.	q_s^2	$q_i^2 \bar{q}_T$	$q_j^2(1-\bar{q}_T)$
Aa	Means	.5	$\dfrac{(3+k)d}{2}$	$\dfrac{(1+k)d}{2}$
	Dev.	$.5-q_s$	$(\frac{1}{2}-q_i)(1-k)d$	$(\frac{1}{2}-q_j)(1+k)d$
	Freq.	$2q_s(1-q_s)$	$2q_i(1-q_i)\bar{q}_T$	$2q_j(1-q_j)(1-\bar{q}_T)$
aa	Means	0	$(1+k)d$	0
	Dev.	$-q_s$	$-q_i(1-k)d$	$-q_j(1+k)d$
	Freq.	$(1-q_s)^2$	$(1-q_i)^2\bar{q}_T$	$(1-q_j)^2(1-\bar{q}_T)$
Means		q_s	$[1+k+q_i(1-k)]d$	$q_j(1+k)d$
Variances		$\dfrac{q_s(1-q_s)}{2}$	$\dfrac{q_i(1-q_i)(1-k)^2d^2}{2}$	$\dfrac{q_j(1-q_j)(1+k)^2d^2}{2}$
Covariances		$(q_s \cdot G)$	$\dfrac{q_i(1-q_i)(1-k)d}{2}$	$\dfrac{q_j(1-q_j)(1+k)d}{2}$

sents the proportion of loci segregating in the stock under selection that are homozygous AA in the tester, then it can be shown (Table 21.2) that average progress in cross performance per locus is:

$$\Delta P_h = [\, \bar{q}_T \cdot \Delta q_i \,(1-k) + (1-\bar{q}_T) \cdot \Delta q_j \,(1+k)\,]\, d \qquad (4)$$

For loci fixed AA in the tester:

$$\Delta q_i = s \cdot r_{P\,G_i} \cdot r_{G_i q_i} \cdot \sigma_{q_i} = \frac{s\,d\,\sqrt{q_T}}{2\,\sigma_P} \cdot q_i\,(1-q_i)\,(1-k) \qquad (5)$$

Similarly for loci fixed aa in the tester:

$$\Delta q_j = s \cdot r_{P\,G_j} \cdot r_{G_j q_j} \cdot \sigma_{q_j} = \frac{s\,d}{2\,\sigma_P} \cdot \sqrt{(1-\bar{q}_T)} \cdot q_j\,(1-q_j)\,(1+k) \qquad (6)$$

From equation (4) we can now express average progress per locus from selection for cross performance with a homozygous tester as:

$$\Delta P_h = [\, \bar{q}_T^{3/2} q_i \,(1-q_i)\,(1-k)^2 + (1-\bar{q}_T)^{3/2} q_j \,(1-q_j)\,(1+k)^2]\,\frac{s\,d^2}{2\,\sigma_P}\quad (7)$$

Rate of improvement in cross performance from reciprocal selection (equation 3) approaches zero as gene frequencies approach the equilibrium expected if rates of reproduction of individuals were directly proportional to their phenotypes (i.e., $q = [1 + k]/2k$). Hence, progress from reciprocal selection may be expressed more usefully in terms of the deviation of gene frequencies from $(1 + k)/2k$, as follows:

$$\Delta P_r = \frac{s\,d^2}{2\,\sigma_P}\left[\, q_1\,(1-q_1)\left(\frac{1+k}{2\,k} - q_2\right)^2 + q_2\,(1-q_2)\left(\frac{1+k}{2\,k} - q_1\right)^2\right]4\,k^2$$

$$- 2\,k\cdot\Delta q_1\cdot\Delta q_2 d \quad (8)$$

Comparisons of expected progress per generation from homozygous tester and from reciprocal selection may be made from equations (7) and (8), respectively. The comparison may be visualized by plotting rate of improvement against deviations of gene frequencies from an initial equilibrium value of $(1 + k)/2k$, using q_1 and q_2 for the two populations under reciprocal selection, and q_i and q_j for loci that are AA and aa, respectively, in the tester, for homozygous tester selection.

In Figure 21.5, it is assumed that $k = 2$, and q_i is shown approaching 0 $(k + 1)/(k - 1)$ times as fast as q_j approaches 1. Actually, q_i would move more slowly than q_j at first because $(Aa - AA) = (k - 1)d$ and $(Aa - aa) = (1 + k)d$. However, Δq_i increases as q_i falls from .75 toward .5 because of the increased variance of q_i and consequent increase in genetic variance and in covariance with progeny means, and then Δq_i declines as q_i moves from .5 toward 0. There is a steady decline in Δq_j as q_j rises from .75 toward 1.0.

Under reciprocal selection, if q_1 and q_2 are near an equilibrium of $(1+k)/2k$ at the outset, initial progress will be slight compared with that from homozygous tester selection and will not equal ΔP_h until q_1 and q_2 differ, in opposite directions from $(1 + k)/2k$, by an average of about .50. Only during the late generations of selection will reciprocal selection surpass homozygous tester selection in effectiveness.

Another possible disadvantage of reciprocal selection is that gene frequencies at most loci for which $k > 1$ may be somewhat below $(1 + k)/2k$. This will occur if the advantage of Aa over AA and aa individuals in rate of reproduction is made greater by intensive individual or family selection than it would be if reproductive rates were directly proportional to phenotypic levels of performance. This would amount to increasing the effective degree of heterozygote advantage from k to k', and hence making actual equilibrium q nearer to .5 (i.e., $\hat{q} = [1 + k']/2k'$).

If actual equilibrium frequencies for the more favorable allele are generally below $(1 + k)/2k$ in both populations, reciprocal selection will tend to raise both q_1 and q_2 toward $(1 + k)/2k$, but at an ever decreasing rate, until q chances to go beyond $(1 + k)/2k$ in one of the populations. However, q_1 and q_2 are unlikely to be equal, even when both are smaller than $(1 + k)/2k$. If $q_1 > q_2$, then q_1 will be closer than q_2 to $(1 + k)/2k$ and will move faster in that direction $(\Delta q_1 > \Delta q_2)$. Consequently q_1 will become larger than $(1 + k)/2k$ and direction of Δq_2 will·be reversed without reducing Δq_1 to zero. Only

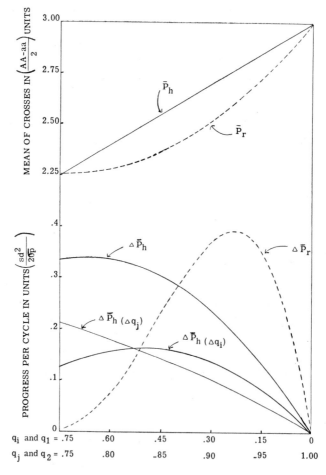

FIG. 21.5—Mean performance of crosses (*upper*) and rates of progress per cycle (*lower*) for homozygous tester (*solid lines*) and for reciprocal (*broken lines*) selection when $k = 2$ and $\bar{q}_T = .75$, as q_i and q_1 approach 0 and q_j and q_2 approach 1.

then can the slow-starting reciprocal selection begin moving q_1 and q_2 toward opposite extremes.

Use of Partially Inbred Tester Lines

In large animals, or even in poultry, discussion of selection utilizing homozygous tester lines is still largely academic. Few very highly inbred and usable lines of swine and chickens exist. However, there are many partially inbred lines of swine and poultry whose average cross performance has been or is now being tested. These partially inbred lines should be extremely useful in overcoming the initial disadvantage of reciprocal selection, because inbreeding will have pushed frequencies of individual genes in these lines much further away from equilibrium than in non-inbred stocks. Since effectiveness of reciprocal selection (equation 8) increases with

$$\left(\frac{1+k}{2k} - q_2\right)^2,$$

even a moderately inbred line used as one of two populations under reciprocal selection would materially increase initial progress per cycle from Δq_1.

Of course, further selection within the inbred line itself on the basis of cross performance would be relatively ineffective (Δq_2 small) until the selection on cross performance has had time to shift q_1 at individual loci in the non-inbred population away from $(1 + k)/2k$ in the opposite direction from q_2. It might be wise to ignore cross performance in selecting replacements within the inbred line for a number of cycles to allow time for q_1 to make this shift at loci where initial q_1 and q_2 chance to deviate from $(1 + k)/2k$ in the same direction. Beyond this point, progress from reciprocal selection between the partially inbred and the non-inbred populations should approach and finally exceed that from selection for cross performance with a homozygous tester.

In selecting a partially inbred line for use in reciprocal selection, one instinctively would choose a line known to be superior in its average cross performance and in its usability as an inbred strain. This seems desirable to assure that the line carries at high frequencies any genes whose favorable effects on total performance are incompletely dominant. In addition, it would be helpful to try a number of different partially inbred lines in crosses with a given non-inbred stock, choosing finally for reciprocal selection the line showing best initial cross performance. Diversity of origin and previous crossing data would of course aid in selecting the lines more likely to be initially complementary to a given non-inbred stock.

Presumably, both initial cross performance and rate of progress from reciprocal selection are likely to be greater if the two populations are of different breeds. However, Dobzhansky's (1949) finding of greater heterozygote advantage from alternative homologous chromosome segments within a single population than in crosses between non-interbreeding populations of

Drosophila suggests the need for further investigation of the importance of diversity of origin for attainment of maximum heterosis in crosses.

Use of an F_1 Cross as the Tester

Hull (1945) also has suggested selection to complement the F_1 cross of two homozygous lines as a means for developing new lines to replace the poorer ones presently used in successful corn hybrids. Here, expected rate of improvement in performance of the 3-line cross (ΔP_f) would be a composite of that expected from selection for cross performance with a homozygous tester, and with a non-inbred strain in which gene frequency is $\frac{1}{2}$ at each locus:

$$\Delta P_f = [\, q_T^2 \cdot \Delta q_i \,(1-k) + (1-q_T)^2 \cdot \Delta q_j (1+k) + 2 q_T (1-q_T) \cdot \Delta q_f] \, d \quad (9)$$

where q_T is average proportion of loci homozygous for the more favorable allele in the lines represented in the F_1 tester; q_i, q_j, and q_f are average frequencies of the more favorable alleles at loci that are AA, aa, and Aa, respectively, in the F_1 tester. The F_1 tester is AA at q_T^2, aa at $(1-q_T)^2$, and Aa at $2q_T(1-q_T)$ of the loci. Hence,

$$\Delta q_i = \frac{sd}{2\sigma_P} q_T q_i \,(1-q_i)\,(1-k)\,, \; \Delta q_j = \frac{sd}{2\sigma_P}(1-q_T) q_j (1-q_j)\,(1+k)$$

and

$$\Delta q_f = \frac{sd}{2\sigma_P}\sqrt{2 q_T (1-q_T)} \cdot q_f (1-q_f)\,.$$

Substituting in equation (9), we obtain as estimated progress per cycle:

$$\Delta P_f = \{\, q_T^3 q_i \,(1-q_i)\,(1-k)^2 + (1-q_T)^3 q_j \,(1-q_j)\,(1+k)^2$$
$$+ [2 q_T \,(1-q_T)\,]^{3/2} \cdot q_f (1-q_f)\,\} \frac{sd^2}{2\sigma_P} \quad (10)$$

Apparently one might expect that selection to complement an F_1 tester (of 2 homozygous lines) would be about one-half as effective as selection to fit a single homozygous tester.

In selection for complementary strains in livestock, the F_1 tester may be a cross of two partially inbred lines, M and N. Selection of a population, L, to complement $M \cdot N$ would tend to improve the $L(M \cdot N)$ cross at a rate intermediate between one-half that for reciprocal selection (ΔP_r)/2 and that for use of an F_1 cross of homozygous lines as the tester (ΔP_f), depending on the degree of inbreeding in lines M and N.

If M and N were being selected to complement each other, gene frequency in the $(M \cdot N)$ linecross tester would tend to be lowered from equilibrium $(1+k)/2k$ toward $\frac{1}{2}$ as the limit. Consequently, rate of improvement in the $L(M \cdot N)$ cross from selecting L to fit $M \cdot N$ should approach that expected from selecting in population L to complement a non-inbred tester in which

$q = .5$ at each segregating locus. Progress per cycle when $q_2 = .5$ should approach

$$q_1 (1 - q_1) \cdot \frac{s d^2}{2 \sigma_P}.$$

Since q_1 would be increased above initial equilibrium of $(1 + k)/2k$, maximum progress per cycle should be

$$\frac{(1 + k)(k - 1)}{4 k^2} \frac{s d^2}{2 \sigma_P},$$

and rate of progress would decline as q_1 became larger than $(1 + k)/2k$. The maximum rate of progress, then, for selecting population L to complement the cross of two highly complementary strains M and N, is expected to be little more than one-half that for selection to complement a homozygous tester.

Other Considerations

Under heterozygote advantage and selection toward complimentary strains by either the reciprocal or the homozogous tester method, the strains themselves may be expected to decline in performance for characters that are depressed by inbreeding. The less favorable allele would tend to become fixed at about half of the loci segregating in the foundation stocks. The effectiveness of this sort of selection in moving gene frequencies toward opposite homozygous extremes in the complementary strains would be greater for those traits in which heterozygote advantage ($k > 1$), and hence inbreeding depression, is larger. That portion of the inbreeding depression arising from loci at which there is no heterozygote advantage ($k \leq 1$) would not be produced by selection for cross performance without inbreeding, because selection would favor the dominant allele in both strains. Therefore, any serious decline in performance of the strains themselves, while under selection for cross performance, is indicative of heterozygote advantage and should be accompanied by compensatory improvement in performance of the cross.

In order to develop complementary strains whose own performance would make them usable in commercial production of crosses, some compromise may be necessary between selection based on test-cross and on individual performance. There is much opportunity for selection in choosing young breeders, especially males, to be tested in the strain-cross. Individual selection for characters little affected by inbreeding would be least apt to impair the effectiveness of the complementary selection. Some selection for individual performance characters important for both the strains and their cross may become necessary to prevent fixation of rare genes with major detrimental effects in the homozygote, but advantageous in the heterozygote. Selection for fertility and maternal influences (e.g, hatchability, prolificacy, or suckling ability) in test-cross matings should help maintain usable strains.

SUMMARY

Genetic Variability in Economic Characters of Swine

1. Inbreeding and crossbreeding effects indicate that degree of heterozygosity exerts a major influence on the important performance characters, and that a high degree either of dominance or of epistacy due to deviations from an optimum genetic intermediate, or both, characterizes genetic variability in performance.

2. Relative ineffectiveness of selection within mildly inbred strains makes ordinary dominance or epistasis doubtful as an explanation of inbreeding decline, and suggests heterozygote advantage for net desirability in prolificacy, suckling ability, viability, and growth rate.

3. "Controlled" selection experiments with swine show that high and low lines for growth rate or feed utilization can be separated, but indicate little improvement of high line over foundation stock, particularly for net performance in all characters.

4. Lower heritabilities and larger inbreeding declines for characters long and intensely selected in one direction, compared with those selected toward an intermediate or in varying directions, indicate a higher degree of dominance for the former.

5. Some sort of negative relationship between components of total performance is indicated by lower heritability for total performance than for its component characters and by direct estimates of correlation. This would correspond to heterozygote superiority, in that increased frequency of genes with dominant favorable effects on one character would constitute decreased frequency of their alleles having dominant favorable effects on other characters.

6. The genetic basis of performance appears to be similar in corn and in swine, as indicated by natural degree of inbreeding, extent of inbreeding decline in performance, and the effectiveness of phenotypic selection. Ordinary dominance is inadequate to account for heterosis already achieved in corn, and by analogy, is unlikely to be adequate in swine.

7. Examples of manifold effects and heterozygote advantage for specific chromosome segments or loci support their inferred importance for quantitative economic characters.

Methods of Selecting for Maximum Heterosis

1. Intensity of selection per unit of time is lower when based on progeny performance in test-crosses than when based on individual and family performance. Hence, methods of selecting for maximum cross performance between complementary strains are indicated only when individual and family selection have become relatively ineffective, and when there is evidence for

important heterozygote advantage with attendant intermediate equilibrium gene frequencies.

2. Cumulative gains from recurrent selection pressure are necessary to obtain efficiently crosses heterozygous for anywhere near the potential maximum proportion of loci, since distribution of F_1 crosses within any generation is narrow relative to the potential range when numbers of loci are large.

3. Expected effectiveness of reciprocal recurrent selection between two populations and recurrent selection for cross performance with a homozygous tester may be compared as follows:

a. They are alike in potential limits of cross performance for loci exhibiting heterozygote advantage, but use of a homozygous tester would be more likely to limit ultimate cross performance if partial dominance or special epistatic effects were important.

b. They would be similar in initial cross performance, except that it should be easier to deliberately select a stock differing materially from a homozygous tester in gene frequency at individual loci than to select two equally complementary non-inbred stocks.

c. As long as gene frequencies in the selected populations are anywhere near their expected equilibria, improvement in cross performance per cycle will be far greater for the homozygous tester than for the reciprocal selection plan. The difference between progenies from A and a gametes under selection approaches zero as frequency of A in the non-inbreed tester approaches an equilibrium of $(Aa-aa)/(2\,Aa-AA-aa)$, but discrimination between A and a gametes under selection is maximum when the tester is homozygous aa or AA.

d. Rate of progress from reciprocal selection accelerates as the difference in frequency of homologous chromosomal units in the two populations becomes larger, and surpasses homozygous tester selection when $q_1 - q_2$ exceeds about .5.

4. Use of a partially inbred line as one of the two populations in reciprocal selection would greatly increase progress in early cycles, since individual gene frequencies will be further away from equilibrium in inbred strains than in non-inbred stocks.

C. R. HENDERSON
Cornell University

Chapter 22

Specific and General Combining Ability

By general combining ability we mean the average merit with respect to some trait or weighted combination of traits of an indefinitely large number of progeny of an individual or line when mated with a random sample from some specified population. The merit of the progeny is measured in some specified set of environmental circumstances. If maternal effects are present, we must specify that the tested individuals are males. If the tested individuals are females, the merit of the progeny is a function of both general combining ability and maternal ability.

General combining ability has no meaning unless its value is considered in relationship to at least one other individual or line and unless the tester population and the environment are specified. For example, suppose two dairy bulls used concurrently in an artificial breeding ring each have 500 tested daughters, and that it can be assumed that the cows to which the two bulls were mated were a random sample of cows from herds using artificial breeding. Suppose that the mean of the butterfat records of the daughters of the first sire is 410 pounds and of the second sire is 400 pounds. Five hundred tested daughters are sufficient to reduce the sampling variance of the progeny mean to a negligible amount. Consequently the general combining ability of the first sire is $410 - 400 = 10$ pounds better than that of the second in this particular population and in this set of environmental circumstances. The general combining abilities of the two sires might differ by more or by less than 10 pounds if they were used in some other region where both the genotypes of the cows to which they were mated as well as the environment could be quite different from those of the test.

SPECIFIC COMBINING ABILITY

We shall define specific combining ability as the deviation of the average of an indefinitely large number of progeny of two individuals or lines from the values which would be expected on the basis of the known general combining abilities of these two lines or individuals and the maternal ability of the female parent. As Lush (1948) has pointed out, apparent specific effects, or what animal breeders usually call *nicking*, also can be a consequence of Mendelian sampling, of inaccurate estimates of the additive genetic values of the two parents, and of environments affecting the progeny which are different from the average environments in which the general combining abilities and the maternal abilities were estimated.

Genetically, specific combining ability is a consequence of intra-allelic gene interaction (dominance) and inter-allelic gene interaction (epistasis). We shall assume in this paper that we can estimate only the joint effect of dominance and epistasis. As an illustration of specific combining ability let us suppose that we know that the general combining ability with respect to weight in swine line A is $+10$ pounds at 154 days, and that the general combining ability plus maternal ability of line B is $+5$ pounds at 154 days. Then if an indefinitely large number of progeny of the cross $A \times B$ has a mean of $+7$ pounds, the specific effect for this cross is $7 - 10 - 5 = -8$.

SELECTION FOR GENERAL AND SPECIFIC COMBINING ABILITY

Under some circumstances selection would be largely for general combining ability, and in other circumstances for a combination of general and specific combining ability. For example, those selecting sires for use in a large artificial breeding ring are interested primarily in obtaining sires with the highest general combining ability with respect to the population of cows and environments in which the bulls are to be used. On the other hand, those wishing to employ crosses among inbred lines for commercial use select for a combination of general, maternal, and specific effects.

Now let us consider some of the problems involved in selecting for general and specific combining ability. There are reasonably good solutions to some of these problems, but almost none for others. Some of the questions which are involved are:

1. Given a particular set of records how can one best estimate the general combining abilities of individuals, families, or lines, and how can one best estimate the value of the progeny of a specific cross between families or inbred lines?

2. What proportion of the breeder's resources should be put into a testing program? For example, if he is dealing with inbred lines, what proportion of his resources should be employed in the making of lines and what proportion in testing them for general and specific combining ability?

3. Having decided on the size of the testing program, what kind of tests should be made? For example, should lines be tested in topcrosses or in line crosses or in some combination of these two procedures? Also what use should

be made of a sequential type of testing in which some lines are discarded on the basis of a very preliminary and inaccurate test?

4. What relative emphasis in selection should be placed on general as compared to specific combining ability?

5. How much inbreeding should be done in the making of lines? How fast should the lines be made?

Obviously a complete discussion of all these problems and their possible solutions in the time at our disposal is impossible. Consequently we shall discuss primarily the problem of estimating general combining abilities of lines and individuals and of estimating the values of specific crosses among lines, given a particular set of records. In addition, since estimates of the variances play an important role in these selection methods, we shall discuss briefly the problem of estimating variance components from the results of line-cross tests.

So far as estimation of general combining abilities of individuals is concerned, the methods to be presented here are essentially those of the selection index. It will be shown that no assumption of normality of distributions is required; that joint estimates of general combining abilities and certain parameters such as the population means, the yearly effect, the age and inbreeding effect, can be obtained; and that certain short-cut computational procedures are sometimes distinctly advantageous. An application of the principles of the selection index to estimation of general combining abilities of lines or families also will be presented. Finally it will be shown that application of the selection index need not be restricted as it has been to selection for additive effects, but can be applied equally well to joint selection for specific effects and general combining ability. The selection index approach to appraising crosses can, under some circumstances, be much more efficient than selection based on the mean of the progeny of a particular cross.

ESTIMATION PROBLEMS IN SELECTION

Before turning to selection for general and specific combining abilities let us consider the type of estimation problem which is involved and some general solutions to it. Later the manner in which the solutions can be applied to our present problem will be discussed. Our estimation problem can be stated in this way. We have a sample of N observations, $y_1, y_2, \ldots, y_N$, from which we wish to estimate $\theta_1, \theta_2, \ldots, \theta_q$. The y's are assumed to have a multivariate distribution (precisely what distribution need not be specified for the present) with means, $b_1 x_{1i} + b_2 x_{2i} + \ldots + b_p x_{pi}$, and variance-covariance matrix,

$$\| \sigma_{y_i y_j} \|.$$

The b's are fixed parameters such as the population mean and the regression of y on age of the dam, and x is an observable parameter, the first subscript denoting with which b it is associated, the second subscript with which sample observation. As an illustration, x_1 might be associated with b_1, the population mean. Then x_{1i} would have the value 1 in each observation; x_{2i} might denote the inbreeding coefficient of the dam.

Now comes the really crucial part of the model. The θ's are regarded as having some multivariate distribution with means zero and variance-co-variance matrix,

$$\| \sigma_{\theta_g \theta_h} \|.$$

Also the θ's and y's are regarded as having a joint distribution with covariances $\sigma_{\theta_h y_i}$. The way in which this problem differs from the ordinary estimation problem in statistics is that here we wish to estimate the values of individual θ's which are regarded as a sample from some specified population.

Selection for Additive Effects in the Normal Distribution

What is the "best" way to estimate the θ's? Suppose that they represent additive genetic values of individuals and that any linear function of the y's is normally distributed. Lush (1948) has shown that, subject to the normality assumptions, improvement in additive genetic merit of a population through selection by truncation of the estimates (indexes) of additive genetic values is maximized by choosing that index which has maximum correlation with additive genetic value. This principle has been used in the index method of selection by Fairfield Smith (1936), Hazel (1943), and others. These workers have shown that the index can be found in a straightforward manner provided certain variances and covariances and all of the b's, the fixed elements of the model, are known.

The values of $K_{\theta i}$ which maximize $r_{\theta \hat\theta}$ where $\hat\theta = K_{\theta 1} w_1 + \ldots + K_{\theta N} w_N$ are the solution to the set of simultaneous equations (1). The w's are the y's corrected for the fixed elements of the model such as the population mean (not the sample mean). Thus $w_1 = y_1 - b_1 x_{11} - \ldots - b_p x_{p1}$.

$$K_{\theta 1} \sigma^2_{y_1} + K_{\theta 2} \sigma_{y_1 y_2} + \ldots + K_{\theta N} \sigma_{y_1 y_N} = \sigma_{y_1 \theta}$$

$$K_{\theta 1} \sigma_{y_1 y_2} + K_{\theta 2} \sigma^2_{y_2} + \ldots + K_{\theta N} \sigma_{y_2 y_N} = \sigma_{y_2 \theta} \qquad (1)$$

$$\cdot \qquad\qquad\qquad\qquad\qquad\qquad\qquad \cdot$$
$$\cdot \qquad\qquad\qquad\qquad\qquad\qquad\qquad \cdot$$
$$\cdot \qquad\qquad\qquad\qquad\qquad\qquad\qquad \cdot$$

$$K_{\theta 1} \sigma_{y_1 y_N} + K_{\theta 2} \sigma_{y_2 y_N} + \ldots + K_{\theta N} \sigma^2_{y_N} = \sigma_{y_N \theta}$$

Selection when Form of Distribution is Unspecified and b's Are Unknown

Maximization of $r_{\theta \hat\theta}$ is a satisfactory solution to the problem of selection for additive genetic values under the normality assumption and the assumption of known b's. Is a comparable solution available when nothing is known of the distribution or of the b's? So far as I am aware there is not.

Consequently let us consider some other criterion of a "best" index. We shall use as our criterion of "best" that index from the class of linear functions of the sample which is unbiased (coefficients of all b's = 0 in $E\hat{\theta}$) and for which $E(\hat{\theta} - \theta)^2$ is a minimum. E denotes expected value. Consequently $E(\hat{\theta} - \theta)^2$ denotes the average in repeated sampling of the squared deviations of the index of θ about the true value of θ. When the b's are unknown, the same criterion of best is applied to them, that is, minimum $E(\hat{b} - b)^2$ for unbiased estimates $(E\hat{b} = b)$ which are linear functions of the sample. It turns out that minimization of $E(\hat{\theta} - \theta)^2$ and maximization of $r_{\theta\hat{\theta}}$ lead to identical indexes. Hence the assumption of normality is not essential to construction of selection indexes as now used.

It must be obvious that the selection index method just described is very laborious when a number of different θ need to be estimated, for the solution to a set of simultaneous equations is required for each θ. In practice this difficulty is avoided to a certain extent by choosing arbitrarily only a few sources of information to be employed in selection. This is not a wholly satisfactory solution, for in most cases if the number of different indexes is not to be entirely too large, information must be rejected which could add at least a little to the accuracy of the index.

By means of a simple modification it becomes necessary to solve only one set of equations no matter how many θ are estimated from a particular set of data, and precisely the same index as in the conventional method is obtained. Using the same notation as before, the index for θ is now

$$\hat{\theta} = C_1 \sigma_{\theta y_1} + C_2 \sigma_{\theta y_2} + \ldots + C_N \sigma_{\theta y_N},$$

where the C's are the solution to a set of equations identical to set (1) except that the right members are $w_1, \ldots, w_N$ rather than $\sigma_{\theta y_1}, \ldots, \sigma_{\theta y_N}$. Consequently once the C's are computed, any number of θ's can be estimated simply by taking the appropriate linear function of the C's.

More tedious computations result if the b's are not known. One solution is of the following general form. In order that each θ be unbiased it is necessary that the K's have these restrictions imposed:

$$K_1 x_{11} + K_2 x_{12} + \ldots + K_N x_{1N} = 0$$
$$K_1 x_{21} + K_2 x_{22} + \ldots + K_N x_{1N} = 0$$
$$\cdot \qquad\qquad\qquad \cdot$$
$$\cdot \qquad (2)$$
$$\cdot$$
$$K_1 x_{p1} + K_2 x_{p2} + \ldots + K_N x_{pN} = 0$$

Subject to these restrictions the values of the K's which minimize $E(\hat{\theta} - \theta)^2$ can then be found.

If we wish to obtain estimates of the b's which are unbiased and have minimum $E(\hat{b} - b)^2$, we impose the restrictions of equations (2) except that the right member of the equation pertaining to the particular b to be estimated is 1 rather than 0.

An easier solution to the problem of unknown b's often can be obtained by regarding the model as,

$$y_i = b_1 x_{1i} + b_2 x_{2i} + \theta_1 z_{1i} + \ldots + \theta_q z_{qi} + e_i ,$$

where the e_i are independently distributed with mean zero and variance $\sigma_{e_i}^2$ and the z's are observable parameters. For example, θ_1 might represent the general combining ability of inbred line A, θ_2 the general combining ability of line B, and θ_3 a specific effect peculiar to the cross $A \times B$. The observable parameters z would have the following values: $z_1 = 1$ when line A is one of the parents, $= 0$ otherwise; $z_2 = 1$ when line B is one of the parents, $= 0$ otherwise; and $z_3 = 1$ when y_i is an observation on the cross $A \times B$ or $B \times A$, $= 0$ otherwise. Now the joint estimates of b's and θ's are the joint solution to the subsets of equations (3), (4), and (5).

$$C_1 \sigma_{y_1}^2 + C_2 \sigma_{y_1 y_2} + \ldots + C_N \sigma_{y_1 y_N} = y_1 - \hat{b}_1 x_{11} - \ldots - \hat{b}_p x_{p1}$$

$$\tag{3}$$

$$C_1 \sigma_{y_1 y_N} + C_2 \sigma_{y_2 y_N} + \ldots + C_N \sigma_{y_N}^2 = y_N - \hat{b}_1 x_{1N} - \ldots - \hat{b}_p x_{pN}$$

$$\hat{\theta}_1 = C_1 \sigma_{y_1 \theta_1} + \ldots + C_N \sigma_{y_N \theta_1}$$

$$\tag{4}$$

$$\hat{\theta}_q = C_1 \sigma_{y_1 \theta_q} + \ldots + C_N \sigma_{y_N \theta_q}$$

$$\hat{b}_1 S x_1^2 + \ldots + \hat{b}_p S x_1 x_p + \hat{\theta}_1 S x_1 z_1 + \ldots + \hat{\theta}_q S x_1 z_q = S x_1 y$$

$$\tag{5}$$

$$\hat{b}_1 S x_1 x_p + \ldots + \hat{b}_p S x_p^2 + \hat{\theta}_1 S x_p z_1 + \ldots + \hat{\theta}_q S x_p z_q = S x_p y ,$$

where

$$S x_1^2 = \sum_i \frac{x_{1i}^2}{\sigma_{e_i}^2}, \qquad S x_1 x_2 = \sum_i \frac{x_{1i} x_{2i}}{\sigma_{e_i}^2}, \quad \text{etc.}$$

These equations can be solved by the following steps. First solve for the C's in equations (3). The results will be in terms of the sample observations and the $\hat{b}$'s. Second, substitute values of these C's in equations (4) to obtain $\hat{\theta}$'s in terms of the sample and the $\hat{b}$'s. Third, substitute these values of the $\hat{\theta}$'s in equations (5) and solve for the $\hat{b}$'s. Fourth, substitute the computed values of the $\hat{b}$'s in (4) and solve for the $\hat{\theta}$'s.

An alternative computational procedure which is less laborious when the θ's are few in number, and in particular when the θ's are uncorrelated, involves joint estimation of the b's and θ's by solution of equations (5) to which are added equations (6).

$$b_1 Sx_1 z_1 + \ldots + b_p Sx_p z_1 + \theta_1(S z_1^2 + \sigma^{11}) + \ldots + \theta_q (S z_1 z_q + \sigma^{1q}) = S z_1 y$$

$$\tag{6}$$

$$b_1 Sx_1 z_q + \ldots + b_p Sx_p z_q + \theta_1(S z_1 z_q + \sigma^{1q}) + \ldots + \theta_q (S z_q^2 + \sigma^{qq}) = S z_q y\,,$$

where

$$\| \sigma^{ij} \| = \| \sigma_{\theta_i \theta_j} \|^{-1}\,,$$

and

$$Sx_1 z_1 = \sum_i \frac{x_{1i} z_{1i}}{\sigma_{e_i}^2}\,, \quad \text{etc.}$$

These equations are simply least squares equations (the θ's are regarded as fixed rather than having a distribution) modified by adding σ^{ii} to certain coefficients.

SELECTION BY MAXIMUM LIKELIHOOD ESTIMATES

Now let us assume that the θ's have the multivariate normal distribution and that the errors are normally and independently distributed. What are the maximum likelihood estimates of the θ's and b's? It just so happens that the estimates which are unbiased and which have minimum $E(\hat{\theta} - \theta)^2$ and $E(\hat{b} - b)^2$ for the class of linear functions of the sample are also the maximum likelihood estimates. Consequently the estimation procedure we have described can be seen to have the following desirable properties: unbiasedness, maximum relative efficiency of all linear functions of the sample, maximization of genetic progress through selection by truncation when the distributions are normal, properties of maximum likelihood estimates when the distributions are normal, and equations of estimation which can be set up in a routine manner.

Unknown Variances and Covariances

An important problem in selection remains unsolved and perhaps there is no practical solution to it. What should be done if the variances and covariances are unknown? If our sample is so large that estimates of the variances and covariances can be obtained from it with negligible errors, we can use these estimates as the true values. Similarly we may be able to utilize estimates obtained in previous experiments. But if there are no data available other than a small sample, the only reasonable advice would seem to be to estimate the variances from the sample, perhaps modifying these estimates somewhat if they appear totally unreasonable. At any rate the estimation procedure serves to point out what additional information is needed if an intelligent job of selection is to be accomplished.

SELECTION FOR ADDITIVE GENETIC VALUES IN INDIVIDUALS

As our first application of the methods described above, consider the estimation of additive genetic values of individuals with respect to a single trait (the single trait might be net merit) from a set of records all made in the same herd or flock. It will be assumed for the present that the population mean is known and that records can be corrected satisfactorily for all non-random environmental factors. For example, the records might represent all of the 305 day, mature equivalent butterfat records made in a herd during the past ten years. It is desired on the basis of these records to decide which cows should be culled, which heifers should be selected for replacements, and which bull calves should be grown out for possible use as herd sires.

In the usual approach to this selection problem by use of the selection index, one would decide what particular subset of the records would contribute most to the estimate of the value of each animal under consideration and would then construct separate indexes. The method to be presented here employs all available records in estimating the value of each animal. That is, no prior decision is made concerning which records to use to construct the index for each animal, but instead all available ones are used.

The first step in the procedure is the computation of what Emik and Terrill (1949) have called a numerator relationship chart and Lush (1948) has called genic variances and covariances for all animals whose records are to be used in the index or whose breeding values are to be estimated. In terms of Wright's (1922) coefficients of relationship and inbreeding, the genic variance of the ith animal is $1 + F_i$, where F_i is the inbreeding coefficient of the ith animal, and the genic covariance between the ith and jth animal is

$$R_{ij} \sqrt{(1 + F_i)(1 + F_j)},$$

where R_{ij} is the coefficient of relationship between the two animals. The numerator relationship or genic covariance, which we shall denote by a_{ij}, is the numerator of the fraction representing relationship. That is

$$R_{ij} = \frac{a_{ij}}{\sqrt{(1 + F_i)(1 + F_j)}}.$$

The computation of $\|a_{ij}\|$ is a routine procedure if it is done systematically as described by Emik and Terrill and by Lush.

Next we need an estimate of heritability of the trait, and if more than one record is available on a single animal, as would be true of butterfat production, an estimate of repeatability. Now let $\bar{y}_1, \bar{y}_2, \ldots, \bar{y}_p$ be the mean of the n_i records of each of p animals, these records having been corrected for non-random environment and expressed as deviations about the population mean. The next step is to solve the following set of equations for $C_1, \ldots, C_p$. In these equations h denotes heritability and r denotes repeatability.

$$C_1\left(F_1 h + \frac{1 + (n_1 - 1)\ r}{n_1}\right) + C_2 a_{12} h + \ldots + C_p a_{1p} h = \bar{y}_1$$

$$C_1 a_{12} h + C_2\left(F_2 h + \frac{1 + (n_2 - 1)\ r}{n_2}\right) + \ldots + C_p a_{2p} h = \bar{y}_2 \tag{7}$$

$$\cdot$$
$$\cdot$$
$$\cdot$$

$$C_1 a_{1p} h + C_2 a_{2p} h + \ldots + C_p\left(F_p + \frac{1 + (n_p - 1)\ r}{n_p}\right) = \bar{y}_p$$

If all available records are to be used in the estimation procedure just described, the number of equations to be solved for the C's is large. It might appear, in fact, that the number is too great for the method to have any value. However, the equations are ideally suited to an iterative solution. The reason for this is that the diagonal elements of the left members of the equations are very large compared to the off-diagonal elements thereby making the iterative solution a particularly rapid one. On the basis of our experience with a few herds a solution to sufficient accuracy can be obtained in three or four rounds of iteration.

Once the C's have been computed the estimate of g_i, additive genetic value of the ith animal, is

$$\hat{g}_i = h\ (C_1 a_{1i} + C_2 a_{2i} + \ldots + C_p a_{pi}).$$

If the ith animal had one or more records included in the computation of the C's the estimate can be computed more easily, for

$$\hat{g}_i = \bar{y}_i - C_i\ \frac{1 + (n_i - 1)\ r - n_i h}{n_i}.$$

The estimate of the real producing ability of a tested animal is even more simple to express. The estimated real producing ability is

$$\bar{y}_i - C_i\ \frac{(1 - r)}{n_i}.$$

It should be pointed out that this estimate differs from the one presented by Lush (1945) since his method does not utilize records on relatives.

Valuable characteristics of the method just described, in addition to its ease of computation and its use of all available information, is that the inclusion of the records of the contemporaries of the ancestors of the animals being appraised automatically eliminates the troublesome problem of what effect selection has had on the phenotypic and genetic variances of the selected group of ancestors. Also changes in additive genetic variances and covariances effected by inbreeding are automatically taken into account. If selection is intense, the sample mean may considerably overestimate the population mean appropriate for subtraction from the records. The safest procedure is to regard μ as unknown and to estimate it by the procedure described earlier (equations 3, 4, 5). It is also of interest to note that joint estimation by this method of such factors as environmental trends and age effects automatically eliminates biases in the estimates resulting from use of selected data.

SELECTION FOR GENERAL COMBINING ABILITY IN TOPCROSS TESTS

When it comes to estimation of the general combining abilities of inbred lines or of the values of specific crosses, apparently no application has been made of the selection index method. This failure may have been due to difficulty in obtaining the estimates of the needed variances and covariances, failure to see that the method was applicable, or the opinion that since inbred lines can be carefully tested more efficient but complex methods of appraisal are not worth the extra computational labor. We propose to show here how the methods can be applied to such selection problems, to indicate some situations in which it may result in considerably more efficiency in selection than the use of the straight means of the lines or crosses as the criteria of selection, and to present some approximate solutions which are relatively easy to compute.

Let us consider first one of the most simple tests of lines, the topcross test. In this test a random sample of individuals from each of several lines is mated to a tester population, and measurements are taken on the resulting progeny. If only one trait is considered important, the lines are usually rated according to the means of their topcross progeny. This method of ranking is as good as any, provided either that the same number of progeny is obtained for each line or that the sampling errors of the line means are negligible. Seldom, at least in large animal tests, would either of these conditions hold. Accidents usually preclude attainment of equal numbers, and sampling errors are usually large. If sequential testing is done, numbers would always be unequal. By sequential testing we mean here that lines are given a preliminary test, and a certain fraction of those performing worst are discarded. Then the remaining lines, accompanied perhaps by some new lines, are given another test, and so on through any number of cycles desired. The lines surviving several such tests would obviously have larger numbers of progeny than the new lines, and it would be a very inefficient procedure to disregard the results of prior tests on the older lines when choosing between them and the newer, less well-tested lines.

The way in which the lines should be ranked on the basis of all information is analogous to choosing between individuals with different numbers of records. In the latter case both repeatability of single records and the number of records need to be considered; in the former case the genetic differences among lines, the environmental variance, and the number of progeny. Also in both cases consideration of the genetic covariances between individuals or between lines increases the accuracy of the ranking.

Assuming that the population mean is known and that it and non-random environmental factors have been subtracted from the means of the progeny of the various lines, the estimate of g_i, the general combining ability of the ith line, is

$$\hat{g}_i = C_1 \sigma_{g_i \bar{y}_1} + \ldots + C_p \sigma_{g_i \bar{y}_p}$$

where $\bar{y}_1, \ldots, \bar{y}_p$ are the corrected means for the p tested lines and the C's are the solution to a set of equations with

$$\| \sigma_{\bar{y}_i \bar{y}_j} \|$$

as coefficients in the left members and corrected $\bar{y}_1, \ldots, \bar{y}_p$ as the right members. Computation of $\sigma_{\bar{y}_i \bar{y}_i}$ and $\sigma_{g_i \bar{y}_i}$ requires good estimates of

$$\| \sigma_{g_i g_j} \|$$

and of σ_e^2. Assuming that the corrected mean of a particular topcross is $\bar{y}_i = g_i + \bar{e}_i$, and that the errors are independent with common variance σ_e^2 we have the following variances and covariances

$$\sigma_{\bar{y}_i}^2 = \sigma_{g_i}^2 + \sigma_e^2 / n_i \qquad\qquad \sigma_{\bar{y}_i g_i} = \sigma_{g_i}^2$$

$$\sigma_{\bar{y}_i \bar{y}_j} = \sigma_{g_i g_j} \quad \text{(where } i \neq j) \qquad \sigma_{\bar{y}_i g_j} = \sigma_{g_i g_j} \quad (i \neq j)$$

Frequently good estimates of μ and non-random environmental factors are not available and consequently must be estimated from the topcross data. For example, it is very likely that the environment is not the same from test to test and must be taken into account if the data from several tests are to be combined into a "best" index. In such cases the method of equations (5) and (6) can be employed to distinct advantage unless

$$\| \sigma_{g_i g_j} \|^{-1}$$

is too difficult to compute. To illustrate this method as applied to topcross data we shall assume that y_{ij}, the record of the jth progeny of the ith line, can be represented by

$$y_{ij} = b_1 x_{1ij} + b_2 x_{2ij} + g_i + e_{ij} .$$

b_1 and b_2 are examples of fixed parameters, g_i is the general combining ability of the ith line, and e_{ij} is a random error. Assuming that the g_i are distributed with means zero and known variance-covariance matrix,

$$\| \sigma_{g_i g_j} \| ,$$

and that the e_{ij} are independently distributed with means zero and common variance σ_e^2, the estimates of the b's and g's which are "best" by the criterion used in this paper are the solution to the following equations:

$$\hat{b}_1 \sum_i \sum_j x_{1ij}^2 + \hat{b}_2 \sum_i \sum_j x_{1ij}x_{2ij} + \sum_i \hat{g}_i x_{1i.} = \sum_i \sum_j x_{1ij}y_{ij}$$

$$\hat{b}_1 \sum_i \sum_j x_{1ij}x_{2ij} + \hat{b}_2 \sum_i \sum_j x_{2ij}^2 + \sum_i \hat{g}_i x_{2i.} = \sum_i \sum_j x_{2ij}y_{ij}$$

$$\hat{b}_1 x_{11.} + \hat{b}_2 x_{21.} + \hat{g}_1 (n_1 + \sigma_e^2 \sigma^{11}) + \sum_{i \neq 1} \hat{g}_i \sigma_e^2 \sigma^{1i} = y_1.$$

$$\begin{matrix} . & & . \\ . & & . \\ . & & . \end{matrix}$$

$$(8)$$

$$\hat{b}_1 x_{1p.} + \hat{b}_2 x_{2p.} + \hat{g}_p (n_p + \sigma_e^2 \sigma^{pp}) + \sum_{i \neq p} \hat{g}_p \sigma_e^2 \sigma^{pi} = y_p.$$

Dots in the subscripts denote summation over that subscript, and σ^{ii} denotes an element of

$$\| \sigma_{g_i g_j} \|^{-1} .$$

The above procedure for appraising lines on the basis of topcrosses assumes either that the lines are homozygous or that only one progeny is obtained from each randomly chosen male. If these assumptions are not correct, the procedure is modified to take into account intra-line variances and covariances and the number of progeny per male.

What are the consequences of appraising lines on the basis of the arithmetic average of their respective progeny as compared to the more efficient method just described? First, the errors are larger than necessary. Second, selection of some small fraction of tested lines will tend to include a disproportionately large number of the less well-tested lines. The more efficient method discounts the higher averages in accordance with the number of tested progeny and the relative magnitudes of σ_g^2 and σ_e^2.

What if the number of lines tested is large and certain lines are related? This means that a large matrix,

$$\| \sigma_{g_i g_j} \| ,$$

has to be inverted and then a large set of simultaneous equations solved. What approximations might be employed in the interest of reducing computations? For one thing, we might ignore the covariances between the g's, thereby reducing the inverse matrix to $1/\sigma_{g_i}^2$ in the diagonal elements and 0 in the off-diagonal elements. Also if we know μ and non-random environmental factors well enough, further simplification is possible. Let $\bar{w}_i$ be the corrected mean of the progeny of ith line. Then

$$\hat{g}_i = \frac{n_i \sigma^2_{g_i}}{n_i \sigma^2_{g_i} + \sigma^2_e} \, \bar{w}_i \, .$$

This result is a straightforward application of the principles of the selection index.

It must be quite apparent that efficient appraisals of the general combining abilities of lines depend on knowledge of the variances and covariances of general combining abilities and of the variance of error. It hardly seems likely that estimates of the line variances and covariances can be obtained with accuracy comparable to estimates of additive genetic variances and covariances with respect to individuals. The latter estimates are based on studies of heritability and on the known facts of the hereditary mechanism. In the case of inbred lines, however, the sample of different lines tested is usually so small as to make the estimates of σ^2_g less reliable than we should like. A way around this difficulty in the case of traits for which heritability is well known is to compute the expected variances and covariances based on knowledge of σ^2_g in the original population from which the lines were formed, the inbreeding of the different lines, and the relationships between pairs of lines. It seems likely that such estimates would be more reliable when the number of lines is small than would estimates arising from the actual line tests. We cannot be any more precise regarding this point until methods are developed for placing confidence limits on estimates of variances and covariances arising from non-orthogonal data.

SELECTION FOR GENERAL COMBINING ABILITY, MATERNAL ABILITY, AND SPECIFIC ABILITY IN LINE CROSS TESTS

If we wish to estimate the general combining ability of lines relative to the population from which the lines themselves can reasonably be regarded as a random sample, line crosses give, for fixed size of testing facilities, more accurate estimates than do topcrosses. The reason for this is that we obtain from each cross estimates of the general combining abilities of two or more lines. Also, line crosses enable one to estimate differences in maternal abilities unconfounded with differences in general combining abilities and to appraise the values of specific crosses. In those species for which hand mating is the customary procedure, little more labor is required for line cross than for topcross tests. The estimation of line and line cross characteristics from line cross data is no different in principle from what we have already described with respect to estimation of additive genetic values of individuals or general combining abilities of lines. As before, we wish to obtain unbiased and most efficient estimates of certain genetic values. For the sake of simplicity of presentation we shall confine ourselves to discussion of the analysis of single crosses. Application of these principles to multiple cross data involves no new principles.

Let us consider first what type of model might be reasonable for a single cross. It is not too difficult to suppose that the value of a particular observation on a single cross is the sum of the general combining ability of the male line, the general combining ability of the female line, a maternal effect coming from the line used as the female, a specific effect due to dominance and epistasis and peculiar to the particular cross, non-random environmental effects, and a multitude of random errors such as Mendelian sampling and the environment peculiar to the particular progeny on whom the record is taken. More complicated models could of course be proposed, but the one which we have just described would seem to account for the major sources of variation among crosses. Furthermore it is amenable to mathematical treatment. Putting the above description in a mathematical model we have

$$y_{ijk} = b_1 x_{1ijk} + b_2 x_{2ijk} + g_i + g_j + m_j + s_{ij} + e_{ijk} ,$$

where y_{ijk} is the observation on the kth progeny of a cross between the ith line used as a male parent and the jth line as a female parent, the b's and x's are related to the mean and other non-random environmental factors as described in the model for the topcross test, $g_i(g_j)$ is the general combining ability of the ith$(j$th$)$ line, m_j is an effect in addition to the additive genetic value which is common to all progeny of the jth line used as a female parent, s_{ij} is an effect over and above the additive genetic and maternal effects and which is common to all progeny of the cross of the ith line by the jth line or of the jth line by the ith line, and e_{ijk} is a random error associated with the particular observation.

In this model the g_i are regarded as having some multivariate distribution with means zero and variance-covariance matrix,

$$\| \sigma_{g_i g_j} \| .$$

The m_j, s_{ij}, and e_{ij} are all regarded as independently distributed with means zero and variances σ_m^2, σ_s^2, and σ_e^2, respectively. It is of course conceivable that the variances of the m_j and s_{ij} and the covariances between them vary with the inbreeding and relationships of the lines. Also g_i and m_j may be correlated. In the absence of any real knowledge concerning such covariances we shall ignore them for our present purposes. If, however, something is known about these covariances, the estimation procedure can be modified to take them into account. The procedure should also be modified if the lines are not homozygous and each parent has more than one progeny.

A single cross test can supply answers to the following questions with respect to the lines tested:

1. What are the best estimates of the relative values of the tested lines

when used as the male parent in topcrosses on the population from which the lines are regarded as a sample?

2. What are the best estimates of the relative values of the tested lines as female parents in crosses with males from the above population?

3. What are the best estimates of the relative values of specific single crosses among the tested lines?

Suppose that n_{ij} progeny of the cross ith line of male by jth line of female are tested (n_{ij} can be zero for some crosses). Now the easiest way to estimate the value of the ith line as a male parent is simply to compute the mean of all progeny of the line when used as the male parent. This simple procedure, however, fails to take into account the distribution among lines of the mates of males of the ith line, the covariances among the general combining abilities of lines, the consequences of specific effects, the size of the error variance, and the number of progeny tested. Furthermore, since the ith line is used also as the female parent in certain crosses, something can be gained by employing the measurements on these progeny. Estimation by the general procedure we have described takes into account all of these factors. Similarly the easiest way to estimate the maternal ability of the jth line is to compute the mean of all progeny out of females of the jth line, but the most efficient procedure takes into account the same factors as are needed in efficient estimation of general combining ability. Finally the easy way to appraise the value of a particular cross is merely to find the mean of all progeny of the specific cross (if that cross has been tested). This latter estimate is subject to large sampling error since it would seldom be feasible to test many individuals of the numerous possible crosses among even a few lines. The error of estimation can be materially reduced by utilizing the fact that the true merit of a cross is a function of the general combining abilities of two lines, the maternal ability of the female line, and the specific effect peculiar to that cross and to its reciprocal. The method to be described places the proper emphasis on estimates of general and maternal abilities and on the progeny averages of the specific cross and its reciprocal. The procedure also enables estimates to be made of the value of a specific cross even though that particular cross has not been tested.

The major step in these efficient estimation procedures is the setting up and solving of a set of simultaneous equations in the $\hat{b}$'s, $\hat{g}$'s, $\hat{m}$'s, and $\hat{s}$'s. These equations are as follows:

$$\hat{b}_1 \sum_i \sum_j \sum_k x^2_{1ijk} + \hat{b}_2 \sum_i \sum_j \sum_k x_{1ijk} x_{2ijk} + \sum_i \hat{g}_i (x_{1i..} + x_{1.i.}) \qquad (9)$$

$$+ \sum_j \hat{m}_j x_{1ij.} + \sum_{i<j} \hat{s}_{ij} (x_{1ij.} + x_{1ji.}) = \sum_i \sum_j \sum_k x_{1ijk} y_{ijk}$$

and similarly for the b_2 equation.

$$\hat{b}_1(x_{11..}+x_{1.1.}) + \hat{b}_2(x_{21..}+x_{2.1.}) + \hat{g}_1(n_{1.}+n_{.1}+\sigma_e^2\sigma^{11})$$

$$+ \sum_{i\neq1}\hat{g}_i(n_{i1}+n_{1i}+\sigma_e^2\sigma^{1i}) + \hat{m}_1 n_{.1} + \sum_{j\neq1} m_j n_{1j} + \sum_{j\neq1}\hat{s}_{1j}(n_{1j}+n_{j1})$$

$$= y_{1..}+y_{.1}.$$

and similarly for the other g_i equations.

$$\hat{b}_1 x_{1.1.} + \hat{b}_2 x_{2.1.} + \hat{g}_1 n_{.1} + \sum_{i\neq1}\hat{g}_i n_{i1} + \hat{m}_1(n_{.1}+\sigma_e^2/\sigma_m^2) + \sum_{i\neq1}\hat{s}_{1i} n_{i1} = y_{.1}.$$

and similarly for the other m_j equations.

$$\hat{b}_1(x_{112.}+x_{121.}) + \hat{b}_2(x_{212.}+x_{221.}) + (\hat{g}_1+\hat{g}_2)(n_{12}+n_{21}) + \hat{m}_1 n_{21}$$

$$+ \hat{m}_2 n_{12} + \hat{s}_{12}(n_{12}+n_{21}+\sigma_e^2/\sigma_s^2) = y_{12.}+y_{21}.$$

and similarly for the other s_{ij} equations.

These equations are not particularly difficult to solve, for each s_{ij} can be expressed as a function of $y_{ij.}$, $y_{ji.}$, $\hat{b}_1, \hat{b}_2, \hat{g}_i, \hat{g}_j$, and $\hat{m}_j$. Utilizing this relationship the equations can be reduced to a set involving none of the $\hat{s}_{ij}$. Also an iterative solution is usually easy because of the relatively large diagonal coefficients. Once the estimates of g_i, m_j, and s_{ij} are obtained it is a simple matter to evaluate the lines and crosses. The estimate of the value of a line as the male parent in topcrosses is $\hat{g}_i$, and the estimate of its average value as the female parent is $\hat{g}_i + \hat{m}_i$. The value of a single cross is estimated simply as $\hat{g}_i + \hat{g}_j + \hat{m}_j + \hat{s}_{ij}$. It is appropriate to add the estimates in this manner because they have the desirable property of invariance.

If solution of the large set of simultaneous equations required for most efficient appraisal of lines is considered too burdensome, certain approximate solutions can be employed. An approximation suggested by the common practice in construction of selection indexes is the choosing of certain information most pertinent to the particular line or cross to be appraised. For example, the estimate of g_i might be based entirely on $y_{i..}$ and $y_{.i.}$, each corrected for the b's as best can be done with the information available regarding their values. As a further simplification it might be assumed that the g_i are uncorrelated and have common variance σ_g^2. Similarly m_i might be estimated entirely from $y_{i..}$ and $y_{.i.}$. These approximate solutions are

$$\hat{g}_i = C_1\sigma_{g_i y_{i..}} + C_2\sigma_{g_i y_{.i.}}$$

$$\hat{m}_i = C_1\sigma_{m_i y_{i..}} + C_2\sigma_{m_i y_{.i.}},$$

where the C's are the solution to

$$C_1\sigma_{y_{i..}}^2 + C_2\sigma_{y_{i..}y_{.i.}} = y_{i..} - \hat{b}_1 x_{1i..} - \hat{b}_2 x_{2i..}$$

$$C_1\sigma_{y_{i..}y_{.i.}} + C_2\sigma_{y_{.i.}}^2 = y_{.i.} - \hat{b}_1 x_{1.i.} - \hat{b}_2 x_{2.i.}.$$

The variances and covariances needed in this approximate solution can be computed easily from σ_g^2, σ_m^2, σ_s^2, and σ_e^2. Approximate values of $\hat{s}_{ij}$ can then be obtained by substituting the approximate $\hat{b}_1$, $\hat{b}_2$, $\hat{g}_i$, and $\hat{m}_j$ in equations (9).

ESTIMATION OF VARIANCES OF GENERAL, MATERNAL, AND SPECIFIC EFFECTS

As mentioned earlier, one might take as the additive genetic variance and covariance among the lines the theoretical values based on relationships among the lines, degree of inbreeding among the lines, and the genetic variance in the original population from which the lines came. It is necessary even then to estimate σ_m^2, σ_s^2, and σ_e^2. It is well known that methods for estimating variance components are in a much less advanced stage than estimation of individual fixed effects. It is seldom possible to obtain maximum likelihood estimates. Consequently many different methods might be used, and the relative efficiencies of alternative procedures are not known.

We shall consider as desirable criteria of estimation procedures for variance components ease of computation and unbiasedness. If the single cross experiment is a balanced one, that is if there are the same number of observations on each of the possible crosses, it is not difficult to work out the least squares sums of squares for various tests of hypotheses, regarding the line and cross line characteristics as fixed. Then assuming that there are no covariances between the various effects and interactions, one can obtain the expectations of the least squares sum of squares under the assumption that the effects and interactions have a distribution (Henderson, 1948). In case the experiment is not a balanced one, it is still possible to obtain least squares tests of hypotheses and to find expectations of the resulting sums of squares· This, however, is ordinarily an extremely laborious procedure (Henderson, 1950).

A much easier procedure is available. It probably gives estimates with larger sampling variance, although that is not really known, and gives almost exactly the same results in the balanced experiments as does the least squares procedure. This involves computing various sums of squares ignoring all criteria of classification except one, taking expectations of these various sums of squares, and solving the resulting set of simultaneous equations. The latter procedure will now be illustrated for single cross data in which we wish to obtain estimates of the variances pertaining to general combining ability, maternal ability, specific effects, and error. It will be assumed that the only fixed element in the model is μ. Now let us compute certain sums of squares and their expectations. These are set out below.

Total: $E\left(\sum_i \sum_j \sum_k y_{ijk}^2\right) = n..(\mu^2 + 2\sigma_g^2 + \sigma_m^2 + \sigma_s^2 + \sigma_e^2)$

Sires: $E\left(\sum_i \dfrac{y_{i..}^2}{n_{i.}}\right) = n_{..}(\mu^2 + \sigma_g^2) + \sum_i \dfrac{\sum_j n_{ij}^2}{n_{i.}}(\sigma_g^2 + \sigma_m^2 + \sigma_s^2) + s\sigma_e^2 ,$

where s denotes number of different lines used as the male line.

Dams: $E\left(\sum_j \dfrac{y_{.j.}^2}{n_{.j}}\right) = n_{..}(\mu^2 + \sigma_g^2 + \sigma_m^2) + \sum_j \dfrac{\sum_i n_{ij}^2}{n_{.j}}(\sigma_g^2 + \sigma_s^2) + d\sigma_e^2 ,$

where d is the number of different lines used as the female line.

Crosses: $E\left(\sum_{i<j} \dfrac{(y_{ij.} + y_{ji.})^2}{n_{ij} + n_{ji}}\right) = n_{..}(\mu^2 + 2\sigma_g^2 + \sigma_s^2)$

$$+ \sum_{i<j} \dfrac{n_{ij}^2 + n_{ji}^2}{n_{ij} + n_{ji}}\sigma_m^2 + c\sigma_e^2 ,$$

where c denotes the number of different crosses (regarding reciprocals as one cross)

Correction Factor: $E\left(\dfrac{y_{...}^2}{n_{..}}\right) = n_{..}\mu^2 + \sum_i (n_{i.} + n_{.i})^2 \sigma_g^2 / n_{..}$

$$+ \sum_j n_{.j}^2 \sigma_m^2 / n_{..} + \sum_{i<j}(n_{ij} + n_{ji})^2 \sigma_s^2 / n_{..} + \sigma_e^2$$

The above sums of squares and expectations are quite easy to compute and once this is done all one needs to do is to subtract the correction factor and its expectation from the other sums of squares and expectations and solve the resulting set of four equations for σ_g^2, σ_m^2, σ_s^2, and σ_e^2.

FURTHER RESEARCH NEEDED

If maximum progress through selection for general and specific combining ability is to be attained, much additional research is needed. From a statistical standpoint we need to know if an index based on minimization of $E(\hat{\theta} - \theta)^2$ comes close to maximizing progress through selection by truncation when the distributions are not the multivariate normal. If such an index does not do so, we need to know what practicable index or indexes will. Further, if nothing is known of the variances and covariances needed in construction of indexes or if there are available only estimates with large sampling errors, we need to know if the index based on the assumption that the estimate is the true value is best from the standpoint of maximizing genetic progress. Finally, much more work is needed on the problem of estimating variance and covariance components and placing confidence limits on such estimates.

Although there is a considerable body of literature on heritability esti-mates, we need more accurate estimates of the heritabilities of most traits of economic importance. Also almost nothing is now known about genetic cor-relations between traits, about genetic-environmental interactions, and about the magnitude of genetic differences among herds. Estimates of these genetic parameters are essential to intelligent selection for additive genetic values. In the case of inbred lines, little is known concerning the variances of general and specific combining abilities. The work of Sprague and Tatum (1942) with corn and Henderson (1949) with swine illustrates the types of estimates which are badly needed in selecting for general and specific combin-ing abilities from the results of line cross tests.

Finally, well designed experiments are needed to test how closely predic-tions made from indexes or other selection procedures check with actual re-sults.

L. M. WINTERS
University of Minnesota

Chapter 23

Rotational Crossbreeding and Heterosis

It is well for all of us, including our most eminent scientists and philosophers, to reduce our thinking to relatively simple terms. Genetics is, after all, basically rather simple. A fertilized zygote results from the union of two germ cells, each of which carries a haploid number of chromosomes, and a haploid number of genes which are resident in the chromosomes. By the very nature of the procedure, genes are paired which are alike or not alike. As the pairing of similar genes is increased, the population approaches increased purification. As the pairing of dissimilar genes increases, the resulting population becomes more heterozygous. Increased heterozygosity has been generally associated with increased vigor which is generally spoken of as hybrid vigor.

PLANNING THE MINNESOTA EXPERIMENTS

I believe the best way to discuss rotational crossbreeding is to relate briefly how the system was developed. When I was asked in 1928 to head the research in animal breeding at the University of Minnesota, I brought with me several proposed projects. One of these was a study of crossbreeding swine. A review of the literature of crossbreeding experiments conducted previous to 1928 shows that for the most part they were small-scale experiments. When the data were all put together, however, the evidence was in favor of crossbreeding. Yet, the general sentiment at that time among the stockmen was overwhelmingly opposed to the practice of crossbreeding. The statement frequently heard was that crossbreeding was quite satisfactory for the production of one crop, but all of the crossbreds must be marketed because it was absolutely disastrous to use any of the crossbreds as breeding animals. By 1928, it was quite evident that corn breeders were revolutionizing the system of breeding corn, and that hybridization was to become the rule rather than the exception in the production of commercial corn. Wright (1922) had several years previously published what has since turned out to be a classic: *The Report of the U.S.D.A. Studies of Inbreeding and Crossbreeding with Guinea Pigs*. Why then should the situation be different in livestock than in corn and in guinea pigs? Was it true that livestock failed to respond to crossbreeding, and if so, why? A likely explanation appeared to be that our breeds of livestock were not truly comparable to inbred lines of guinea pigs and corn because they did not possess sufficient genetic purification.

I am sorry now that I did not record in advance of this experiment the results that I expected to derive. Had I recorded them, they would have been something like this: The crossing of the breeds of livestock will result in a slight increase in vigor. The increase will be so slight that it is scarcely worth while for the commercial producer, in contrast to the more simple procedure of grading or the maintenance of a registered herd. Most of my severe critics regarding crossbreeding will be quite surprised to read this statement. As nearly as I can tell at this time, there were two major reasons for my belief. The first was the accumulation of the continued absorption of a large amount of teaching toward that end. The second was the general belief on the part of geneticists that our breeds of farm animals had not been sufficiently purified nor separated genetically to yield hybrid vigor when crossed.

If I had recorded all of my thoughts, they would have included this reservation: If the crossing of the breeds *does* result in increased performance sufficient to make crossing worth while, then the standard advice that had been given through the years regarding the use of crossbred females for breeding must be erroneous. This reservation was based on the results that Wright had previously obtained in his use of crossbred guinea pigs as dams, and from the information already available regarding the production of hybrid corn. At this time there was no thought regarding continuous crossbreeding by either rotation or crisscross breeding. The objectives were merely to find out if there was any advantage in crossing the breeds for the market production of swine. If there was an advantage in crossing the breeds for market production of swine, was there then any advantage in retaining these crossbreds to become future parents?

In planning the experiment, provision was made whereby as nearly as possible the same genetic material was put in the crosses as was produced in the purebreds. In planning the use of crossbreds as parents, the original plan called for the use of both crossbred females and crossbred males. My senior officers informed me that they were willing to go along with me quite a way in this crossbreeding study, but that when it came to the use of crossbred males, that was going just a bit too far and I would have to compromise. I compromised on this point all too willingly. How I have wished, during the last few years, that I had insisted on carrying out my original plan of using both crossbred females and crossbred males in the experiment. But little did any of us realize at that time that within twenty-two years we would be in the midst of a flourishing hybrid boar business. None of us know much about their true merits and demerits. Nevertheless, the crossbred boars were not included in the experiment.

Experimental Results

The experiment did proceed as planned for the production of first cross offspring from the mating of purebred females of one breed to purebred males of another breed. Crossbred females were then retained as breeding animals to be mated in one case to a boar of one of the two parental breeds and in the other case to a boar of a third breed. The results of this experiment showed that there was a very definite advantage in the production of firstcross pigs. There was a slightly greater advantage in the production of backcross pigs (that is, where crossbred females were mated back to a boar belonging to one of the parental breeds). There was a still greater advantage where the crossbred females were mated to a boar of another breed.

As I mentioned before, you bring together either genes that are alike or genes that are not alike. There appears to be very little likelihood of bringing about any more heterozygosity as a result of a three-breed or a four-breed cross than there is in a two-breed cross. The advantages derived from the backcross and from the cross to a third breed appear therefore to have been derived from the fact that the female parents were crossbreds or in a more hybrid state than their purebred half sisters. Why should this be the case? The female produces the eggs, carries the fertilized eggs, and develops them to the point where, after a period of about 114 days, they are ready for birth and then nurses the little pigs for another 56 days. In general, the advantage derived from the crossbred female in contrast to the purebred female is about equal to that derived from having the progeny crossbred in contrast with having progeny that are purebred.

The above are the general deductions that I made at the close of our crossbreeding experiment. Now I am not so certain that this interpretation is absolutely correct. The reason for my questioning is that recently I had a long visit with one of the largest hybrid seed corn producers in this nation. He is a man who has had many years of experience in the field. He told me that he had not yet seen a single cross of hybrid corn that was as useful for commercial corn production as the double hybrid. He elaborated further to the effect that the single cross hybrid often would yield as heavily as the double hybrid, but that under adverse environmental conditions the double hybrid fared better. This he attributed to the fact that the double hybrid developed from four inbred lines possessed greater genetic diversity toward adversity. This appears to be somewhat in contrast to the experimental results and interpretations of those results in some of the present-day fundamental studies of Drosophila genetics. Undoubtedly, with time and more experimental results, we will be in a better position to bridge this gap. My experiences have convinced me, however, that it is a mistake not to take seriously the observations made by competent practical men in the field of operations. I am inclined to believe that very often these men see more, although they measure less accurately, than we in the field of research, with our eyes glued carefully to the job of measuring certain details.

In this experiment we used four standard measurements for appraisal of the pigs' worth. These were: number of pigs born alive, number of pigs weaned, rate of gain, and feed per unit of gain. Since then we have added a fifth measure—appraisal of body form on the basis of judgment. When we took the first four factors and compared the performance of the crosses with the comparable purebreds, we obtained an advantage of the crosses over the purebreds of 6.3 per cent for the first cross, 7.5 per cent for the backcross, and 11.7 per cent for the three-breed cross. This was obtained by throwing the four factors together as equal in importance.

By another method of comparison, wherein more factors were thrown into the pool, we obtained an advantage for the first cross of 7 per cent, the backcross 6 per cent, and the three-breed cross of 17 per cent. If, however, we were to take litter weight at weaning, which in one sense is comparable to yield in corn, we would have an advantage of the first cross of approximately 25 per cent, the backcross 39 per cent, and the three-breed cross 61 per cent. If we were to take total litter weight at the close of the experiment, the advantages of the crosses would be still greater. In my opinion, total litter weight as a sole measure of merit exaggerates the difference. On the other hand, I do not consider the method we have used entirely satisfactory. I do not know of an entirely satisfactory measure of performance in livestock. We in the livestock field need to do a great deal in the matter of perfecting our methods of measurements. The important question to the practical man is whether one procedure is better than another, rather than whether this procedure gives me exactly 20 per cent or 18 per cent increase.

ROTATIONAL CROSSBREEDING

On the basis of these results, we developed and put forward our plan of rotational crossbreeding. Even at the time that I started to analyze the data, I did not believe that our three-breed cross had given us any worth-while advantage over the single cross. I mention this merely to show how strongly entrenched the old teaching had become regarding the limitations of crossbreeding in livestock production. The results of the experiment were, however, very definite. I calculated and recalculated, and the results were always essentially the same—the three-breed cross possessed distinct advantages over the first cross and over the backcross.

Simple calculation shows that, on the average, the first cross will possess 50 per cent of the chromosomes, or more properly speaking, linkage groups of breed 1, and 50 per cent of breed 2. The second year, wherein three breeds are used, the resulting pigs will, on the average, possess: 25 per cent of the chromosomes from breed 1, 25 per cent from breed 2, and 50 per cent from breed 3. The third year, the pigs will possess 62.5 per cent of the chromosomes from breed 1, 12.5 per cent of breed 2, and 25 per cent of breed 3. The fourth year, the pigs will carry, on the average 31.25 per cent of the linkage groups from breed 1, 56.25 per cent from breed 2, and 12.5 per cent from breed 3. The fifth year, the pigs will possess, on the average: 15.63 per cent from breed 1, 28.12 per cent from breed 2, and 56.25 per cent from breed 3. From that time on, they will remain in a continuous cross, in about that general state of equilibrium, but the percentage of relationship to the different breeds will change.

On the basis of these calculations, we advocated rotational crossbreeding. Some of our critics could not understand how we felt justified in recommending rotational crossbreeding when our experiments had been carried only to the three-breed cross. Calculations showed so clearly that if the three-breed cross was good, then the continuous cross, by rotation, could not help being successful, insofar as the system of breeding was concerned. On the basis of the theory I have always contended that there was very little advantage in a four-breed cross. Now, however, I am not so sure that that is correct, if we are to take seriously what my commercial hybrid corn producer told me regarding the merits of the double cross of corn in contrast to the single cross. There may be merits in the four- or even the five-way cross that are not generally revealed in short-time experiments.

We have recommended rotational crossbreeding for commercial swine production, and it seemed, on the basis of theory again, that the rotational scheme of crossing had a particular aptitude for swine production, and was perhaps questionable with other classes of four-footed farm animals. The reason for this is that in swine it is possible for the commercial producer to turn a generation every year if he so desires. I have, however, a number of friends who are breeding commercial flocks of sheep after this general pattern with remarkably good results. If you look at their flocks with the strictly commercial viewpoint, they do not have the variance that most critics of the plan have contended would result. Further than that, the experiments conducted by the United States Department of Agriculture with beef cattle and dairy cattle have shown that the same basic principles apply to these classes of livestock as in swine. Dairymen have perhaps been more reluctant to depart from the purebred philosophy of breeding than any other group of livestock breeders. Yet by a strange coincidence, the experiments of the United States Department of Agriculture are showing a greater increased yield as the result of crossing dairy cattle than the crossing of any of our other species of farm animals. Their data show an increase of 25 per cent in milk and 32 per cent in butterfat yield.

ROLE OF INBRED LINES

The next logical question then is: Where and how do inbred lines enter this general picture? I cannot see that it changes the picture appreciably unless perhaps it gives an added reason as to why four or five inbred lines may (theoretically speaking) prove of advantage over the three-line rotational cross. We have now carried the continuous rotational cross of three inbred lines in two series of crossings to the seventh continuous generation of crossing. We have several others in the sixth, and several in the fifth generation. The comparative results of the different line crosses have been remarkably similar and uniform from generation to generation.

I have already given the average increased performance of the different breed crosses as being 6.3 for the first cross, 7.5 for the backcross, and 11.7 for the three-breed cross. What then are the increases obtained from crosses of inbred lines? By the same method of comparison used in breed crosses, except in this case including an estimate on type, we obtained an average of approximately 12 per cent increased performance for the crossing of inbred lines belonging to the Poland China breed, and an increased performance of 18 per cent when we crossed the Minnesota No. 2 with our inbred Poland China lines, and 20 per cent when we crossed Minnesota No. 1 with Minnesota No. 2 or crossed Minnesota No. 1 with our inbred Poland China lines. This is an increased performance over the performance of the inbred lines.

I am constantly asked what the comparative performance of our crosses of inbred lines with the performance of outbred stock is. By the best methods with which we have been able to make comparisons to date, the increased performance of our crossbred lines in comparison to the performance of the old-line breeds is an increase of about 20 to 25 per cent. One of these comparisons was made with outbred stock from our own University of Minnesota purebred herds. The other comparison is with the performance of purebred herds as given by Lush and Molln (1942). I do not regard either of these comparisons as entirely adequate, and again I will frankly state that I do not know how to make a comparison that will be entirely adequate. I would be much obliged if someone would present me with a plan by which a satisfactory comparison can be made.

I cannot conceive of any sampling method (sampling of the breeds) that will constitute an adequate sample of the breeds for comparative purposes, unless we go far beyond any funds that I can conceive of being made available for this purpose. Field trials such as have been conducted for comparisons with corn have been advocated. Some of the corn breeders inform me that they are not at all satisfied that these field trials are adequate. One reason is that yield is not a sufficient measure. Many farmers have told me that our own estimates of the advantages of crossing both the standard breeds and the use of our inbred lines is in error, due to an underestimate rather than an overestimate of the benefits.

Contrary to expectations, our three-line crosses have not given us as much increased performance over the two-line crosses as I expected on the basis of the results with breed crosses and theoretical expectations. I do not know the cause, but I am inclined to believe that it is due to inadequate sampling, and that as our samples become larger the advantages of the three-breed continuous cross will become more pronounced.

FARM APPLICATIONS

How does this work out on farms? The records on one of the large farms with which I am working show that their percentage of survival from the purified lines (230 litters) is 75 per cent, whereas their survival from the crosses of lines (248 litters) is 92 per cent under the same conditions. The survival of crossbred pigs out of crossbred sows is 91 per cent, but the crossbred gilts weaned an average of 9.1 pigs, to 8.3 for the first cross pigs and 7.2 for the purified lines.

This discussion would not be complete without reference to hybrid boars and how they are entering the picture. I have not seen sufficient data to allow me to appraise properly the advantages and disadvantages of the so-called *hybrid* boar, but he does seem to be proving popular with a number of farmers. If, then, the hybrid boar is here to stay, what is his place in rotational breeding? In my opinion, it will not change the basic situation materially, except that at least six inbred lines will be needed to produce the boars for the rotational crossing of the production of commercial stock. In this case, we will then use hybrid boar of lines 1 and 2, the following year hybrid boar of lines 3 and 4, the next year hybrid boar of lines 5 and 6, and then we will go back to 1–2, to 3–4, and to 5–6 in rotation.

In thinking about rotational crossing, we need to keep in mind that it is merely a procedure whereby we are able to maintain our breeding females (and perhaps our breeding males), as well as the offspring, in a relatively permanent hybrid state. It in no way affects the basic concepts of hybridization. It is just a means of utilizing hybridization, and if at some future date our methods of production change, as for instance the general development of so-called *pig hatcheries,* then we may well find some other method of crossbreeding better suited to the swine industry.

E. L. PINNELL
E. H. RINKE
and
H. K. HAYES
University of Minnesota

Chapter 24

Gamete Selection for
Specific Combining Ability*

Gamete selection as a breeding method was designed for more efficient sampling of open-pollinated varieties. It was suggested by Stadler in 1944. The method was outlined in detail by Stadler (1945) and preliminary data presented. Hayes, Rinke, and Tsiang (1946) proposed that the same technic could be used to select gametes from such sources as synthetic varieties, single or more complex crosses, and inbred lines. They discussed gamete selection in its relation to the improvement of a particular double cross combination.

MATERIALS AND METHODS

In 1945, three double crosses, Minhybrids 602, 607, and 406, were selected for a method study in gamete selection. Single cross performance data shown in Tables 24.1 and 24.2 indicate that A344 is low in combining ability in Minhybrids 602 and 607, and that the same is true for inbreds A25 and A73 in Minhybrid 406.

A344 was crossed to Minnesota #13 (Morris strain) and to 8 inbred lines namely, Oh51A, A97, I234, A315, A348, A367, A396, and Ill. 4226 as sources of gametes. The inbreds were selected because of their diversity of origin and good general combining ability. In addition, A367 had yielded well in specific tests with A357, A385, and A392. A315 and A348 had performed well in crosses with A392. The remaining five inbreds had not been crossed to A357, A385, or A392 in previous years. A25 was crossed with Golden King and A73 with Murdock. In 1946, individual F_1 plants of these crosses were

* Paper No. 2591 of the Scientific Journal Series, Minnesota Agricultural Experiment Station.

selfed and crossed to the *opposing* single cross parent of the double cross. Table 24.3 gives the number and type of test crosses made.

Approximately 60 inbred × variety F_1 plants from each of the three sources were selfed and crossed to the testers. Selection of the better F_1 plants at harvest reduced the number for further study to 35, 32, and 38 as listed in Table 24.3. Experiments 1 and 2 were tested in separate randomized blocks

TABLE 24.1

PERFORMANCE OF A344 AND A334*

INBREDS	AV. OF CROSSES	
	% Moist.	Bu.
A344×A357, A392, A385.....	28.3	69.8
A334×A357, A392, A385.....	30.1	84.3

* As indicated by average moisture and yield when crossed in non-parental single cross combinations of Minhybrid 602 (A344× A334) (A357×A392) and Minhybrid 607 (A344×A334) (A357× A385).

TABLE 24.2

PERFORMANCE OF A25, A334, A73, AND A375*

INBREDS	AV. OF CROSSES	
	% Moist.	Bu.
A25 ×A73, A375............	24.6	76.2
A334×A73, A375............	24.7	79.4
A73 ×A25, A334............	24.6	74.8
A375×A25, A334............	24.7	80.8

* As indicated by moisture and yield in non-parental single crosses of Minhybrid 406 (A25×A334) (A73×A375).

using two replicates at each of three locations in central Minnesota. Data from the two testers were averaged to give a total of 12 replicates as a test for each gamete. Experiments 3 and 4 were also grown in randomized blocks with three replicates at each of four locations in southern Minnesota. One location of experiment 3 was discarded and one replicate of experiment 4 was abandoned prior to harvest.

On the basis of yield trial results in 1947, gametes were selected from all varieties and from two inbreds, for use as parents in the development of new lines by straight selfing and by backcrossing to the sampler inbred.

Study of the performance indices and agronomic characters of the test crosses led to the selection of three Golden King gametes and four Murdock gametes as higher in general desirability than the sampler inbred parent. In addition, gametes of low yield potential but of relatively satisfactory agronomic characters were selected from both varieties, three from Golden King and two from Murdock.

F_2 populations were grown in 1948 from the selfed ears of the twelve F_1 plants selected in the above manner. Visual selection was practiced for desirable plant and ear characters, and these individual plants were crossed to the appropriate single cross tester. Remnant seed of the test crosses of the selected F_1 plants was used to make a direct yield comparison in 1949 with the test crosses of the selected F_2 plants. Two randomized block experiments were made at each of three locations in southern Minnesota with three

TABLE 24.3

GAMETE SOURCES, TESTERS USED, AND TEST CROSSES
MADE IN SELECTING GAMETES FOR IMPROVEMENT
OF INBREDS A344, A25, AND A73

Experiment Number	Inbreds	Gamete Source	Tester	Number of Crosses
1........	A344	Morris 13 gametes	A357×A392	35
	A344	Inbred gametes	A357×A392	8
		A344	A357×A392	1
2........	A344*	Morris 13 gametes	A357×A385	35
	A344	Inbred gametes	A357×A385	8
		A344	A357×A385	1
3........	A25	Golden King gametes	A73×A375	32
		A25	A73×A375	1
4........	A73	Murdock	A25×A334	38
		A73	A25×A334	1

* Same plants as in experiment 1.

replications per location. One experiment consisted of the crosses of 6 F_1 plants (remnant seed) from A25 × Golden King, and 34 F_2 plants by the tester compared with the cross of A25 × tester. The other included test crosses of 6 F_1 and 37 F_2 plants from A73 × Murdock gametes in comparison with A73 × tester.

EXPERIMENTAL RESULTS

The Morris strain of Minnesota 13 has been a very outstanding open-pollinated variety in Central Minnesota for many years. Yield trial data from plants of A344 × Morris 13 crossed with the testers show that a large proportion of Morris 13 gametes have higher yield potential than A344. Table 24.4 gives the distribution of yield and moisture data obtained from thirty-five test crosses of A344 × Morris 13. Sixteen of the thirty-five gametes gave test-cross yields significantly in excess of A344 × tester. Although not higher in yield, five other gametes may be considered superior to A344 because of their significantly lower moisture content at harvest and yields not significantly different in test crosses from A344 × tester.

The eight inbreds tested as possible sources of germ plasm for the improvement of A344 were A97, A315, A348, A367, A396, Oh51A, Ia234, and Ill.4226.

TABLE 24.4

DISTRIBUTION OF PER CENT MOISTURE AND YIELD OF 35 F₁ PLANTS OF A344 × MORRIS 13 CROSSED TO S.C. TESTERS A357 × A392 AND A357 × A385*

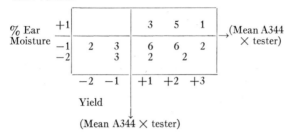

* Classes separated by one or more than one LSD (5 per cent) from the mean of A344 × tester.

TABLE 24.5

DISTRIBUTION OF PER CENT MOISTURE AND YIELD OF TEST CROSSES OF 8 INBRED LINES AS SOURCES OF GAMETES. CROSSES ARE OF THE TYPE (A344 × INBRED) × TESTERS*

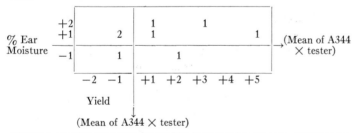

* Classes separated by one or more than one LSD (5 per cent) from the mean of A344 × tester.

The distribution for yield and moisture of test crosses of A344 × Inbred is given in Table 24.5. Three inbreds, Ia234, A396, and A97, demonstrated yield potential significantly higher than A344.

Golden King and Murdock are old, well-adapted varieties formerly grown extensively in southern Minnesota. Test crosses of thirty-two Golden King gametes × A25 and thirty-eight Murdock gametes × A73 are shown in Tables 24.6 and 24.7, respectively.

No gamete from Golden King exceeded A25 significantly in test-cross yields. However, eight not different in yield were significantly earlier, and are considered superior in yield performance on the basis of maturity. Eight gametes from Murdock demonstrated yield potential greater than A73, as indicated by significantly higher yields in crosses. In addition, fourteen gametes not different from A73 in yield were significantly earlier in maturity.

The proportion of promising gametes extracted from the three varieties and the eight inbreds is summarized in Table 24.8. About 25 per cent of the total number tested were superior to the sampler inbred in yield potential. Another 25 per cent would be considered desirable parents because they had a yield potential equal to and a maturity potential which was significantly earlier than the sampler inbreds.

SELECTION OF GAMETES AS PARENTS AND TESTS OF F_2 PROGENIES

Years of testing at Minnesota have led to the conclusion that, in general, there is a direct relation between yield and moisture content at husking among hybrids of equal genetic desirability. On this basis the combining ability of inbred $\times$ gamete plants was determined by considering both yield and moisture percentage at husking. They were effectively placed on a comparable basis by calculation of a performance index using the test cross of the sampler inbred as 100 for both ear moisture and yield. For example, if the moisture percentage of an A25 $\times$ Golden King plant (in test cross) was 93.5 as compared with A25 $\times$ tester, and its yield was 106.5 per cent, its performance index would be $+13$. Where the comparative moisture percentage is higher than the yield percentage the index becomes a negative value.

The performance indices for the selected gametes for both 1947 and 1949 trials and similar data for the F_2 plant progeny tests appear in Tables 24.9 and 24.10. The tests of F_2 plants from gametes of both high and low yield potential were made as explained in "Materials and Methods". This was carried out by selfing selected F_2 plants and also crossing them with the appropriate tester, and again comparing the results with the crosses of the appropriate inbred with the same tester. Agreement between the two tests of the gametes was very good except for Murdock gametes numbered 12 and 49.

On the average there was good agreement between F_1 and F_2 progeny performance. Tables 24.11 and 24.12 show that there is evidence of segregation for yield factors within almost all of the F_2 families tested.

Mean performance of the F_2 progeny from the high testing gametes was little different from the F_1 for either ear moisture or yield (Table 24.13). However, the F_2 progeny from the gametes of low yield performance exceeded the F_1 parent plant in yield performance on the average. This indicates that visual selection of plants within the F_2 populations was more effective among the progenies arising from the gametes of low yield performance than for those F_2 plants that were selected from high performing F_1 crosses (gamete $\times$ inbred).

TABLE 24.6

DISTRIBUTION OF PER CENT MOISTURE AND YIELD OF 32 F_1 PLANTS OF A25 × GOLDEN KING CROSSED TO A73 × A375*

% Ear Moisture	−2	−1	+1	+2
+2		1		
+1		3	2	
−1	2	8	5	
−2	3	5	3	

Yield

* Classes separated by one or more LSD (5 per cent) from the mean of A25 ×tester.

TABLE 24.7

DISTRIBUTION OF PER CENT MOISTURE AND YIELD OF 38 F_1 PLANTS OF A73 × MURDOCK CROSSED TO A25 × A334*

% Ear Moisture	−2	−1	+1	+2
+3	1			
+2				
+1		1	1	
−1		5	7	3
−2	1	2	9	3
−3		2	1	2

Yield

* Classes separated by one or more LSD (5 per cent) from the mean of A73 ×tester.

TABLE 24.8

NUMBER AND SOURCE OF GAMETES SUPERIOR IN PERFORMANCE TO SAMPLER INBREDS

Source of Gametes	Sampler Inbred	Total Gametes Tested	Higher in Yield and as Early or Earlier in Maturity	Not Different in Yield but Earlier
Morris 13......	A344	35	16	5
8 inbreds......	A344	8	2*	0
Golden King...	A25	32	0	8
Murdock......	A73	38	8	14
Total......	....	113	26	27

* An additional gamete higher in yield was also later in maturity.

TABLE 24.9

PERFORMANCE INDICES OF TEST CROSSES OF
SELECTED F₁ PLANTS AND F₂ PROGENY
FROM A25 × GOLDEN KING

F₁ PLANT NUMBER	PERFORMANCE INDEX			NUMBER OF F₂ PLANTS
	1947	1949		
	F₁	F₁	F₂	
19 H*....	+11	+19	+25	5
20 H.....	+14	+ 9	+14	7
36 H.....	+ 9	+16	+11	7
5 L.....	−11	− 3	+ 5	7
29 L.....	−11	− 1	− 0	1
46 L.....	− 5	+ 1	+ 2	7

* H = high- and L = low-performing gametes.

TABLE 24.10

PERFORMANCE INDICES OF TEST CROSSES OF
SELECTED F₁ PLANTS AND F₂ PROGENY
FROM A73 × MURDOCK

F₁ PLANT NUMBER	PERFORMANCE INDEX			NUMBER OF F₂ PLANTS
	1947	1949		
	F₁	F₁	F₂	
12 H........	+18	− 3	− 6	8
14 H........	+25	+33	+27	5
49 H........	+20	+ 1	+ 5	6
50 H........	+29	+19	+18	7
6 L........	−10	−23	−10	5
35 L........	− 4	−24	− 7	6

TABLE 24.11

FREQUENCY DISTRIBUTION OF PERFORMANCE IN-
DICES OF F_2 PROGENY PLANTS FROM A25 ×
GOLDEN KING AROUND MEAN PERFORMANCE
OF A25 × TESTER

F_1 PLANT NUMBER	INDICES FOR F_2 PLANTS					
	−15	−5	+5	+15	+25	+35
19 H.....				1	2	2
20 H.....			2	3	2	
36 H.....			3	4		
5 L.....		3	2	1	1	
29 L.....		1				
46 L.....	1	1	5			

TABLE 24.12

FREQUENCY DISTRIBUTION OF PERFORMANCE
INDICES OF F_2 PROGENY PLANTS FROM A73 ×
MURDOCK AROUND MEAN PERFORMANCE OF
A73 × TESTER

F_1 PLANT NUMBER	INDICES FOR F_2 PLANTS					
	−15	−5	+5	+15	+25	+35
12 H.....	5	1	1		1	
14 H.....				1	2	2
49 H.....		2	2	2		
50 H.....			2	2	2	1
6 L.....	2	2	1			
35 L.....	2	3	1			

TABLE 24.13

COMPARISON OF F_1 PLANTS AND THEIR F_2 PROGENY IN 1949 TEST
CROSS PERFORMANCE FOR EAR MOISTURE, YIELD,
AND PERFORMANCE INDEX

PARENTS	No. PLANTS TESTED		EAR MOISTURE %			YIELD IN BU.			PERFORMANCE INDEX		
	F_1	F_2	F_1	F_2	Diff.	F_1	F_2	Diff.	F_1	F_2	Diff.
A25×G. King H....	3	19	20.3	20.2	−0.1	54.0	54.5	+0.5	+14.4	+15.8	+ 1.4
A25×G. King L.....	3	15	23.3	23.8	+0.5	52.9	56.3	+3.4**	− 2.1	+ 3.3	+ 5.4
A73×Murdock H....	4	26	21.8	21.1	−0.7*	56.0	55.0	−1.0	+12.5	+ 9.6	− 2.9
A73×Murdock L....	2	11	22.8	22.4	−0.4	41.7	48.7	+7.0**	−23.6	− 8.6	+15.0

* Exceeds 5% point of significance.   ** Exceeds 1% point of significance.

DISCUSSION

Almost 50 per cent of the gametes studied showed evidence of having combining ability in excess of the sampler lines. The gametes chosen as parents appear to furnish a desirable source of germ plasm for a selection program designed to improve the yield potential of A344, A25, and A73 in combining ability in specific crosses.

Where a high combining varietal gamete is chosen for an inbred selection program, the F_1 plant of which it is a parent represents a high×low type of cross so far as combining ability is concerned. To the extent that such F_1 plants are comparable to crosses of inbreds, the breeding results should be similar to those from crosses of inbreds differing in combining ability. At Minnesota (Hayes and Johnson, 1939), crosses of high×low combiners have given F_5 lines ranging from high to low, but with a good proportion of high combiners.

Whether selection of gametes should be followed by test controlled selection in the F_2 is an important question. In these studies more than 50 per cent of the F_2 plants from high combining gametes tested at least ten performance index units higher than the sampler inbred. Thus without further test crosses, the chances of choosing high combining F_2 plants would still have been very good. The number of F_2 plants that could be handled in test crosses was quite limited. This may make for greater difficulty in recovering or improving the agronomic type of the sampler lines. It was very evident from field observations that the proportion of agronomically desirable F_3 lines appeared lower than usually found from crosses of highly selected inbreds.

The greater effectiveness of visual selection among the F_2 progenies of the low testing gametes is at this stage only an interesting development. Only a small proportion of the plants arising from the low testing gamete parents exceeded the sampler inbred in performance by a significant amount.

It was not possible to determine by visual examination which F_2 populations were derived from high gametes and which from low gametes, although there were wide differences in plant type between populations.

Gametes from eight inbred lines compared fairly well with varietal gametes from Morris 13, in offering promising sources of germ plasm for the improvement of specific combining ability of A344. Where a breeder has available large numbers of inbred lines of diverse origin the use of test selected inbred parents rather than varietal gamete parents may be the more feasible approach. Selection for characters other than yield would presumably be done more economically. The same advantage can be claimed for the use of complex crosses of inbreds. On the other hand, utilization of varietal gametes in improvement work does not "use up" inbreds so far as their combination in hybrids for commercial use is concerned. Lines recovered from crosses of inbreds may be more restricted than their inbred parents in commercial use because of relationship. It seems probable to the writers that the method of gamete selection is worthy of considerable use for further selection of material from open-pollinated, desirable commercial varieties.

Studies of lines recovered from selected varietal gametes will have to be carried to F_5 or later generations to determine if the large amount of outcross testing is justified economically. The writers would like to emphasize the importance they attach to method studies of the type presented here. New ideas in breeding must be explored constantly if continued progress is to be made in corn improvement.

SUMMARY

Since 1945, a program has been underway at Minnesota to attempt improvement of Minhybrids 602, 607, and 406 by the method of gamete selection. The hybrid pedigrees are respectively: (A344×A334) (A357×A392), (A344×A334) (A357×A385), and (A25×A334) (A73×A375). Detailed studies of the non-parental single crosses among the inbred parents of each hybrid led to the conclusion that A344 in Minhybrids 602 and 607, and A25 and A73 in Minhybrid 406 were low in combining ability.

A344 was crossed to the Morris strain of Minnesota 13 and to eight inbreds of diverse origin. A25 was crossed to the Golden King variety and A73 to Murdock. (Inbred×gamete) (tester) crosses were made using the opposing single cross parents as testers. These were compared with the appropriate cross of inbred×tester. Yield trial performance was obtained from a total of 113 gametes, 35 from Morris 13, 8 inbreds, 32 from Golden King, and 38 from Murdock.

Sixteen gametes from Morris 13, three from the inbreds, and eight from Murdock gave significant increases in yield over the test crosses of the checks A344 and A73. Five gametes from Morris 13, eight from Golden King, and fourteen from Murdock were not significantly different in yield but were significantly earlier so that yield performance could be considered better than the checks on the basis of ear moisture at harvest. These varieties and the three high testing inbreds thus appear to be good sources of gametes for improving the relatively low performing inbreds in specific combining ability for yield.

Both high and low testing varietal gametes were selected for use in a study of the development of new inbreds. From the crosses, A25×Golden King and A73×Murdock, selected F_2 plants×the appropriate tester were compared with the progeny of their F_1 parental plants when crossed on the same tester. While there was excellent agreement, on the average, for combining ability in the F_1 and F_2, there was evidence of segregation for combining ability from almost all of the twelve F_2 families which were studied. Visual plant selection within the F_2 generations appeared to be effective in increasing yield performance of the plants from the low testing gametes, but appeared to have no effect in further increasing the yield performance of the F_2 plants from the high testing gametes.

The economic feasibility of F_2 plant testing in a gamete selection program is questioned.

SHERRET S. CHASE
Iowa State College

Chapter 25

Monoploids in Maize*

Haploid sporophytes have been reported in jimson weed (Blakeslee *et al.*, 1922), cotton (Harland, 1920), tobacco (Chipman and Goodspeed, 1927), evening primrose (Gates, 1929), maize (Randolph, 1932a, 1932b), wheat (Gaines and Aase, 1926), rice (Ramiah *et al.*, 1933) tomato (Lindstrom, 1929), pepper (Christensen and Bamford, 1943), and in many other genera which have been subjects of cytogenetic study.

A haploid organism, strictly speaking, is one which has only one set of chromosomes, that is, one genome per cell. In the common usage of botanists, geneticists, and others, a sporophyte originating by reduced parthenogenesis or by an equivalent process, and consequently carrying the reduced or gametic complement of chromosomes in each cell instead of the normal zygotic complement, is referred to as a *haploid*.

Thus the term, as applied to a sporophyte, has come to carry the connotations of both parthenogenetic origin and gametic chromosome number, and the actual genomic condition tends to be ignored. Many so-called haploids are actually diploids or polyploids. Thus the haploids of common wheat are triploids, since the parent species, *Triticum vulgare*, is a hexaploid. To emphasize the fact that the haploids of maize carry only one set of chromosomes per cell, that is, only one chromosome of each type instead of the normal pair, the alternate term *monoploid* is used here to designate these aberrant plants.

In normal sexual reproduction in maize the pollen tube penetrates the eight nucleate embryo sac. One of the two male gametes released fuses with the egg nucleus to form the zygote, while the other fuses with the two polar nuclei to form the primary endosperm nucleus. In the abnormal type of reproduction giving rise to monoploid sporophytes the processes apparently are the same except that for some reason the *first* male gamete fails to fuse with the egg nucleus and is lost. The egg nevertheless is activated and devel-

* Journal Paper No. J-1906 of the Iowa Agricultural Experiment Station, Ames, Iowa. Project 1201.

389

ops into an embryo. Evidence for this is indirect—monoploid embryos are found in kernels having normal (3n) endosperm. It is possible that some or all monoploids arise from reduced cells of the embryo sac other than the egg, from the synergids perhaps.

As tools for experimental research monoploids offer many possibilities: in the cytological field for studies of the meiotic distributions of unpaired chromosomes, *non-homologous* synaptic relations of the chromosomes and mechanics of chromosome doubling; in the genetic field for direct observation of mutational effects, measurement of mutation rates, studies of cytoplasmic effects, and biochemical investigations; in the agronomic field for the production of diploid, homozygous stocks directly from the monoploids. The following discussion is concerned primarily with my own investigations into the latter possibility.

A monoploid carries in each of its cells, or nuclei, only one chromosome of each type. Thus if the chromosome complement of any cell can be doubled, the affected cell and any derivative of it will consequently be both diploid and homozygous. If such homozygous diploid sectors include the reproductive tissues, meiosis should then be normal and the gametes produced functional. Thus such plants can produce diploid progeny—homozygous diploid progeny if the individual is successfully self pollinated—since every gamete of the plant is genetically equivalent to every other gamete. In a monoploid without diploid sectors, since the chromosomes lack synaptic mates, meiosis is highly irregular. Only rarely are functional gametes carrying the full complement of chromosomes produced. If two of these rare functional gametes from a single monoploid do fuse in syngamy, the zygote produced will be diploid, and homozygous, unless the gametic chromosomes were subject to chromosomal aberration during the irregular meiosis.

Production of homozygous diploid progeny from monoploids results in the fixation of a single gametic complex. In any population, desirable gametes are more frequent than desirable zygotes. For example, if one has on hand an individual heterozygous for three pairs of genes and wishes to obtain from it a definite homozygous product by selfing, *one* individual in *sixty-four* of the immediate self progeny (S_1) will, on the average, carry the desired genotype. *One* gamete in *eight*, extracted as a monoploid and then converted into a homozygous diploid, will furnish the same genotype (see Fig. 25.1).

Successful production of homozygous diploids in quantity from monoploids depends upon the adequate solution of two main problems. The first of these is the production and recognition in the seedling, or in earlier stages, of large numbers of monoploids. This problem has been solved to the extent that thousands of monoploids can be produced with relatively small expenditure of effort. The second problem is that of deriving self, and consequently homozygous, diploid progeny from the monoploids isolated. This problem also has a practical, though partial, solution.

MONOPLOIDS IN MAIZE

It has been known for some time that monoploids occur naturally in maize in measurable frequency. Data of Randolph (Randolph and Fischer, 1939) and of Einset (1943) suggest that monoploids occur spontaneously at a rate of about one per thousand. Data of Stadler (unpublished) indicate a rate of about one per hundred in a genetic stock. At the start of the studies reported

♀ \\ ♂	ABC	ABc	AbC	Abc	aBC	aBc	abC	abc
ABC	$\frac{ABC}{ABC}$	$\frac{ABc}{ABC}$	$\frac{AbC}{ABC}$	$\frac{Abc}{ABC}$	$\frac{aBC}{ABC}$	$\frac{aBc}{ABC}$	$\frac{abC}{ABC}$	$\frac{abc}{ABC}$
ABc	$\frac{ABC}{ABc}$	$\frac{ABc}{ABc}$	$\frac{AbC}{ABc}$	$\frac{Abc}{ABc}$	$\frac{aBC}{ABc}$	$\frac{aBc}{ABc}$	$\frac{abC}{ABc}$	$\frac{abc}{ABc}$
AbC	$\frac{ABC}{AbC}$	$\frac{ABc}{AbC}$	$\frac{AbC^*}{AbC}$	$\frac{Abc}{AbC}$	$\frac{aBC}{AbC}$	$\frac{aBc}{AbC}$	$\frac{abC}{AbC}$	$\frac{abc}{AbC}$
Abc	$\frac{ABC}{Abc}$	$\frac{ABc}{Abc}$	$\frac{AbC}{Abc}$	$\frac{Abc}{Abc}$	$\frac{aBC}{Abc}$	$\frac{aBc}{Abc}$	$\frac{abC}{Abc}$	$\frac{abc}{Abc}$
aBC	$\frac{ABC}{aBC}$	$\frac{ABc}{aBC}$	$\frac{AbC}{aBC}$	$\frac{Abc}{aBC}$	$\frac{aBC}{aBC}$	$\frac{aBc}{aBC}$	$\frac{abC}{aBC}$	$\frac{abc}{aBC}$
aBc	$\frac{ABC}{aBc}$	$\frac{ABc}{aBc}$	$\frac{AbC}{aBc}$	$\frac{Abc}{aBc}$	$\frac{aBC}{aBc}$	$\frac{aBc}{aBc}$	$\frac{abC}{aBc}$	$\frac{abc}{aBc}$
abC	$\frac{ABC}{abC}$	$\frac{ABc}{abC}$	$\frac{AbC}{abC}$	$\frac{Abc}{abC}$	$\frac{aBC}{abC}$	$\frac{aBc}{abC}$	$\frac{abC}{abC}$	$\frac{abc}{abC}$
abc	$\frac{ABC}{abc}$	$\frac{ABc}{abc}$	$\frac{AbC}{abc}$	$\frac{Abc}{abc}$	$\frac{aBC}{abc}$	$\frac{aBc}{abc}$	$\frac{abC}{abc}$	$\frac{abc}{abc}$

$AAbbCC^*\ldots AbC\ldots AbC$ (left label for row AbC)

* Desired homozygous individual. $\frac{1}{8}$ of gametes and $\frac{1}{64}$ of zygotes.

Fig. 25.1—Efficiency of Monoploid Method Compared with Selfing to S_1 for Obtaining Homozygous Individual $AAbbCC$ from Heterozygous Parent $AaBbCc$.

here it was assumed that naturally occurring monoploids would furnish a sufficient supply at a rate of occurrence of the order of one in one or two thousand plants of a progeny provided the bulk of the diploids could be screened out by some simple device during the seed or seedling stages. This has proven feasible.

It was also assumed that some method for inducing doubling of the monoploid chromosome complement would have to be developed. Though this still appears desirable and possible, artificial induction of chromosome doubling has not been necessary in order to obtain diploid self progeny from a portion of the monoploids. The reason for this is that the fertility of the plants is increased naturally by spontaneous doubling of the chromosome complement. About 10 per cent of untreated monoploids have yielded successful self progeny, largely as a result of this spontaneous somatic diploidization.

Since monoploids are for the most part of maternal origin, these plants should resemble their seed parents. Thus the search for monoploids is greatly facilitated if one looks for them among the progeny of markedly dissimilar parents. If one crosses a purple maize stock as pollen parent onto plants which lack this color and then finds non-purple seedlings in the progeny, one has reason to think these aberrant plants may be monoploids. In practice, the marker phenotype is used to indicate the diploid plants. These are discarded as recognized. Morphological and cytological tests are used for positive recognition of the monoploids.

In brief, the techniques used in isolating monoploids are as follows. The stock from which one wishes to obtain monoploids is pollinated with pollen from a genetic marker stock. The marker may carry the purple plant color genes ($A_1 A_2 B Pl R$) or brown ($a_1 A_2 B Pl R$), purple plumule ($A Pu_1 Pu_2$), or any suitable complex of marker genes not carried by the seed stock. The ears at harvest are checked for kernels resulting from accidental self or cross pollinations. This check is made possible by using marker stocks which carry endosperm marker genes as well as plant marker genes. The markers which have been used, as appropriate, are purple aleurone ($A_1 A_2 A_3 C R i Pr$), red aleurone ($A_1 A_2 A_3 C R i pr$), starchy endosperm (Su), and yellow endosperm (Y).

The kernels *not showing* the endosperm marker phenotype are discarded (if the pollinations have been carefully made few discards are necessary). Then the kernels saved are germinated and a check made of the embryos or seedlings for the plant marker phenotype. All *showing* this character are discarded. The remainder are transplanted after first taking from each a root tip or two for cytological study. A second screening off of diploids is carried out after the first seedling leaves of the putative monoploids are fully extended. Those having the first leaf as long as the comparable leaf of the seed parent are almost without exception diploid and are therefore discarded. The true monoploids are then recognized by chromosome number determinations. Errors in classification at each stage result primarily in loss of monoploid plants. Consequently monoploid frequencies as reported are likely to be less than the actual frequencies of occurrence.

The putative monoploids screened off as a result of the genetic check include the actual monoploids and also diploids of the following types: diploid hybrids mutant for marker genes, hybrids carrying strong color suppressor genes, hybrids in which disease (generally fungus infection) has suppressed the development of the color phenotype, and a few maternal diploids. Occasionally paternal monoploids also are produced. These may be recognized when the hybrid phenotype is unlike that of either the pollen or the seed parent, as is the case in crosses in which the brown marker stocks are used as pollen parents. In such crosses, maternal monoploids of the progeny should resemble the seed parent. Paternal monoploids should be brown (green at early stages) and the hybrids purple. The particular brown stocks used carry recessive markers, liguleless or japonica. These also serve to mark the very rare paternal monoploids.

When the monoploids reach the reproductive stage the practice has been to self these plants if any self pollen is shed, to cross them by other monoploids shedding excess pollen, or to pollinate them by diploids if self pollen is lacking.

FERTILITY OF MONOPLOIDS

The estimate of the fertility of monoploids, based on the assumption of 10 chromosomes distributed independently at meiosis, is one normal egg in 1024. That is, if abundant normal pollen were used in pollination these plants should set one good kernel in 1024 ovules. Actual fertility of the monoploids studied has been much higher than this, in spite of the fact that the amount of pollen used has often been scant. Little is known of the mechanics of meiosis in maize monoploids. Studies of the reactions of unpaired chromosomes at meiosis suggest that monoploid meioses may produce some functional gametes with structurally altered chromosomes (Kostoff, 1941). A proportion of the syngamic products in such cases would consequently be structurally heterozygous. If the reproductive tissue of a monoploid becomes diploidized before meiosis is initiated the gametes produced should all be structurally normal and strictly equivalent genetically. Some progenies were checked to determine the extent of chromosome aberration. The percentage of nonviable (actually, non-stainable) pollen produced by the monoploid derivatives was used as an indication of chromosome abnormalities. Among the progenies of diploid seed parents by monoploid pollen parents about 1 per cent had 10 per cent or more bad pollen. Among the progenies of monoploid seed parents by diploid pollen parents about 8 per cent had 10 per cent or more bad pollen. Among the progenies of monoploid by monoploid, 17 per cent had 10 per cent or more bad pollen. In the latter two classes, both of those in which monoploids were used as the seed parents, the monoploids thus used were those which had shown no evidence of diploidization in the tassels.

In a group of 298 monoploids, 282 matured. Of these 139 shed some pollen, 68 formed kernels, and 34 yielded successful self progeny. The fertility of this group of plants and of the whole series to date was far in excess of that expected of maize monoploids on theoretical grounds. The difference can be ascribed largely to spontaneous doubling of the chromosome complement in cells giving rise to reproductive tissue (Chase, 1949b).

PARTHENOGENESIS

A number of interesting facts have come out of studies of the frequency of reduced parthenogenesis in maize. One unanticipated fact has been that of the effect of the male (pollen) parent on parthenogenesis. Although this parent does not contribute its genes to the maternal monoploid, the particular pollen parent used in any cross does have an effect on the rate of occurrence of maternal monoploids (Chase, 1949a). In Table 25.1 the results of

TABLE 25.1

FREQUENCIES OF OCCURRENCE OF MONOPLOIDS FROM SEVERAL INBREDS AND HYBRIDS WHEN INBREDS A385 AND 38-11 WERE USED AS THE POLLEN PARENTS

SEED PARENTS	A385 AS POLLEN PARENT				38-11 AS POLLEN PARENT			
	Number of Progeny	No. n	Freq. per Thousand	Av.	Number of Progeny	No. n	Freq. per Thousand	Av.
Os420.........	1,715	1	.58	.29	4,909	9	1.84	1.83
M14..........	2,074	0	.00		2,738	5	1.83	
WF9..........	1,792	0	.00	.00	5,065	6	1.19	1.24
W22..........	1,839	0	.00		2,322	3	1.29	
Os420/M14....	6,238	0	.00	.19	6,648	11*	1.66	2.52
WF9/W22.....	5,148	2	.38		3,554	12	3.38	
(Os420/M14)/ (WF9/W22)..	5,068	1	.20		4,868	2*	.41	
Averages			.17				1.66	
Golden Cross Bantam......	12,324	2	.16		6,638	20	3.01	

* Known to be too low.

paired crosses involving two different pollen parents, inbreds A385 and 38-11, are summarized. Both of these inbreds carry the purple plumule marker system. From the genetic point of view A385 is the more satisfactory of the two. That is, in its hybrids the marker phenotype is generally well developed. In the hybrids of 38-11 the phenotype is often obscure. Consequently few monoploids were lost by misclassification in the progenies of A385, whereas a considerable number may have been lost in those of 38-11. In spite of this the data show 38-11 to be ten or more times as effective as A385 as a *stimulator* of parthenogenesis. This effect seems to be general. That is, the several dent stocks and also the sweet corn hybrid show about the same proportionate effect of the pollen parents. Other data involving other crosses and data taken in other seasons are in agreement with those summarized here.

Data summarized in Table 25.2 are presented to show the variation in monoploid frequency dependent on the seed parent. Summaries are given of frequencies in crosses in which a single pollen parent, a brown marker, was used. The differences, expressed in terms of frequencies per 1000 seedlings and also as the frequency per seed parent, are quite striking. The rate of parthenogenesis seems to be roughly proportional to the intensity of agronomic selection to which these various stocks have been previously subjected.

TABLE 25.2

FREQUENCIES OF OCCURRENCE OF MONOPLOIDS IN SOME
DENT STOCKS WHEN CROSSED BY A UNIFORM
POLLEN PARENT

Seed Parent	Pollen	Number Progeny	No. n	Freq. per Thousand	Freq. per Seed Parent
Lancaster.....................	N*	10,173	4	.39	.12
Reid's........................	N	14,650	11	.75	.38
Stiff Stalk Synthetic (SSS₀)†......	N	91,125	90	.98	.37
Early Synthetic (ES₀)............	N	8,226	10	1.13	.36
Dent Inbreds and Hybrids‡........	N	....	......	1.35	....
Stiff Stalk Synthetic (SSS₁)†......	N	121,764	176	1.45	.51
Averages	....	....	....	1.01	.35

* Brown, liguleless stock, *a B Pl C Rᵍ Pr lg;* Randolph 43687-1.
† Original and first cycle Stiff Stalk Synthetic.
‡ 1947 data (Chase 1949), averages of frequencies per thousand.

Other data, including that from sweet corn varieties, hybrids and inbreds, bear out this relation. A likely explanation, other things being equal, is that the frequency of occurrence of *viable* monoploids is correlated inversely with the frequency of lethal genes in the source stocks. That the frequency of lethal genes in a stock is not the sole basis of differences between stocks becomes evident when one compares stocks which have been subject to an equivalent degree of selection.

It also becomes evident that there is another genetic basis for differences in rates of parthenogenesis when one analyzes the frequency of occurrence of monoploids as a function of the individual seed parent plants. In Table 25.3 summaries are given of the numbers of monoploids per seed plant in crosses in which the Stiff Stalk Synthetic variety was used as the seed parent. The distribution of none, one, two, and three monoploids per parent is about what one might expect on a chance basis. But the likelihood of getting five, six, and seven monoploids per seed plant by chance in three, three, and two cases respectively in a sample of 1065 parent plants is remote. The likeliest explanation is that certain genotypes favor parthenogenesis. Whether this is a function of the sporophyte or of the gametes is not certain. It appears more likely that the effect originates in the individual gametes (eggs).

Emerson (unpublished) and Lindstrom (unpublished) and others have attempted to stimulate parthenogenesis in maize by the application of hormones and other chemicals to the ovules before or during fertilization. The results were uniformly discouraging. Randolph (1932b) found a number of

TABLE 25.3

DISTRIBUTION OF MONOPLOIDS PER SEED
PARENT, STIFF STALK SYNTHETIC

Number of Monoploids per Seed Parent	Number of Seed Parents in Each Class
0	776
1	195
2	60
3	19
4	7
5	3
6	3
7	2
Total	1,065

TABLE 25.4

MONOPLOID FREQUENCIES AMONG THE
PROGENIES OF MONOPLOID
DERIVATIVES

Seed Parents	Pollen Parent	Number of Progeny	Number of Monoploids	Freq. per Thousand
H159	V	1,716	15	8.70
(H15/H25), S_1	V	1,792	14	7.81
(H19/H25), S_1	V	537	5	9.34
(H152/H143)	V	550	10	18.18

monoploids in material which had been subjected to heat treatments designed to induce polyploidy. Though it is a question whether the heat induced parthenogenesis, this type of treatment should be repeated on material in which the natural rate of parthenogenesis is known. In connection with the general monoploid study reported here a number of special treatments have been tried. Among these are hormone treatments, X-radiation of pollen, intergeneric crosses, pollination with pollen from tetraploid maize, and delayed pollination. These experiments are incomplete.

There is presently available one method by which high rates of parthenogenesis can be had. This is by selection of the pollen and seed parents used in a cross. As shown in Table 25.4, monoploid derivatives are particularly favorable parthenogenetic stocks. In this series of crosses the stock V used as the pollen parent is a purple marker which is better than average as a stimulator of parthenogenesis. The seed parent in each case was a monoploid derivative; either a homozygous diploid (H159), or a single cross hybrid between two monoploids (H152/H143), or an advanced generation of such a hybrid.

The average frequency per 1000 for the stock from which H159 was derived (the Stiff Stalk Synthetic) is about 1.21. In each case the frequency of parthenogenesis is higher than that of the stock or stocks from which the monoploid derivatives were obtained. The hybrid H152/H143 and the frequency of monoploids in its progeny are particularly interesting in that H152 was a monoploid extracted from Inbred P39 and H143 a monoploid from Inbred P51. Thus the cross of the two is the single cross hybrid Golden Cross Bantam, based on monoploid parents. Normal Golden Cross Bantam crossed by marker stock V has a monoploid frequency of about 4.00 per thousand. A high rate of parthenogenesis is characteristic not only of the four stocks listed in Table 25.4 but of all monoploid derivatives adequately tested.

H159 not only has a high rate of parthenogenesis among its progeny but also a high degree of fertility among the monoploids produced. Of the 15 monoploids obtained from the cross with stock V, 12 were grown to maturity. All of these had one or more diploid sectors in the tassel and all set good seed.

On the average about one monoploid in ten is self fertile—in the sense that it yields a successful homozygous diploid progeny. One would like to obtain diploid self progeny from all monoploids. Since any increase in the rate of somatic diploidization should result in increased fertility, a number of treatments with polyploidizing agents have been tried. Colchicine, as used, brought about an increase in fertility but injury to the plants killed so many that no over-all gain was effected. In these treatments, solutions of approximately .5 per cent aqueous colchicine were injected into the scutellar nodes of the monoploid seedlings. It is possible that use of more dilute solutions injected repeatedly would be more effective.

Podophyllin, as a saturated aqueous solution, produced drastic stunting and inhibition of the development of the ears and tassels. Heat treatment, tried on a very minor scale, seemed to be about as effective as colchicine and had the same disadvantage. In this problem, as in that of increasing the rate of parthenogenesis, genetic methods seem to offer the best available solution. That is, stocks derived from self fertile monoploids are better sources of self fertile monoploids than the stocks from which the original monoploids were obtained.

Synthetic varieties that combine high monoploid frequency, high monoploid fertility, and high general agronomic desirability can probably be developed from homozygous diploids, both sweet and dent, already on hand.

FIG. 25.2—Sweet corn monoploid sporophyte derived from Golden Cross Bantam.

FIG. 25.3—Ears of homozygous diploid dent (H502) and inbred WF9. H502 is a Stiff Stalk Synthetic derivative. The ears shown are from plants of the first diploid generation.

Such synthetic varieties should be 10–20 times more effective as sources of new homozygous diploid lines than the better heterozygous stocks already tested.

About fifty homozygous sweet corn diploid stocks and about fifty homozygous dent stocks have been developed at Ames during the past two years of exploratory work. These are being tested for combining ability in comparison with related inbred lines. Though there is no reason *a priori* to expect that these lines will be better than average combiners, there is reason to think they should carry well balanced genetic systems, since passage through the sporophyte phase as a monoploid involves drastic selection against lethal and sublethal genes. In appearance the homozygous lines seem better than average unselected inbreds in general vegetative vigor.

CONCLUSIONS

It has been demonstrated that homozygous diploid stocks of maize can be produced from monoploid sporophytes. The method as now developed is practical from the point of view of the plant breeder as an alternate to inbreeding for the production of homozygous lines. As a method of gamete selection it offers unique possibilities. Improvements now being attempted should increase the efficiency of the procedure very considerably. It is not known yet whether the homozygous lines produced will prove to be better or poorer or equal to unselected advanced generation inbred lines on the average in respect to combining ability.

G. F. SPRAGUE
USDA and Iowa State College

Chapter 26

Early Testing and Recurrent Selection

It appears desirable to review the history of corn breeding very briefly in order that early testing and recurrent selection may be placed in their proper perspective. The first breeding method used in corn was undoubtedly mass selection. The fact that the corn ear is large, and that harvesting for a long period of time was essentially a hand operation, provided excellent opportunities for selection to be practiced on ear length, diameter, and kernel characteristics. This type of selection undoubtedly was practiced from the beginning of the domestication of the corn plant until well into the twentieth century. This type of selection was quite effective in modifying ear and kernel characters even though it provided no opportunity for parentage control. Variation in ear size, etc., due to soil fertility were assumed to be genetic.

Varietal hybridization was the next breeding procedure tried. The results obtained in some cases were very promising, but no extensive use was made of the method. Varietal hybrids, however, did provide source material from which many of the widely grown varieties were isolated.

The ear-to-row method of breeding was suggested by C. G. Hopkins of the Illinois Station in 1896. This procedure, as the name implies, involved selecting a group of ears, planting these ear-to-row and obtaining information on performance. In such tests, marked differences in yield were obtained among the ears tested. This method was tried rather extensively, but was finally abandoned when it became apparent the cumulative improvement in yielding ability was not realized.

The ear-to-row breeding method provided for selection on the basis of the visual characters of the original parent ears and some measure of performance based on the progeny of the selected ears. Opportunities for genetic control were limited, and the original high yielding progenies were hybrids of unknown ancestry which could not be duplicated. The ear-to-row method of breeding was quite effective in modifying chemical composition, plant and

400

ear height, and leaf area. These characters, for which selection was effective, differ from yield in that the genetic basis is undoubtedly much less complex and environmental variability less likely to lead to mistaken classifications. We now know that the plot technics used in these ear-to-row trials were quite inadequate, and some of the failure to achieve improvements in yields must certainly be ascribed to this cause. Many of the modifications of the ear-to-row method of breeding which were introduced to minimize inbreeding probably had an opposite effect, and the rate of inbreeding was actually increased. On the basis of data now available, it is impossible to fully assess the relative importance of various causes resulting in the ineffectiveness of this method in increasing yields.

SELECTION WITHIN AND AMONG INBRED PROGENIES

The next method tried, and the one still used most extensively, involved selection within and among inbred lines and the evaluation of the lines retained in hybrid combinations. Some of the early work which served as a foundation for this breeding method has been reviewed in other chapters of this book. Extensive breeding programs were established at the various stations in the early 1920's, and a large percentage of the lines now used in the production of commercial hybrids had their origin in this early work.

In the earlier days of these programs any inbred line which could be maintained was considered to have potential value. As the work progressed it became apparent that inbred lines must meet certain minimum standards of performance as lines in order to merit testing in hybrid combinations. Studies were undertaken by Jenkins (1929) and somewhat later by Hayes and Johnson (1939) to determine which, if any, characters of the inbred lines were correlated with yield in hybrid combinations. In the studies reported by Jenkins correlations were used to measure the relationship between (1) various characters of the parental inbreds and the same character in their F_1 hybrids, and (2) between characters of the parental inbreds and the means of the same characters for all of their crossbred progeny. The results obtained under 1 and 2 were somewhat different. In the first case, none of the characters of the parental inbreds were closely related to the yield of their F_1 hybrids. The correlations reported ranged from $-.10$ to $+.24$. The correlations between yield of the parents and yield of their F_1 hybrids were .14 and .20. Multiple correlations considering various grouping of characters of the inbreds and the yield of their hybrids ranged from .20 to .42.

In the second series which involved characters of the parental lines and the means of the same characters for all crossbred progeny, the correlations obtained were materially larger. With different groups of material the correlations involving yield ranged from .25 to .67. In some cases the degrees of freedom were few and the relationship therefore poorly determined. A weighted r calculated for the entire series was .45. The difference between these two series can be readily accounted for by the assumption of epistasis, though no claim is made that this is the only or even the correct explanation. Where the correlations involve some character of the inbred parent and the same character in their F_1 crosses, epistatic effects would be expected to be at a maximum. When a character of the parent is correlated with the mean of all crossbred progeny opportunity would be provided for a considerable degree of cancellation of the epistatic effects.

The results reported by Hayes and Johnson are more directly comparable with Jenkins' group 2. Various characters of the inbred parent were correlated with the yield of their topcross progeny. The correlations for individual characters ranged from .19 to .54, and the multiple r for 12 characters of the inbred parent and yield of the topcross progeny was .67.

As a result of these studies some investigators have decided that the correlations were too low to provide a wholly satisfactory basis for prediction, and the only safe measure of the worth of an inbred line was to evaluate it in hybrid combinations.

EARLY TESTING

Since the characteristics of the inbred lines did not provide an adequate index as to the value of a line, and since this value must be determined by crossbred progeny tests, it seemed advisable to determine whether crossbred performance could be evaluated at an earlier stage of inbreeding. Several lines of reasoning suggested that this might be feasible and desirable. First the ear-to-row tests with all of their limitations suggested that there were marked differences in yielding ability between individual carefully selected open-pollinated ears. The genotype of such high yielding ears was modified or diluted in ear-to-row testing procedure, but the identity of these individual ears could readily be maintained by self-pollination. Second, it appeared logical to assume that a potential ceiling was established for any derived line at the time of the selfing of the S_0 or F_2 parent plant. This ceiling is established by the genotype of the parent plant and the most desirable combination of genes which can be isolated from this gene sample.

The small population commonly grown from each selfed ear, the hindrance of linkage in preventing random recombination of genes, and the limited efficiency of visual selection would all operate to render the probability of isolating this most desirable gene combination very unlikely. The effort expended in growing and continued inbreeding and selection of strains having the less desirable genotype might represent a considerable waste. Third, if facilities were limited, as they always are, greater progress might be achieved by the early discarding of the less desirable genotypes and the growing of larger progenies of the more desirable genotypes in the early generations of selfing when variability and the efficiency of visual selection would be expected to be at a maximum.

Before these ideas could be put to a test, data were presented by Jenkins

(1935) which seemed to lend considerable support to the general ideas mentioned above. Remnant seed of 14 lines from the variety Lancaster and 14 lines from the variety Iodent representing eight generations of selfing were chosen in Jenkins' study. These 28 lines represented a random sample of the lines from these two varieties which had survived the eight generations of inbreeding. Two sibs were chosen to represent each generation, one representing a selected ear in the direct line of descent and the second a discarded sib. These 56 ears were grown ear-to-row, and pollen from 10–12 plants of each line were mixed and applied to ten ear shoots of the tester variety Krug.

Due to variation in stands and the unfavorable season neither the sampling of plants within a strain nor the topcross parent was as adequate as planned. Only 12 of the lines originally chosen were represented in each of the eight generations of selfing. The yield trials of the topcrossed progeny were grown in 1932. Information on several important problems is presented in this paper, but the items of most importance in the present discussion deal with the performance of the lines after successive generations of selfing. In the Iodent series, represented by seven lines, the mean square associated with generations was not significant. In the Lancaster series, represented by five lines, the variation associated with generations was significant but there was no indication of a consistent trend.

On the basis of these results Jenkins concluded that, "The inbred lines acquired their individuality as parents of top crosses very early in the inbreeding process and remained relatively stable thereafter." Since this paper was published, several people have assumed that the stability mentioned by Jenkins was synonymous with homozygosity, and therefore experiments demonstrating segregation in F_2 or F_3 were disproof of this stability. However Jenkins took particular pains to point out that the stability he was assuming did not arise from homozygosity, but was a sampling phenomenon. This sampling stability, if confirmed, makes the early testing procedure even more attractive, but stability is neither assumed nor required as a prerequisite for early testing.

Results from Early Testing

Experiments on early testing were started in Missouri in 1935. However due to unfavorable seasons, no critical data were obtained until 1938. The experiments were continued in Iowa in 1939 and subsequent years. The results of these studies were summarized in 1946 (Sprague, 1946). Some 167 selected S_0 plants from a strain known as Stiff Stalk Synthetic were self pollinated and outcrossed to the double cross tester parent Iowa 13. The yields of the test crosses ranged from 61.8 to 100.8 bushels per acre. Four of the test crosses were significantly lower yielding than the synthetic parent, and two were significantly higher yielding than the tester parent. The plants chosen for selfing represented a carefully selected group on the basis of phenotypic desirability. The wide range in topcross yields obtained is evidence of the poor relation between phenotype and performance in hybrid combinations.

The frequency distribution of topcross performance was subjected to two types of samplings. In one sample the S_1 lines representing the best 10 per cent of the population were grown, and individual plants again self pollinated and outcrossed to the tester parent, Iowa 13. The distribution of the S_0 and S_1 topcrosses are illustrated in Figure 26.1. (The S_0 topcross yields have been adjusted to the S_0 topcross level on the basis of the performance of the tester

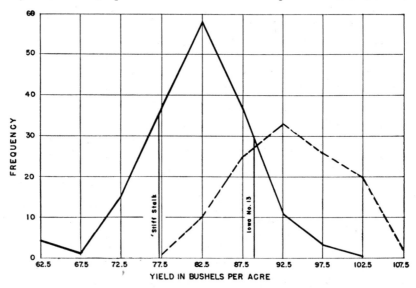

FIG. 26.1—A comparison of the frequency distributions of 167 topcrosses of S_0 plants (*solid line*) with a series of topcrosses of S_1 plants (*dotted line*), representing the highest yielding 10% of the original S_0 population.

parent, Iowa 13.) The distribution of the S_1 topcross yields clearly indicate that the S_0 plants exhibiting high combining ability transmitted this characteristic to their S_1 progeny. Segregation within progenies was quite apparent, indicating that opportunities for additional selection existed.

A group of twelve lines was chosen which provided a seriated sampling of the frequency distribution of S_0 topcross yields. These were grown in 100 plant progenies, and an attempt was made to self pollinate 25 of the better plants in each progeny and to outcross these to the tester parent. Because of differences in time of pollen shedding only 6 of the 12 lines chosen were finally used (Table 26.1).

Significant differences in yielding ability were obtained within each of the six S_1 families. The range in yield was of about the same magnitude in each family, suggesting that the S_0 plants having the highest test cross performance were no more heterozygous than the S_0 plants having poor test cross performance. The distributions arising from the four highest yielding families were not significantly different, but were significantly different from the distributions arising from the two lowest yielding families. These same general types of results were obtained when stalk breaking was considered.

Finally, three of the lines arising from selected sample when in the S_3 generation of inbreeding were compared with five standard lines. These eight lines were crossed in all possible combinations and compared in replicated yield trials (Table 26.2). The S_3 lines, as a group, were superior to the stand-

TABLE 26.1

FREQUENCY DISTRIBUTION OF ACRE YIELDS IN BUSHELS FOR
20 S_1 TOPCROSSED PROGENIES DERIVED FROM
6 S_0 LINES (SPRAGUE, 1946)

FAMILY No.	YIELD		DISTRIBUTION OF 1942 ACRE YIELDS IN BUSHELS					
	1940	1942	87.5	92.5	97.5	102.5	107.5	112.5
SSS 278.......	100.8	105.9	....	....	3	5	9	3
SSS 295.......	92.9	104.6	....	1	2	8	7	2
SSS 393.......	92.9	102.2	....	....	6	10	3	1
SSS 130.......	82.5	103.3	....	....	6	5	8	1
SSS 227.......	73.5	94.1	4	8	5	3	....	....
SSS 407.......	64.9	97.3	1	5	9	5	....	....

TABLE 26.2

RELATIVE AVERAGE PERFORMANCE OF
STANDARD AND NEW S_3 INBRED LINES
OF CORN BASED ON SINGLE CROSS YIELD
TRIALS (SPRAGUE, 1946)

INBRED DESIGNATION	RELATIVE PERFORMANCE AS MEASURED BY		
	Yield in Bu. per Acre	Root Lodging Per Cent	Stalk Breaking Per Cent
L317...............	78.4	11.8	2.7
187-2.............	79.2	8.0	0.9
WF9..............	87.5	8.0	0.7
38-11.............	78.8	1.1	1.2
Oh67A............	72.7	5.6	2.1
Average........	79.3	6.9	1.5
SSS 211-300........	86.7	3.2	0.5
SSS 278-161........	81.0	1.2	1.5
SSS 507-193........	89.1	3.6	0.8
Average........	85.6	2.7	0.9

ard lines in yield, and in resistance to root lodging and stalk breaking. On the basis of these results it was suggested that early testing might be a valuable tool in a breeding program. However it was pointed out that the method might be of limited value under some conditions. This warning has to some extent been ignored and some have assumed that the early testing procedure is useful at any stage of the breeding program and with any parental material.

Additional trials of the early testing procedure have been conducted by Dr. John Lonnquist (1950) of the Nebraska Station. In this experiment a series of selected plants from a strain of Krug were self pollinated and outcrossed to a series of plants of the same variety. When test cross performance data were available two samplings were made. One consisted of the group of lines exhibiting the highest topcross yields and the second group those exhibiting the lowest topcross yields.

In each group in subsequent generations selection was practiced in both directions. In the high group the phenotypically most desirable and least desirable plants were self pollinated and outcrossed to the tester. In the low group again the most and least desirable plants were selfed and outcrossed. This plan had to be modified somewhat as inbreeding progressed, since seed was not always obtained on the least desirable plants. The group actually used were the least desirable plants which could be propagated. After each test cross generation the selection of lines to be continued was based on combining ability. The single cross WF9×M14 was substituted for Krug as the tester parent after the original series of test crosses.

The results obtained during the first four selfed generations clearly indicate that topcross combining ability can be readily modified by a combination of selection and testing (Fig. 26.2). In the high group selected for high combining ability, the average topcross yields of all lines represented increased from 98.6 to 107.5 bushels. In the high group selected for low combining ability after the S_1 yields decreased from 98.6 bushels to 93.3 bushels. In the low group selected for high combining ability after the S_1 generation yield increased from 85.9 to 94.0. Where selection was practiced for low combining ability in each generation, yields decreased from 85.9 to 77.9 bushels.

Thus selecting for high combining ability for three additional generations when the original lines exhibited poor combining ability produced S_4 lines which were not significantly different in combining ability from those of the high group selected for a similar period for poor combining ability. Selection in the low group therefore would be largely wasted effort. Continued selection and testing after the S_1 would be most profitable for only those lines exhibiting the highest S_1 topcross combining ability.

Limitations of Early Testing

Three papers have been published which are somewhat critical of the value of early testing. These will be reviewed briefly. Payne and Hayes (1949) have presented data on a comparison of combining ability in F_2 and F_3 lines of corn. On the basis of these comparisons they concluded that early testing was of doubtful practical value. The material used in this study was 30 selfed ears from early segregates from the single cross A116×L317. Each of the 30 selfed ears was grown ear-to-row and pollen from approximately 30

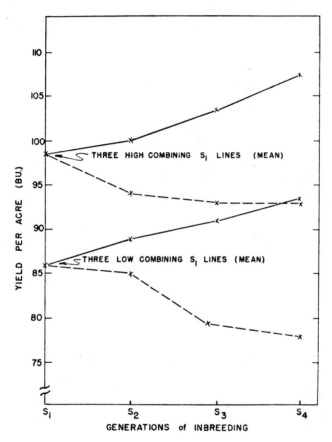

FIG. 26.2—The effects of visual selection and testing for combining ability during four generations of selfing in the variety Krug.

plants in each progeny was bulked and applied to the four inbreds chosen as testers; A334, A357, A340, and A392.

In addition, five individual plants selected at random were also outcrossed to the same four testers. The test crosses arising from the bulked pollinations were considered as representing a random sample of the gametic production of the individual F_2 plants and the five individual test crosses as samples of the F_3 progenies. Adequate seed was obtained from 26 of the original 30 families. Within the different tester groups correlations between F_2 and F_3 test cross means ranged from .51 to .76.

Payne and Hayes stated that:

The extent of relationship between the performance of F_2 test crosses and of the performance of their F_3 progenies in test crosses leads the writers to conclude that in these studies there was some doubt of the practical value of early testing for combining ability as a means of selecting desirable sources of F_3 lines. By a test however of relatively few F_3 lines it was possible to select F_3 lines that seemed to be a desirable source for improving, or substitution for certain inbred lines in Minhybrid 608.

It may be well to emphasize again that the only claim made for early testing was that it enables the separation of a population into two groups on the basis of combining ability. Also, continued selection in the more desirable group will yield a larger number of high combining lines than will the less desirable group or a random sample of lines selected solely on the basis of

TABLE 26.3

FREQUENCY DISTRIBUTIONS OF YIELD IN BUSHELS PER ACRE FOR 1 TO 3 F_3 PROGENIES DERIVED FROM F_2 LINES OF A116 × L317 CROSSED WITH 4 DIFFERENT TESTERS (AFTER PAYNE AND HAYES, 1949)

Tester Parent	F_2	Distribution of F_3 Test Cross Yields in Bu. per Acre						Number of Test Crosses Yielding 60.0 Bu. or More
		47.5	52.5	57.5	62.5	67.5	72.5	
A334	Higher 50%	......	......	3	5	9	7	21
	Lower 50%	3	1	4	7	3	......	10
A340	Higher 50%	......	3	10	14	5	......	19
	Lower 50%	3	9	11	2	1	......	3
A357	Higher 50%	......	......	2	1	10	6	17
	Lower 50%	1	2	5	9	6	2	17
A392	Higher 50%	......	1	5	16	7	4	27
	Lower 50%	1	5	9	10	6	1	17

phenotype. The frequency distributions of test cross combining ability for F_2 and F_3 progenies seem to fulfill this claim very nicely. In the table that follows, each F_2 distribution has been divided into the higher yielding 50 per cent and the lower yielding 50 per cent. The distribution of F_3 test crosses for each of these subgroups was taken from their paper. The results are presented in Table 26.3.

The writer would conclude from these distributions that the testing of F_2 would have been a desirable practice. Within each test cross series it would have permitted of the discarding of a considerable number of lines. If the number of F_3's to be tested had been held constant and all of the lines to be tested derived from the higher yielding F_2 subgroup, even greater progress might well have been expected.

The results obtained in this study are exactly those to be expected under the postulates of early testing. Early testing obviously cannot be used as a substitute for the more refined tests possible when the lines are more nearly homozygous. This limitation was clearly outlined in the 1946 paper (Sprague, 1946).

Data have also been presented by Singleton and Nelson (1945) which they interpret as demonstrating the ineffectiveness of early testing. In the study reported, forty-eight ears were chosen from the variety Whipple early yellow. These were grown ear-to-row and one self made within each lot. The selfed plants were also outcrossed to the inbred line P39. Selfing was continued for three generations. In each generation the plants chosen for selfing were outcrossed to P39. At the end of this period of selfing and testing, ten lines were chosen for this special study. By using remnant seed, test crosses were

TABLE 26.4

ANALYSIS OF VARIANCE FOR YIELD. 1940 AND 1941
(AFTER SINGLETON AND NELSON, 1945)

Source of Variation	DF	MS	F
Blocks..........................	8	1194.81	2.91*
Years...........................	1	275362.56	66.99**
Varieties.......................	9	230.49	.56
Varieties×Years................	9	722.66	1.76
Var.×Blks.×Yrs................	72	411.08	....
Generations....................	3	2163.57	14.35**
Linear......................	1	4586.95	30.42**
Quad.......................	1	1170.96	7.75*
Cubic......................	1	732.79	4.86
Generations×Years............	3	296.04	1.96
Generations×Var..............	27	885.76	5.87**
Gen.×Var.×Yrs................	27	212.88	1.41
Error Term....................	238	150.80	....

produced involving S_0, S_1, S_2, and S_3 generations. No data are given in the publication but an analysis of variance for the two-year test period is presented in Table 26.4.

At least two points concerning the analysis are worthy of mention. First there were no significant differences among the ten lines studied. In view of the extensive testing back of the group of lines chosen, and because they were selected to be very similar in yield, it is not surprising that the early testing procedure failed to disclose differences. The early testing procedure is certainly not suited to the measurement of very small differences. However the degree of genetic uniformity with respect to combining ability would normally not be expected in sampling with open-pollinated or F_2 populations.

The second comment bears on their interpretation of improvement in combining ability during the course of inbreeding. The appropriate test of significance in this case depends upon the specific question the data are asked to answer. If conclusions are to be confined to the particular lines used, then the variation associated with generations is correctly judged significant. If, however, the experimental material is assumed to represent a random sample of lines and therefore typical of lines in general, the appropriate test indicates generations to be non-significant. Since no yield data were presented, no test of significance can be calculated for the linear component of generations. Their results, as presented, have little bearing on either early testing or the effectiveness of visual selection in modifying combining ability during the course of inbreeding.

Richey (1945, 1947) has presented a re-analysis of Jenkins' (1935) data on combining ability after successive generations of inbreeding and reached conclusions differing from those presented by Jenkins. He questions the stability of combining ability and the effectiveness of early testing in providing a satisfactory criterion of combining ability when the lines approach homozygosity. He also presents some information on tester parents and their effectiveness in revealing segregation. This latter is a very important problem but will not be discussed here.

We return to the first criticism raised by Richey, namely that lines do not reach stability early in the course of inbreeding. To demonstrate his ideas, Richey has combined the eight generations into pairs, thus providing four groups. Then by selecting certain inbreds he has shown by graphs that, visually, quite different slopes are obtained over the period under study. Other groupings than those used by Richey may be selected with equal validity. These different groupings show quite an array of slopes upon visual inspection. However if one extends the original analysis of variance presented by Jenkins separating *generations* into a linear and remainder component, the linear component is not significant. This, of course, does not prove that trends are absent. It does indicate that such trends as may exist are small in comparison with the random variation.

Richey's second criticism deals with the effectiveness of early testing as a measure of combining ability as the lines approach homozygosity. He concludes that early testing would have been quite ineffective. The real basis for the evaluation of any breeding or testing system depends upon the lines which are produced or revealed which have sufficient value for use in commercial hybrids. Of the twenty-seven lines on which Jenkins presented data, two lines of the Lancaster series have been of sufficient value to be used extensively. These are L289 and L317. These two ranked in the upper half of the lines tested and would have saved under an early testing procedure.

Two other lines have been used to a limited extent. One of these, I224, exhibited the highest yields in the Iodent S_1 test cross series and would certainly have been saved. The other line L304A was in the upper 50 per cent of the S_1 Lancaster series. If early testing had been used with this material, saving the upper 50 per cent of each frequency distribution, no commercially useful lines would have been discarded. The early discarding of the remaining lines would have resulted in a very great saving of time and money as compared with testing at a more advanced stage of inbreeding.

RECURRENT SELECTION

Superficially recurrent selection has a considerable resemblance to the ear-to-row method of breeding. However recurrent selection differs in several important respects. It provides for a much more accurate genetic control, and the plot technic can be modified to give any desired degree of accuracy. Our use of the recurrent selection technic was a direct outgrowth of the work on early testing. It appeared logical to assume that if the individual S_0 plants selected on the basis of test cross performance were a superior group, intercrosses among this group to provide source material for a new cycle of selection would minimize certain of the limitations arising from continued selfing. Accordingly a group of the best lines from the early testing series were intercrossed to provide material for the evaluation of this method.

Somewhat earlier, studies were started to compare the relative efficiency of recurrent selection and inbreeding in isolating material having a high oil percentage. At the time the work was started we were of the opinion that this was a new idea. It was some time later that we discovered that essentially the same ideas had been published independently by East and Jones (1920) and by Hayes and Garber (1919). In neither of these cases was any extensive use made of the method and no critical data were published. The first detailed description of recurrent selection was made by Jenkins (1940). The breeding procedure did not receive a name however until Hull (1945) published his article dealing with recurrent selection for specific combining ability.

Because of the shorter time period required per cycle we have much more information on recurrent selection as a method for modifying chemical composition than we have for the modification of combining ability (Sprague and Brimhall, 1949). We shall report in some detail only one study—that contrasting recurrent selection and inbreeding in modifying oil percentage in corn. The source material for this study was obtained from S_1 ears from reciprocal backcrosses involving the single cross wxOs420×Ill. High Oil. Individual plants were self-pollinated in each backcross population and analyzed individually for oil percentage in the grain. The five ears having the highest oil percentage in each population were planted ear-to-row the following season and all possible intercrosses made among the ten progenies. Equal quantities of seed from each cross were bulked and used as source material for a new cycle of selfing, analyzing, and intercrossing.

A duplicate planting of the ten ears mentioned above was made in 25 plant, ear-row progenies. The phenotypically most desirable plants in each progeny were self-pollinated. At harvest time approximately five ears were saved and analyzed individually for oil content of the grain. The two ears of each family having the highest oil percentage were again grown in progeny rows for continued inbreeding and selection. When the analyses were available the sibling progeny having the lowest average oil percentage was discarded. The two selfed ears having the highest oil percentage in the selected sibling were used to propagate the family. This process was continued through five generations. The general procedures used in selection, with the exception of the chemical analyses, are essentially those commonly employed in the development of inbred lines by the standard method.

It should be emphasized that the time requirement, number of pollinations and analyses, land requirements, and selection differentials were essentially the same for the recurrent and the selfing series. The relative efficiencies of the two methods therefore should be directly comparable.

RECURRENT SERIES

The results from the recurrent series will be presented first. The material from the Ill. High Oil$\times$wxOs420 series has been carried through two cycles after the original selfings. The frequency distributions are shown in Figure 26.3. The distribution presented for the original population is a composite for the two backcrossed populations. The solid vertical line represents the population mean and the dotted vertical line the mean of the selected sample. These selected ears were grown in ear-row progenies the following year and all possible intercrosses made by hand. Bulked seed from these intercrosses provided the source material for the next cycle of selfing and selection. The mean of the first cycle population was essentially the same as the mean of the selected parents—the full selective advantage of the parents had been retained. In the second cycle population the mean was further shifted to the right by an amount equal to 2.1 class intervals, but still failed to equal the mean of the selected parents by an amount equal to 1.1 class intervals. The mean of the original population was 7.2 per cent of oil. The mean of the second cycle population was 10.5 with the extreme deviate at 13.5.

The ranges and standard deviations of these three populations are of some interest in indicating any changes in genetic variability. Considering first the range: in the original population the range was from 4.5 to 10.5, in the first cycle 5.5 to 12.5, and in the second cycle 7.5 to 13.5—a difference of 6, 7, and 6 class intervals respectively. The first cycle had the greatest, the original population intermediate, and the second cycle the smallest standard deviations. The fact that the second cycle exhibited the smallest standard deviation may indicate some loss in genetic variability. However 65 per cent of the selective advantage of the parents was retained indicating that a considerable amount of genetic variability exists.

SELFING SERIES

The selfing series presents a strikingly different picture. The results are presented graphically in Figure 26.4. The values plotted for the S_1 generation represent the oil percentages of the original selfed ears. Two lines were lost during the course of inbreeding because of failure to produce any phenotypically desirable plants. The eight lines remaining however represent eight of the ten lines comprising the recurrent selection series. The values presented for the S_2 generation represent the mean of all ears of a particular family which were analyzed. In S_3 to S_5 the value plotted represents the

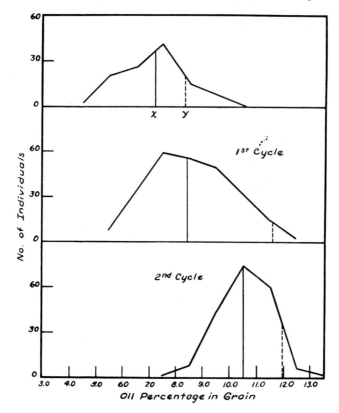

FIG. 26.3—A comparison of the frequency distributions of oil percentage in the corn kernel, in the original population, Illinois High Oil × wxOs420, and after one and two cycles of recurrent selection.

mean for the sibling population in the direct line of descent. If the highest values in each generation had been plotted instead of the means, the picture would have been essentially the same except that the fluctuation from generation to generation would have been increased. The eight lines exhibited somewhat different patterns during the course of inbreeding. Six of the eight lines exhibited an increase, and two a decrease in oil percentage. There does not appear to be any consistent trend within the families from generation to generation. It would appear that chance has played a very important role in spite of the intensive selection practiced.

Comparisons between the two systems of breeding may be made in a number of ways. Selection during inbreeding is normally practiced within and among families. If only the two families having the highest oil percentage were retained and these compared with the mean of the second cycle population, the differences are very slight but in favor of the selfing series. If these

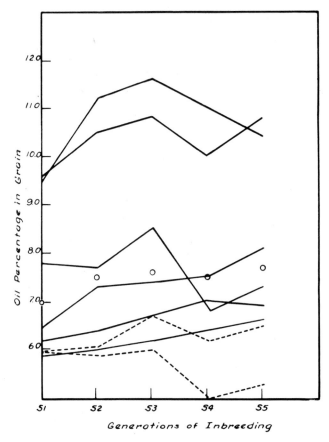

Fig. 26.4—A comparison of mean oil percentages in the corn kernel from the reciprocal backcrossed Illinois High Oil × wxOs420 during five generations of inbreeding and selection.

two lines are compared with the extreme deviate of the recurrent series the lines are lower in oil by nearly three per cent. If the comparison is made between the mean of the S_5 lines and the mean of the second cycle population the lines are again lower, the contrast being 7.5 and 10.5 per cent of oil respectively.

Any comparison involving these two series must also take into account the time at which the comparisons were made. In the selfing series, genetic variability, and therefore opportunity for selection, would be largely exhausted after five generations of selfing. For reasons mentioned earlier, it is assumed that a considerable degree of genetic variability remains in the recurrent series. The disparity between the two systems would therefore be expected to increase with additional generations of selfing and cycles of selection.

Recurrent selection has been practiced for oil percentage in two additional populations. One series had its origin in an F_2 population of the single cross I198×Hy. This population started with a much lower average oil percentage, but the effectiveness of selection was essentially the same as in the Ill. High Oil×wxOs420 series.

In a third series a strain known as Stiff Stalk Synthetic served as parental material. This material also has been divided into a selfing and a recurrent series to supplement the material already presented. This experiment has not yet been completed. The difference between the two series, in so far as data are available, closely parallels the wxOs420×Ill. High Oil series already discussed.

Data on the effectiveness of recurrent selection in modifying combining ability are still quite limited. One such comparison is shown in Figure 26.5. The original stock used was the Stiff Stalk Synthetic, and the double cross Iowa 13 was used as the tester parent. The yields for the two years were not greatly different, but to facilitate a direct comparison the lower frequency distribution has been displaced to the right so that the yield of Iowa 13 for the two years falls on the same ordinate. Stands were somewhat variable in the test crosses comprising the first cycle. The effect of this variation was minimized by adjusting all yields to an average stand by means of a covariance analysis. This adjustment reduced the range in yields so that the contrast between the two frequency distributions does not necessarily present a true picture of the relative variation in the two populations.

RECIPROCAL RECURRENT SELECTION

A modification of the recurrent selection scheme has been suggested by Comstock *et al.* They have designated this procedure reciprocal recurrent selection. Under this modification two diverse foundation sources, A and B, are to be used. Individual selected plants in A are self-pollinated and outcrossed to source B as a tester parent. Similarly selected plants from source B are self-pollinated and outcrossed to source A as a tester. When test cross data become available, a group of selfed ears from source A having the best test cross performance are recombined to produce A^1. AB^1 population is formed in a similar manner. A^1 and B^1 then serve as source material for a new cycle of selfing and test cross evaluation followed by the intercrossing of the most desirable plants. No data are yet available from either their experiments or ours using this method.

In the original paper by Comstock *et al.* (1949) a comparison is presented of improvement limits of three definite breeding procedures. These were (1) selection based on general combining ability using at least two single crosses as testers, (2) recurrent selection for specific combining ability as proposed by Hull (1945), and (3) reciprocal recurrent selections. The assumptions on

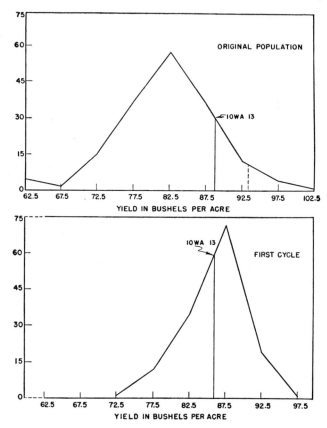

FIG. 26.5—A comparison of the frequency distributions for yield in bushels per acre for top crosses from the original Stiff Stalk Synthetic and after one cycle of recurrent selection.

which these comparisons were based were stated by Comstock *et al.* and will not be repeated here. The conclusions reached are briefly as follows:

1. When dominance is incomplete methods 1 and 3 are essentially equal and superior to method 2.

2. If over-dominance is of major importance methods 2 and 3 will be essentially the same and superior to method 1.

3. When dominance is complete all three methods would be rather similar.

Thus method 3, reciprocal recurrent selection, would appear to be the safest and most efficient method to use with our present lack of knowledge concerning the relative importance of partial dominance, dominance, and over-dominance in determining combining ability.

In the discussion presented so far no emphasis has been placed upon choice of testers. It is obvious that either early testing or recurrent selection can be carried out giving special emphasis to either general or specific combining ability depending upon the tester parent chosen. In the experiments involving oil percentage of the grain this problem does not arise. In the experiments involving test crosses for yield evaluation, double crosses or open-pollinated varieties have been used as tester parents thus giving special emphasis to general combining ability.

SUMMARY

In the data which have been presented bearing on early testing, the method has demonstrated all of the characteristics which have been claimed for it. This is not to be interpreted as meaning early testing is the ideal corn breeding method and equally applicable under all circumstances. It is useful under some conditions. The ideal method of corn breeding probably is still to be devised.

Recurrent selection has been found to be quite effective in modifying the chemical composition of the corn grain. Tests of this method in modifying combining ability have been less extensive. Here again this method may not be equally valuable under all conditions and circumstances, but on the basis of results to date it is certainly deserving of more extensive use.

E. J. WELLHAUSEN
Rockefeller Foundation, Mexico City

Chapter 27

Heterosis in a New Population

Data recently presented by Mangelsdorf and Smith (1949) indicate that corn was being grown in what is now southwestern United States and Mexico at least four thousand years ago. The corn grown in these prehistoric times was both a pod corn and a pop corn of relatively low yield capacity. Today in this same area an enormous variation exists. Direct derivatives of the ancient low yielding pod-pop type still can be found on a very limited scale in certain areas of Mexico, but these low yielding ancient corns now have been replaced largely by more vigorous and productive types.

Tremendous changes have been brought about in both type and yield capacity since ancient times. The modern varieties of Mexico have a yield capacity many times more than the ancient types. On the high plateau of Mexico a variety known as Chalqueño, whose pedigree in part can be traced back to an ancient pop corn, has yielded up to 125 bushels per acre. If the various evolutionary processes and the kinds of gene actions involved in the development of such high yielding varieties from the low yielding prehistoric types were known, we would certainly have a better understanding of the phenomenon of heterosis.

It is the purpose of this chapter to present, first, what seems to have been involved in the development of the modern, relatively high yielding varieties over a period of about four thousand years; and second, a discussion of the methods used and results obtained in the further improvement of some of the modern varieties in a short period of six years.

Perhaps the title might best have been "Heterosis in an Old Population" in the sense that the Mexican corns as a whole are much older than those in the United States. However, from the standpoint of modern corn breeding, it is a new population in that it involves new material on which to try the modern techniques of corn breeding developed in the United States. The successes and failures of standard techniques in this new population, together with certain modifications that are being tried, will be discussed.

HETEROSIS IN NATIVE OPEN-POLLINATED VARIETIES

The first obvious step in any breeding program in a new area is adequate testing of the varieties at hand. In the early years of the program, therefore, considerable time was devoted to a study and classification of the present-day varieties in Mexico (Wellhausen *et al.*, in collaboration with Mangelsdorf, 1951). Evidence presented in this report strongly indicates that many factors have been involved in the evolution of corn in Mexico, the most important of which are repeated here as follows:

1. Varieties in the ancient pod-pop corn type were probably at first chiefly brought about through mutation and by a partial release from the pressure of natural selection by man. There are four ancient races in Mexico which definitely trace back to a common parent. Where this common parent originated is still unknown. All have a sufficient number of different characters to warrant their classification as separate races, yet they all have a number of characters in common; namely, all are pop corns, two of the four are pod corns, all are early maturing, all have a low chromosome knob number, and all are relatively low in yield capacity compared to modern varietal standards. Since no record of the common ancestor is available, no direct comparisons can be made of the yield capacities of the ancient indigenous races as they exist today in Mexico and of their common ancestor. Judging from the Bat Cave material (Mangelsdorf and Smith, 1949) it is not at all unlikely that considerable increase in yield capacity was brought about through gene mutation alone.

2. It is distinctly evident from a study of the various collections that sometime during the history of the Mexican corns there was an influx of exotic types from countries to the south. As a result of the introgression of the ancient indigenous types into the exotic types, and vice versa, many new varieties and races came into existence.

3. Superimposed upon the above two evolutionary mechanisms was the introgression of teosinte germplasm. If Mangelsdorf and Reeves (1939) are right in their theory that teosinte originated as a cross between corn and Tripsacum, then this teosinte germplasm is largely Tripsacum germplasm. Practically all the modern more-productive types of corn contain some teosinte germplasm.

4. The fourth important factor in the evolution of corn in Mexico has been the geography of Mexico itself. Mexico is a mountainous country with many different climates and geographically isolated valleys. Corn is grown from sea-level up to 10,000 feet elevation under a wide range of rainfall conditions. In some areas rainfall is limited to five to ten inches for a period of four months. Other areas receive up to 100 or more inches in a period of six to ten

months. Different temperatures due to changes in elevation and different amounts of rainfall may occur in areas separated only by a few miles. Such conditions are conducive to the development of many different varieties of corn.

As a result of the above evolutionary factors operating over a period of at least four thousand years, there is a greater variation in the corns of Mexico today than in any country in the world. Without doubt the greatest single factor in the development of the modern high yielding agricultural types in Mexico has been the introduction of exotic types from the south. These exotic types were largely big-grained flour corns, which no doubt brought in a series of genes for higher yield that had not existed in Mexico before.

The various processes and types of gene action involved in the development of higher yielding varieties from the reciprocal introgression between the indigenous and exotic types, plus introgression of teosinte, are not easily explained.

Gene Combinations

These processes probably involved a gradual sifting of the gene combinations brought together by hybridization, and continuous backcrossing or rehybridization of resulting hybrids or segregants. The complex pedigree of some of the modern high yielding varieties in Mexico, taken from Wellhausen *et al.* in collaboration with Mangelsdorf (1951), are shown in Figures 27.1–27.4. In these pedigrees each product of the indicated hybridization between two different races, or species in the case of teosinte, was higher yielding or better adapted to its native habitat than either one of the putative parents. For example, in Figure 27.1 Cónico is a better corn than either Palomero Toluqueño or Cacahuacintle, and Tuxpeño is a more productive corn than either Olotillo or Tepecintle. Chalqueño, which is somewhat more recent in the evolutionary scale, is more productive than either Cónico or Tuxpeño.

This does not necessarily mean that the same races crossed today would all show considerable heterosis in F_1. As a matter of fact many of the crosses indicated in the diagrams have been made and studied. In certain cases the F_1 hybrid, when tested in the environment best suited to one or both parents, showed considerable heterosis. In other cases it was no better than the better parent or was intermediate between the two parents. In some crosses the F_1 was definitely unadapted to the environment of either parent.

In the natural development of higher yielding corns from the intercrossing of different races, there were no doubt many instances in which the F_1 hybrids that first occurred between a native and an introduced variety were very poorly adapted to native conditions and showed no heterosis. A 50 per cent random dosage of an introduced variety is often more than sufficient to completely upset the physiology of a native variety that has adapted itself to a fixed environment over a long period of natural selection. Under natural conditions, however, any crossing that might take place between two varieties is purely at random and not complete. Hybrid plants that appear in a field of native corn in the succeeding generation, therefore, might be widely scattered. But no matter how little seed these F_1 plants may produce, if their flowering periods coincide, then germplasm would be passed on to the native variety through backcrosses.

Thus by repeated backcrossing and the sifting action that always takes place through natural and artificial selection, certain genes from an introduced population may be readily transferred to a native population. These might be additional favorable yield genes that express themselves in the native gene complex, or they might be other genes which permit the fuller expression of the yield genes which the native variety already contains, or both.

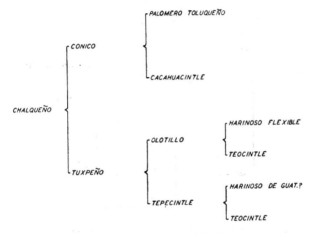

Fig. 27.1—Probable origin of Chalqueño.

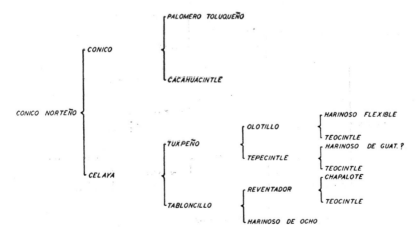

Fig. 27.2—Probable origin of Cónico Norteño.

A classical example of such introgression is the introgression of genes from teosinte into corn, a process which is still taking place in many areas of Mexico. Teosinte grows as a weed in the corn fields of certain areas. Also the Mexican farmers in some areas have been known to plant teosinte in their corn fields based on a belief that such a practice would make their native corns more drought resistant. The F_1 hybrids between corn and teosinte are very small-eared, and ears are difficult to collect because of their very brittle rachis. As such, the F_1's have no value in artificial selection. However, the F_1's shed pollen about the same time as the native corn variety, and a large number of backcrosses result with the corn parent as the female. Some of these are unconsciously selected as seed for the following year since they cannot be

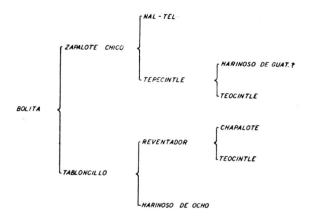

FIG. 27.3—Probable origin of Bolita.

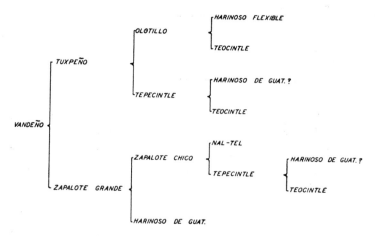

FIG. 27.4—Probable origin of Vandeño.

separated at time of harvest from the non-hybrid grains. These backcrosses then, bring about a second generation of backcrosses.

Through this sifting action certain genes from teosinte, such as those that condition greater drought resistance when in combination with the native corn gene-complex, become fairly well established. In a dry area any genes bringing about greater drought resistance would immediately affect the yield, and gene frequency for such characters would increase in the population through subsequent natural and artificial selection. Thus a new, improved higher yielding population under dry conditions may be brought about which will replace all other populations in its range of best adaptation. It must have been in this way that the old superstition of a greater protection from drought by interplanting corn with teosinte arose. How many other factors of survival value were obtained from teosinte is difficult to ascertain.

This is probably the most common manner in which higher yielding varieties for specific areas, especially the old corn areas, were built up. However, as old land wore out, new methods of corn cultivation and new areas in which corn could be produced were constantly sought. New environments for corn production thus came into existence throughout the years. These new environments often consisted of the artificial or natural drainage of old lake beds which brought into cultivation highly fertile areas with high water-holding capacity. In such areas, due to reserve moisture in the soil from the previous rainy season, corn could be planted as much as two months ahead of the beginning of the normal rainy season. This provided a six or eight month growing season instead of the usual four to six months. It was in such new environments, where plants could develop and fully express their yield capacity, that certain F_1 hybrids presented a much higher degree of heterosis and adaptation than in the native habitat of either one of their immediate parents.

Hybridization

Perhaps the outstanding example of a highly productive hybrid race that has developed in a relatively new environment in the central high plateau of Mexico is a late maturing race called Chalqueño. This race (Fig. 27.1) probably came into existence through the hybridization of the two distinct races, Cónico and Tuxpeño. Cónico is an early maturing corn that originated on the high plateaus of Central Mexico from the hybridization of an ancient indigenous high altitude pop corn called Palomero Toluqueño and an exotic race called Cacahuacintle. Tuxpeño, the other parent of Chalqueño, is a cylindrical dent adapted to the lowland coastal areas of Mexico. It probably came into existence through the intercrossing of two prehistoric races, Olotillo and Tepecintle, which in turn probably were derived from two different exotic flour corns through the introgression of teosinte.

Chalqueño, in the areas where it is grown today, is much more productive than either of its putative parents Cónico and Tuxpeño. In the highland regions to which Cónico is best adapted, neither Chalqueño nor Tuxpeño will mature, and in addition Tuxpeño is very heavily attacked by rust. On the other hand, in the lowland areas where Tuxpeño is best adapted, Chalqueño produces very little and Cónico produces practically nothing. A similar relationship has held with an artificial cross between Cónico and Tuxpeño in which half the germplasm was from one parent and half from the other. The artificial hybrid, as one might expect, was not as well adapted to the Chalqueño area as Chalqueño itself. Chalqueño over a period of many years of gene sifting no doubt concentrated those favorable growth genes best suited to its present environment and practically eliminated the frequency of other genes which were unnecessary or deleterious to its maximum development. The hybrid, nevertheless, was much superior to the two parents in the environment best suited to Chalqueño.

Here then is an example of the process which often happens in nature or in planned breeding programs. A hybrid between two parents adapted to widely different environments shows no hybrid vigor, as measured in yield, over either one of the two parents when grown in the native habitat of either parent. But in a new environment different from the one under which either parent developed, the hybrid may show extreme vigor. It is highly probable that many new varieties came into existence when new areas of land were brought under cultivation or when the native inhabitants migrated to new areas. Very often several different corns were brought together in these new environments which were not as well adapted as the hybrids that resulted between them. It is also highly probable that the first varietal hybrids were not as good on the whole as the varieties that developed from them through successive generations of backcrossing and gene sifting.

From a study of the origin and development of the various types of corn in Mexico, it seems that the most important factor in the evolution of the different productive races has been the gradual accumulation of favorable growth or yield genes in combination or balance with the proper "governing or regulating" genes in each specific environment. Maximum yield in a specific environment is not only dependent on favorable genes for such quantitative characters as ear and kernel size, number of ears, leaf area or photosynthetic efficiency, but also on genes which govern such functions as maturity, disease and drought resistance, or general adaptation.

The latter group might well be genes which some investigators have termed *bottleneck* genes. Such genes may inhibit the full expression of certain quantitative yield genes and thus prohibit the organism from reaching its maximum production allowed by a specific environment. An increase in yield capacity, therefore, often may not involve the accumulation of more favorable yield genes, but rather the removal of certain bottleneck genes. In new environments these bottleneck genes might be *relic* genes carried over from their old native habitat where they existed because they had survival value.

It would seem, therefore, that heterosis is the result of the combined effect of individual gene action (for growth) plus the interaction of all genes within the genotype (its genetic environment) in relation to the sum-total of all external influences acting upon the organism and governing expression of its gene complex. If heterosis in a cross between $A \times B$ is measured as the excess vigor or yield over the average of A and B, there may be no heterosis in the environment to which A or B is best adapted as shown with Chalqueño. Yet in some new environment different from that in which A and B developed, the excess vigor may be great, even exceeding that of A and B in their native environment, if such comparison could be made. Certainly the genotype is no different in any of the areas. The difference must be due to different interactions between over-all gene action and environment. It is no wonder that so many different ideas exist when it comes to the explanation of heterosis. It has no simple explanation.

IMPROVEMENT THROUGH BREEDING

In the evolution of corn in Mexico, the different varieties and races were brought together in a haphazard manner. Relatively few of the total combinations of races and varieties possible have been made, and when two varieties or races come together in a specific region by chance, there is no reason to believe that the particular combination was the best that could have been made for the area. Although some fairly productive varieties did develop, especially in the more fertile areas with higher rainfall, the possibilities of further over-all improvement are astonishing and offer a challenge to modern corn breeders.

The cooperative corn improvement program of the Mexican Government and the Rockefeller Foundation was begun about six years ago. Its objective was to provide higher yielding varieties or hybrids for the many different environments in the main corn producing areas. In most of Mexico, selection has been going on for many centuries for adaptation to low soil fertility and extreme climatic conditions. A variety or strain capable of producing something in the years of extreme drought or early frost was highly prized by the native Indians, even though it produced only a little more in good years. Low yields meant hunger, but a crop failure meant starvation. With modern means of transportation, crop failures in a region no longer mean starvation for the people of that region, and low fertility can and must be remedied before corn production can be greatly increased. The breeding program, therefore, was geared to the development of productive varieties or hybrids adapted to the average climatic conditions of a particular region, and a level of fertility that could permit maximum production under these average conditions. More productive varieties would pay the cost of soil improvement and pave the way for a generally higher level of corn production.

The program also is based on a gradual improvement year by year. As soon as a variety or hybrid was found to be superior to native varieties in a particular area, it was increased and distributed, although it still may have had many minor defects. When better varieties or hybrids become available, they are substituted for those previously released in the increase and distribution program.

The different steps involved in this gradual improvement program for any particular area have been as follows:

1. Variety testing. In this way good open-pollinated varieties were sometimes isolated for immediate distribution and as basic material for the breeding program to follow.

2. The improvement of the best native open-pollinated varieties through the formation of synthetics which could be propagated through open-pollination.

3. The formation and distribution of double cross hybrids which were good not only as double crosses but also as synthetics in advanced generations. For this purpose one generation selfed lines were used.

4. Finally, after many of the farmers have learned how to use hybrid corn, greater emphasis may be devoted to the formation of more specific, higher yielding uniform hybrids with highly selected and proven inbred lines.

Areas in Which Improvement Work Has Been Concentrated

The methods used and results obtained may be understood more clearly if the areas in which improvement programs were initiated are identified. Although corn is grown everywhere in Mexico, the most important commercial corn growing areas are found on the central plateau between 18 and 22 degrees latitude. It is within this area that the breeding work has been concentrated. To facilitate the work still further, the area was divided into five zones on the basis of elevation as follows:

Zone 1—2200–2600 meters elevation
    a) Late varieties with six months' growing season planted under irrigation
    b) Early varieties with four months' growing season under natural rainfall conditions
Zone 2—1800–2200 meters
Zone 3—1400–1800 meters
Zone 4—1000–1400 meters
Zone 5—0–1000 meters

The main breeding stations for these five zones are located in Zone 1 at 2200 meters, Zone 3 at 1600 meters, and Zone 4 at 1200 meters. With these three main stations and with the cooperation of farmers in making yield tests in outlying regions, it has been possible to cover the central plateau and certain tropical areas fairly completely.

Utilization of Good Native Open-pollinated Varieties

Since it is entirely possible that the original gene populations in the many different isolated valleys of a particular zone were not the same, one might expect to find a different variety in each valley as a result of natural and artificial selection. Often this was precisely the case. Out of 240 samples of corn collected in Zones 2 and 3 from areas with elevations ranging from 1400 to 2000 meters, and tested under conditions representative of these two zones, 15 varieties were outstanding. These consisted of three early, five medium, and seven late maturing varieties in relation to the normal growing or rainy season of the area in which tests were made. The best early varieties (Wellhausen, 1947) yielded from 15 to 49 per cent more than the average of 26 varieties of the same maturity. The best medium maturing varieties yielded from 30 to 54 per cent higher than the average of 57 varieties of medium maturity. The best late varieties yielded from 25 to 60 per cent more than the average of the 62 late varieties of similar maturity included in the tests.

A similar situation was found to exist in the valleys at higher elevations in the high plateau (Zone 1) among both the late and early varieties. A late variety commonly grown under irrigation in the fertile valleys of the State of Hidalgo was found to yield about 20 per cent more than a variety called Chalco widely used for irrigation plantings in the States of Mexico and Puebla (Wellhausen and Roberts, 1948). The best early varieties for Zone 1 were found in the State of Mexico, north of Mexico City, and these yielded from 15 to 20 per cent more than the average early varieties grown in Zone 1. On the whole, from 15 to 20 per cent increase in yield often could be obtained in some parts of all zones through the wider distribution of the best open-pollinated variety found within each zone.

Fundamental Methods in the Formation of Good Inbred Lines

Steps 2 to 4, as outlined above, imply the formation and use of inbred lines, and the degree of improvement one might expect depends upon the isolation of good, vigorous, disease-resistant lines that combine well with each other when used in synthetics or hybrids. In the formation of lines we have, in general, adhered to the following principles:

1. The use of diverse varieties adapted within a particular zone.
2. Rigid selection based on vigor and desirable agronomic characters.
3. Tests for combining ability after one generation of selfing.

Approximately 35 different varieties of corn belonging to eight different races have been inbred in the improvement program for central Mexico. These eight races are listed as follows in order of adaptation to elevation:

Race	Zone to Which Adapted
Cónico	1
Chalqueño	1
Cónico Norteño	2
Celaya	3 and 4
Bolita	3 and 4
Tabloncillo	3 and 4
Vandeño	4 and 5
Tuxpeño	5

All are races which have come into existence in more recent times and all have rather complex pedigrees as shown in Figures 27.1–27.4. So far only the outstanding varieties of each race have been inbred. It was concluded early in the breeding program that inbred lines for immediate use in a particular zone might best be obtained from the high yielding varieties adapted to that zone. It is entirely possible that in the future better hybrids may be obtained through the utilization of a wider base of germplasm. The latter procedure would require more time and more adequate testing. It would involve the extraction of the favorable yield factors from several races and their convergence into a synthetic variety or hybrid along with the proper *governing genes* for a given environment.

In the inbreeding program it has become apparent that vigor in the original plant or first generation selfed progeny (S_1) can be used to a considerable extent as a measure of the number of favorable yield genes with which the particular plant or line has been endowed. But vigor becomes less and less useful as an indicator of the number of yield genes in a particular line in the second, third, or fourth generations of inbreeding because of a greater number of bottleneck genes that are fixed with successive generations of inbreeding. In advanced inbred generations, two lines might be greatly different in vigor, yet equal in combining ability with a specific tester, because of similarities in their yield gene complex. As lines, they may be different in relative vigor because of certain different specific bottleneck genes or loci that mask the expression of genes or loci for growth and development.

The Mexican corn program not only involves the actual improvement of corn, but also the development and training of young corn breeders. In order to demonstrate more vividly that considerable effort may be saved by selecting only the best and most vigorous plants or lines for further work, several students visually classified the inbred lines available after one generation of selfing from five different varieties into four classes on basis of vigor. The most vigorous lines were classified as *A* lines. Those somewhat less vigorous or desirable were classified as *B*, and so on, with the least vigorous lines classified as *D*.

Although classifications were originally made into four categories, the *D* lines were discarded without further consideration. Of the remaining lines saved from each of the five different varieties, 3–6 per cent in each were classified as *A*, 12 to 15 per cent as *B*, and the remaining 79 to 85 per cent as *C*. All were topcrossed to a common tester, but only the topcrosses involving *A* and *B* lines were finally included in yield tests because of lack of space. Comparative yields of the *A* and *B* topcrosses are summarized in Tables 27.1–27.3.

Table 27.1 shows the results obtained with *A* and *B* lines from a variety known as Leon Criollo topcrossed on the variety Urquiza and tested at three locations. At each place the average yield of the topcrosses involving the *A* lines was slightly higher than those involving *B* lines. But what is more important, the percentage of lines increasing the yield over the tester parent was much higher among the A lines than among the B lines.

Table 27.2 shows the performance of A and B lines from Urquiza topcrossed on Leon Criollo when tested at two different locations. Again the average yield of the A topcrosses was higher than that of the B topcrosses, and the percentage of topcrossed lines yielding more than the tester was higher among the A lines than among the B lines.

The same thing was true in A and B lines obtained from three other varieties when topcrossed on Urquiza, as summarized in Table 27.3. These data definitely indicate that the probability of obtaining good general combiners

TABLE 27.1

COMPARATIVE YIELDS OF A AND B S_1 LINES
OF LEON CRIOLLO IN TOPCROSSES
WITH URQUIZA AT 3 LOCATIONS*

Location	Class	No. of Lines	Average Yield of Topcrosses in % of Check	Per Cent of Lines Increasing Yield 25% or More of Check
I........	A	31	116	32
	B	60	113	23
II........	A	33	122	39
	B	64	108	20
III.......	A	33	92	18
	B	45	90	14

* Variety Urquiza was used as check.

TABLE 27.2

COMPARATIVE YIELDS OF A AND B S_1 LINES
OF URQUIZA IN TOPCROSSES WITH LEON
CRIOLLO AT TWO LOCATIONS*

Location	Class	No. of Lines	Average Yield of Topcrosses in % of Check	Per Cent of Lines Increasing Yield of Check
I........	A	13	111	69
	B	33	97	40
II........	A	19	102	63
	B	56	90	28

* Leon Criollo was used as check.

as measured by the testers used, is higher among the more vigorous and agronomically better lines.

The experiment has been carried somewhat further. Inbreeding was continued in the various S_1 families originally classified as A, B, and C. After three generations of selfing, the advanced lines on hand were topcrossed on two different testers and the resulting topcrosses were tested for yield. On the basis of average topcross performance, certain of the advanced inbred lines were selected as worthy of keeping for further work. The number selected from each of several varieties together with their classification is given in Table 27.4.

TABLE 27.3

COMPARATIVE YIELDS OF A AND B S_1 LINES OF MICH. 21, PUE. 16, AND MEX. 39 IN TOPCROSSES WITH URQUIZA*

Variety	Class	No. of Lines	Average Yield of Topcrosses in % of Check	Per Cent of Lines Increasing Yield of Check
Mich. 21........	A	21	110	76
	B	21	105	67
Pue. 16.........	A	22	85	9
	B	10	74	0
Mex. 39........	A	11	101	55
	B	14	92	29

* Urquiza was used as check.

TABLE 27.4

NUMBER OF LINES SELECTED FROM FOUR VARIETIES ON BASIS OF TOPCROSS TESTS AFTER THREE GENERATIONS OF INBREEDING AND THEIR CLASSIFICATIONS IN S_1

VARIETY	No. of Original S_1 Lines Inbred	No. of S_3 Lines Selected	No. Originally Classified as A and B in S_1	
			A	B
Mich. 21.......	219	9	8	1
Mex. 39.......	131	2	1	1
Leon Criollo....	218	5	4	1
Chalqueño.....	67	22	15	7

As pointed out before, in the first three varieties listed above, 3–6 per cent of the lines were classified as A, 12–15 per cent as B, and the rest were classified as C. In Chalqueño, the S_1 families were discarded more heavily and the 67 S_1 families selected for further inbreeding were classified as follows: $16A$, $35B$, and $13C$. It is clearly evident that by far the majority of S_2 lines saved for further study after testing in topcrosses came from the S_1 families originally classified as A.

In the early stages of the program, about five hundred plants were inbred in each variety. At harvest, about two hundred, or 40 per cent, were selected for further work. The above data indicate that, as far as the varieties listed were concerned, the same results might have been obtained with a more drastic elimination of lines at the beginning of inbreeding.

Selection of testers for use in the isolation of good inbred lines is always a problem. In Mexico, chief concern in the early stages of the breeding program was the isolation of lines with good general combining ability. For this purpose the inbred lines in each zone were topcrossed on at least two different testers, usually unrelated adapted open-pollinated varieties. The good combiners, when selected on average topcross performance, often were disappointing when crossed inter se. In those zones where two varieties were available which, when crossed, produced a desirable hybrid agronomically, a reciprocal method of testing was used. With this method, inbreds from variety A were topcrossed on variety B, and inbreds of variety B were topcrossed on variety A. Good combiners thus isolated from variety A were crossed with good combiners from variety B to form single crosses and subsequently double crosses. This method of double cross formation was more efficient than the recombination of lines with so-called general combining ability from the above method. Where a good single cross of first generation inbred lines was available that could be used as a tester to isolate inbred lines which combine well with it, this cross proved more efficient than either of the above two methods in the formation of good double crosses.

Utilization of Semi-inbred Lines in Synthetics and Hybrids

Almost from the beginning of hybrid corn production, breeders have sought to discover methods of utilizing superior inbred strains in more or less permanent combinations. In a country such as Mexico, where the majority of the farmers will not readily adopt a practice of securing new hybrid seed for each planting, superior synthetic varieties would have real advantage.

As Sprague and Jenkins (1943) pointed out, four factors operate to determine the yield of advanced generations of hybrids: (1) the number of lines involved, (2) the mean yield of these lines, (3) the mean yield of all of their possible single crosses, and (4) the percentage of self pollination. Since maize is almost wholly cross-pollinated, the last factor may be largely ignored.

Which of the remaining three factors is the most important has not been determined to date.

Wright (1922) has shown that with random mating the vigor and productiveness of an F_2 is less than that of the F_1 by an amount equal to $1/n$th of the difference between the F_1 and the average of the parental lines where n is the number of parental lines involved. These theoretical conclusions of Wright are adequately supported by experimental data from maize (Neal, 1935; Kiesselbach, 1933; Wellhausen and Roberts, 1949).

In the past, in estimating the number of lines to use in a synthetic, apparently it was assumed that the F_1 mean in Wright's formula could be taken as a constant value regardless of the number of lines involved. If this assumption were correct, then the more lines involved the higher would be the yield of the resulting synthetic. In actual practice, however, synthetics with a large number of lines have yielded little more than the open-pollinated varieties adapted to the same area. As indicated by Kinman and Sprague (1945), the assumption of a constant mean yield for all F_1 combinations seems unwarranted. In any series in inbred lines, there are some that combine better than others, and it is much easier to obtain four inbred lines that yield well in all possible combinations than ten or sixteen. Therefore, to bring about the highest mean yield of all possible single crosses, the use of relatively few lines is indicated.

It can be shown by holding the F_1 yields as a constant that a better synthetic might be made with four more productive lines than with eight less productive. For example, assuming the mean yield of all single crosses involved to be 120 per cent, an F_2 of a synthetic involving four lines with a mean yield of 80 per cent will be 110 per cent, while a synthetic involving eight lines yielding only 30 per cent will yield 109 per cent in F_2. Kinman and Sprague (1945) concluded that in general the most efficient number of lines to be included in a synthetic will vary with the range in combining ability among the inbreds available as parents. However, on the basis of their study, four to six lines appeared to be the most efficient number, the smaller number being most efficient when more productive lines, yielding at least 75 per cent of open-pollinated variety, were involved.

Theoretically, therefore, the best synthetics would result from the use of four to six lines which are as productive as possible and which are good combiners inter se. Certain practical aspects also must be taken into consideration. If the inbred lines that are combined into a synthetic are greatly different in type and maturity, the resulting F_2 may be extremely variable for these two characters and may require considerable selection before distribution as a new variety. Variation is often a serious objection for many farmers who have become used to their more-uniform highly selected old varieties. The resistance of farmers to synthetic varieties which are variable and which are not strikingly higher yielding is often so great that it is difficult to obtain wide scale distribution and use.

Considerable success was achieved in the formation of synthetic varieties from double topcrosses in the early stages of the Mexican program, as described by Wellhausen and Roberts (1949). Nevertheless, in consideration of all factors, it seemed that the most logical procedure would be the formation of good double cross hybrids which would also make good synthetics in advanced generations. In this way, the more progressive farmers could take advantage of the higher yield capacity of hybrids, while less progressive farmers would still benefit by planting the advanced generation progeny. Also much wider use of improved seed could be obtained more easily and rapidly since hybrids always make a better showing than synthetics. With time, through education, demonstration, and the formation of better hybrids, the demand for hybrid seed could be increased gradually, and use of advanced generation seed gradually would decrease. Some of the hybrids obtained for Zones 1 and 3 and their relative value as synthetics will be discussed below:

Results in Zone 1

In Zone 1, for March and April plantings under irrigation or under conditions where subsoil moisture is sufficient for germination, the race Chalqueño has become widely distributed. Some of the results obtained in the attempt to improve this long season race are given in Table 27.5.

The variety listed as Chalco in Table 27.5 represents an average variety of the race Chalqueño, and its yield for the sake of comparison has been taken as 100. Variety V-7 is one of the best varieties found in the race, and has been widely distributed as an improvement of the common variety Chalco. Its two-year average yield in comparison to Chalco was 118 per cent.

Hybrid H-2 is a cross between two composites, one of which (Hgo. Comp. 1) was made up of a composite of five first generation selfed lines (S₁) from the variety V-7, that were good in topcrosses with the variety Urquiza, of the race Cónico Norteño. The other (Urq. Comp. 1) was made up of a composite of five S₁ lines from the variety Urquiza, selected on the bases of their combining ability in topcrosses with a variety similar to Chalco. Urquiza was the only variety of the different races tried in Chalqueño territory that was fairly well adapted. Hybrids between two such composites are of interest because the parents may be propagated as open-pollinated synthetic varieties, thus eliminating the necessity of forming single crosses and the maintenance of four inbred lines, as is the case in a double cross.

The yield of hybrid H-2 was only slightly higher than the open-pollinated variety V-7. Work is under way to find out how much this hybrid might be improved through reciprocal recurrent selection.

The three-way hybrid H-1 was made by using a single cross involving an

S_1 line of Urquiza (Urq. 54) and an S_1 line of Chalqueño (Hgo. 3-5) as the female parent, with a very vigorous first generation selfed line Mex. 37-5 also from Chalqueño as the pollinator. This hybrid involving one Urquiza line and two Chalqueño inbreds has been one of the best combinations to date of Urquiza and Chalqueño lines. In general, hybrids of inbred lines from Chalqueño and inbred lines of Urquiza have been disappointing in comparison with the yield of the variety V-7, although the Chalqueño lines in the crosses were selected on the basis of combining ability with the variety Urquiza, and Urquiza lines on the basis of their combining ability with a variety of Chalqueño. None of the hybrids, including H-1, approached very closely the

TABLE 27.5

RELATIVE YIELDS IN PER CENT OF CHALCO FOR THREE
LONG SEASON VARIETIES AND HYBRIDS
IN 1948 AND 1949

Variety or Hybrid	Pedigree	Relative Yields in Per Cent		
		1948	1949	Average
Chalco.........	Open-pollinated	100	100	100
Variety V-7.....	Selected O.P.	117	120	118
Hybrid H-2.....	Hgo. Comp. 1× Urq. Comp. 1	120	125	122
Hybrid H-1.....	(Urq. 54×Hgo. 3-5)× Mex. 37-5	134	130	132

yield, ear size, and depth of grain of the best 10 per cent of the plants in the variety V-7.

If a hybrid could be made in which 80–90 per cent of the plants approached the yield of the best 10 per cent of the plants in the variety V-7, it would be an excellent hybrid. If such a hybrid is to be obtained, another line of approach seems warranted. The best approach to this immediate ideal is probably through the recombination of lines from V-7 or other varieties within the race Chalqueño rather than bringing in outside germplasm, since no race or variety has as yet been found which in F_1 crosses with V-7 has been as good as V-7. The question of selecting the proper tester for use in isolating the high-combining genotypes, inter se, needs further study. Perhaps a tester made up as a double cross or as a synthetic of the most vigorous, most agronomically desirable, highest yielding, and best combining Chalqueño lines would be the one to use. Against this nucleus of concentrated adapted germplasm, other lines from V-7 or lines from other varieties of Chalqueño, regardless of vigor, could be tested for their combining ability. Those that increased the yield of the tester could then be pooled, and this pool could be concentrated further by another round of selfs and outcrosses to the tester. The objective would be to concentrate the factors which complement those of the tester to bring about the ideal hybrid. If successful, the final hybrid could consist of a cross between two pools of germplasm, rather than individual inbred lines, with the tester used as the female parent if so desired.

The race Cónico (Figs. 27.1 and 27.2) is almost universally distributed in Zone 1 where it is used for June plantings at the beginning of the rainy season. With respect to general plant characters it is probably the poorest corn in Mexico. The plants are sparsely leafed, have a poor tassel, and have an extremely weak root system. As a normal practice, dirt is hilled around each individual stalk to keep the plants upright until harvest. Its one outstanding feature is its ability to grow and develop grain of high test weight under relatively low temperature conditions.

To improve this race, incorporation of germplasm from another race with a strong root system seemed highly desirable. The materials most likely to be of use were the earliest varieties of the race Cónico Norteño. For the purpose of improving the corn varieties for the rainy season of Zone 1, therefore, two varieties were selected. One, designated as Mex. 39, was one of the best yielding varieties of the race Cónico at 2200 meters elevation. The other, designated as Leon I, was a good yielding early variety of the race Cónico Norteño commonly grown in Zone 2 at 1800 to 2000 meters elevation. This second variety was a little late in maturity in Zone 1 and was not as well adapted to the cool growing season as was Cónico. Selected first generation selfed lines from Mex. 39 were topcrossed on Leon I and selected S_1 lines from Leon I were tested with Mex. 39. The best combiners with the respective testers under conditions best suited to Cónico were then crossed in all possible combinations, and tested for yield. From these results a double cross that might also make a good synthetic was predicted, made, and tested. The pedigree of this double cross, its yield relative to Mex. 39, and its probable yield in F_2 are given in Table 27.6.

The female parent of this double cross consisted of a single cross between two S_1 lines from Leon I (Race Cónico Norteño). The male parent consisted of a cross between an S_1 line and a composite of four S_1 lines all from Mex. 39 (Cónico). This pollinator also is being propagated and used as a synthetic variety with good results.

Although based on only one year's results, the data in Table 27.6 indicate substantial differences in yield capacity between the hybrid and the open-pollinated variety Mex. 39. Perhaps what is more important at the moment is that the advanced generation progeny of this hybrid shows promise of being substantially superior in yield capacity to Mex. 39 which is one of the better varieties of the race Cónico. The actual yields of the double cross and the six possible single crosses between the four parental lines, together with the open-pollinated variety Mex. 39 as check in Table 27.6, were all determined in the same experiment under the same conditions. In calculating the yield of the F_2 generation, however, the average yield of the four parental lines was estimated as 70 per cent of Mex. 39. In view of the fact that the S_1 lines involved were the most vigorous within their respective varieties, this estimation is conservative. Actual yields of the F_2 generation in comparison with Mex. 39 and the double cross hybrid are not yet available.

Results in Zone 3

Zone 3 comprises the corn belt of Mexico and produces more commercial corn than any other area. In the eastern part of Zone 3, an area commonly referred to as the Bajío, the race Celaya (Fig. 27.2) is widely distributed

TABLE 27.6

YIELD AND PER CENT DRY MATTER OF A DOUBLE CROSS
HYBRID COMPARED TO THE OPEN-POLLINATED
VARIETY MEX. 39 AND TO ITS F_2 YIELD*

Hybrid	Av. Yield Kg./Ha.	% D.M.	Yield in % of Check
(LI 27 × LI 193) × Mex. 39-26 × Mex. 39 Comp. 1	3795	71	148
Mex. 39 O.P. (check)	2568	69	100
Av. of all possible singles	3506	70	136
Av. of parental lines (est. 70% of check)	1798	......	70
F_2 (calculated by Wright's formula)	3079	......	120

* Calculated from average yield of the three inbreds and one composite and their six possible single crosses.

and is apparently a recent introduction into the area. The predominating corn in the Bajío area at one time must have been the race Cónico Norteño. But as the root rot organism populations built up, the varieties of Cónico Norteño rapidly dropped in yield because of their almost complete root rot susceptibility. Celaya probably originated in the State of San Luis Potosí which is adjacent to the Bajío, but at a lower elevation than is common in Zone 3. When introduced into the Bajío, it was a late variety and was first grown only by farmers who had irrigation and could plant corn considerably ahead of the rainy season. As irrigation farming increased, the race Celaya became very popular and widespread. Selection pressure operated in the direction of earliness, and certain varieties were developed which were more productive than Cónico Norteño on the better soils and under conditions of a normal rainy season. The rainy season begins about July 1 and ends in October.

In the western part of Zone 3, the predominating types are varieties of the race Tabloncillo and inter-mixtures of Tabloncillo, Celaya, and a third complex from the mountains in southern Jalisco. The breeding work for Zone 3 was concentrated in the Bajío and had the following objectives:

1. The development of hybrids and synthetics higher yielding than Celaya, with a high degree of root and ear-rot resistance, which have general adaptation to Zone 3 under irrigation.

2. The development of early drought resistant hybrids and synthetics for Zone 3, which are adapted to the normal rainy season of the area, and which have a high degree of root and ear-rot resistance.

Since the variety Celaya already had considerable root and ear-rot resistance, it was used as basic breeding material in the attempt to attain the above objectives.

One of the first attempts at the improvement of Celaya involved the pro-

TABLE 27.7

YIELDS OF TWO DOUBLE TOPCROSSES IN COMPARISON TO THE OPEN-POLLINATED VARIETY CELAYA

Hybrid	Pedigree	Yield Kg./Ha.	Yield in % of Celaya
H-305.......	(M30-60×Gto. 59A)× (L II 123×Jal. 35)	4845	120
H-301.......	(L II 123×Gto. 59A)× (M30-33×Jal. 35)	4411	108
Celaya*.....	Open-pollinated variety	4092	100

* The variety of Celaya used as a check in this and in the following tables is the one being maintained by the Agricultural Experiment Station in Leon, Gto.

duction of double topcrosses. In this method, two different high yielding varieties adapted to Zone 3 were used as testers. One of these, designated as Gto. 59A, was one of the better late varieties found within the race Celaya. The other, designated as Jal. 35, was a high yielding variety obtained from southern Jalisco. This latter variety apparently was derived from a highly heterogeneous mixture of several races that came together in southern Jalisco: Tabloncillo, Celaya, and the Jaliscan mountain complex (Wellhausen et al.). Inbred lines (S_1) from Gto. 59A and other varieties of the race Celaya were topcrossed with Jal. 35, and S_1 inbred lines from Jal. 35 and similar varieties were topcrossed on Gto. 59A. These topcrosses were then tested in three locations in Zone 3 with Celaya as a check. As a result of these tests, the ten best topcrosses with Gto. 59A were selected and each crossed with each of the ten best topcrosses with Jal. 35. Subsequently, the resulting double topcrosses were tested at two different locations in Zone 3. Finally, two double topcrosses were selected and released for commercial production. The yields of the two double topcrosses for commercial production together with the yields of Celaya are given in Table 27.7. These comparative yields are based on an average of four replications in each of 20 experiments in two different localities and are highly significant statistically.

The double topcross hybrid H-305 yielded 20 per cent more than Celaya and was equal to Celaya in maturity. Hybrid H-301 yielded only 8 per cent more than Celaya but was about ten days earlier. In normal years this is a decided advantage in adaptation to the variable rainy season of the Bajío. The major portion of the 2000 hectares planted in 1948 for hybrid seed production in the Bajío was used for the production of these two double topcross hybrids. According to a formula presented by Mangelsdorf (1939), the gain in yield of these two double topcrosses in F_2 would be about half of what they showed in F_1 over Celaya. The results of an experiment set up to measure the difference in yield between the F_1 and F_2 generations of eight different double topcrosses made up as described above are given in Table

TABLE 27.8

COMPARISON OF F_1 AND F_2 GENERATION YIELDS OF EIGHT
DOUBLE TOPCROSSES IN PER CENT OF CELAYA

GENERA-TION	DOUBLE TOPCROSSES								AVERAGE
	1	2	3	4	5	6	7	8	
F_1......	132	115	111	99	94	101	98	89	105
F_2......	123	104	70	92	93	117	114	114	103
Celaya...	100	100	100	100	100	100	100	100	100

27.8. The data are based on an average of four replications in each of two locations.

According to the data presented in Table 27.8, the differences in yield between the F_1 and F_2 generations were statistically significant only in the double topcrosses 3 and 8. In topcross 8 the difference was in favor of the F_2 generation. Some of the double topcrosses undoubtedly held a certain advantage in yield over Celaya in the F_2, but further data are needed before accurate conclusions can be drawn with respect to the comparative yield capacities of the F_1 and F_2 generations of double topcrosses.

Although some improvement was achieved over Celaya by means of the multiple topcross method, the direct recombination of lines from Celaya has given better results. Celaya definitely offers the best breeding material for Zone 3. Crosses between Celaya and other races in Zone 3 such as Cónico Norteño and Tabloncillo have been disappointing. The race Cónico Norteño introduces some earliness, but it also contributes susceptibility to root rot and ear-rots. The race Tabloncillo of western Mexico behaves in a similar manner. In addition, it introduces certain undesirable ear characters.

As shown in Table 27.9 some outstanding hybrids have been attained through a recombination of lines from Celaya. The Celaya lines used in the hybrids of Table 27.9 were isolated by topcrossing with a variety of the race Cónico Norteño and with the variety Jal. 35. The two hybrids, H-309 and H-307 were made with S_1 lines, while H-310 was made with S_2 lines. Both H-309 and H-307 gave slightly better all around performance in yield and in disease resistance than did H-310, but H-309 was the best of the three in yield, disease resistance, and general agronomic characters. Its yield, as

TABLE 27.9

YIELDS OF DOUBLE CROSSES MADE FROM S_1 AND S_2 LINES
COMPARED WITH THE AVERAGE YIELD
OF CELAYA, H-301, AND H-306*

Hybrid	Pedigree	Yield Kg./Ha.	% of Av. of Checks
H-309...	(C 123×C 243) ×(C 90×Ag. 172)	4549	123
	Av. of checks	3703	....
H-307...	(Ag. 172×C 79)×(C 67×C 90)	4032	119
	Av. of checks	3375	....
H-310...	(M30-60-3×C 243-2-2) ×(Ag. 172-2×G 61-5-4)	4437	118
	Av. of checks	3760	....

* An average of two years' data from two locations.

shown in Table 27.9, was 23 per cent higher than an average of the three varieties used as checks. The checks, in addition to Celaya, included two double topcross hybrids (H-301 and H-306) which brought the level of yield of the checks up to 107 per cent of Celaya. The actual difference between H-309 and Celaya, therefore, would be somewhat greater than 23 per cent.

Hybrid H-309 should also make a good synthetic because: (1) the average yield of the six single crosses possible between the four inbred lines is very nearly the same as the yield of the double cross H-309, and (2) because the four S_1 lines were among the most vigorous obtained from Celaya. The actual yield relationship between F_1, F_2, and F_3 progenies, where available for a series of double crosses in a randomized block experiment with eight replications, is given in Table 27.10.

All yields in Table 27.10 are expressed in per cent of Celaya. All double cross hybrids with the exception of No. 1, involve S_1 lines from varieties of the race Celaya. Hybrid No. 1 was made with S_2 lines from varieties of the race Celaya. Hybrid No. 2 contains the same lines as H-309 in Table 27.9, but in a slightly different combination. This combination has resulted in slightly higher double cross yield, but should have no effect on yields of the F_2.

As shown in Table 27.10, the F_2 generation progeny of the better double cross hybrids with S_1 lines retained a substantial advantage in yield (12 to 20 per cent) over the open-pollinated variety Celaya. Hybrid No. 1 with S_2 lines was included to see if it would actually show a greater drop in yield between F_1 and F_2 than the others.

From Table 27.11 it is evident that the F_2 or F_3 yields of the double

TABLE 27.10

YIELDS OF F_1, F_2, AND F_3 GENERATION PROGENY OF
SEVEN DOUBLE CROSS HYBRIDS IN PER CENT
OF THE VARIETY CELAYA

No.	Pedigree	F_1	F_2	F_3
1....	(Gto 61-5-4×Ag. 172-2)×(M30-60-3×C 243-2-2)	118	103	101
2....	(C 123×C 90)×(C 243×Ag. 172)	140	112	......
3....	(C 123×M30-60)×(C 90×C 243)	139	107	111
4....	(C 123×C 90)×(C 243×M30-60)	150	118	......
5....	(C 123×C 90)×(C 243×Ag. 32)	149	119	......
6....	(C 123×C 90)×(Ag. 32×Ag. 172)	146	120	......
7....	(C 123×C 243)×(L II 67×L II 90)	127	......	101
8....	Celaya	100	100	100

L. S. D. = 12.5%

TABLE 27.11

YIELD OF F_1, F_2, AND F_3 PROGENIES IN PER CENT OF F_1

No.	Pedigree	F_1	F_2	F_3
1....	(Gto 61-5-4×Ag. 172-2)×(M30-60-3×C 243-2-2)	100	87	86
2....	(C 123×C 90)×(C 243×Ag. 172)	100	80	.....
3....	(C 123×M30-60)×C 90×C 243	100	77	80
4....	(C 123×C 90)×(C 243×M30-60)	100	79	.....
5....	(C 123×C 90)×(Ag. 32×C 243)	100	79	.....
6....	(C 123×C 90)×(Ag. 32×Ag. 172)	100	82	.....
7....	(C 123×C 243)×(L II 67×L II 90)	100	.....	80

crosses with S_1 lines was consistently about 80 per cent of the yield in F_1, whereas the F_2 of the double cross with S_2 lines was 87 per cent of the F_1. This is not significantly higher, but also not significantly lower as one might expect on the basis of the lower yields of the S_2 lines.

The few F_3 yields available were not greatly different from those of the F_2. The assumption that in general, barring selection, there is no further reduction in yield beyond F_2 has been adequately supported by experimental data. Sprague and Jenkins (1943) tested the F_1, F_2, F_3, and F_4 of one 24 line and four 16 line synthetics in various districts in Iowa. There was little difference between the various advanced generations, the F_2, F_3, and F_4 yielding 94.3, 95.4, and 95.1 per cent as much as the F_1 respectively. Kiesselbach (1933) compared the yield of the F_2 and F_3 generations of 21 single crosses. The yield of F_2 and F_3 was approximately the same, being 38.4 and 37.8 bushels per acre respectively. Wellhausen and Roberts (unpublished) compared the average yields of the F_1, F_2, F_3, and F_4 generations in 18 topcrosses. The average yield was 10.8, 9.9, 9.6, 9.8 kilos per plot for the F_1, F_2, F_3, and F_4 generations respectively.

In the attempt to obtain still greater yield over Celaya, approximately 1000 S_2 and S_3 lines were crossed with the single cross C 67 $\times$ C 90. Both lines in this single cross were first generation selfs from Celaya, and the majority of the lines crossed with it were from varieties of this race. It is of interest to note the kind of lines that gave the highest yields in combination with C 67 $\times$ C 90. Among the ten that were finally selected as the best combiners with C 67 $\times$ C 90, three were from the variety Jal. 35, one from a variety from the State of Coahuila in northern Mexico, and the rest were from Celaya. The total number of lines included from Jal. 35 and from other varieties not classified as belonging to the race Celaya were relatively small compared to the total number of Celaya lines involved in the test. However, four of the ten best combiners with respect to yield came from varieties outside the race Celaya. This is in line with the belief that the possibility of obtaining high yielding hybrids is greater in the combination of lines from different varieties than in the combination of lines from the same or closely related varieties. Nevertheless, hybrids obtained from a recombination of Celaya lines were satisfactory in yield and generally more disease resistant and more acceptable from an agronomic standpoint than hybrids between Celaya and non-Celaya lines.

In the yield test results of all possible single crosses between the ten selected good combiners with the tester C 67 $\times$ C 90, the two lines C 110-3 and C 126-5 from Celaya (the same variety from which the tester lines were obtained) were of considerable interest. These two lines were not only good combiners with the single cross tester C 67 $\times$ C 90, but also combined well with each other. The single cross C 110-3 $\times$ C 126-5 was among the highest of all the 45 possible single crosses among the ten selected lines.

The tester single cross which was made up of two average S_1 Celaya lines would tend to isolate genotypes which contribute the greatest number of additional yield factors to its own genotype. These genotypes could be very much alike or greatly different. Apparently the two genotypes represented by the lines C 110-3 and C 126-5 were greatly different both genotypically and phenotypically. In ear type they seemed to be opposite extremes in the range of segregation among Celaya lines. As shown in Figure 27.5, C 110-3 is a line with a fairly long 8-rowed ear, and phenotypically appears to be a segregant in the direction of Tabloncillo which is one of the probable progenitors of the race Celaya. The other, C 126-5, has a fairly short ear and a high row number and apparently is a segregant in the direction of Tuxpeño which is the other probable progenitor of the race Celaya.

If selection for ear type, using Celaya as the ideal, had been a factor in the development of inbred lines, then both C 110-3 and C 126-5 probably would have been discarded. Selection for type may be a mistake in those varieties

FIG. 27.5—Typical ears of the two inbreds C 110-3 (*left*) and C 126-5 (*right*). Both are from the race Celaya, which probably originated from the hybridization of Tabloncillo and Tuxpeño. C 110-3 phenotypically appears to be a segregant in the direction of Tabloncillo and C 126-5 appears to be a segregant in the direction of the tropical many-rowed cylindrical dent Tuxpeño.

which apparently have not reached equilibrium, or in which segregants closely resembling one putative parent or other appear. It may be an especially bad practice if the lines from the same variety are to be recombined into hybrids. In the recombination of lines from the same variety, it remains to be seen whether good hybrids can be more readily made by a recombination of lines which phenotypically are opposite extremes, or from those lines which resemble more closely the type of the variety from which they came. Probably both types are needed.

Hybrids and synthetics developed from Celaya lines were well adapted to regions with supplemental irrigation, and to certain of the regions in Zone

3 where rains are generally well distributed throughout the rainy season. However, in many areas of Zone 3, the corn is often subjected to long periods of drought. Since drought generally reduces the total length of time for growth, varieties are needed which are not only drought resistant, but also earlier in maturity than Celaya.

So far, no good hybrids earlier than Celaya have been obtained from a recombination of early Celaya lines. It became necessary to look elsewhere for material which would give the desired earliness and drought resistance when combined with Celaya. The two races Cónico Norteño and Tabloncillo, which overlap Celaya in its distribution in Zone 3, were found to be undesirable because of their high susceptibility to both root and ear-rots, although they were early in maturity. In the search for suitable material, a race called Bolita, found in a small valley in Oaxaca about 500 miles from the Bajío, has shown considerable promise. It probably originated in the Valley of Oaxaca through the hybridization of Tabloncillo and an early maturing tropical race called Zapalote Chico (Fig. 27.3). The Valley in Oaxaca where Bolita probably originated has the same elevation and has a climate similar to parts of the Bajío. Bolita, when grown in the Bajío, was found to be early maturing, very resistant to ear-rots, and generally resistant to root rots. Its yield capacity, however, was considerably below that of Celaya in years with good rainfall distribution.

Through a method of reciprocal testing of lines of Bolita with Celaya and lines of Celaya with Bolita, S_1 lines of Bolita were isolated, which when combined with certain S_1 lines of Celaya, produced hybrids superior to both Bolita and Celaya in the drier areas of Zone 3. One of these hybrids, made with a single cross of two S_1 Celaya lines (C 90 $\times$ C 67) as a female parent and a synthetic of four S_1 Bolita lines as a pollinator, is now being produced for large scale testing. Preliminary data obtained on this hybrid, called Celita, are given in Table 27.12.

In the first three localities where Celita was tested, the rainfall was either well distributed or supplemented by one irrigation in a period of extreme drought. Under these conditions as evident in Table 27.12, Celita was about equal in yield with the standard variety Celaya. But at Irapuato under extreme drought conditions, Celaya yielded only 741 kilos per hectare (about 12 bushels per acre) while Celita yielded 1441 kilos per hectare, or about 23 bushels per acre. Also as indicated in Table 27.12 by the differences in per cent dry matter at harvest, Celita was considerably earlier in maturity than Celaya. Celita is also fairly resistant to root rots and much more resistant to ear-rots than the best hybrids made with Celaya lines.

It appears, therefore, that the hybrid Celita, under conditions normal for Celaya, is equal to it in yield, but under severe drought conditions it is greatly superior. This hybrid also is superior to Bolita under both normal and dry conditions although the data are not presented in the table. Here then is another case where a hybrid between S_1 lines of two different races under one set of conditions is no better than the better of the two parents, but, under a different set of conditions, is superior to both.

Double cross hybrids made from S_1 lines of Celaya in combination with S_1 lines of the race Cónico Norteño have in general given good results in Zone 2, with yields ranging from 20 to 25 per cent higher on the average than the native varieties commonly grown in the area.

TABLE 27.12

YIELD OF CELITA AND PERCENTAGE DRY MAT-
TER AT HARVEST COMPARED TO CELAYA AT
FOUR DIFFERENT LOCATIONS, 4 REPLICATIONS
EACH

LOCALITY	YIELD KG./HA.		% DRY MATTER	
	Celita	Celaya	Celita	Celaya
Vista Hermosa. . .	3793	3806	68	60
Guadalajara.	4069	3760	80	69
León.	4273	4223	75	66
Irapuato.	1441	741	81	77

In the tropical areas (Zones 4 and 5) hybrids were under test for the first time in 1950. These involved principally combinations of S_1 and S_3 inbred lines from the races Tuxpeño and Vandeño (Fig. 27.4).

Lines Selfed Once versus Lines Selfed More Than Once in Hybrid Formation

The use of S_1 lines in the early stages of a breeding program has many advantages. It means that testing for combining ability can begin in the first generation of selfing. It can, in fact, begin with selected open-pollinated plants which may be simultaneously selfed and crossed. Lines thus isolated in a breeding program where uniformity is not of prime importance can be utilized immediately in the formation of hybrids and synthetics. Since S_1 lines are more vigorous than advanced generation selfed lines, they also have a definite advantage in the formation of synthetics. It has never been definitely determined whether high yielding hybrids can be obtained more readily with homozygous lines than with heterozygous lines. Jenkins (1935) has shown that crosses of lines selfed only once are on the average as productive as crosses involving the same lines selfed six to eight generations. This may indicate, as Jenkins suggests, that the effects of selection are almost exactly balanced by the loss of good genes through the rapid attainment of homozygosity.

Some data have been accumulated to date in the Mexican program which may have some bearing on the relative value of S_1 lines versus more homozygous lines in the formation of hybrids.

Preliminary data on the relative combining ability between S_1 and the S_3 lines selected from each S_1 are available from topcrosses to the same tester. Each topcross with an S_1 line was tested for yield in the same experiment with the corresponding topcrosses involving the lines obtained from that S_1 after three generations of selfing and selection for desirable agronomic characters. The number of S_3 lines in each S_1 family varied from one to sixteen, some families having a larger number of desirable S_3 lines with respect to agronomic characters than others.

A frequency distribution of the differences in topcross yields in per cent between S_1 line topcrosses and the average of the S_3 line topcrosses within each family is given in Table 27.13. The differences are expressed as S_1 minus

TABLE 27.13

DISTRIBUTION OF DIFFERENCES IN TOPCROSS YIELDS BE-
TWEEN S_1 LINES AND THE AVERAGE OF THE S_3 LINES
WITHIN EACH FAMILY (S_1 — AVERAGE OF S_3's)

	MINUS														
Class center.....	75	70	65	60	55	50	45	40	35	30	25	20	15	10	5
Frequency.......	1	..	..	..	..	1	..	2	2	4	6	3	9	12	12

	PLUS												
Class center.....	0	5	10	15	20	25	30	35	40	45	50	55	60	65
Frequency.......	25	18	18	3	3	3	4	4	2	..	4	1	..	1

Number of observations = 138   Mean = +0.90

the average of the S_3 within the respective S_1 family. The class mid-points, therefore, range from 0 to 65 per cent positive and from 0 to 75 per cent negative, with class intervals of 5 per cent. A positive difference means that the S_1 topcross yield exceeded the average of the S_3 topcrosses. A negative difference indicates that the average of the S_3 topcrosses was higher than the S_1 topcross within the same family. It is evident from Table 27.13 that the distribution of the differences approaches very closely that of a normal curve. That is, there were as many cases in which the S_1 exceeded the average of the S_3 as there were cases in which the average of the S_3 exceeded the S_1. The mean difference between the 138 pairs was +0.90 per cent. These data indicate that visual selection in advanced selfed generation progeny based on agronomic characters is largely at random with respect to combining ability. If visual selection in successive generations of inbreeding had been effective in increasing combining ability, then the above curve would have been skewed in the direction of the negative differences.

Upon further inbreeding of S_1 lines at random without selection for combining ability, one would expect to end up with about as many advanced generation inbred lines which exceed the S_1 in combining ability with a specific tester as lines which were below that of the S_1. In other words, the distribution in relation to the S_1 yield would follow that of a normal curve.

In Table 27.14 are given the distributions of the yields of S_1 and S_3 top-

TABLE 27.14

FREQUENCY DISTRIBUTIONS OF S_1 AND S_3 LINE-TOPCROSS YIELDS OF 12 FAMILIES. CLASS IN WHICH S_1 LINE-TOPCROSS OF EACH FAMILY FALLS IS INDICATED BY NUMBER IN BOLD FACE TYPE

Class Midpoints (Yield of Topcrosses in % of Checks)	65	75	85	95	105	115	125	135	145	155	165	175	185	195	205
Family and Frequency															
Hgo. 9-4								**1**	2						7
Ch. II 148							1	**2**	1						3
M. 37-5					1	2		**1**	1	3	1				
Hgo. 4-5				1	1		**4**	2	3	3		1			
Hgo. 1-5			1				**1**	1	1						
Hgo. 3-4						1		**2**							
Hgo. 2-3					1			**2**							
Ch. II 187					1	2									
Hgo. 1-8				1	1	1									
Hgo. 6-11	1	1	1	**3**				1							
Hgo. 3-5	1	2			2	1	1								
Ch. IV 146		2			1										

crosses of 12 families from the same race of corn (Chalqueño). All of the S_1 and S_3 lines within each family were topcrossed on an S_1 line from the race Celaya, and all topcrosses were tested under the same conditions. The class in which the S_1 topcross of each family fell is indicated by the number in bold face type. It is evident from the table that the number of S_3 lines from each family tested are insufficient to show a normal distribution. However, in nearly every case where more than three S_3 lines were available for comparison, some were no better, some were significantly better, and still others were significantly worse than the respective S_1 line in combining ability. It appears, therefore, that in certain cases considerable increase in the yield of specific combinations involving S_1 lines can be obtained through further inbreeding and selection for specific combining ability.

Further evidence that better yields can be obtained through the substitution of S_2 or S_3 lines in a specific S_1 combination is presented in Table 27.15.

This table is divided into two parts. In column A is given the yield of each specific single cross made with S_1 lines. In column B is given the yield of each corresponding single cross of two advanced lines selected from the S_1 lines given in column A in the second or third generation of inbreeding. Selection of the S_2 or S_3 lines in each case, however, was not based on test crosses for specific combining ability with the other line involved. The advanced lines used were picked from among their sister lines largely on the basis of desirable agronomic characters. It may be seen in Table 27.15 that, although in many instances the differences were small, the yield of the crosses of S_2 or S_3 lines exceeded that of the corresponding cross with S_1 lines in every

TABLE 27.15

YIELDS OF SINGLE CROSSES BETWEEN
S_1 LINES COMPARED TO YIELDS OF
SINGLE CROSSES BETWEEN TWO
LINES*

Crosses	Yields of Crosses between S_1 Lines (A)	Yields of Crosses between S_2 and/or S_3 Lines (B)	Differences A−B
1.......	5935	6873	−938
2.......	6074	6630	−556
3.......	6340	6560	−220
4.......	5172	6514	−1342
5......	5056	6479	−1423
6......	5669	6306	−637
7.......	5588	6259	−671
8.......	5970	6202	−232
9......	5970	6190	−220
10......	6005	5935	+70
11.......	5334	5843	−509
12.......	4535	5577	−1042
13.......	5368	5473	−105
14......	5542	4964	+578

N = 14.
Mean difference = 517.6 ± 147 kilos (or 9.2 per cent).

* Derived from the respective S_1's after two or three generations of inbreeding and selection for agronomic characters only. (Kilos per hectare.)

case except two. The average difference between the fourteen paired crosses was 9.2 per cent. It is highly probable that a greater increase would have been obtained had the various S_2 or S_3 lines also been picked on the basis of tests for specific combining ability. However, since selection can make a choice only between the alleles present in a particular S_1, a point of diminishing returns may be rapidly reached upon straight selfing. Experiments are under way to determine in what generation of selfing maximum gains may be reached.

The data in Table 27.14 are of further interest from the standpoint of relationship between the combining ability of S_1 lines and the advanced generation selfed lines obtained from them. In this table it is evident that in those families where the S_1 lines were poor combiners with a given tester, the S_3 lines obtained from them on the average also tended to be poor. In those families where the S_1 lines were good combiners, the S_3 lines obtained from them were also good. A correlation coefficient of 0.69 was obtained between the topcross yields of S_1 lines and the average topcross yields of the S_3 lines derived from each. This highly significant correlation coefficient, based on the same 138 pairs whose differences were distributed as shown in Table 27.13, indicates a high degree of relationship between the performance of S_1 and the average performance of lines obtained from each through subsequent generations of inbreeding. It seems, therefore, that tests for combining ability in the S_0 or S_1 generation would serve to separate the families that are good combiners from families that are poor combiners with respect to a given tester in the early stages of the inbreeding program.

CONCLUSIONS AND SUMMARY

Although the yield results are based on relatively few years' data, it is evident that the methods used in the improvement of corn in Mexico during the six years that the Mexican program has been under way have given excellent results. In some areas considerable improvement in corn yields was obtained by the wider distribution of certain good native, open-pollinated varieties that had developed in isolated areas through chance hybridization and subsequent natural selection. In areas where two different adapted varieties were available which expressed a certain degree of heterosis when crossed, the formation of double topcrosses offered a means of rapid improvement over the native varieties.

It has also been shown that excellent three-way or double cross hybrids can be made from first generation selfed lines. Some of these same double crosses in advanced generations have made good synthetics. This means that those farmers who cannot or are unwilling to plant newly crossed seed every year may still have a 12–20 per cent advantage in yield over their native varieties. Hybrids made from crosses of two synthetics, each consisting of a pooled set of closely related S_1 lines that combined well with a different pooled set of related S_1 lines, have shown some promise in the greater simplification of hybrid seed production. In this way the maintenance of lines for hybrid seed production can be greatly simplified.

The use of first generation selfed lines in the early stages of a new breeding program obviously has many advantages. Whether such lines can be maintained for a reasonable period of time without much change in combining ability remains to be determined. So far through a composite sib method of propagation they have been maintained reasonably "pure."

Data have been presented which indicate that hybrids made from more homozygous lines might be superior to those made with lines selfed only once.

It remains to be shown whether more uniform hybrids actually would be superior to hybrids made with S_1 lines in a country such as Mexico. Variations in climate from year to year in any one valley in Mexico are usually extreme. Under such conditions, a high degree of uniformity in a hybrid may actually be a detriment over a period of years.

The problem of what tester or testers to use in isolating lines of high combining ability continues to be a difficult one. Usually the tester chosen depends upon the use to be made of the lines. Judging from the segregants obtained upon inbreeding in some of the races of maize, a point may have been overlooked in the selection of lines and testers. This appeared to be especially true in those races where it was necessary to recombine lines from the same race to obtain immediate improvement. In some of the races upon inbreeding, especially Bolita, Chalqueño, and Vandeño, inbred line segregants often appeared which were very similar to the putative parents of the particular race (Wellhausen et al. in collaboration with Mangelsdorf, Fig. 98). If these races had reached equilibrium on an individual gene loci basis, one would not expect to get the parental types in subsequent inbred generations from 500 ears selfed at random in the original population. It appears, therefore, that many of the modern races in Mexico are not in equilibrium on an individual gene loci basis, but consist of blocks of genes in equilibrium with each other. Although it is difficult to estimate the age of some of the modern varieties, these gene blocks obtained from the various ancestors seem to have persisted more or less intact through many generations.

If blocks of germplasm as received from various ancestors are still intact in some of the modern high yielding races, then it may not be as difficult as it once seemed to reconstruct a hybrid that would approach the yield of the ideal plant in a particular variety by the recombination of inbred lines from that variety. Isolation of good lines for such recombination may involve different procedures. A method based on selection for origin and type, with subsequent crossing to an unrelated variety or varieties for the determination of combining ability, may not be the best procedure.

Selection for vigor and type in an environment best suited to a race such as Chalqueño, which probably originated from the hybridization of two different races neither of which is adapted to the environment best suited for Chalqueño, would eliminate those segregants in the direction of either one of the putative parents. It is probable that with the elimination of such segregants, many genes are discarded that are needed to reconstruct the ideal chance hybrids which often appear in a particular variety or race through open pollination. Selection for vigor and type also would tend to select those genotypes which are similar, and more nearly like those of the variety from which they came, than the extreme segregants.

Tests for combining ability of a group of lines from the same variety, based on crosses with an unrelated variety or varieties, tend to select those genotypes which combine well with the particular tester, but do not differentiate lines that combine well among themselves. Thus it seems that new methods of isolating the good combiners must be sought in those races of hybrid origin in which improvement is desired through inbreeding and recombination of lines within the race.

FRED H. HULL

Florida Agricultural Experiment Station

Chapter 28

Recurrent Selection
and Overdominance

For many breeders, in considering problems that lie ahead and methods of meeting them, the main problem is whether to continue with varieties or breeds, or to work with inbred lines and F_1 crosses. Behind this question are the problems dealing with the relative importance of general and specific combinability, or of prepotency and nicking:

Is the yield gain of hybrid corn due mainly to selection within and among inbred lines, or to selection among F_1 crosses of inbred lines?

Is it due to improved frequencies of dominant favorable genes in elite inbred lines which are parents of elite-yield hybrids?

Is selection within and among inbred lines to accumulate higher frequencies of dominant favorable genes many times more powerful in one cycle without recurrence, than is selection without inbreeding through many recurring cycles?

To what extent may higher levels of specific combinability be reached by recurrent selection?

How may heritability of specific combinability be evaluated?

Why have the less favorable alleles of vigor genes been retained in such high frequencies?

May selection for general combinability and selection for specific combinability sometimes have counter effects on gene frequencies?

Does superiority of F_1 crosses of inbred lines over varieties or breeds necessarily depend on overdominance?

If this choice of problems is approximately correct, the research emphasis may begin to shift from effects of inbreeding to effects of selection.

EARLY EXPLANATIONS FOR HYBRID CORN

East and Emerson in an early paper considered the theoretical problem of recovering two traits together from a crossbreeding population in which the frequency of each trait was 1/1000, and the two were independent. The authors offered two solutions: first to select at the rate of one per million in one generation, and second at the rate of one per thousand in two generations recurrently, first for one trait and then for the other. It is clear now that selec-

451

tion for both traits together each time, with normal distribution, would provide theoretical recovery in two generations at the rate of 1 per 400 or less. Multiplication of selection differentials in recurrent selection was sufficiently understood at the inception of hybrid corn. Nevertheless, hybrid corn has been developed with virtually no use or benefit from recurrence of selection. Hybrid corn is almost wholly an empirical development, but I think we may now consider applications of genetic science to improve the process.

Recurrent selection (Hull, 1945a) was meant to include reselection generation after generation, with interbreeding of selects to provide for genetic recombination. Thus, selection among isolates, inbred lines, or clones is not recurrent until selects are interbred and a new cycle of selection is initiated. Recurrent selection for specific combinability would seem to require a special breeding plan to provide heritability through successive cycles.

Shull's original plan for developing superior corn hybrids was designed for maximum immediate employment of specific combinability. Selection was mainly among specific F_1 crosses of lines which had been isolated and stabilized by inbreeding, thus providing repeatability of crosses. This plan was consistent with a theory of heterozygosis of a degree here termed overdominance. Shull's plan did not involve recurrent selection to accumulate higher frequencies of favorable genes in successive cycles.

The apparent heterozygosis which Shull proposed to use was interpreted by Jones about ten years later as the expectation of repulsion phases of random linkages of dominant favorable factors and recessive less favorable alleles. This interpretation was particularly attractive because it seemed to eliminate any necessity of accepting overdominance. Overdominance is a contradiction of the time-honored principle that purity of blood is to be sought and maintained. Vigor was no exception to the old principles of *like begets like* and *breed the best to the best*. Moreover, the postulated linkage relations would appear to be inevitable where many loci are involved.

In the decade following appearance of the Jones hypothesis, most corn breeders began more intense selection for vigor within and among lines during the inbreeding process, and selection among lines for general combinability. Most of the very considerable success of hybrid corn came quickly after these modifications of Shull's method were adopted. Selection within and among inbred lines to improve frequencies of dominant favorable factors became the guiding principle for developing superior hybrids of corn, other crops, and of livestock. Selection among specific F_1 crosses was retained as a final step, but with very little verbal emphasis.

Initial successes with hybrid corn (which so far have not been greatly surpassed) were obtained with inbred lines which were, for the most part, isolated directly from the open-pollinated varieties. Corn breeders then had at least two alternatives for further work. Empirically, the choice might well have been to continue isolation and testing of additional new lines from the same sources, abandoning recurrent selection entirely. Usually, successful but mysterious processes are not modified on theoretical grounds alone. However, most of us, and myself most of all I suspect, chose the alternative course without question. New lines for a second cycle of selection were isolated from crosses of elite first-cycle lines. Since it was soon apparent that second-cycle lines as a group were a vast improvement over first-cycle lines, it was clear that we were on the right track. Recurrent selection for higher frequencies of dominant favorable genes was fulfilling expectation admirably. That it had failed in ear-to-row selection (progeny testing without inbreeding) meant that "selection within and among inbred lines" was the key. Apparently the protagonists of "early testing" have not fully appreciated this latter point.

DISAPPOINTMENT WITH SECOND-CYCLE HYBRIDS

My first suspicion that all was not well was aroused by disappointing yield performance of second-cycle hybrids in 1941. The first reaction then was to conclude that heterosis might involve complex gene interactions to a greater extent than I had supposed. Cytoplasmic-nuclear interactions could not be ruled out entirely. But no thought of heterozygosis, of overdominance, was entertained at all, so thoroughly had I been weaned from it.

In 1942 we began the process of separating Florida inbred lines into two permanently distinct groups on the basis of combining values with two single cross testers which were thought to make a good double cross. Subsequent breeding operations after the initial separation were to consist of isolating new lines within each group from crosses of the older lines within the group. New lines were to be stabilized by at least three self-pollinations with accompanying selection for vigor and type, and then tested for combinability with the reciprocal group. This, of course, was reciprocal recurrent selection without *early testing*. I still adhered firmly to the efficacy of "selection within and among inbred lines."

Segregation of the breeding mass into two permanently distinct reciprocal groups, first of all, did not cost anything. A search for satisfactory substitutes for each of the four master tester lines was well in order. It seemed that the necessity of recovering specific combinability again as the last step of each breeding cycle might be avoided to some extent. Possibly higher levels of specific combinability might be accumulated.

Two years later, after interviews with a number of other corn breeders, it seemed that a still higher rating might be in order for specific combinability. Second and third-cycle hybrids were not much superior to first-cycle hybrids in yield of grain. Recurrent selection for general combinability was not proving to be very effective.

An early test of recurrent selection for specific combinability seemed desirable. One way to intensify the process already in operation was to adopt a more specific tester. This was done by abandoning the reciprocal feature of the plan—by reducing one of the reciprocal groups to the single-cross tester alone. That tester is to be continued indefinitely. Another way to intensify the operation was to increase the frequency of recurrence of selection. This was done by adopting the general principle of early testing, by abandoning the inbreeding interphase of each cycle, by testing S_0 plants rather than S_3 lines or higher. Inbred lines, including the tester lines, of the second reciprocal group were intercrossed to provide one crossbred group of S_0 plants. Repeated selection within this crossbred group for combinability with the permanent unrelated tester is the proposed plan. It is only for practical reasons that one homozygous line is not employed as the tester for field corn. With sweet corn a line tester might well be used.

The working definition of *specific combinability* employed in designing the foregoing breeding plans was about thus: that part of the genetic superiority of specific F_1 crosses of homozygous lines which is not transmitted into or through general recombinations. The concurrent definition of *general combinability* then is: that part which is transmitted into and through general recombinations. That these definitions are perhaps inadequate for analyses of variance does not necessarily mean that they are not admirable for the other purpose.

Shull, East, and others who isolated inbred lines and crossed them discovered that inbreeding did little or no irreparable harm to the germ plasm. Gametes of inbred lines hardly differ basically from gametes of crossbred varieties. The inbreeding effect is very nearly or entirely a zygotic phenomenon. Vigor genes in both homozygous and heterozygous associations were obeying Mendel's first law of non-contamination. All of this was an important discovery.

Shull in addition invented *selection for specific combinability*, which was certainly something new under the sun; yet to be generally recognized as one of the great inventions. Shull was led, I suspect, to this invention by the empirical evidence before him, not by considering the more abstract concept of heterozygosis. Shull must have recognized very soon that reconciliation of his invention with his knowledge of genetics required heterozygosis, and perhaps the more inclusive *heterosis*.

RECURRENT SELECTION FOR SPECIFIC COMBINABILITY

A little more than thirty years later the inevitable invention of *recurrent selection for specific combinability* was made from matter-of-fact empirical considerations as outlined above. Again it seemed necessary soon afterwards to embrace some theory of heterozygosis for reconciliation with genetics. The breeding plan was presented (Hull, 1945a) with confusing emphasis on the abstract concept of overdominance, I fear, and too little emphasis on the actual motivation.

May it be said now that the first proposal was to determine with direct tests if higher levels of specific combinability could be accumulated by recurrent selection. There is no need to await incontrovertible evidence of overdominance; indeed even if it were in hand the direct test would still be needed.

The second proposal was that if recurrent selection for specific combinability should be important, selection within and among inbred lines had been greatly over-emphasized. The inbreeding interphase could be abandoned. This would provide an enormous saving in time and otherwise, particularly with poultry and other livestock. Curiously, some reviewers have described the proposed breeding plan as a "laborious method."

Grain yield of corn depends appreciably on resistance to new and sporadic diseases, insects, and adverse environmental complexes. Here it would seem that overdominance is not likely, but that selection within and among inbred lines is yet of real value. Significant resistance where it exists will eventually be identified in continuing a stable line. Selected crosses will be generally superior insofar as the several resistances are dominant and matched combinations are found. Here again I am not certain that rapidly recurring progeny tests without inbreeding may not be equally or more effective in the main. One resistant line among some hundreds of susceptible ones in an epidemic provides a striking field illustration—perhaps a deceptive one.

Breeding plans to accumulate specific combinability may be designed in many ways, the better ones to be determined by actual tests. Testers might best be the male parent of the hybrid in some cases, or the female parent in others. The inbreeding interphase may be omitted or included in any practicable degree. It has been thought that the problem of the preceding paragraph might be met well enough by direct selection in the crossbred lot and selection among S_0 testcrosses. But in some cases there might be an advantage with S_1 or S_2 testcrosses. With S_0 or S_2 some of the selection may be for general combinability, for higher frequencies of genes which are favorable in any combination.

The early view (Hull, 1945a, Proposition 7) was that where aA is generally intermediate to aa and AA, A should be in high frequency, in improved varieties. Not much further opportunity for improving combinability would remain.

Crow's viewpoint, as he has presented it here, seems to be that without overdominance long continued selection in any form would have carried favorable alleles to high frequency in equilibrium with reverse mutation, where heterozygosity is infrequent and heterosis not large.

If recent shifts of environment or of emphasis in artificial selection should have provided important loci with intermediate gene frequencies, Crow's argument may not be germane. Here I may venture an opinion (Hull, 1945b) that without overdominance rapidly recurring mass or ear-row selection should continue to surpass contemporary selected F_1 crosses of homozygous lines. Or we may consider the more efficient technic of recurrent testing of controlled testcrosses of S_0 plants with the parent variety and recombining the better ones into an improved variety. We know this will not work, although it has not been fairly tried. Finally, in modern corn breeding the same technic with S_4 and higher lines has been extensively advanced through at least two cycles. Most corn breeders will admit that a general recombination or synthetic blend of parent lines of present elite-yield hybrids would hardly yield more than a random blend of parent varieties of today or of 50 years ago.

A few recombinations of lines selected wholly for general combinability have been reported with significantly higher yields than improved varieties. This result I will attempt to show later is a different matter, fully consistent with overdominance theory.

It seems likely that improvement of general combinability, accumulation of dominant favorable genes with respect to grain yield, in the field corn of our central Corn Belt in the past fifty years has been hardly significant except for that depending on disease resistance, resistance to lodging, to ear dropping, etc. Almost any one of the common breeding technics is quite effective with general improvement of morphology of the corn plant, or with oil and protein of the grain. Genetics of vigor would appear to differ in some important respect from genetics of the other traits.

Overdominance has seemed the more likely, but I have never meant to insist that the existence of every other alternative had been disproven. Refractory repulsion linkage has seemed insufficient alone to explain the apparent degree of overdominance in corn (Hull, 1945a).

The main point now is accumulation of general combinability with recurrent selection. It is axiomatic with most of us, including the corn breeders, that general combinability is the first consideration, despite the evidence cited here. This kind of evidence has been largely ignored and almost taboo.

Comstock *et al.* (1949) have proposed Reciprocal Recurrent Selection to obtain maximum utilization of general and specific combinability together. In this they have accepted that specific combinability might be accumulated in successive cycles, and that the inbreeding interphase could be abandoned entirely. This variation of the general plan was compared on theoretical considerations with selection in a crossbred for combinability with a homozygous tester. Now, since a homozygous tester is clearly impracticable in many cases and heterozygosity would impair efficiency of a tester except for reciprocal selection, there is an advantage in the reciprocal plan which the authors did not record.

It has never been my intent, however, to attempt to rule out judicious reciprocal selection. We have crossed each of the two tester lines of corn to a goodly number of unrelated strains, and have backcrossed in bulk to each tester line separately. The two lots are being held in separate crossbreeding reserves with nominal selection for agronomic type. If either tester line should develop a serious fault, or if the present main selection for specific combinability should seem to reach a ceiling, reversal of selection would seem almost inevitable. A tester would be chosen from the current crossbred and the two bulk backcrosses would furnish a reciprocal crossbred to reverse the process, temporarily at least.

An accessory operation with bulk backcrosses is hardly practicable with livestock. But here the tester would be one inbred line which would need to be 50 per cent inbred for equal efficiency with the single cross of homozygous lines employed as the corn tester. The tester should be the male parent of the improved hybrid in livestock to avoid any impairment of the female function by inbreeding.

Beginning with a partly inbred or non-inbred stud flock or herd as the tester, and continuing mild inbreeding, it is inevitable that choices among young males for herd sires of the stud herd would depend partly on their testcross progeny. Sufficient vigor must be retained in this herd to provide satisfactory sires of commercial hybrids. The problem is real and obvious enough, but I have thought the details must await a demonstration that specific combinability can be accumulated in important amounts by recurrent selection. For an early test the more homozygous tester is probably to be preferred. If uniformity of the product is of some moment, the operator of reciprocal selection may expend considerable effort for it. Such expenditure might be avoided by partial inbreeding of one of the groups.

The two breeding plans, selection in a crossbred to a homozygous tester and reciprocal selection between two crossbreds, are the extremes of recurrent selection for specific combinability. Between these we may have any practicable degree of inbreeding of one of the groups at the start, or subsequently. Inbreeding restricts reciprocal selection but, aside from that, the reciprocal feature may be varied at will. I do not know what factors may determine the more efficient plans except that general combinability with respect to vigor is probably not an important one. Nor is it likely to be important to choose an inbred tester with above-average general combinability.

PHYSIOLOGICAL NATURE OF OVERDOMINANCE

Overdominance has been defined (Hull, 1946a) as $aA > AA$, which is a sufficient definition for present purposes. However, there may be some value in considering what the underlying physiology may be. Heterozygosis as considered by Shull and his early contemporaries is entirely or very nearly the same concept. Fisher (1918, 1932) has discussed this concept more generally as *super-dominance*. Some recent writers have employed *heterotic alleles* or *heterotic interaction of alleles* as a modern form of *heterozygosis*. But since any degree of dominance of the more favored allele is essentially a heterotic interaction, heterotic alleles does not necessarily imply $aA > AA$.

In the current sense that any interaction of alleles is dominance, $aA > AA$ is overcomplete dominance, overdominance. In a similar sense all interactions of non-alleles are epistasis. Dominance and epistasis differ in distribution on chromosomes, but not necessarily in underlying physiology so far as I can see. Overepistasis would excite no particular comment.

Dominance and epistasis are no more fundamental properties of genes than is interaction a property of a unit of nitrogen or phosphorus. These fertilizer elements may exhibit an interaction in plant growth if made available to a living plant, or they may seem to act independently. One quantity of nitrogen may be adequate for the needs of the plant. Adding the same quantity again may produce no further effect. There is an interference or decreasing returns interaction.

East (1936) has discussed dominance as a decreasing returns or interference interaction of active alleles A_1 and A_1 in the homozygote. The amount by which the two together failed to do twice as much as either alone was a the dominance effect—a loss which could not explain heterosis. East then proposed that if A_1 should develop by successive steps to A_4 (analogous to replacing successive parts of one bag of nitrogen above with phosphorus until there is one of phosphorus and one of nitrogen) of a different quality, A_1 and A_4 might interfere very little or none in A_1A_4. The principle as East states it is: "*The cumulative action of the non-defective allelomorphs of a given gene approaches the strictly additive as they diverge from each other in function.*"

The effect of the phosphorus and nitrogen together is the sum of their separate effects—no interference. Dominance by interference disappears when A_1 and A_4 are independent in functions, leaving A_1A_4 superior to either A_1A_1 or A_4A_4. Now it must be clear that any deviation of A_1A_4 from the mid-point between the two homozygotes must be interpreted as dominance of A_1 to A_4 for the A_1 function or dominance of A_4 to A_1 for the A_4 function or both. If the primary dominance in each case is complete, A_1A_4 will just equal the sum of A_1A_1 and A_4A_4 in total effect beyond a neutral aa.

Overdominance may occur when: (1) aa is neutral and aA is nearer to an optimum dose of A than is AA, (2) A' and A are both active for separate supplementary functions and each is dominant to the other for its own function (cf. East, 1936), (3) A' and A are both active for separate primary functions, and the primary functions interact to produce an effect greater than those of either $A'A'$ or AA (Hull, 1945a).

Pseudo-overdominance may occur when A and B are linked: (1) with no epistasis, aB and Ab combinations simulate the second case above, (2) with positive epistasis aB and Ab simulate the third case.

If $(aB \times Ab)$ is superior to both $(ab \times AB)$ and $(AB \times AB)$, selection may tend to tighten the repulsion linkage until ab and AB disappear and the paired blocks are hardly distinguishable from alleles with primary overdominance.

It is clear enough that the frequency of heterozygotes is greater and of homozygotes less for any locus with multiple alleles present in a crossbreeding population. If heterozygosity should be of general advantage, multiple alleles would provide more heterosis. East was at some pains to explain the development of A_4 from A_1 by successive steps to the end of a superior heterozygote. He apparently did not accept that heterozygote superiority might be general, with multiple alleles affecting vigor. I do not accept it either as a likely proposition.

It seems likely that production of grain, meat, eggs, or milk may consist of main effects and interactions of many, perhaps most, of the genes of the plant or animal. Main effects must be of many kinds and magnitudes. Where inbreeding depression and heterosis are evident there must be bias of positive dominance or interactions of alleles to provide a gain in heterozygotes over the arithmetic mean of homozygotes. Whether the interaction is basically a stimulation of unlike alleles in the heterozygote, an interfering depressing interaction in the top homozygote, or some other kind of interaction is an important problem in gene physiology. Present concern, however, is only with the magnitude and frequency of the effect without regard to its basic physiology.

Various writers have noted that dominance is not an absolute property. If the phenotype is fruit size, degree of dominance is hardly the same for both diameter and volume. The same genes might also affect stem length and exhibit a third degree of dominance there. Gene effects are often greatly subject to environmental fluctuations and to presence or absence of genes at other loci.

Within reasonable limits of soil fertility and climate, grain yield of selected homozygous corn is about 30 per cent of the yield of crossbred corn. Seventy per cent of the apparent yield of crossbred corn consists of dominance effects and perhaps of interactions of dominance with other gene effects. The 30 per cent yield of homozygous corn consists of main effects and epistatic interactions of main effects.

One difficulty in resolving the present situation without regard to how it may have evolved is that the absolute zero of the genetic yield range cannot be easily estimated. However, it might be assumed that it is less than zero on our data scale. More specifically, the homozygotes with more than two-thirds of the concerned loci aa or less than one-third AA may be inviable or have an average yield potential of zero. The 100 per cent of measured yield then would represent only the upper two-thirds of the total genetic range. With dominance of high yield complete at each locus and the foregoing assumption the present situation is adequately explained without resort to epistatis or overdominance.

LINEARITY OF INBREEDING DEPRESSION AND HETEROZYGOSITY

Any appreciable degree of interaction of dominance with other gene effects might be detectable in a non-linear relation of inbreeding depression to predicted frequency of heterozygosity in succeeding generations of inbreeding. Since the considerable body of data on inbreeding effects on yield of corn fails to show any such non-linearity at all, I have been inclined to dismiss interaction of dominance with other gene effects. Since, in addition, backcrosses of F_1's to homozygous parent lines fail to show significant non-linearity I have been inclined to dismiss epistasis in general as an appreciable part of the explanation of the disparity of yields of homozygous and crossbred corn.

Overdominance alone is an adequate explanation of the disparity. Pseudo-overdominance from random linkage is not an adequate explanation by itself since the totals of gene effects are independent of linkage (Hull, 1945a).

REGRESSION OF F_1 YIELD ON YIELDS OF PARENT LINES

Corn breeders have frequently chosen a small sample (usually 10) of inbred lines and have made all or most of the specific crosses. Comparable yield records on parent lines and F_1's have become available now in 25 sets of data. F_2 records are included with 3 of them. None of these data are mine. Some of them were analyzed in part by simple regression of yield of F_1 on yield of parents, which would seem to provide the significant information from the general combinability viewpoint. Interaction of parents is mostly neglected.

Within each column or each row of a (10 × 10) table as described are nine F_1's or nine F_2's with one common parent. The common parent is the tester of the other nine lines. Each line serves as the tester of one such group.

On the assumption that the partial regression of offspring on parent within a group having one common parent is a relative measure of heritability within the group, or of efficiency of the common parent as a tester, it has seemed worth while to calculate all of the regression coefficients for individual columns of the twenty-five F_1 and three F_2 tables. We tacitly accept that yield may be a heritable character. Beyond this we need no fine-spun theory nor any genetic theory at all to warrant direct regression analysis of the data. However, Mendel's final test of his theory was with backcrosses to aa and AA separately. He noted essentially that with completely dominant characters the expected regression of offspring phenotype on gene frequency of parent gamete was unity with the aa tester and zero with the AA tester. We may be dealing with multiple factor cases of such testcrosses and of course with different degrees of dominance at the several loci. The significant differentiation of our homozygous testers may be in relative frequencies of aa and AA at the a_1, a_2, a_3—a_n loci.

Results with the first two examples are shown in Table 28.1. Yield of the tester parent (P) is in bushels per acre. Directly below are the partial regression coefficients (b_p) for the respective testers. Since there are apparently negative trends of b_p with respect to P, the second order regression (b_2) of

b_p on P has been calculated. The second order regression function has been solved for the special case $b_p = 0$, to obtain an estimate of P_c the critical value of P where the regression surface is level and heritability is zero.

The third summary in Table 28.1 is for average yields in six states of the

TABLE 28.1

REGRESSION OF YIELD OF F_1 AND F_2 CORN HYBRIDS ON YIELD OF INBRED PARENTS WITHIN GROUPS HAVING ONE COMMON PARENT

Yield of parents (P) is recorded in bushels per acre, with the partial regression coefficient (b_p) below each one for the group of which it is the tester. The second order regression b_2 is regression of b_p on P. Critical P (P_c) is estimated value of P for $b_p = 0$.

*Stringfield, G. H. Unpublished. Ohio Agr. Exp. Sta. and USDA**

P	14	28	30	46	51	55
$b_p(F_1)$	.68	.41	.31	.22	.07	.05
$b_p(F_2)$	.55	.45	.33	.24	.26	.17

Mean $b_p(F_1)$ .29, (F_2) .33; $b_2(F_1)$ −.014, (F_2) −.008; Mean P 37; P_c 58; Mean F_1 97; Mean F_2 70.

*Kinman and Sprague, Agron. Jour. 1945**

P	3	15	20	26	28	28	32	39	40	50
$b_p(F_1)$	.63	.75	.84	.69	.13	.30	.25	.39	.22	.01
$b_p(F_2)$	.26	.36	.42	.69	.24	.29	.37	.58	.54	.47

Mean $b_p(F_1)$ .42, (F_2) .42; $b_2(F_1)$ −.016, (F_2) +.005; Mean P 29; P_c 54; Mean F_1 80; Mean F_2 51.

*USDA and State Regional Tests, Midseason 1943; Iowa, Kans., Ill., Ind., Ohio, Penn. P values from Kinman and Sprague above; their F_1's included here**

$b_p(F_1)$ −.05+.11+.08−.13−.20−.11+.12−.01−.18
  Mean b_p −.01; b_2 −.004; P_c 25.

* Sources of data.

same F_1's as those of Kinman and Sprague in Iowa. The Iowa test included parent lines and F_2's as well as F_1's. The third summary has been made with Iowa records on parent lines. An analysis was made also of the F_1 records for each state separately with the same values of P. Regression trend was positive for the Indiana data, thus failing to support any theory of dominance of high yield. Regression trends for the other four states were negative with estimates of P_c all lower than the one for Iowa.

The eighteen other sets of data not summarized in the table are from Minnesota, Iowa, Illinois, Ohio, New York, and North Carolina. They are believed to be generally independent genetically and ecologically. Regression trends are positive in eight cases. Taking the five cases summarized together in Table 28.1, as five separate ones, we have seventeen with negative regression trend to eight with positive. Estimates of P_c for the seventeen negative trends are near to or within the range of data as in Table 28.1 for each case but one. With one of the least extensive tests the estimate of P_c is roughly 12 times the top inbred line, thus agreeing nicely with incomplete dominance.

Insofar as regression trends are due to heterozygosity they may be expected to disappear with inbreeding of the crosses. The first two examples in Table 28.1 are the two more extensive of the three cases which include F_2, and it is apparent that the negative trend of F_1 has decreased or become positive in F_2. It is positive in F_2 of the third case also with a strong negative trend in F_1.

The regularity of regression trends apparent in the first two examples in Table 28.1 is by no means so readily apparent in any of the other twenty-three cases. The eight cases with positive trends do not appear worse in this respect than the others.

The possibility that the 10 inbred lines of Kinman and Sprague do not comprise a representative sample has been tested by dividing the 10 into two groups of 5 each in various ways. This provides a 5×5 table in each case with a unique sample of 25 F_1's from the total of 45. These 5×5 tables do not have vacant cells which arise when one parent line is included on both margins of a table. Each tester in one group is rated with the same five lines in the other group. Estimates of b_2 and P_c from such 5×5 tables have consistently substantiated those reported in Table 28.1, for the 10×10 table.

Analyses of six of the twenty-five cases have been done also with logarithms of P and F_1 records, with results generally in agreement with those of the original data.

Most or all of the individual values of b_p and b_2 are not statistically significant. The distribution of the twenty-five b_2's is distinctly bi-modal. Eight are positive indicating dominance of low yield, one is negative and small enough to indicate intermediate dominance of high yield. Sixteen are negative and decidedly in the overdominance range. No explanation of the bi-modality is apparent now. The eight positive values of b_2 are in some degree suspect since they are inconsistent with so many facts. All of these tests could be repeated with the same unique samples of genotypes insofar as the parent lines were homozygous and are still available. We need more comprehensive and precise data.

Present evidence from regression analysis is slightly in favor (2 to 1) of the conclusion that a zone of nearly level regression, nearly zero heritability, exists near the upper end of the range of present data. This conclusion would be more consistent with the failure of selection for general combinability if it should be that selection for specific combinability should favor aA over AA, and thus tend to degrade gene frequencies below that equilibrium where heritability and regression change from positive to negative.

GENETIC INTERPRETATION OF THE REGRESSIONS

The problem of genetic interpretations of b_p and b_2 may be approached first with the simpler case of no epistasis. Consider the multiple gene set a_1A_1 to a_nA_n. Let $(1 - v)$ and v be relative frequencies of a and A in the gametes of P_i with respect to the n loci, and w similarly for P_j. The product of the two gametic arrays provides expected frequencies of aa, aA, AA in $F_1(P_i \times P_j)$ with respect to n loci.

$$F_1 \simeq n\,(1-v)\,(1-w)\,aa + n\,[\,v\,(1-w) + w\,(1-v)\,]\,aA + n\,vw\,AA$$

Define[1] phenotypes:

$$a_1a_1\,a_2a_2 \ldots a_na_n = T$$
$$a\,A \qquad\qquad = T + d + kd$$
$$A\,A \qquad\qquad = T + 2d$$

$$F_1 = n\,(v+w)\,(d+kd) - n2\,vw\,(kd) + T \tag{1}$$

This is the regression of F_1 phenotype on gene frequencies of parents and is independent of degree of inbreeding of parents.

If P_i is homozygous it has $n(1-v)aa$ and $nvAA$ loci.

$$P_i = n\,v\,(2d) + T\,, \qquad v = (P_i - T)/n2d$$
$$P_j = nw\,(2d) + T\,, \qquad w = (P_j - T)/n2d \tag{2}$$

Substituting for v and w in (1)

$$F_1 = (1+k+kT/nd)\,(P_i+P_j)/2 - (k/n2d)\,(P_iP_j) - kT^2/n2d - kT \tag{3}$$

This is the regression of F_1 phenotype on phenotypes of homozygous parents, the equation of a surface in three dimensions, F_1, P_i, P_j. The surface is a plane if $b_2 = k/n2d$ is zero, if $k = 0$, if there is no dominance, no interaction of P_i with P_j. Then, $F_1 = (P_i + P_j)/2$, by setting $k = 0$ in (3).

Taking P_i constant as the common tester of one column of the regression table,

$$F_1 = [\tfrac{1}{2}\,(1+k) - k\,(P_i - T)/n2d]\,P_j + C' \tag{4}$$

b_p is the coefficient of P_j, within brackets,

$$b_p = (-k/n2d)\,P_i + \tfrac{1}{2}\,(1+k) + kT/n2d\,. \qquad \text{If } k = 0\,, \qquad b_p = \tfrac{1}{2}$$

Regression of b_p on P_i is $b_2 = -k/n2d$. Since $P_i = nv(2d) + T$, $bp = \tfrac{1}{2}(1+k) - kv$. If $bp = 0$,

$$v = (1+k)/2k \tag{5}$$

With no dominance,

$$k = 0\,, \qquad v = 1/0 \text{ at equilibrium}$$

1. T, d, and kd are defined here in units of bushels/acre or pounds/plot, for example. Then, $k = kd/d$ is in units of (bu./A)/(bu./A), likewise b_p, but b_2 is in units of 1/(bu./A), making the whole term $b_2P_iP_j$ in bu./A.

In terms of selective values it is convenient to define d_s in terms of number of progeny surviving to breed. Then, k_s may be greater or less than k, depending on artificial breeding plan. If roan in Shorthorn cattle is intermediate, k is essentially zero, but if roan is favored in artificial selection over red and over white, $k_s > 1$ and there is overdominance with respect to artificial selective values.

With corn yield no single locus is identified, no heterozygote may be favored to provide $k_s > 1$, except that $k > 1$. Then, k_s may depend on gene frequency and on rate of culling.

Complete dominance

$$k = 1 , \qquad v = 1 \qquad \text{at equilibrium}$$

$$k = 2 , \qquad v = 3/4 \text{ at equilibrium}$$

For the more general case where P_i and P_j are (not inbred) individuals in a crossbreeding population, equations paralleling (2), (3), and (4) are second, fourth, and second degree, respectively. The simplification obtained with homozygous parents is reduction of the three functions to first, second, and first degree, respectively, by removing dominance effects (allelic interactions) from parent phenotypes P_i and P_j. Mendel found the simplification obtained with homozygous parents to be of considerable value in his early studies of monogenic inheritance.

The Mendelian model (2), (3), (4) may be complicated with innumerable kinds of interactions (epistasis) by simple, compound or complex transformations (log, anti-log, exponential, etc.) of (2), (3), and (4). It is not intended to imply, however, that interactions of alleles must precede interactions of non-alleles in living organisms.

The estimate of b_p for any tester parent line is independent of gene frequencies of the other parent lines with respect to dominance interactions. If obtained estimates of b_p for the same tester with samples of weak and strong lines respectively should differ significantly, the necessary interpretation would seem to require some kind of interaction other than between alleles, or that the lines were not strictly homozygous.

Interpretation of b_p, b_2, etc., by the Mendelian model presented here will not be biased by linkage of two loci if frequencies of ab, aB, Ab, and AB do not deviate significantly from expectation from random recombination of gene frequencies of the two loci with respect to all of the parent lines. Free assortment of the two loci is then effectively simulated. But any union of two unlike gametes must contain some cases of repulsion linkage close enough to retain the aB and Ab combinations in high frequency through several generations. A sample of lines all derived directly by selfing from one heterozygous parent plant may well contain many cases of repulsion linkage to simulate overdominance. This effect would not be counterbalanced by high frequencies of coupling linkage of other pairs of loci. Lines within each of the 25 samples reported here are in most or all cases no more closely related than plants within one or more varieties.

Variations of d and k from locus to locus would contribute to total variance, but would not seem to impair seriously the validity of the estimates of regression coefficients, nor of P_c when $b_p = 0$.

When all loci are aa or all loci are AA, $P_i = P_j = F_1 = F_2 = x$. With this restriction (3) becomes a quadratic with roots equal to the phenotypes at the two limits. The difference is $n(2d)$, the genetic range, the denominator of $b_2 = -k/n2d$. Values of k, calculated thus, for the nine cases where parent and F_1 yields are strictly comparable and b_2 is negative, are: 2.25, 1.50, 1.88 (2.18), 1.83, 1.78, 2.45, 1.41, 2.25, 1.69. The 1.88 (2.18) entry is F_1 and F_2 respectively of Stringfield's example, Table 1. The value 1.09 from F_2 data was doubled to correct for the effect of inbreeding.

If these independent estimates of k should be unbiased operationally, we must still be cautious in attempting any unique physiological interpretation. All of the several types of apparent overdominance listed here and others too may be operating in corn yield.

Estimates of backcrosses B_i and B_j may be written by inspection of (1) and (2). F_1 is transformed to F_2 (by selfing F_1) by multiplying the coefficient of each k term in (1) by $\frac{1}{2}$. This provides three linear sets F_1, F_2, bar P; F_1, B_i, P_i; and F_1, B_j, P_j, on the assumption of no epistasis. F_1, F_2, and $\bar{P}$ are alike in gene frequency. They differ only in frequency of heterozygosity. Differences in the backcross comparisons arise from both gene frequency and frequency of heterozygosity.

GRAPHIC TRANSFORMATIONS TO REMOVE EPISTASIS

Where the two intervals in any one of the three comparisons are not equal, epistasis may be suspected and a transformation of data may help to eliminate some of its effects. No transformation of the corn yield data would be warranted by all of the considerable amount of published data I have found, since the data fit the linear hypothesis very closely with F_2 and backcross comparisons.

Where transformation is clearly indicated, I may suggest a graphical determination of the best function. Plot the data, P_i, P_j, $\bar{P}$, F_1, F_2, B_i, B_j, and $\bar{B}$ on the vertical axis, and the same values on the horizontal axis linearly with no dominance, with any arbitrary scale. If the plotted points do not seem to provide a smooth curve, move F_1 to the right a trial distance. Move F_2, B_i, B_j, and $\bar{B}$ the same direction one-half as far. Move to the right or left (F_1 twice as far as the others each move) until the best fit visually to a smooth curve is found as the best transformation function. The only excuse for suggesting such a crude process is that if it is carefully carried out with good data the function is so much more refined than any arbitrarily chosen function for the purpose of correcting a complex of different kinds of epistasis together.

The transforming function determined by the above process with all available data on grain yield of corn would not differ sensibly from a straight line. From this I have said earlier that epistasis is unimportant in corn yield. Considerable amounts of increasing and decreasing returns types of epistasis may be effectively balanced, of course. In that case, epistasis would provide no explanation of the disparity of inbred and crossbred yields.

MAXIMUM YIELDS FROM CROSSING HIGH BY LOW?

For four loci with v and $w = \frac{3}{4}$, the gametes are $a_1A_2A_3A_4$, $A_1a_2A_3A_4$, $A_1A_2a_3A_4$, $A_1A_2A_3a_4$. Equations (1) or (3) with appropriate substitutions calculate the mean of the 16 F_1 combinations of four gametes of equal gene frequency. Deviations of the individual F_1's from the mean are not predictable from parent phenotypes. They are due to specific combinability arising from varying frequencies of heterozygosity. No more than two loci can be heterozygous in this example. But if $v = \frac{3}{4}$, $w = \frac{1}{4}$, six of the sixteen F_1's are heterozygous at all four loci. In the event of overdominance $\frac{6}{16}$ of high $\times$ low combinations may exceed the best high $\times$ high combination. If $1 < k < 2$, and $v = \frac{3}{4}$, the mean of high $\times$ high is greater than the mean of high $\times$ low. From the general combinability viewpoint we see only the difference of means. Selection of the very few elites among specific F_1's would, however, find them more frequently in high $\times$ low combinations. Hayes and Immer (1942, Table 21) present data of Johnson and Hayes which seem to agree with this interpretation in that the mean of high $\times$ high is best, but the highest specific combination is more likely in high $\times$ low.

EQUILIBRIUM FREQUENCIES OF GENES

We may substitute for v in equation (1) the mean gene frequency of a group of lines or of a variety, a general tester, to be held constant. Then if v is less than $(1 + k)/2k$, and $k > 1$, regression of F_1 on w is positive. Selection for general combinability with the same tester should continue to fixation of A except for reverse mutation. But if selected lines are recombined for each cycle and the recombination is the tester for the next cycle, selection comes to equilibrium when gene frequency of the tester reaches $(1 + k)/2k$, short of fixation if $k > 1$.

If concurrent with the foregoing process there should be selection of the high specific combinations (high $\times$ low) with lower gene frequencies, the combined effect on gene frequency may be nil. It may even be to degrade gene frequency when gene frequency is so near the equilibrium that heritability of general combinability is weak. From this view we may expect in the event of overdominance to find the equilibrium zone nearer the upper end of the range of data, providing some degree of positive heritability, some degree of positive regression of F_1's on inbred parents.

Ear-to-row selection should have progressed toward equilibrium gene frequencies except for the counter effect of selection of superior plants within ear-rows and within recombinations, selections of elite specific combinations of two gametes with above-average heterozygosity and lower gene frequency.

Modern corn breeding is failing largely beyond the first cycle for the same reasons that caused the failure of ear-to-row selection, except that inbred lines provide for a more efficient identification of elite specific combinations which may have the lower gene frequencies.

The whole of the evidence fits the generalized Mendelian model neatly enough if we may accept overdominance and otherwise proceed without prejudice to those conclusions more consistent with the data.

In familiar theory, selective advantage of a heterozygote leads to an equilibrium gene frequency in natural selection, where every individual leaves progeny (no culling) in proportion to fitness or where fitness is in fact fertility or more specifically, number of offspring surviving to breed. We must distinguish now between k for a physical trait, k_{ns} for natural selection of the same trait, and k_s for artificial selection. Since there is little apparent difference between bushels per acre and potential number of offspring surviving to breed, it may be supposed that k and k_{ns} are about the same for yield factors in corn. But if $k > 1$, artificial selection including strong culling may make k_s appreciably greater than k, and $(1 + k_s)/2k_s$ appreciably less than $(1 + k)/2k$. The expected effect of any single cycle of artificial selection is to shift gene frequency towards $(1 + k_s)/2k_s$, if $k > 1$. The operator's success (measured by k_s) in culling out homozygotes will improve as gene frequency approaches $\frac{1}{2}$ and frequency of aA approaches maximum. The limit is reached when k_s is infinite, and gene frequency is $(1 + \infty)/2\infty$ or $\frac{1}{2}$; e.g., as when saving only roan Shorthorns for breeding stock. The roans then have infinitely more progeny than whites or reds, which have none.

It does not seem likely that the limit equilibrium of $q = \frac{1}{2}$ can be reached or maintained with multigenic complexes such as corn yield, because of inability to cull absolutely all homozygotes. On this theory, strong selection will seem to degrade vigor. Relaxation of selection may allow vigor of the corn variety to improve. But there may be important loci where overdominance does not obtain, which tend to obscure the overdominance effect.

If artificial control should maintain fertility continually proportional to the physical trait where $k > 1$, gene frequency should progress to equilibrium at $(1 + k)/2k$; cf. recurrent selection for general combinability for corn yield. The population mean is maximum for the physical trait when $q = (1 + k)/2k$.

If overdominance should be important in vigor of cattle at a number of unfixed loci and a herd is close to $(1 + k)/2k$ for those loci, mild culling of females would tend to raise gene frequencies above $(1 + k)/2k$. Strong culling of males might have the opposite effect. Founding an *elite* herd with choice females from many herds and an expensive bull might be more likely to degrade gene frequency below optimum in the event of overdominance. The offspring of the choice animals might be disappointing aside from expected regression towards the mean of the breed.

EFFECTIVENESS OF RECURRENT SELECTION

Most of the selection practiced with plants and animals is recurrent. Exceptions are selection among homozygous lines or among clones. Inbreeding may curtail the efficiency of recurrent selection by lengthening the cycle. Selection within inbred lines during the process of inbreeding is recurrent but inefficient to the extent that freedom of recombination is curtailed. I have suggested before that breeders of self-fertilized crops might find greater efficiency in more frequent recombinations. It was to emphasize these considerations that the term *recurrent selection* was introduced. The sense of recurring back to the same tester was never intended.

Breeders of open-pollinated corn need to save no more than 1 ear from 500 or more to plant the same acreage again. If selection is only 20 per cent effective, the net effect in ten years is $(\frac{1}{10})^{19}$. The number of corn plants grown in the world in one year is roughly $(10)^{11}$. In 100 million times the world acreage of corn there might be one plant as good as the farmer's whole field after he has done 10 to 12 years of recurrent[2] selection. That this seemingly fantastic theoretical concept is essentially correct is supported very well, I think, by results of selection for oil and protein of the corn kernel in the well-known Illinois experiments and in many other less well documented cases with animals, too. East has proposed that selection for oil and protein in corn might be more efficient with inbred lines. However, East proposed that S_1 lines from the selected ears after chemical analyses be recombined for another cycle of selection. He employed inbreeding only to avoid open-pollination of the ears to be analyzed. It is unthinkable that East meant to propose that selection within and among inbred lines for oil or protein without recurrence of selection should be the more effective process.

Open-pollinated corn varieties of 50 or 30 years ago were actually pretty good, in yield and in many other respects. The selection differentials by which they were isolated were probably enormous. Nevertheless, specific combinations of inbred lines are sometimes 20 to 30 per cent above the varieties in yield. That this gain is mainly due to higher frequencies of dominant favorable genes in the elite inbred lines isolated from only a few hundred without recurrence of selection is really inconceivable.

A single corn plant in the variety is a product of two gametes. An F_1 of two homozygous lines is a product of two gametic types. The plant and the F_1 are genetically the same in mean, variance, and expectation of homozygosity in advanced generations as well as the first. It should not be difficult, if asexual propagation were possible, to isolate from the single plants clones that are easily superior to the present elite F_1's. That the reservoir of specific combinability in corn is far from exhaustion by present hybrids is evident in comparisons of F_1's with the range of individual plants in varieties. The animal breeder may look upon a family of full sibs (from four grandparental gametes) as a double cross of unselected but homozygous lines, for a rough estimate of possibilities with hybrids. But, aside from that, the breeder of open-pollinated corn was selecting among specific combinations of two gametes the same as in selection among F_1's. Continued selection within varieties might have degraded gene frequency below $(1 + k)/2k$ at any locus

2. Cf. Huxley, *Genetics in the 20th Century*, p. 595. "Recurrent selection," natural or artificial, is designed to multiply improbabilities; requires heritability in the strictest sense. Selection among inbred lines may go on and on without "recurrence."

where $k > 1$, thus providing the positive mild regression of offspring on parent, the heritability which so many have taken as strong evidence against $k > 1$.

Many traits of the corn plant are mostly independent of genes concerned with yield. Many others may be optimum for yield at intermediate points genotypically as well as phenotypically. It should hardly seem surprising if, subsequent to intense selection for yield, we should find evidence of intermediate gene frequencies and very little inbreeding depression or heterosis with such characters. An intermediate optimum may place some premium on aA, but hardly to the extent of explaining the evident heterosis of corn yields, so far as I can see.

Evidence cited here of overdominance in the genetics of grain yield of corn consists of:

1. Failure of mass selection and ear-to-row selection beyond the level of the adapted variety.

2. Crossbreeding recombinations of parent lines of elite hybrids yield little more than the original varieties.

3. Hybrids of second-cycle and third-cycle lines yield little more than those of the first cycle.

4. Homozygous corn yields 30 per cent as much as heterozygous corn.

5. No evidence of epistasis in corn yield.

6. Regression analyses of yields of F_1's and inbred parents indicate a zone of nearly level regression near the upper end of the range of present data, where it might be predicted with the kind of artificial selection which has been practiced, and in the event of overdominance.

7. There is some evidence that selection for general combinability alone with respect to yield is effective and this too is consistent with the expectation of overdominance theory.

8. The fact of hybrid corn is hardly to be explained as other than a result of selection for specific combinability, which in turn is manifestly dependent on heterozygosity of corn yield genes.

My proposal (Hull, 1945a) that recurrent selection for specific combinability be given a trial was made on the assumption that recurrent selection for general combinability or for accumulation of dominant favorable genes had been fairly tried in mass selection and subsequently. The tentative conclusion was that varieties (and breeds perhaps) were near equilibrium, with mean gene frequencies approximately at $(1 + k)/2k$. Regression analyses a little later indicated that the corn samples were below equilibrium. Since then it has been proposed orally many times that two parallel breeding plans restricted respectively to specific and to general combinability might well be run with corn and with small laboratory animals as pilot experiments. I have later come to believe that recurrent selection among homozygotes might also provide results of considerable theoretical interest.

Present-day corn breeding is done in three steps: selection among inbreds based on their own phenotypes; selection among inbreds for general combinability; selection among specific F_1's of the remaining inbreds. These steps are the three processes of the preceding paragraph. The corn breeder applies the three processes in the order named to the same stock, then recombines the elite lines and begins the cycle again. The present proposition is to apply the three processes separately to parallel stocks, and thus attempt to learn which ones are primarily responsible for superior hybrids.

RECURRENT SELECTION AMONG HOMOZYGOTES

This process can be done effectively enough in corn, perhaps with S_2 lines. Two selfings would amount statistically to reducing the degree of dominance to one-fourth of the original value. One-half of the S_1 lines could be discarded in the first comparison. About fifty S_2 lines should be retained in the recombination. Selection within ear-rows should be rigidly excluded.

There is no reason to suppose that a physiological barrier would be reached short of the level of elite hybrids. Recurrent selection towards an extreme has been very effective with many characters where not much dominance is apparent. In noted cases no limit of genetic variance has been reached. What genetic limit might be reached with vigor or yield genes of corn when the confusion of dominance is artificially eliminated is to be explored. Theoretically, this process of recurrent selection should be much superior to any non-recurrent selection among gametes or doubled haploids.

RECURRENT SELECTION FOR GENERAL COMBINABILITY

Strictly, the tester should be the variety. S_0 plants or S_n lines are to be testcrossed with several plants of the variety. The S_0 plant must be selfed at the same time. Parents of elite testcrosses are recombined into an improved variety which becomes the tester for the next cycle. If gene frequency of the variety is improved to approach $(1 + k)/2k$, where $k > 1$, heritability will approach zero and the variety mean its maximum. If pseudo-overdominance from repulsion linkage is important the equilibrium may advance to higher levels as recombinations occur. But, aside from that, we have now no experimental verification of a selection equilibrium, and a test would seem desirable. Concurrent selection for specific combinability should be strictly avoided in this test.

RECURRENT SELECTION FOR SPECIFIC COMBINABILITY

This process has been adequately described both here and earlier (Hull, 1945a). From the theoretical viewpoint it would be best to use a homozygous tester and avoid selection within the crossbred except that based on testcross performance. The purpose is to determine first how much specific combinability may be accumulated in early cycles and eventually to determine where this process may reach physiological or genetic limits.

Now if we are convinced that overdominance is not very important and that, perhaps for other reasons too, selection for general combinability will eventually win, or at least not lose, we may proceed at once with recurrent selection for general combinability to render hybrid corn obsolete. Some of us may find it necessary to include an inbreeding interphase between cycles. Breeders of livestock may as well return to improvement of pure breeds by progeny testing. We will run these pilot tests merely for the sake of verification.

But if it should seem likely that recurrent selection for specific combinability may win, the breeder of livestock may begin now with recurrent reciprocal selection for specific combinability. For my part, I would choose two crossbreds for the start and would begin mild inbreeding in one of them which would become the stud herd. On one side of this is the Comstock plan with no inbreeding in either herd. On the other side we might choose a line with 50 per cent inbreeding at the start and practice reciprocal selection along with continued mild inbreeding. Evaluation of these alternatives of the reciprocal plan with small laboratory animals, along with the other two main plans, would be of considerable interest theoretically. The cost might be minute in comparison with the total of wasted effort in current breeding practices.

Recurrent selection for general combinability without the inbreeding interphase is a fairly obvious technic which has been employed and described variously. The first discussion of it from the overdominance viewpoint with the restriction against selection for specific combinability was that of Hull (1946b). Since then I have continued to urge parallel tests with fast breeding species as pilot experiments. Recurrent selection for superior homozygotes is proposed here for the first time, I believe.

Reciprocal selection for specific combinability was a counter proposal to me of several corn breeders in 1944 and later, when I proposed selection in a crossbred for combinability with a fixed tester, a homozygous line or F_1 of two homozygous lines.

For simplicity of illustration we may consider a 4-factor example with gene frequency in a homozygote or gamete (v or w) taking values, $0, \frac{1}{4}, \frac{2}{4}, \frac{3}{4}, \frac{4}{4}$. Gene frequencies intermediate to these values may occur in heterozygotes and in whole populations. Let us take $k = 2$ for the degree of dominance as suggested roughly for corn yield by estimates reported here. Then regression of offspring phenotype on gene frequency of parent in any column of the (5×5) Mendelian checkerboard is $b_p = \frac{1}{2}(3) - 2v$, where v is gene frequency of the common parent of the column. Substituting the five values of v provides the five values of b_p, $1\frac{1}{2}, 1, \frac{1}{2}, 0, -\frac{1}{2}$, for the five columns. Heritability changes from positive to negative where $v = (1 + k)/2k = \frac{3}{4}$. These values of b_p for the given values of v are the same for any number of loci. In any case the zone of near-zero heritability for one locus is relatively broad on both sides of the critical value of zero. Reciprocal selection between two crossbreds is at equilibrium for one locus when gene frequencies are $(1 + k)/2k$ in both, and $k > 1$. It is conceivable that gene frequencies of the two crossbreds may wander in the zone of low heritability through many cycles of reciprocal selection, but they must eventually separate on opposite sides to approach aa and AA respectively with increasing velocities. When the two gene frequencies are on opposite sides of the equilibrium initially, reciprocal selection will tend to drive them farther apart. If they are on the same side both will tend to approach equilibrium. Comstock's statement here that the one nearest equilibrium may approach it more rapidly and continue beyond to reverse the trend of the other, thus obtaining a quick separation, seems good. I had overlooked this point and hope it may be experimentally verified.

Gametes with critical gene frequencies in the present model are $aAAA$, $AaAA$, $AAaA$, $AAAa$. A general tester composed of the four homozygous lines producing these four gametes respectively will provide zero heritability. So also will a crossbred tester for every locus where gene frequency is $\frac{3}{4}$. One of the homozygous lines alone as a specific tester provides mean $b_p = 0 = [\frac{3}{2} + 3(-\frac{1}{2})]/4$. But here the individual values of b_p for each locus are at maximum, $\frac{3}{2}$ for the aa locus, and $-\frac{1}{2}$ for each AA locus, providing maximum heritability in selection to a homozygous tester.

Defining phenotypes of aa, aA, AA alternatively as $1 - s$, $1 - hs$, 1, provides $b_p = 1 - h - (1 - 2h)v$. Then with $h = -\frac{1}{2}$ for the same degree of dominance as the present model, $b_p = \frac{1}{2}(3) - 2v$ again. The only inconsistency between the two systems of defining phenotypes which may be encountered here, I think, is failure to distinguish between physical values and selective values, e.g., body weight and number of offspring surviving to breed.

It seems fairly clear that overdominance of the degree considered here may provide considerable variation of heritability within a finite sample, a herd or a variety on one farm. Mean b_p may be positive and fairly large, yet $b_p = 0$ near the upper range of gene frequency in the sample. Moreover, the degree of dominance for selective values might be appreciably greater than for the physical trait. For these reasons, selection indexes made up with average heritabilities of physical traits could be misleading.

Parallel operations of the foregoing breeding plans with heavy dosages of mutagenic agents in addition might provide significant information on progressive improvement, where the objectives respectively are the superior homozygote, the mean of the population, and the superior heterozygote. This proposal will be subject to criticism by those who are convinced that it is only in gene-by-gene analysis that real advances in knowledge of genetics can be obtained. I have no quarrel with that viewpoint except that where many genes with minute effects may be involved the gene-by-gene approach still seems fairly remote.

Recurrent selection in prolific species such as corn, chickens, mice, and Drosophila may soon build up very large selection intensities, perhaps to recover high frequencies of rare natural or mutant alleles. Chemists have employed high pressures and temperatures to obtain reactions of great interest. They have concentrated rare elements and rare isotopes by various ingenious processes. With selection intensities and mutation rates well above natural values it might be possible to obtain estimates of the minimum ratio of selection to mutation for survival or improvement of the variety or breed.

JOHN W. GOWEN
Iowa State College

Chapter 29

Hybrid Vigor in Drosophila

Experience has defined hybrid vigor as the evident superiority of the hybrid over the better parent in any measurable character as size, general vegetative vigor, or yield. For any one species it is left for us to show that, within the possible crosses of pure lines, hybrid vigor actually exists and what particular morphological and physiological characters express it best.

With this in mind, investigations with wild-type Drosophila of diverse geographical origin were begun in 1934 and continued to date. The group working on this problem has included Dr. Leslie E. Johnson, Dr. F. S. Straus, Miss Janice Stadler, Dr. S. Y. Loh, and myself. The material reported here is the result of our joint efforts. To specify the problem of hybrid vigor, five characteristics were chosen for investigation in eight inbred lines of Drosophila and a hybrid between two of the lines. The characteristics chosen were egg production throughout the full life of the fly, the days the females laid the eggs, the hatchability of the eggs, and the duration of life of the males and females in each line.

To determine egg production, a pair of flies of a particular line was placed in a quarter-pint milk bottle sealed with a paraffin paper cap on which was placed a disk of nutrient banana agar colored with charcoal. The female laid her whole day's egg output on this disk when it was properly seeded with yeast and a little acetic acid. The caps, a sample shown in Figure 29.1, were changed daily and the eggs were counted for each day.

The characteristic performances of the different pure lines and the hybrid are shown in Table 29.1.

The average egg production for the different inbred races varied from 263 to 1701 eggs. There is some correlation between the intensity of the inbreeding and the production of the particular race. Ames I and II are less inbred

474

races than Inbred 92 or Homozygous. Correlation exists between the egg production of the race and its fitness to survive as judged by its duration of life as measured by the survival of either males or females.

The hybrid race came from the cross Inbred 92 and Ames I. The mean productions of the parents were 389 and 1000 eggs respectively over the life-

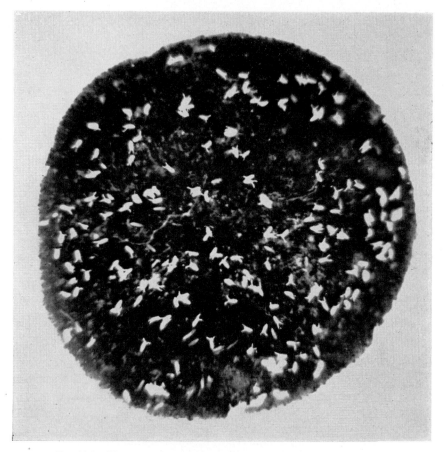

Fig. 29.1—Photograph of laying cap with eggs and some hatched larvae.

time period. The mean production of the hybrid was 2034 eggs, or 203 per cent greater than that of its high producing parent, Ames I, and 422 per cent greater than that of its other parent, Inbred 92. The hybrid showed more eggs than any of the pure races. The excess of the hybrid over the pure parents is greater in this particular experiment than in several other similar experiments.

The females of the different races showed average egg laying periods of 17.2 to 46.0 days. The hybrid lays eggs nearly as long as the higher producing purebreds, 43.4 days, but does not exceed the range. The parents entering into the cross for this hybrid laid eggs for an average of 38.4 and 17.2 days respectively. Hybrid vigor is only 113 per cent for the length of the productive period.

The physiological fitness of the purebred races, as measured by their duration of life, ranged from 22 days to 58 days. The average life of the hybrid was 52.2 days. The hybrid's parents lived for 38.7 and 50.2 days respectively. This character showed little hybrid vigor—104 per cent.

These results show that egg production is the most favorable of the Drosophila characters analyzed for the study of hybrid vigor. The lifetime

TABLE 29.1

CHARACTERISTIC VARIATION OF DROSOPHILA RACES
IN EGG PRODUCTION AND DURATION OF LIFE

RACE	EGG PRODUCTION		SURVIVAL OF FEMALES IN DAYS OF LIFE		DAYS FEMALES LAID EGGS		SURVIVAL OF MALES IN DAYS OF LIFE	
	No.	Mean	No.	Mean	No.	Mean	No.	Mean
Ames II.........	56	1701	48	56.1	56	46.0	30	58.7
Ames II.........	56	1511	41	51.5	56	40.0	39	53.6
Princeton........	56	814	45	48.4	56	35.4	43	46.7
Inbred 92........	56	389	43	33.4	56	17.2	42	44.0
Florida-45	54	610	49	28.5	54	22.4	52	32.6
Oregon R-C-44....	54	413	49	36.4	54	28.7	48	35.5
Swede-b-40.......	53	398	50	26.7	53	16.5	50	35.7
Homozygous 42...	54	263	54	22.7	54	16.7	51	27.9
Ames I..........	54	1000	51	50.9	54	38.4	50	49.6
Hybrid..........	54	2034	52	50.0	54	43.4	51	55.4
Pooled Variance...	d/f 537	236847	......	......	d/f 537	179.5	......	......

distributions of egg productions for the inbred and hybrid races are shown in Figure 29.2.

Newly hatched females require a short period after emergence for maturing. Heavy egg production begins on the fourth day and rises rapidly to a maximum in early life. From the high point, production gradually declines. The rate of this decline varies with the different races. The average slope is shown by straight lines.

Drosophila egg production presents a single cycle as contrasted with the series of cycles or egg clutches observed in the egg production in certain other forms—the domestic fowl or the fungus fly, Sciara. This fact makes Drosophila egg production an easier character to study. The egg yield curve is determined by the initial high point in production and the rate of loss in productivity with age.

The form of the egg production curve in Drosophila fits in with Ashby's hypothesis of metabolic reserves being responsible for hybrid vigor. The hy-

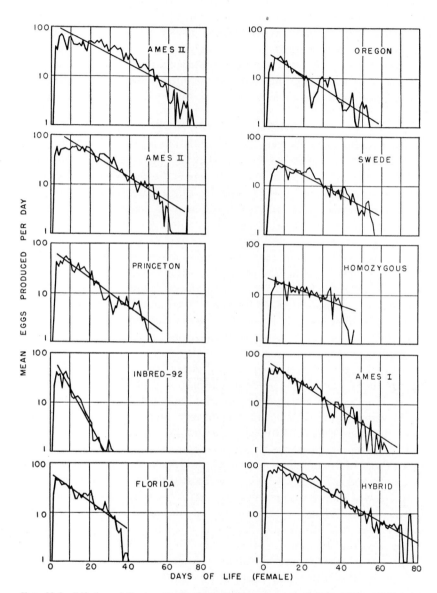

FIG. 29.2—Lifetime daily egg production of different races of *Drosophila melanogaster*, number of initial females tested, 53 to 56.

brid has a higher initial production than its parents, or, for that matter, any of the purebred races. The hybrid expends its metabolic reserves less rapidly than either of its parents. Taking all inbred races together, the hybrid utilizes its reserves at slightly less than the average rate. The hybrid is chiefly characterized by its large initial production. Examination of the pure lines indicates that there are slight differences in the rate of expenditure of the initial reserve, even when the obviously different Inbred 92 is not considered.

WHAT IS HYBRID VIGOR?

These results show that the vigor of the hybrid is greatest for lifetime egg production, 203 per cent; is less if length of egg laying period is considered, 113 per cent; and is still less with life span as the character, 104 per cent. What is the explanation of egg production's high heterosis? Egg production is a character which is in turn dependent on other component characters. A simple breakdown would be, lifetime egg yield is determined by the length of egg laying period, the decline (slope) representing the loss of ability to produce eggs with age, and maximum egg production at the initial phase of the egg laying cycle. Length of egg laying period has already been shown to have 113 per cent heterosis. The slopes of the decreasing egg yields with advancing ages are Inbred 92—0.17, Ames I—0.06, and their F_1 hybrids—0.05. The hybrids show heterosis in that their egg productions decline less rapidly than their best parent, but the heterosis is only 121 per cent.

Maximum productions, as judged by the three highest days' average yields of the strains, are Inbred 92, 40.7; Ames I, 52.7; and F_1 hybrid, 81.4 eggs, or the heterosis is 154 per cent. The highest of the component heterosis values is only about half of that noted for lifetime egg yields. It seems not unlikely that if the division into components could be carried further, it would be found that the heterosis values would approach closer and closer to 100. The results consequently argue for heterosis, as the result of the combined action of two or more groups of distinct characters which, when jointly favorable, and as frequently truly multiplicative in action, lead to heterosis.

Analysis of the variation in egg production between races—the heritable fraction controlled through inbreeding—as contrasted with the variability within races—the fraction due largely to environment—shows that about 56 per cent of the lifetime egg production is fixed within the races and 44 per cent is due to gene segregation, environment, etc.

Consideration of the individual records further support this view. Contrasting the performances of the individual females within the hybrid groups with those in the different inbred races shows that the hybrid has no females with greater production than those of the inbred races. The hybrids are good because, on the average, all members of the cross are good producers. The hybrids include one female laying 3083 eggs and twenty-seven others laying between 2000 and 3000 eggs. The Ames I has one female laying 2016 eggs;

Ames II, in two similar experiments, has two females laying 3168 and 3108 eggs and thirty-two others laying between 2000 and 3000 eggs. The other pure races have no individuals laying more than 2000 eggs. Hybrid vigor contributes consistently high performance to all individuals rather than exceptional performances to a few. It is the consistency of high performance which calls for explanation.

MEASURES OF HETEROSIS

As lifetime egg production is a difficult character with which to work, a less tedious measure of productivity was sought. The character chosen was daily egg yield 5, 6, 7, 8, and 9 days after the female emerged from the pupa. These records are at the general maximum of the female's productive life. The correlation with lifetime production is high.

Chromosomal and Cytoplasmic Basis for Hybrid Vigor

The possibility of creating homozygous races of Drosophila through outcrossing offers a unique opportunity for analyzing the causative agents behind hybrid vigor. Hybrid vigor has been postulated as due to differences in allelic genes and to differences in the cytoplasms which combine at fertilization. The reduction in yield of inbred races is accompanied by increasing identity in both the combining alleles and the cytoplasms which combine to form succeeding generations. Both these factors have been invoked to explain the low yield of such inbred races. Production of homozygous types through outcrossing furnishes a contrast between these two possible causes of low productivity. The allelic genes are made homozygous so that any undesirable recessive gene would have full expression in the different races and thus lower the yield. The cytoplasms which combine are diverse and as such should give high yield to the individuals if hybrid vigor is an expression of differences in combining cytoplasm. This contrast is shown as follows:

	Genes tend toward		Cytoplasms tend toward
		Inbreeding	
♂ Gametes			
	identity		identity
♀ Gametes			
		Homozygous by outcrossing	
♂ Gametes			
	identity		diversity
♀ Gametes			

The effects of genes as contrasted with the effects of the cytoplasm may be measured by comparing inbred performance with that of a race made homozygous for the same genes. Table 29.2 shows this comparison.

For Princeton 1, the inbred progeny resulting from brother-sister mating for 28 generations had an egg production of 73.6 eggs per day over the test period. The homozygous Princeton 1 race, coming from the outcross breeding system, had an average egg production of 62.7 eggs, or, the homozygous production was 10.9 eggs less than the inbred. The differences of the different inbred-homozygous comparisons range from −22.0 to +10.6 eggs. In nineteen comparisons the inbred races produce more than the homozygous. In five instances the homozygous races yield more than the inbred. Of the nineteen trials in which the homozygous races had less production than the in-

TABLE 29.2

VARIANCE ANALYSIS FOR PROGENY OF IN-
BRED (BROTHER BY SISTER) AND OUT-
CROSS (LEADING TO HOMOZYGOSIS) MAT-
ING SYSTEMS

Race	Mean Difference	Value F
Princeton 1	−10.9	5.9*
Princeton 1	− 2.8	.3
Princeton 1	− 9.9	3.7
Princeton 8	+ 6.6	2.1
Princeton 8	− 6.3	2.9
Princeton 8	− 1.3	.1
Princeton 10	+ 6.0	1.9
Princeton 10	+ 0.1	.0
Princeton 10	−15.9	9.6**
Princeton 10	+ 0.8	.1
Florida 2	− 7.3	.8
Florida 2	− 8.7	3.4
Florida 2	−20.5	20.1**
Florida 2	−16.6	8.3**
Florida 5	− 5.5	.8
Inbred 3	+10.6	3.1
Inbred 4	−19.2	7.9**
Inbred 4	− 9.6	2.6
Inbred 4	− 9.3	1.6
Inbred 4	− 6.6	.7
Inbred 9	−13.7	4.4
Inbred 9	−21.1	7.6*
Inbred 9	−16.2	3.9
Inbred 9	−22.0	7.9*
Average	− 8.4	....

breds, there are four differences which are highly significant and three differences that are in the significant range when account is taken of chance variations. In no instance was the homozygous egg yield significantly larger than that of the inbreds. The data were consistent in showing the homozygous poorer in egg production than the inbred, even though the particular homozygous is only a sample of the germ plasm of the highly inbred strain.

The average difference between the homozygous and inbred progeny is −8.38. Considering each observation as equivalent, the probability that the homozygous are on the whole poorer producers than the inbreds is well beyond the 1 per cent range by the test.

There are three major hypotheses to account for the vigor of race crosses. One hypothesis assumes an as yet unexplained physiological stimulation resulting from the union of gametes of unlike origin. The second hypothesis attributes hybrid vigor to the union of gametes carrying different favorable dominant genes for vigor, which cover up defects which may exist in each of the original parent races. The third hypothesis also depends on genic action. It assumes that the vigor of the hybrid comes from the association of unlike alleles brought in from the two parental races, these unlike alleles are postulated as contributing different, as well as like, chemical or physical stimulations favorable to the vigor of the hybrid. The results of these experiments presented in Table 29.2 are in favor of a genic basis rather than a physiologic stimulation as the cause of hybrid vigor, since throughout this work, diverse cytoplasm has shown less yield than like cytoplasm when put on a background of homozygous or inbred inheritance.

INBREEDING EFFECTS ON HETEROSIS AS RELATED TO DEFECTIVE GENES

The creation of homozygous types tests the parent race for heterozygosity of particularly undesirable genes, lethals, and semi-lethals. Table 29.3 shows the results obtained in mating the homozygous races.

TABLE 29.3

GENOTYPES OF INBRED RACES FOR VIABLE, LETHAL, AND RECESSIVE VISIBLE ALLELES

Race	Line	No. Lethal	Lethal	Recessive Visible	Total Isolation
Princeton.........	1	9	7	0	16
Inbred...........	9	0	17	0	17
Florida...........	5	98	20	2	118
Florida...........	2	0	12	2	14

The lethals observed were all in chromosomes 2 and 3. They range in frequency from 17 per cent for one race to 100 per cent for another. The visible recessives picked up were also semi-lethal. The mathematical model employed in inbreeding calculations postulates random recombination and fertilization. Conclusions are misleading when these postulates are not met. The above evidence for mechanisms to maintain heterozygosity in races even though the matings are of relatives as close as continued full brother × sister seems unmistakable. The defective genes are in the races. Residual defective genes can contribute both toward and away from greater heterotic effects in particular crosses. As these defective genes arise ultimately by mutation and as the number of the genes is large, the ultimate possible genetic changes are appreciable and may be an important force toward heterosis.

EFFECT OF THE GENOME COMPONENTS ON HYBRID VIGOR

The combining capacity of a genome may be analyzed into its components
—the individual chromosomes. To make this analysis, Dr. Straus in our genetics laboratory carried through duplicated experiments based on the cross of
Inbred 92 and Ames I. This cross, as noted previously, showed high hybrid
vigor. The following data were taken from his thesis (1942).

The results showed no cytoplasmic effects. Effects of reciprocal crosses
also were found negligible.

The first step in these investigations required that 8 possible homozygous
lines be created for the first, second, and third chromosomes. About 98.5 per
cent of the genes would be homozygous in each of the eight types. Crosses
of the eight different homozygous lines will give all the other types ranging
from those heterozygous in one chromosome pair to those heterozygous for
each chromosome. The productivities of these 27 different types together
with their chromosomal constitution are as follows:

	Type	Average Daily Egg Yield
Heterozygous for 3 chromosome pairs	1	76.9
Heterozygous for 2 chromosome pairs		
6 chromosome combinations	2	64.7
	3	64.4
	4	51.5
	5	65.5
	6	66.5
	7	62.9
Heterozygous for 1 chromosome pair		
12 chromosome types	8	55.2
	9	52.7
	10	55.8
	11	60.6
	12	46.5
	13	53.6
	14	35.3
	15	56.1
	16	56.2
	17	52.4
	18	51.7
	19	41.7
Homozygous		
8 types	20	45.0
	21	51.3
	22	40.4
	23	36.3
	24	37.0
	25	35.9
	26	27.8
	27	31.9

The analysis of the variance of the 1440 daily egg productions in this completely balanced factorial experiment shows that the difference between
chromosome effects makes the most important contribution to variation.

From type 20 to 27, all types are homozygous or are of zero heterozygosity.
Types 8 to 19 have one chromosome heterozygous. Since each chromosome

enters in equal frequency, this means that one-third of the genes are on the average heterozygous. Types 2 to 7 have 2 chromosomes heterozygous, or the average of these types is two-thirds heterozygous. Type 1 is completely heterozygous or 100 per cent. Plotting the average egg production for the four groups shows the effects of different degrees of heterozygosity on the hybrid vigor.

The property of additivity of the heterotic gene effects would seem to be the logical explanation for this linear relation and also for the absence of interactions between the genes of the different chromosomes. It must be realized, however, that the chromosomes themselves represent interacting gene effects which give the block reactions. The trend so far considered is an average trend, each point, except that for the completely heterozygous, being based on several types. Interaction—combination effects which are larger or smaller than the sum of the chromosomal effects separately—may exist. Such effects, it is true, must be in opposite directions and equal. The factorial design of the experiment facilitates evaluation of these interactions. The data following gives the three levels of effect each of the chromosomes can assume, together with the two and three chromosome interactions.

VARIANCE ANALYSIS OF CHROMOSOMAL EFFECTS

Source of Variation	d/f	Mean Square	Apportionment of Variation Per Cent
I chromosome...................	2	574	11
II chromosome..................	2	1916	44
III chromosome.................	2	1010	22
I and II chromosomes...........	4	81	0
I and III chromosomes..........	4	62	0
II and III chromosomes.........	4	116	1
I, II, and III chromosomes.......	8	103	22

The effects of the direct order actions of the first, second, and third chromosomes are highly significant. None of the interactions show large variations. Nor are any of these interactions in excess of what would be expected from random differences. Apportioning the variance to its various chromosomes, 11 per cent is attributable to the first chromosome, 44 per cent to the second, and 22 per cent to the third.

Analysis of this material shows that the hybrid vigor of the egg yields receives a significant contribution from the heterozygosity of each chromosome pair, and that none of the chromosome interactions are significant. The homozygous chromosomes of the two parental inbreds do not differ in either their direct or interaction effects from zero.

The linearity of the effect on egg yield and the absence of interactions show that the chromosomes with their contained genes behave as integrated units

—much like major genes—with given degrees of dominance. Within each group the genes may have any known type of gene action so long as the quality of additivity of their effect between chromosomes is maintained.

EFFECT OF CHROMOSOME LENGTH ON HYBRID VIGOR

The analysis of variance shows that the effects of the three chromosome pairs differed widely. These differences could be due to differential numbers of gene loci within the separate chromosomes, to varying magnitude of gene effects, or to both. The data do not allow us to positively distinguish between these hypotheses. Proportionality between the effects of the three chromosomes and their sizes would favor the first interpretation.

There are several different measures of chromosome size. These measurements of the different chromosomes may be compared with their heterotic effects in a least square test.

The proportionality between heterotic effects and chromosome lengths was as follows:

	CHROMOSOMES			CLOSENESS OF AGREEMENT	
	I	II	III	7-Day Data	All Data
Metaphase length............	1.56	2.21	2.80	✕	✕
Salivary length..............	220	460	485	✕	✕
Salivary bands...............	1024	2134	2077	✕✕	✕
Per cent visible loci..........	.69	1.00	.77	✕✕	✕✕
Cross over length............	.62	1.00	.98	✕✕	✕
Observed heterotic {7 day....	248	386	325	✕ significantly closer 1:20 or	
effect {All data..	192	305	174	✕✕ highly significant 1:100	

Excellent agreements are observed between per cent of visible loci or the crossing-over units with the heterotic effects of the chromosomes. Less agreement is noted between the number of bands in the salivary chromosomes and the heterotic effect. The metaphase lengths of chromosomes or the physical lengths of the salivary gland chromosomes are less closely related to heterotic effects. All comparisons of chromosome sizes with heterotic effect give excellent to fair correlations. In general, the heterotic effect is distributed according to random distribution of several genes to the various chromosomes. This favors the view that the heterotic effect is due to many gene pairs in each chromosome, rather than to one having a specific additive phenotypic effect. These genes would be randomly distributed to the different loci within the chromosome.

GENOME CONTRIBUTIONS TO HYBRID VIGOR

Average combining ability of one inbred line when mated to several lines is called general. The genomes of an inbred line can be regarded as uniform and good or bad according to the genes which they contain. These genes could be additive in effect making the genomes of uniform effect with other inbred lines. Specific combining ability represents unlike combining ability of the genomes from one race with those of a succession of other races. This variation in hybrids could be due to different allelic distributions as complementary or epistatic reactions of the different gene combinations with which the given genome was combined. The relative effects of general vs. specific combining ability for a particular group of crosses may be measured in data containing all possible combinations between a series of different inbreds. Table 29.4 presents the egg productions for the possible hybrids of five inbred races.

TABLE 29.4

EGG PRODUCTIONS OF 5 INBRED RACES AND THEIR CROSSES
AVERAGE YIELDS FOR 5, 6, 7, 8, AND 9TH DAYS
OVER 4 EXPERIMENTS

FEMALE PARENT RACE	MALE PARENT RACE					TOTAL
	A	B	C	D	E	
A.............	....	2509.0	2681.0	3479.4	2503.8	11173.2
B.............	2908.6	....	2712.8	3427.4	1822.2	10871.0
C.............	1804.8	2827.8	....	3298.8	3116.0	11047.4
D.............	2321.4	3485.6	3215.2	....	3447.6	13467.8
E.............	2109.8	1908.2	2498.2	3301.0	....	9817.2
Total........	10144.6	10728.6	11107.2	13506.6	10889.6	56376.6
Inbred Race Yields........	2595.2	2586.4	1996.6	2173.4	1859.4	....

Table 29.4 shows 14 of the race hybrids have higher average yields than their inbred parent races. The average hybrid produced 2818.8 eggs, the average inbred 2242.2, or the increase over the average inbred was 25.7 per cent. These data serve to re-emphasize the fact pointed out earlier, that characters built up of components of lesser characters generally show more heterosis than observed for each of the components taken separately.

The individual race crosses differed in their ability to unite into favorable hybrids. Race D is evidently high in its general combining ability. The other four races show about equal combining ability. Race D has this high general combining ability even though its own productivity is rather low—2173.4— eggs as against 2595.2 for another of the races.

For individual flies the range in egg production was from 0 to 146 eggs. The zero egg producing flies are an important class which give an insight into female sterility. We have dissected over 300 such flies. These observations have led to the opinion that this class is the result of a variety of causes and definitely differs genetically and otherwise from that of the flies which produce even one egg in their lifetimes. For this reason and the fact that heterosis is a phenomenon of quantitative inheritance, we have excluded such flies from consideration in these studies.

The general analysis of the variations within these hybrid egg yields is presented in Table 29.5.

TABLE 29.5

DISTRIBUTION OF VARIANCE IN EGG PRODUCTION

Source of Variation	Designation	d/f	Mean Square	Components of Variation	Per Cent Contributed
Total..........	......	5624	....	....	.....
Experiments....	E	3	116461	$W+11.2ERA+280EA+56ER$ $+1400E$	7.3
Races..........	R	24	37405	$W+11.4ERA+57ER+45RA$ $+225R$	15.4
Inbreds......	......	4	12630		
Hybrids......	......	19	36811	....	.....
Inbreds vs. Hybrids....	......	1	147779	....	.....
Ages..........	A	4	6665	$W+11.4ERA+285EA+45RA$ $+1125A$	1.2
Exp×Races....	ER	72	5800	$W+11.2ERA+56ER$	9.8
Exp×Ages.....	EA	12	18202	$W+11.2ERA+280EA$	6.8
Races×Ages...	RA	96	767	$W+11.4ERA+45RA$	0.2
Exp×Races× Ages.........	ERA	288	830	$W+11.2ERA$	3.1
Residual.......	W	5125	510	W	56.2

100.0

Table 29.5 presents data on the factors which may be of importance in the interpretation of heterotic effects. The percentage contribution of each factor is shown in the right hand column. The largest contribution, residual, is made by the variation within flies of a given age. It is half of the total observed. This variation shows what minor differences in seemingly constant conditions can be responsible for differences in egg yields.

Differences in races represent the next most significant contribution to yield variations—15 per cent. Major contributor to this effect is the difference between the productivities of the inbred parent races and their hybrids. These differences may be looked upon as the effects of additive genetic factors for yield, and the effects of specific gene combinations leading to the expression of dominance, overdominance, or epistacy in the phenotypes.

A point of currently even more importance brought out by these data is the dependence of yield on the close interrelation of environment and genotype. The interaction of experiment × race accounts for 9.8, and experiment, race, and age, 3.1 per cent of the variation. The total is 12.9 per cent. Even with great care to closely control conditions both within and between experiments, the environment is sufficiently important to the yield of the particular race to account for nearly as much of the total yield variation as race alone. With widely ranging environments, given genotypes may show much more variation in phenotypic expression. The interaction terms show that genes in quantitative inheritance are not stable in their effects. In one condition the phenotypic reaction, in some degree, could be such as to suggest recessive action; in another dominant, in another additive or epistatic.

These interpretations may be brought out by another analytical approach. In analyzing data of this kind it has been customary to neglect the genotypic environmental interactions. This neglect finds expression in the models adopted to explain the yield. For the data above it is sometimes assumed that yield, y_{ijk}, may be accounted for by a basic value common to all crosses, the mean; deviations due to additive general combining ability of the different races g_a, g_b, etc.; deviations due to specific combining ability, s_{ab}, s_{ac}, etc., such as dominance variations, and epistatic effects common only to members of that particular cross; reciprocal effects, r_{ab} vs r_{ba}, etc., of any differences between members of reciprocal crosses; and a term representing residual variations, e_{abk}, e_{ack} etc., due to unknown causes. These variables are set up in the linear equation:

$$y_{ijk} = m + g_i + g_j + s_{ij} + r_{ij} + e_{ijk}$$

Analysis of the data for the contributions of these variables to the yield variance gives these results:

EXPERIMENT 35

General combining ability.... 11.3%
Specific combining ability.... 9.7
Reciprocal effects........... 2.3
Residual effects............. 76.6

Two sets of experiments are available. One is for five and the other for six inbred line hybrids. The test as presented above shows that 11.3 per cent of the variance is due to differences in general and 9.7 per cent to differences in specific combining ability. Differences in reciprocal crosses account for 2.3 per cent. Experiment 36 shows similar contributions attributable to general and to specific combining ability, but the effect of reciprocal crosses is insignificant. The two experiments are concordant in showing that general and specific combining ability account for most of the variation attributable to known causes. In both cases general combining ability is somewhat more important to productivity than specific combining ability.

These results from Drosophila are entirely without any previous selection for combining ability. They are comparable to the observations which were obtained in corn when combining ability was tested for the early crosses of inbred lines. It is significant that Sprague's analyses of such crosses show general combining ability twice as important as specific. This difference is like that of Drosophila but gives even more emphasis to general combining ability.

In later corn hybrids, the products of more stringently selected inbreds, the emphasis was reversed. The specific combining ability was zero to five times as important as the general. Improved utilization of hybrid vigor has seemingly selected and fixed general combining ability in the approved inbreds. Further progress is dependent on specific combining ability. One comparison weakens this evidence. On exactly the same ten inbred combinations one set grown at Ames, the other at Davenport, the specific combining ability was five times that of the general at Ames, while at Davenport the general and specific were identical. A place × genotype interaction in the general-specific combining ability similar to that observed above for Drosophila egg yield is also important even in these highly selected lines.

SIGNIFICANCE OF ENVIRONMENT-GENOTYPE INTERACTION IN HETEROSIS

An experiment by Dr. Loh evaluating the significance of early or late testing furnishes data on the part played by environment in the stability of the hybrid phenotypes (1949). Fifty full brother × sister lines were formed from each of three wild stocks having different geographical or chronological origin. Each line was then doubled and mated full brother × sister for as long as possible, or until 37 generations were reached. The average productivity of the initial lines crossed to the same synthetic strain at the start of the inbreeding was Ames 1947, 179 ± 2; Ames 1943, 176 ± 3; and Amherst 1947, 166 ± 3 eggs for the 5, 6, and 7th days after the hybrid females hatched. All surviving inbred lines were crossed to the same synthetic stock, and the hybrid females tested at the 8, 9, 16, 23, and 30th generations. The results were consistent for the three stocks. The egg productions of the hybrids declined 2.4 eggs per generation on the average. This result was surprising, but may possibly be accounted for by the fact that the inbred lines surviving in the three stocks were becoming more and more like the synthetic tester due to the fact that they were cultured on the same media and in the same way. The favorable gene differences between the crossed lines became less each generation and resulted in a progressive lowering of hybrid yield. As the generation times were confounded with time of year, it was also possible that the egg yields showed some effects of the progressive changes in season.

The surviving inbred lines were tested for egg yield on the 21, 26, and 31st generations. They showed an average decrease in egg yield of 4.3 eggs per generation. This decrease was greater than that observed for the inbreds × synthetic cited above. This was not entirely unexpected, although it did indicate continued and persistent heterozygosity in the inbred lines to a much greater extent than was sometimes realized. The inbred lines produced 20 to 40 per cent less than the hybrids. The differences became greater as the inbreeding advanced.

The inbreds of the 15, 24, and 34th generations were crossed in all possible ways. The line crosses were 17, 30, and 62 per cent better than their inbred parents. They were also 2 to 4 per cent better than the inbred × synthetic crosses. Figure 29.3 shows these trends for the three types of progenies.

Coefficients were calculated for the like cross performances at different generations. The synthetic × inbred lines had correlations for the 1, 8, 9, 16, 23, and 30th generations. Like numbers of comparisons were available in the reciprocal crosses, inbred lines × synthetic. The correlations were similar for generations and their reciprocals. The average for the thirty comparisons was −0.01. In terms of the data, the synthetic × inbred line cross of one generation gave no information on the relative performance of the same cross in a succeeding test. The hybrids showed random variation within themselves, but at the same time averaged out to be distinctly better than the inbreds.

The inbred lines of the 21, 26, and 34th generations were crossed in all possible ways. Again the correlations between the productivities of the like crosses in different generations showed variation. The average correlation was 0.25. The performance of the cross uniting two of these inbred lines did have some predictive value for the performance of like crosses made subsequently. Again these hybrids showed most of the variation within the crosses to be random, but that the yield level of the hybrids was significantly better than the inbred parent lines. The over-all value for larger yield came as a consequence of the cross rather than as an effect of specific cross differences.

This fact is brought out in another way. The inbred crosses were analyzed for general and specific combining ability, as described earlier, for the three different generations of inbreeding, 15, 24, and 34. The average results were:

General combining ability...... 12%
Specific combining ability...... 5
Residual variation............ 83

These results are comparable with those presented earlier. General and specific combining ability can be estimated for each line in the particular crosses and experiments. The values can be compared as between the different generations, to determine how consistent in combining ability is the behavior of each line. The correlations for these comparisons were as follows:

	15 and 24	15 and 34	24 and 34
General combining abilities......	−0.02	−0.27	−0.17
Specific combining abilities.......	0.13	0.02	0.26

These correlations are so small as to indicate that combining abilities are not consistent from one generation (in this case also season) to the next. The hybrids are uniformly better than the inbreds in yield, but again the genotypic system does not appear to have a fixed reaction. The explanation of this fact appears in Table 29.4 where a high experiment genotype interaction was observed. It means that each genotype may react differently to different environment. As these environments change from place to place, season to season, and even between simultaneous carefully controlled experiments, it is not surprising that the general and specific inheritance effects show variations. A particular fitting of strains to place and season, etc., appears essential for highest yields. In view of this conclusion, it is important to remember that this effect is within hybrids, and that hybrids, in general, are distinctly better than the inbreds (see Fig. 29.3).

Through the kindness of Dr. G. F. Sprague, making available certain of his extensive data on F_1 crosses of some 62 inbred lines of corn, we have been able to extend this analysis and compare the stability of general and specific

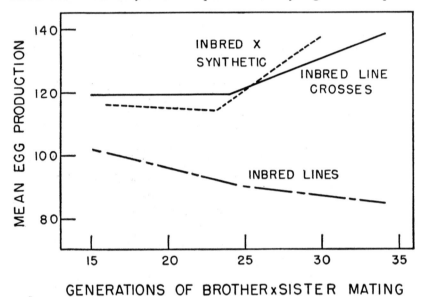

FIG. 29.3—Changes in productivity with advancing generations of brother × sister mating of inbred lines, inbred line crosses, and inbred × synthetic.

combining ability in the two species. The trials were conducted yearly from 1940 to 1948. The F_1 hybrids were planted in ten different areas chosen as representative of the different climatic conditions of Iowa. Any one trial may contain all possible single crosses of 4 to 14 inbred lines. The trials contain many individuals, and are replicated several times so the record for the F_1 is an average of numerous F_1's instead of an individual as in the data on Drosophila. As would be expected, a particular cross was occasionally lost from a test. When this happened, the missing plot value was calculated from the mean and the general combining abilities of the lines entering the test. The specific value was considered zero. The data for the general and specific combining abilities of the lines in the remaining plots were used for further study. Our study considered the first order values, as these are the only values which have operational significance in breeding for heterosis.

General and specific combining abilities are strictly applicable to the particular experiment from which they are calculated. The values for the different lines vary with the group of lines from which they are calculated. This is a serious defect, for the results have no significance unless they may be used for the prediction of the future performance of the particular line or line combination. As the interest is in the operational use of these parameters in guiding breeding work, the theoretical objections to comparing successive values for general or specific combining abilities are outranked by the practical consideration. This study measures the repeatability of the estimates of general and specific combining ability for particular inbred lines when the crosses are grown in different locations, different years, and in different combinations.

Sixty-two inbred lines were the parents of the F_1 crosses. The data include 451 determinations of general and 2033 estimates of specific combining ability. As pointed out above, these determinations are not of equal weight because of differences in numbers and lines in the different F_1 hybrid tests. However, for the purposes of this comparison they are regarded as of equal weight, since it is on this basis that the data will be used for guiding future breeding operations.

The intraclass correlation between the repeated tests of the general combining abilities was 0.29; that for the specific combining abilities of the repeated crosses of the pairs of lines was 0.27. These correlations are definitely higher than those observed for the Drosophila data. They are high enough to be of reasonable importance in practice. The data for the general combining abilities become of somewhat greater value when the determinations are restricted to particular regions of the state, the over-all correlation becoming 0.31. When arranged within years but allowing free range over the 10 different geographical regions of the state, the over-all correlation becomes 0.53. The specific combining abilities do not show an equal improvement in predictive values when subdivided by these categories. Specific combining abilities drop when the data are subdivided by geographical regions of the state, the over-all correlation becoming 0.18. When the subdivision is made by years, the over-all correlation becomes 0.34.

These results reemphasize the effects of the environmental-genotypic interactions on performance as discussed earlier. The corn hybrids are fitted to the geographical regions of the state by selection of the place of planting for season of maturity. Little or no selection is possible for fitting the plantings to the vagaries of the different years. The effects are noted in the intraclass correlations. Double selection for genotypic environmental correlation when the data are subdivided by years leads to definitely increased correlations for the general combining abilities of the particular lines and to slightly increased correlations for the specific combining abilities of these same lines. Where the years $\times$ genotypic effects are allowed to express themselves, the correlations are no greater than those of the whole or are reduced.

SUMMARY

Consideration of egg production and other component characters in *Drosophila melanogaster* shows that hybrids are uniformly better producers than inbreds even though the inbreds be the parents of the hybrids. The hybrids themselves are not exceptional in production when contrasted to the best random bred individuals. Rather, hybrid vigor contributes consistently high performance to all individuals rather than very superior performance to a few.

Lifetime egg productions show greater heterosis than any of the component factors which ultimately determine it. Length of egg laying period has 113 per cent heterosis, maximum egg production 154 per cent, and resistance to decline in vigor, as measured by egg production with advancing age, 120 per cent, while the over-all character lifetime egg yield has 203 per cent heterosis. Heterosis appears to be a consequence of the combined action of two or more groups of distinct and more elementary characters which when jointly favorable lead to generally high yields.

Tests show that hybrid vigor is attributable to nuclear contributions of the two parents rather than to possible cytoplasmic differences in the uniting gametes. Inbred races frequently contain or soon attain mechanisms to slow down or prevent reaching complete homozygosis through continued close inbreeding. Lethal genes, deficiencies, or defective genes residual in all stocks or acquired through mutation, balance to prevent free interchange of genes within chromosome groups, and thus retard or stop the formation of the homozygous types. In the light of these results, mutations as a heterosis mechanism assume much greater importance than ordinarily supposed.

When the egg yields were analyzed by the degree of heterozygosity it was found that flies homozygous for all loci in chromosomes I, II, and III or 0 heterozygous, produced 38.2 eggs on the average. Those heterozygous for one-third of the unlike parental genes in the cross produced 51.5 eggs on the average. Those heterozygous for two-thirds of the unlike parental genes laid 62.6 eggs, and those heterozygous for all unlike parental genes, three-thirds heterozygous had a mean yield of 76.9 eggs. The differences are additive, about 12.9 eggs being added with each increase of one-third of the genes heterozygous. The additivity of the mass gene effects would suggest additivity of the individual gene actions on egg yield. This is an important point but does not necessarily follow, because the dominance or recessiveness or interallelic interactions could be balanced by the mass of gene pairs comprising one-third of the heterozygous loci.

Study of the contributions to the heterosis made by the different chromosomes shows that they are all first order contributions, there being no interaction between chromosome pairs. Comparison of the heterosis attributable to the different chromosomes with different measures of the numbers of gene loci which they contain, shows that as the method of chromosome measurement approaches what appears to be the likely loci number, the better this method agrees with the heterosis which is observed when the chromosome is made heterozygous. The evidence favors several to many gene pairs per chromosome as necessary for the heterotic effects.

Heterotic effects of parental genomes as shown by a series of F_1 hybrids were analyzed. For the individual the most significant contribution to variation was that due to a large number of unanalyzed causes. This component contributed over half of the total variation. Differences due to races contributed 15 per cent, while those due to race-experiment and age interactions, 13 per cent. The interaction term shows that genes in quantitative inheritance are not stable in their effects. In one condition the genes could react as recessives; in another as dominants; in a third, show epistacy.

The dependence of yield on the interrelation of environment and genotype is of even greater importance. The model customarily chosen to represent genetic and environmental effects ordinarily considers the interactions of these terms zero when in truth they may be quite large. The data on both Drosophila and corn general and specific combining abilities of inbred lines show these interactions to be of major importance. Further progress in the utilization of heterosis appears to lie in the adjustment of the hybrid genotype to the environment.

R. E. COMSTOCK
and
H. F. ROBINSON
North Carolina State College

Chapter 30

Estimation of Average Dominance of Genes

This discussion will center around three experimental procedures used at the North Carolina Experiment Station for investigating the degree of dominance involved in the action of genes that affect quantitative characters of economic plants. The objective is twofold: (1) to outline and, in so far as possible, evaluate these methods; and (2) by example, to point up the role of statistics in genetical research.

Basic criteria for the usefulness of a projected experiment are: (1) Will data obtained provide a logical basis for inference relative to the research objective? (2) Will the random variability in the experiment be of an order that will permit satisfactory certainty of conclusions? The latter has obvious statistical overtones, but statistics is not always deeply involved in the former. In genetic work, random variability in the experimental material is generated in part by the genetic mechanism, and can therefore be used as a basis for inference in genetic problems. Hence statistics plays an inescapable role in both aspects of the evaluation of many genetic experiments.

Examination of any proposed basis for inference must obviously center on the premises involved and the validity of deductions predicated on those premises. We will turn first, therefore, to description of the experiments and the logical basis for the estimates they are designed to provide.

THE EXPERIMENTAL DESIGNS

The designs of each of these experiments have two aspects: (1) the genetic background and (2) the field arrangement of the material on which data are collected.

494

Experiment I

The experimental material is produced from matings among plants of the F_2 generation of a cross of two inbred lines. Each plant used as a pollen parent is mated with n seed parents, no seed parent being involved in more than one mating. Thus, if sm pollen parents are used there will be smn seed parents used in smn matings. The progenies of these smn matings comprise the experimental material. All parent plants are chosen from the F_2 population at random.

Pollen parent and seed parent plants will for brevity be referred to in what follows as males and females, respectively. A group of n progenies having the same male parent will be referred to as a male group.

The field arrangement of the material is based on division of the sm male groups into s sets each of which contains mn progenies in m male groups. Each set of progenies comprises the material for a distinct unit of the experiment and is planted in a randomized block arrangement having mn entries and r replications. Thus the total field arrangement is composed of s independent units, each unit being devoted to a different set of progenies. Data on characters of interest are collected on k plants per plot.

Experiment II

This is a modification of Experiment I that can be used when dealing with multi-flowered plants. The foundation stock is again the F_2 generation of a cross of inbred lines. In this case, however, a set of mn progenies is produced by making all of the mn possible matings of m males and n females chosen at random from the F_2 population. With annual plants this can be done (and the progenies kept distinct) only if more than one pistillate flower per plant is available. It could not be done, for example, with single-eared corn.

The field arrangement is as described for Experiment I, the sets arising from the mating plan being maintained intact in the units of the field structure of the experiment.

Experiment III

The experimental material is produced from backcross matings of F_2 plants to the two inbred lines from which the F_2 was derived; the F_2 plants are used as pollen parents. A set of progenies is made up of the $2n$ progenies obtained from backcrossing n random F_2 plants to each of the parent inbreds. The number of inbred plants used in production of each backcross progeny is important only with respect to insuring sufficient seed.

The total experimental material consists of s sets of n pairs of progenies. The members of each pair have the same F_2 (male) parent but different inbred parents. The two inbred parents are, of course, the same for all pairs of progenies.

The field arrangement is analogous to that for Experiments I and II. The unit in this case is a randomized block arrangement ($2n$ entries and r replications) of r plots of each of the progenies of a set.

ANALYSIS OF DATA

The appropriate variance analyses for the data of the three experiments are outlined in Tables 30.1 to 30.3. The expected value (the value that

TABLE 30.1

VARIANCE ANALYSIS (EXPERIMENT I)

Source of Variance	d.f.	m.s.	Expectation of m.s.*
Sets...................	$s-1$	....	....
Replications in sets........	$s(r-1)$	....	....
Males in sets............	$s(m-1)$	M_{11}	$\sigma^2 + r\sigma_f^2 + rn\sigma_m^2$
Females in males in sets....	$sm(n-1)$	M_{12}	$\sigma^2 + r\sigma_f^2$
Remainder among plots....	$s(mn-1)(r-1)$	M_{13}	σ^2

* σ^2 is the error variance among plots of the same progeny (due in part to soil variation among plots in the same block and in part to variation among plants of the same progeny).

σ_f^2 is progeny variance arising from genetic differences among female parents.

σ_m^2 is progeny variance arising from genetic differences among male parents.

TABLE 30.2

VARIANCE ANALYSIS (EXPERIMENT II)

Source of Variance	d.f.	m.s.	Expectation of m.s.*
Sets...................	$s-1$	....	....
Replications in sets.......	$s(r-1)$	....	....
Males in sets...........	$s(m-1)$	M_{21}	$\sigma^2 + r\sigma_{fm}^2 + rn\sigma_m^2$
Females in sets...........	$s(n-1)$	M_{22}	$\sigma^2 + r\sigma_{fm}^2 + rm\sigma_f^2$
Males×females in sets....	$s(m-1)(n-1)$	M_{23}	$\sigma^2 + r\sigma_{fm}^2$
Remainder among plots...	$s(mn-1)(r-1)$	M_{24}	σ^2

* σ_{fm}^2 is progeny variance arising from interaction of genotypes of male and female parents. Other symbols are defined in Table 30.1.

would be approached as a limit if the amount of data were made infinitely large) is listed for each mean square to be used in interpretations.

In order to specify the significance of components of the total variance of which estimates can be used for inferences about dominance, some additional symbolism must first be established. Consider the three genotypes possible at a locus where there is segregation between two alleles. Let the difference in effect of the two homozygous genotypes on a measured character be $2u$ and the deviation of the effect of the heterozygous genotype from the mean effect of the homozygous genotypes be au. Note that u and au have the same significance as d and h, respectively, in the symbolism used by Fisher *et al.* (1932). Also, they have the same significance as d and k in the symbolism employed earlier in the Heterosis Conference. The symbols u and au are used here for consistency with usage in articles by Comstock and Robinson (1948) and Comstock *et al.* (1949). Let the number of segregating gene pairs that affect a particular character be symbolized as N, and a numerical subscript to u or a specify the locus to which the symbolized quantity is relevant. Thus $2u_3$ is the difference in effect of the two homozygous genotypes of the third locus and a_5u_5 is the dominance deviation for the fifth locus.

Now granting validity of several assumptions (to be listed and discussed later) σ_m^2, σ_f^2, σ_{mf}^2, and σ_{ml}^2 have genetic meaning as set out in Table 30.4.

TABLE 30.3

VARIANCE ANALYSIS (EXPERIMENT III)

Source of Variance	d.f.	m.s.	Expectation of m.s.*
Sets......................	$s-1$	....	....
Replications in sets...........	$s(r-1)$	....	....
Inbred line in sets............	s	....	....
F_2 parent in sets............	$s(n-1)$	M_{31}	$\sigma^2 + 2r\sigma_m^2$
F_2 parent$\times$line in sets........	$s(n-1)$	M_{32}	$\sigma^2 + r\sigma_{ml}^2$
Remainder among plots.......	$s(2n-1)(r-1)$	M_{33}	σ^2

* σ_m^2 is progeny variance arising from genetic differences among F_2 (male) parents.

σ_{ml}^2 is progeny variance arising from interaction of genotypes of F_2 and inbred parents.

THE ESTIMATE OF AVERAGE DOMINANCE

The magnitude of a measures the degree of dominance in the action of any one pair of genes, being related to qualitative classification of dominance as follows:

Class of Dominance	Numerical Value of a
No dominance	$a = 0$
Partial dominance	$0 < a < 1.0$
Complete dominance	$a = 1.0$
Overdominance	$a > 1.0$

However, a problem arises concerning the best way to represent the average dominance for all loci with a single number. An obvious possibility is the unweighted mean of a's for all gene pairs. On the other hand, it can be argued that a mean in which individual a's are weighted relative to the importance of loci would be more useful. This in turn raises the question of how the relative importance of loci should be measured. However, the matter will not be pursued further, since the experiments under consideration offer no choice of measure to be estimated.

The estimate that can be made is of

$$\bar{a}^2 = \frac{\Sigma a^2 u^2}{\Sigma u^2} \qquad \text{or} \qquad \bar{a} = \sqrt{\frac{\Sigma a^2 u^2}{\Sigma u^2}}$$

$\bar{a}^2$ is a weighted average of all a^2s, weighting being relative to the square of u (one of the possible measures of the importance of loci). $\bar{a}^2$ and $\bar{a}$ can exceed unity only if one or more individual a's are larger than one, but values of $\bar{a}^2$ in excess of one do not exclude the possibility of partial dominance at numerous

TABLE 30.4

GENETIC NATURE OF COMPONENTS
OF PROGENY VARIANCE*

Component	Experiment		
	I	*II*	*III*
σ_m^2	$\frac{1}{8}\Sigma u^2$	$\frac{1}{8}\Sigma u^2$	$\frac{1}{8}\Sigma u^2$
σ_f^2	$\frac{1}{8}\Sigma u^2 + \frac{1}{16}\Sigma a^2 u^2$	$\frac{1}{8}\Sigma u^2$	
σ_{mf}^2		$\frac{1}{16}\Sigma a^2 u^2$	
σ_{ml}^2			$\frac{1}{4}\Sigma a^2 u^2$

* Summation is in all cases over loci, i.e.,
$\Sigma u^2 = (u_1^2 + u_2^2 + \ldots u_N^2)$ and
$\Sigma a^2 u^2 = (a_1^2 u_1^2 + a_2^2 u_2^2 + \ldots a_N^2 u_N^2)$

loci. On the other hand, $\bar{a}^2$ will not be less than one unless dominance is less than complete at one or more loci, but values less than one do not insure absence of overdominance at all loci.

Experiment I

In accordance with the mean square expectations of Table 30.1 we can estimate

$$\sigma_m^2 \quad \text{as} \quad (M_{11} - M_{12}) / rn$$

and

$$\sigma_f^2 \quad \text{as} \quad (M_{12} - M_{13}) / r$$

and from Table 30.4 we see that in this experiment

$$\sigma_m^2 = \tfrac{1}{8}\Sigma u^2$$

and

$$\sigma_f^2 - \sigma_m^2 = \tfrac{1}{16}\Sigma a^2 u^2$$

Hence,

$$\frac{2\,[\,(n+1)\,M_{12} - M_{11} - nM_{13}]}{M_{11} - M_{12}} \quad \text{is an estimate of} \quad \frac{\Sigma a^2 u^2}{\Sigma u^2} = \bar{a}^2 .$$

Experiment II

Note first from Table 30.4 that in this experiment $\sigma_m^2 = \sigma_f^2$. If the experiment is designed with $m = n$ (this will be assumed in what follows since it is a rational procedure where possible) this means that the expectation of M_{21}

and M_{22} (see Table 30.2) are equal and hence that the two mean squares may be pooled.[1] Let the pooled mean square be symbolized by M_{20}. Then

$$(M_{20} - M_{23}) \, / \, rn \text{ estimates } \sigma_f^2 = \sigma_m^2$$

and

$$(M_{23} - M_{24}) \, / \, r \quad \text{estimates } \sigma_{fm}^2$$

In this experiment (see Table 30.4)

$$\sigma_f^2 = \sigma_m^2 = \tfrac{1}{8} \Sigma u^2$$

and

$$\sigma_{fm}^2 = \tfrac{1}{16} \Sigma a^2 u^2$$

It follows that

$$\frac{2n \, (M_{23} - M_{24})}{M_{20} - M_{23}} \text{ estimates } \frac{\Sigma a^2 u^2}{\Sigma u^2} = \bar{a}^2 .$$

Experiment III

Following Tables 30.3 and 30.4 we see that

$$(M_{31} - M_{33}) \, / \, 2\, r \text{ estimates } \sigma_m^2 = \tfrac{1}{8} \Sigma u^2$$

$$(M_{32} - M_{33}) \, / \, r \text{ estimates } \sigma_{ml}^2 = \tfrac{1}{4} \Sigma a^2 u^2$$

so that

$$\frac{M_{32} - M_{33}}{M_{31} - M_{33}} \text{ estimates } \bar{a}^2 .$$

ASSUMPTIONS

Evaluation of procedures described above should obviously begin with examination of assumptions underlying derivations of mean square expectations listed in Tables 30.1 to 30.3 and genetic interpretations placed on variance components in Table 30.4. Premises involved in the derivation of mean square expectations were as follows:

1. Random choice of individuals mated for production of experimental progenies.
2. Random distribution of genotypes relative to variations in environment.
3. No non-genic maternal effects.

The first of these can be assured easily in the conduct of the experiment. The second is equally easy to assure in so far as environmental variations within the experiment are concerned. On the other hand, the environments encountered in an experiment conducted within the confines of a single year

1. By taking an unweighted mean since degrees of freedom will also be equal when $m = n$.

and location do not constitute a random sample of the environments that occur within the wider limits of time and space for which we would like experimental findings to apply. The consequence of this is that, if interaction of genotype with environment is a source of variation, each mean square arising from variation among progenies will contain some variance from such interaction. Thus, to have been rigorously correct, the expectations of all mean squares between progenies should have included terms recognizing contributions from this source. Separate estimation of the genetic and interaction components of mean squares between progenies could not be effected with data collected in a single year and location. If the ratio of these two sorts of variance is constant for the several mean squares, and there is no obvious reason why it should vary, the presence of interaction variance does not bias the estimates of $\bar{a}^2$ since numerator and denominator are affected proportionately. Nevertheless this constitutes a possible weakness of the methods but one which, if important, can be corrected by replication of all progenies over years and locations.

There are many characters and organisms for which it appears safe to assume maternal affects are absent or of no consequence. This assumption must be viewed with some suspicion when dealing with seedling characters of plants or any character for which there is any hint that cytoplasmic inheritance may be operating, and it is definitely not tenable for pre-maturity characters of mammals. Maternal effects do not contribute to the pertinent mean squares in the variance analysis of Experiment III and only to M_{22} in that of Experiment II. Thus these two experiments are useful in the presence of maternal effects, though if II is used Σu^2 must be estimated from M_{21} instead of jointly from M_{21} and M_{22}.

Assumptions involved in deriving the genetic interpretations of variance components are as follows:

1. Regular diploid behavior at meiosis.
2. Population gene frequencies of one-half at all loci where there is segregation (not necessary for Experiment III).
3. No multiple allelism.
4. No correlation of genotypes at separate loci. This implies no linkage among genes affecting the character studied or that, if linkages exist, the distribution of genotypes is at equilibrium with respect to coupling and repulsion phases.
5. No epistasis, *i.e.*, the effect of variation in genotype at any single locus is not modified by genes at other loci.

In accord with the first of these, usefulness of the procedures described is limited to studies with diploids or amphidiploids in which multivalent meiotic associations are entirely absent or are absent in meiotic divisions giving rise to fertile gametes.

Save for deviations due to natural selection, the second assumption is assured by the fact that the population used is an F_2 of a cross of homozygous lines. Moreover, natural selection strong enough to have more than a trivial effect on gene frequencies can only occur if the development of a moderately large proportion of F_2 plants is so slow or aberrant as to prevent their effective use as parents. Thus a good stand of usable plants constitutes insurance that this assumption is satisfied.

Number three is also assured by the origin of the populations. Multiple alleles in an F_2 of homozygous lines can result only from mutation, and in the light of present knowledge of mutation rates would be expected very infrequently.

On the other hand, complete validity of the fourth assumption is improbable. Present day geneticists are in general agreement that quantitative characters, and particularly physiologically complex ones such as yield, are influenced by many genes. If that is so, there may well be linkages among some of the genes affecting any single character. Furthermore, specific linkage relationships in an F_1 of homozygous lines must be in either the coupling or repulsion phase, and equilibrium between the phases cannot occur in the F_2. In fact the approach to equilibrium in later generations is rather slow unless linkage is very loose (see Wright, 1933).

The effect of linkage is to cause upward bias in estimates of $\bar{a}$. Thus Comstock and Robinson (1948) in discussion of Experiments I and II and Robinson et al. (1949) in discussing results obtained using Experiment I indicated that values of $\bar{a}$ larger than one can result either from true overdominance or from repulsion linkage of genes that are completely or partially dominant to their alleles. The same conclusion can be inferred from Mather (1949).

The situation can be summarized in another manner by stating that values of $\bar{a}$ in excess of unity do not distinguish true overdominance in the action of alleles from what Mangelsdorf has termed pseudo-overdominance or overdominance at the gamete level. However, in defense of the procedures under discussion, it must be emphasized that knowing one or the other of these two phenomena is at work is an advance over being uncertain as to whether either is operative. On the other hand there is good reason to attempt to distinguish which is responsible if estimates of $\bar{a}$ by the methods described are much greater than one. One source of such supplementary information is an extension of Experiment III to be considered briefly in the next section.

The assumption of no epistasis is no more realistic than that of no linkages. It has been pointed out (Comstock and Robinson, 1948) that epistasis probably causes upward bias in the estimates of $\bar{a}$, but that the amount of bias may not be large. Subsequent investigation of several simple epistatic models with respect to expected values of estimates of $\bar{a}$ from Experiments I and II have turned up nothing to change that point of view. It must be emphasized that the matter has not been considered exhaustively, and the possibility remains that in some materials epistasis would be responsible for serious overestimation of $\bar{a}$ by the methods being discussed.

The authors' knowledge of the situation may be summarized briefly as follows. It appears possible that with complete dominance the rule, $\bar{a} = 1.0$, epistasis might bias estimates upwards by as much as .10 to .25. This cannot be considered serious against the background of an actual estimate of 1.6 as reported for grain yield in corn by Robinson *et al.* (1949). On the other hand, genetic models can be specified in which the consequences of epistasis would be serious, but to date no such models have been discovered that seem likely to have reality in nature.

Much investigation of the epistasis problem remains to be done. Theoretical studies of a variety of epistatic models are needed as a basis for understanding (1) how and to what extent inferences based on expectations derived from non-epistatic models may be in error, and (2) how epistasis may be measured and characterized experimentally. Equally important are experimental investigations of the role of epistasis in inheritance of quantitative characters of various organisms. The problem in this connection is one of knowing how to obtain critical information. The most familiar approach is that of studying the regression of character measurements on levels of homozygosity as represented at the extremes by inbred lines and F_1's and at intermediate levels by F_2's and various sorts of backcrosses. While this approach has admitted shortcomings, it has not been exploited to the limit of its usefulness. Other possibilities are suggested by Mather (1949).

EVALUATION OF THE ROLE OF LINKAGE

It was pointed out above that repulsion linkages are a source of upward bias in estimates of $\bar{a}$. In fact if a moderately high number of genes is postulated, one finds on careful examination that estimates in excess of one seem inevitable unless dominance at the locus level is considerably less than complete. From the point of view of breeding methods it then becomes important to distinguish between true overdominance and pseudo-overdominance. Particularly is this true if the latter is to any important degree a consequence of linkages that are loose enough to allow their effects to be dissipated by recombination in a few generations of random breeding, as opposed to the rather durable associations that appear to be postulated by Anderson (1949).

If the assumption that frequencies of genes at all segregating loci are one-half were tenable for generations beyond the F_2, any of the three experiments would provide a basis for obtaining information on the role of linkage. The procedure would be to compare estimates obtained as described with others obtained when parents were taken from an advanced generation (produced under random mating, not with inbreeding) rather than from the F_2. In fact one might systematically repeat the experiment using each successive generation as it became available. Then if loose linkages were of much importance in the first estimate, one would anticipate a downward trend in the estimates of $\bar{a}$ as more and more advanced generations were employed. Natural selection too weak to have much effect on results when the F_2 is used could be the source of significant changes in gene frequencies over a period of generations. Hence the effects of recombination and of shifting gene frequencies would be confounded in trends observed using either Experiment I or II.

Fortunately, Experiment III does not depend on any assumption about gene frequencies. Letting q symbolize the population frequency of any gene and $1 - q$ that of its allele, the genetic interpretation of σ_m^2 and σ_{ml}^2 can be expressed more generally than in Table 30.4 as $\frac{1}{2}\Sigma q(1 - q)u^2$ and $\Sigma q(1 - q)a^2u^2$, respectively. One possible weakness of the proposal is apparent. If shifts in gene frequency are variable by loci the weighting of individual a's in $\bar{a}^2$ is shifted slightly since it is now relative to $q(1 - q)u^2$ rather than u^2. However, barring shifts greater than .2 which are unlikely unless a gene has a very important effect, shifts in weights will be of minor magnitude since $q(1 - q)$ varies only between .21 and .25 as q varies from .3 to .7. Furthermore, shifts in weight are not a source of bias unless degree of dominance (size of a) is correlated with importance of the gene. While this weakness should not be overlooked, it appears of minor consequence. A partial check could be made by accumulating seed of each generation for a yield comparison of the successive generations. If major gene frequency trends have occurred at important loci they should be evidenced in higher yields by the later generations.

The suggested extension of Experiment III is intrinsically the same sort of technic as Mather (1949) has outlined for investigating linkage effects on genetic variances.

DERIVATION OF GENETIC INTERPRETATIONS OF COMPONENTS OF VARIANCE BETWEEN PROGENIES

The genetic constitution of σ_m^2 and σ_{ml}^2 of Experiment III will be derived as examples. Derivations for components of the other two experiments are given elsewhere (Comstock and Robinson, 1948). Initial assumptions will include only the following: regular diploid behavior at meiosis, no multiple allelism, no epistasis. Restrictions are not being placed on gene frequencies or linkage. To that extent the derivations to be given below are more general than those cited above which assumed absence of linkage and gene frequencies all equal to one-half.

The population sampled in Experiment III is outlined in Table 30.5. It consists of an infinity of pairs of backcross progenies, one pair for each variable parent that might be chosen from the F_2 or a later generation from crossing the two homozygous lines. Expected genetic values of each progeny are indicated symbolically. Because all progenies must be of finite size, there will be a sampling deviation between the actual and expected values of the progenies. The variation among expected values is the variation due to genetic differences among parents, and hence that to be considered in evaluating σ_m^2 and σ_{ml}^2. σ_m^2 is the progeny variance due to genetic differences among the variable parents, $i.e.$, the variance of the pair means indicated in the next to the last column of Table 30.5. σ_{ml}^2, the progeny variance from interaction of genotypes of the variable and homozygous parents, is one-half the variance of the pair differences indicated in the final column.[2]

TABLE 30.5

POPULATION SAMPLED IN EXPERIMENT III

| VARIABLE PARENT* | HOMOZYGOUS PARENT | | MEAN | DIFFER-ENCE |
	Line A	Line B		
1	X_{a1}	X_{b1}	$\bar{X}_1$	D_1
2	X_{a2}	X_{b2}	$\bar{X}_2$	D_2
3	X_{a3}	X_{b3}	$\bar{X}_3$	D_3
.				
.				
.				
s	X_{as}	X_{bs}	$\bar{X}_s$	D_s

* The one chosen from F_2 or later generation of the cross between lines A and B.

s symbolizes an infinitely large number.

X's are expected genetic values of progenies, subscripts indicate parentage of individual progenies.

$\bar{X}_i$ = mean of X_{ai} and X_{bi} [where the subscript i identifies the variable parent, e.g., $\bar{X}_1 = (X_{a1} + X_{b1})/2$].

$D_i = X_{ai} - X_{bi}$.

Now note that a pair mean or difference is the sum of contributions from individual loci. Let

x_{ij} be the contribution of the jth locus to the ith pair mean, and

d_{ij} be the contribution of the jth locus to the ith pair difference.

Then

$$\bar{X}_i = x_{i1} + x_{i2} + \ldots x_{iN}$$
$$D_i = d_{i1} + d_{i2} + \ldots d_{iN}$$

where N is the number of contributing loci. Then the variances of pair means and differences must be as follows:[3]

$$\sigma_{\bar{X}}^2 \ (= \sigma_m^2) = \sum_j \sigma_{xj}^2 + 2 \sum_{j,k} \sigma_{xjk} \tag{1}$$

$$\sigma_D^2 \ (= 2\sigma_{ml}^2) = \sum_j \sigma_{dj}^2 + 2 \sum_{j,k} \sigma_{djk} \tag{2}$$

2. It is well known and easily verified that in the analysis of variance of any $2 \times s$ table, the interaction variance is one-half that of the pair differences.

3. Since the variance of the sum of any number of variables is the sum of the variances of those variables plus twice the sum of all covariances among them.

where σ_{xj}^2 is the variance of contributions from the jth locus to pair means,

σ_{xjk} is the covariance of contributions from the jth and kth loci to pair means,

σ_{dj}^2 is the variance of contributions from the jth locus to pair differences,

σ_{djk}^2 is the covariance of contributions from the jth and kth loci to pair differences, and $\sum\limits_{j,k}$ indicates summation over all pairs of loci.

From equations (1) and (2) it is apparent that general expressions for σ_m^2 and σ_{ml}^2 can be written as soon as we know (i) the variance of contributions of any single locus to pair means and differences, and (ii) the covariance of contributions of any two loci to pair means and differences.

With respect to two loci, there will be ten types of variable parent (when classification is by types of gametes giving rise to the parent plant). Table 30.6 lists these, together with their frequencies in the population and the

TABLE 30.6

FREQUENCIES OF VARIABLE PARENT TYPES AND CONTRI-
BUTIONS* OF INDIVIDUAL LOCI TO EXPECTED
GENETIC VALUES OF PROGENIES

VARIABLE PARENT	FREQ.†	HOMOZYGOUS LINE				MEAN		DIFFERENCE	
		B_1b_2/B_1b_2		b_1B_2/b_1B_2		x_1	x_2	d_1	d_2
		1st locus	2d locus	1st locus	2d locus				
B_1B_2/B_1B_2	p^2	u_1	a_2u_2	a_1u_1	u_2	$(u_1+a_1u_1)/2$	$(u_2+a_2u_2)/2$	$u_1-a_1u_1$	$a_2u_2-u_2$
B_1B_2/B_1b_2	$2pr$	$u\ddagger$	$(au-u)/2$	au	$(u+au)/2$	$(u+au)/2$	$au/2$	$u-au$	$-u$
B_1b_2/B_1b_2	r^2	u	au	$-u$	au	$(au-u)/2$	$(au-u)/2$	$u-au$	$-u-au$
B_1B_2/b_1B_2	$2ps$	$(u+au)/2$	au	$(au-u)/2$	u	$au/2$	$(u+au)/2$	u	$au-u$
B_1B_2/b_1b_2	$2pt$	$(u+au)/2$	$(au-u)/2$	$(au-u)/2$	$(u+au)/2$	$au/2$	$au/2$	u	$-u$
B_1b_2/b_1B_2	$2rs$	$(u+au)/2$	$(au-u)/2$	$(au-u)/2$	$(u+au)/2$	$au/2$	$au/2$	u	$-u$
B_1b_2/b_1b_2	$2rt$	$(u+au)/2$	$-u$	$(au-u)/2$	au	$au/2$	$(au-u)/2$	u	$-u-au$
b_1B_2/b_1B_2	s^2	au	au	$-u$	u	$(au-u)/2$	$(u+au)/2$	$u+au$	$au-u$
b_1B_2/b_1b_2	$2st$	au	$(au-u)/2$	$-u$	$(u+au)/2$	$(au-u)/2$	$au/2$	$u+au$	$-u$
b_1b_2/b_1b_2	t^2	au	$-u$	$-u$	au	$(au-u)/2$	$(au-u)/2$	$u+au$	$-u-au$

 * Coded by subtraction of $u_1 + z_1$ (or $u_2 + z_2$) where z is the contribution from the locus when homozygous for the b allele.

 † On the basis that frequencies in which B_1B_2, B_1b_2, b_1B_2, and b_1b_2 gametes are produced in the generation preceding that used for variable parents are p, r, s, and t, respectively. $p + r + s + t = 1.0$.

 ‡ For ease of printing, subscripts to a and u are omitted in rows beyond the first. However, the subscript used in the first row of each column applies throughout the column.

contributions of the two loci to the expected genetic values of progenies and to pair means and differences. As is evident from genotypes indicated for the homozygous lines, the initial linkage phase assumed is repulsion. The required variances and covariances can be worked out directly from information in the table. For example, the variance of contributions from the 1st locus to pair means is

$$(p^2 + 2pr + r^2)(u_1 + a_1u_1)^2/4 + (2ps + 2pt + 2rs + 2rt)\,a_1^2u_1^2/4$$
$$+ (s^2 + 2st + t^2)(a_1u_1 - u_1)^2/4 - (\Sigma x_1)^2$$

and the covariance of contributions to pair means from the 1st and 2d loci is

$$p^2 (u_1 + a_1 u_1)(u_2 + a_2 u_2)/4 + 2p\,r\,(u_1 + a_1 u_1)(a_2 u_2)/4 + \ldots$$

$$\ldots + t^2 (a_1 u_1 - u_1)(a_2 u_2 - u_2)/4 - (\Sigma x_1)(\Sigma x_2).$$

The algebraic reductions are tedious, particularly for the covariances, and will not be written out. However, the final expressions, for both the repulsion and coupling phase, are listed in Table 30.7.

TABLE 30.7

VARIANCES AND COVARIANCES OF SINGLE
LOCUS CONTRIBUTIONS TO PAIR
MEANS AND DIFFERENCES

ITEM	INITIAL LINKAGE PHASE	
	Coupling	Repulsion
σ_{x1}^2	$\frac{1}{2}(p+r)(s+t)u_1^2$	$\frac{1}{2}(p+r)(s+t)u_1^2$
σ_{x2}^2	$\frac{1}{2}(p+s)(r+t)u_2^2$	$\frac{1}{2}(p+s)(r+t)u_2^2$
σ_{x12}	$\frac{1}{2}(pt-rs)u_1 u_2$	$\frac{1}{2}(pt-rs)u_1 u_2$
σ_{d1}^2	$2(p+r)(s+t)a_1^2 u_1^2$	$2(p+r)(s+t)a_1^2 u_1^2$
σ_{d2}	$2(p+s)(r+t)a_2^2 u_2^2$	$2(p+s)(r+t)a_2^2 u_2^2$
σ_{d12}	$2(pt-rs)a_1 u_1 a_2 u_2$	$2(rs-pt)a_1 u_1 a_2 u_2$

Note now that if the frequencies of B_1 and B_2 (in the population from which the variable parents are taken) are symbolized as q_1 and q_2, then

$$p + r = q_1 \qquad s + t = 1 - q_1$$

$$p + s = q_2 \qquad r + t = 1 - q_2$$

and

$$\sigma_{x1}^2 = \tfrac{1}{2} q_1 (1 - q_1) u_1^2$$

$$\sigma_{x2}^2 = \tfrac{1}{2} q_2 (1 - q_2) u_2^2$$

In general

$$\sigma_{xj}^2 = \tfrac{1}{2} q_j (1 - q_j) u_j^2$$

and

$$\sigma_{dj}^2 = 2 q_j (1 - q_j) a_j^2 u_j^2$$

Substituting in equations (1) and (2), we have

$$\sigma_m^2 = \sigma_x^2 = \frac{1}{2}\sum_j q_j (1 - q_j) u_j^2 + \sum_{j,k} (pt - rs)_{jk} u_j u_k \tag{3}$$

and

$$\sigma_{ml}^2 = \tfrac{1}{2}\sigma_D^2 = \sum_j q_j (1 - q_j) a_j^2 u_j^2 + 2\sum_{j,k}^{c} (pt - rs)_{jk} a_j u_j a_k u_k$$

$$+ 2\sum_{j,k}^{r} (rs - pt)_{jk} a_j u_j a_k u_k \tag{4}$$

where $\sum\limits_{j,\,k}^{c}$ indicates summation over all pairs of loci for which the initial

linkage phase was coupling and $\sum\limits_{j,\,k}^{r}$, summation over pairs for which the

initial phase was repulsion.

When the associations between alleles at two loci are at equilibrium with respect to coupling and repulsion phases, either because the loci are not linked or because there has been sufficient opportunity for recombination

$$p = q_j q_k \qquad\qquad r = q_j (1 - q_k)$$
$$s = (1 - q_j) q_k \qquad t = (1 - q_j)(1 - q_k)$$

and $(pt - rs) = 0$. Thus assuming no linkages (3) and (4) reduce to

$$\sigma_m^2 = \tfrac{1}{2}\Sigma q (1 - q) u^2$$
$$\sigma_{ml}^2 = \sigma q (1 - q) a^2 u^2$$

as indicated in the preceding section. If, in addition, gene frequencies at all segregating loci are assumed to be one-half, σ_m^2 and σ_{ml}^2 reduce to the values assigned them in Table 30.4.

If there are linkages and equilibrium has not been reached, $(pt - rs)$ will be negative if the initial phase was repulsion, positive if the initial phase was coupling. Thus covariances from repulsion and coupling linkages will tend to cancel in σ_m^2. In fact if one assumes that enough loci are involved so that the number of linked pairs must be high and that there is no reason why the closer linkages should be predominantly in one phase, one is tempted to conclude that the sum of covariance will not be very important in σ_m^2.

On the other hand the covariance term is always positive in σ_{ml}^2, being a function of $(pt - rs)$ for coupling and of $(rs - pt)$ for repulsion.[4] Thus presence of any linkage, regardless of whether the two phases are equally frequent, will cause σ_{ml}^2 to be greater than $\Sigma q(1 - q)a^2 u^2$, except in the improbable event that a for either or both members of pairs of linked loci is zero. And unless all linkages were in the coupling phase (in which case the ratio of σ_m^2 to $\tfrac{1}{2}\Sigma q(1 - q)u^2$ would be the same as of σ_{ml}^2 to $\Sigma q(1 - q)a^2 u^2$ and hence the ratio of σ_m^2 to σ_{ml}^2 unaffected by the linkages) $\sigma_{ml}^2/2\sigma_m^2$ would overestimate $\Sigma q(1 - q)a^2 u^2/\Sigma q(1 - q)u^2$ so long as equilibrium in linkage associations had not been attained through recombination. However, as stated in the preceding section, the linkage bias becomes progressively smaller as equilibrium is approached.

For purposes of illustration, consider application of the formulae in a simple hypothetical situation. Assume that Experiment III is applied as first described, with variable parents taken from an F_2, and that the quanti-

4. This assumes generality of dominance of the more favorable allele—that a will almost always be positive.

tative character to be studied is affected by seven pairs of genes that are distributed as follows in the parent lines:

$$\text{Line } A—B_1B_1 b_2 b_2 b_3 b_3 b_4 b_4 B_5 B_5 B_6 B_6 b_7 b_7$$

$$\text{Line } B—b_1 b_1 B_2 B_2 B_3 B_3 B_4 B_4 b_5 b_5 b_6 b_6 B_7 B_7$$

with u's and a's having the following values:

	1	2	3	4	5	6	7
				Locus			
u.....1	2	1	2	1	2	1	
a.....6	.6	.8	.8	.8	1.0	.8	

Note that less than complete dominance has been assumed for every locus. Gene frequencies should be one-half in an F_2, so $\frac{1}{2}\Sigma q(1 - q)u^2$ becomes $\frac{1}{8}\Sigma u^2$ and $\Sigma q(1 - q)a^2u^2$ becomes $\frac{1}{4}\Sigma a^2 u^2$. Substituting numerical values of u and a listed above, we obtain

$$\tfrac{1}{8}\Sigma q (1 - q) u^2 = 2.0$$

and

$$\Sigma q (1 - q) a^2 u^2 = 2.57$$

Now assume the following recombination values for pairs of loci:

Pair	Recombination Value (v)
1 and 2	.3
3 and 4	.2
5 and 6	.1
5 and 7	.2
6 and 7	.1
All others	.5

Thus the seven loci fall in three groups that are either on three separate chromosomes or, if on the same chromosome, far enough apart to allow free recombination. In an F_2 the values of p, r, s, and t will depend on v, the recombination value, and the original linkage phase as follows:

	p	r	s	t
Coupling.....	$(1-v)/2$	$v/2$	$v/2$	$(1-v)/2$
Repulsion....	$v/2$	$(1-v)/2$	$(1-v)/2$	$v/2$

Hence $(pt - rs)$ takes the following values:

		v		
	.1	.2	.3	.5
Coupling........	.20	.15	.10	.0
Repulsion.......	-.20	-.15	-.10	.0

Substituting these and the numerical values of the a's and u's, we find

Locus Pair	Linkage Phase	$(pl - rs)u_j u_k$	$(pl - rs)a_j u_j a_k u_k$	$(rs - pl)a_j u_j a_k u_k$
1 and 2	Repulsion	$-.2$		.0720
3 and 4	Coupling	.3	.1920	
5 and 6	Coupling	.4	.3200	
5 and 7	Repulsion	$-.15$		.0960
6 and 7	Repulsion	$-.40$		.3200
		$-.05$	.5120	.4880

With these three sums and the values found above for $\frac{1}{2}\Sigma q(1 - q)u^2$ and $\Sigma q(1 - q)a^2 u^2$ we compute

$$\sigma^2_m = 2.00 + (-.05) = 1.95$$

and

$$\sigma^2_{ml} = 2.57 + 2(.512) + 2(.488) = 4.57$$

Thus, while

$$\bar{a}^2 = \frac{\Sigma a^2 u^2}{\Sigma u^2} = \frac{2.57}{2(2.0)} = .64,$$

the experiment would estimate

$$\frac{\sigma^2_{ml}}{2\sigma^2_m} = \frac{4.57}{2(1.95)} = 1.17.$$

Put differently, the estimate of $\bar{a}^2$ provided by Experiment III would in this case have positive bias in the amount $1.17 - .64 = .53$.

The foregoing example is given only to clarify the meaning of the formulae, not to suggest the amount of bias that may actually be present in practice. The actual bias with any specific material would depend on the amount of linkage and the relative prevalence of coupling and repulsion phases. However, the bias can only be positive and may range from a negligible to a large amount depending on the prevalence of repulsion linkage. While such bias detracts from the described estimate as a criterion of average dominance at the locus level, it is worth emphasizing that it represents a pseudo-overdominance effect which if persistent (due to closeness of linkages responsible) has much the same significance for short-run breeding practice as true overdominance. If the bias declines fairly rapidly as opportunity is provided for recombination, Experiment III offers a means of measuring that decline and thereby gaining an idea of the extent to which apparent dominance stems from linkage relationships that are loose enough to allow a near approach to equilibrium of linkage phases within a moderate number of generations.

AMOUNT OF DATA REQUIRED

An exhaustive consideration of this problem would require more space than can be devoted to it here. Detailed discussion will therefore be limited to one specific question. Let P symbolize the probability of an estimate of $\bar{a}$

that is significantly[5] greater than one. The question to be considered is as follows: Assuming a particular value (> 1.0) for $\bar{a}$ how much data is required if P is to be one-half? Procedure and the argument involved will be given in detail for Experiment III; only comparative results will be indicated for the other two.

If the values of σ_m^2 and σ_{ml}^2 listed in Table 30.4 are substituted into the expectations of M_{31} and M_{32} of Table 30.3, we have

$$E\,(M_{31}) = \sigma^2 + \frac{r}{4}\,\Sigma u^2$$

$$E\,(M_{32}) = \sigma^2 + \frac{r}{4}\,\Sigma a^2 u^2$$

Note that when $\Sigma u^2 = \Sigma a^2 u^2$, i.e., when $\bar{a} = 1.0$, the two expectations are equal. But if $\bar{a} > 1.0$, which means $\Sigma a^2 u^2 > \Sigma u^2$; then $E(M_{32}) > E(M_{31})$. Also, the estimate of $\bar{a}$ will exceed one only where $M_{32} > M_{31}$. It follows that a one-tailed test of the hypothesis that $E(M_{32}) - E(M_{31}) \leqslant 0$ is also a test of the hypothesis that $\bar{a} \leqslant 0$. Since both mean squares are functions of random variables (fixed effects do not contribute to either of them) the variance ratio test, the F test, is applicable and P is equivalent to the probability that the test ratio, M_{32}/M_{31}, will exceed F_a, where a is the probability level of the test.

Let $E(M_{32})/E(M_{31}) = \phi$. If $\phi = 1.0$, M_{32}/M_{31} will be distributed in samples in the same manner as F, otherwise it will be distributed as ϕF, i.e., M_{32}/M_{31} for any probability point in its distribution will be exactly ϕ times the value of F for the same point in the F distribution. Thus the probability of a sample value of M_{32}/M_{31} equal or greater than F_a is the same as that of a sample value of F equal or greater than F_a/ϕ. When degrees of freedom are equal for the two mean squares, as will always be true in Experiment III, the 50 per cent point of the F distribution is 1.0. Hence P will be one-half when the amount of data is that for which F_a (the lowest value of M_{32}/M_{31} to be considered significantly different from one) is equal to ϕ.

We now must know the magnitude of ϕ when $\bar{a}$ is not unity.

$$\phi = \frac{E\,(M_{32})}{E\,(M_{31})} = \frac{4\sigma^2 + r\Sigma a^2 u^2}{4\sigma^2 + r\Sigma u^2}$$

It varies with r, the number of replications in the experiment; with the ratio of $\Sigma a^2 u^2$ to Σu^2 which is $\bar{a}^2$; and with the ratio of σ^2 to Σu^2. Let $c = \sigma^2/\Sigma u^2$. Then

$$\phi = \frac{4c + r\bar{a}^2}{4c + r}$$

Number of replications is subject to the will of the experimenter, but c and $\bar{a}$

---

5. In the statistical sense, that the probability of the observed or a larger estimate as a consequence of random sampling is small.

are not. The logical procedure is to compute ϕ for various combinations of values of r, c, and $\bar{a}$. This is tedious but very useful if the three items are varied over rational ranges. A set of values for ϕ is presented in Table 30.8. Choice of rational values for $\bar{a}$ presented no difficulty since, in this connection, we are not so much concerned with its actual value as with the smallest for which sufficient data to make $P = .50$ are not beyond the reach of the experimenter.

TABLE 30.8

VALUE OF ϕ FOR $r = 2$ AND VARYING
VALUES OF c AND $\bar{a}$

Expt.	$\bar{a}$	c				
		.25	.50	1.00	2.00	4.00
III	1.2	1.29	1.22	1.15	1.09	1.05
	1.4	1.64	1.48	1.32	1.19	1.11
	1.6	2.04	1.78	1.52	1.31	1.17
	2.0	3.00	2.50	2.00	1.60	1.33
II	1.4	1.27	1.17	1.09	1.05	1.03
	1.6	1.44	1.27	1.15	1.08	1.04
	2.0	1.80	1.50	1.29	1.15	1.08
I	1.4	1.13	1.10	1.06	1.04	1.02
	1.6	1.21	1.15	1.10	1.06	1.03
	2.0	1.38	1.28	1.18	1.11	1.06

Appropriate values for c will vary with the experimental material. The range listed in the table was chosen for application to work with grain yield of corn. σ^2 is plot error variance which, judging from experience, will usually be between 50 and 160 when yield is measured in bushels per acre.[6] This corresponds to a range of about 10 to 18 per cent for the coefficient of variation if mean bushel yield is 70. Σu^2 is twice the additive genetic variance in the F_2 population used. Robinson *et al.* (1949) worked with three F_2 populations and reported .0056 as an estimate of the average amount of additive genetic variance where yield was measured as pounds per plant. Converted to bushels per acre this figure becomes 78.4. More recent work at the North Carolina Experiment Station has yielded estimates of the same order of magnitude. From these results it appears that additive genetic variance will in many cases be between 20 and 100 and hence that Σu^2 will be between 40 and 200. The extreme values for c, if σ^2 and Σu^2 are within ranges suggested above,[7] are $50/200 = .25$ and $160/40 = 4.0$.

6. In work at the North Carolina station it has been quite close to 50.
7. Note that the suggested range for σ^2 is off-center upwards and that for Σu^2 is off-center downwards with respect to estimates from North Carolina data. This was done deliberately in an effort to be on the safe side. Efficiency of the experiment suffers from large σ^2 or small Σu^2.

All values of ϕ listed in the table are for $r = 2$. However, the effect of multiplying r by any constant is the same as dividing c by the same constant. Hence, ϕ for $c = 1$ and $r = 8$ is the same as for $c = .25$ and $r = 2$; ϕ for $c = 4$ and $r = 4$ is the same as for $c = 2$ and $r = 2$; etc.

Table 30.9 lists the approximate degrees of freedom required for M_{31} and M_{32} if $F_{.05}$ is to be equal ϕ so that P will be .50. As an example to clarify the significance of this table, assume that $c = 1.0$, $\bar{a} = 1.4$, and $r = 2$. Then if the data provide 142 degrees of freedom for both M_{31} and M_{32}, the probabili-

TABLE 30.9

APPROXIMATE DEGREES OF FREEDOM* RE-
QUIRED TO MAKE $P = .50$ IN
EXPERIMENT III

$\bar{a}$	c				
	.25	.50	1.00	2.00	4.00
1.2	168	275	555	1460	4550
1.4	45	72	142	360	995
1.6	23	34	63	150	450
2.0	10	14	24	50	134

* Obtained assuming normal distribution of Fisher's z and employing the facts that $\sigma_z^2 = \frac{1}{2}(1/f_1 + 1/f_2)$ (where f_1 and f_2 are degrees of freedom for the two mean squares) and $F = e^{2z}$.

ty of the estimate of $\bar{a}$ being significantly greater (at the 5 per cent point) than one is one-half. Degrees of freedom can be related to amount of data as follows. Suppose that n, the number of progeny pairs per set, is 8. Then degrees of freedom will be 7/8 the number of progeny pairs, and assuming two replications, $r = 2$, degrees of freedom will be 7/32 the number of plots in the experiment. The 142 degrees of freedom indicated in the specific instance singled out above would require data on a total of about 650 plots.

An obvious question is whether increasing replications is as effective as increasing the number of progeny pairs. Consider the case where $c = 4.0$ and $\bar{a} = 1.6$. Degrees of freedom required are 450 when $r = 2$. But remembering that multiplying r by a constant has the same effect on ϕ as division of c by the same constant, we see that with four replications degrees of freedom required would be only 150. Thus with two replications a total of about 2056 plots would be required, whereas with four replications only about 1370 would be needed. The same is not true for the entire area of the table. Careful inspection will show that when c is 1.00 or less, doubling the number of progeny pairs is more effective than increasing replications from two to four. But when c is 2.0 or greater, the opposite is true.

Also pertinent are (1) the effect on P of increasing data above amounts indicated in Table 30.9, and (2) the probability of an estimate of $\bar{a}$ that is less than one even though the true value exceeds one. P becomes about .75 if the data are doubled, between .85 and .9 if the data are tripled, and about .95 if the data are quadrupled. With the degrees of freedom indicated, the probability of an estimate less than 1.0 for $\bar{a}$ is in all cases close to .05, and that of an estimate significantly less than one is much smaller. This is an important point since it means a very small chance of erroneously concluding that $\bar{a}$ is less than one if its real value is greater than one by any very important amount.

The general point to note is that the amounts of data indicated in Table 30.9 are moderate for any combination of $c \leqslant 1.0$ and $\bar{a} \geqslant 1.4$. In addition, it is not prohibitive when both $\bar{a}$ and c are (within the ranges considered) either large or small. Actually, as indicated by earlier references, estimates of c for corn yield from data collected to date at the North Carolina Experiment Station have been somewhat less than .50.

An exact F test of the hypothesis that $\bar{a} \leqslant 1.0$ is not provided in the variance analysis of either Experiment I or II. In both instances there is a function (R) of three mean squares that provides an approximate F test. They are given below. Remember for Experiment II that we are assuming $m = n$

Experiment	R
I	$R_1 = (2n+3)M_{12}/(3M_{11}+2nM_{13})$
II	$R_2 = (2n+1)M_{23}/(M_{20}+2nM_{24})$

and using M_{20} to symbolize the mean of M_{21} and M_{22}. As was true for the test ratio of Experiment III, the expectations of numerator and denominator are equal in both of these ratios when $\bar{a} = 1.0$, but when $\bar{a} > 1.0$ the expectation of the numerator exceeds that of the denominator. Also, the estimate of $\bar{a}$ is greater than one only when the test ratio is greater than one. Values of ϕ for Experiments I and II in Table 30.8 are the ratios of expectations of numerator and denominator in these test ratios. As suggested by relative sizes of ϕ for the three experiments, more data are required in Experiment II than in III, and still more are required in I. However, the degrees of freedom supplied are greater relative to numbers of plots used than in III so differences in data required cannot be judged properly in terms of the ϕ's.

The data requirement cannot be determined as accurately as for Experiment III, primarily because degrees of freedom that should properly be assigned to the denominators of the test ratios cannot be known exactly though they can be approximated by the method of Satterthwaite (1946). For the same reason, determination of the approximate data requirement is more time-consuming. Attention will therefore be confined to the three situations indicated below. Degrees of freedom for Experiment I refer to the mean square, M_{12}, and for Experiment II to M_{23}. In both cases, n was assumed to be 4.0. Thus in II, progenies per set would be 16 as was assumed for Experiment III. This would make degrees of freedom for M_{23} be 9/32 of the number of plots, if $r = 2$. If male groups per progeny set are 4.0, in Experiment I, as in the work of Robinson et al., there would also be 16 progenies per set and degrees of freedom for M_{12} would be 12/32 of the number of plots.

Experiment III is obviously the most powerful and I the least powerful of the three. In the three cases examined, the plot requirement for I is from ten to twelve times that of III. Experiment II is intermediate, requiring from two to four times the data needed in III. It may be of interest that in the

c	$\bar{a}$	DEGREES OF FREEDOM REQUIRED			PLOTS REQUIRED IF $r = 2$		
		Expt. I	II	III	I	II	III
.50	1.4	1525	315	72	4066	1120	329
1.00	2.0	440	120	24	1173	426	110
.25	1.6	480	60	23	1280	213	105

work reported by Robinson et al. (1949) in which Experiment I was used in studying corn yield there were about 500 degrees of freedom for M_{12}. The estimate of $\bar{a}$ was 1.64 and, by the approximate F test, was just significant at the 5 per cent point.

Before leaving the subject, it should be noted that the problem of data required has been dealt with under the original assumptions. If what have been called estimates of $\bar{a}$ are biased upward by linkage or epistasis, their expected values are larger than $\bar{a}$, and the foregoing has relevance to the expected values of the estimates rather than to $\bar{a}$ itself. To exemplify, suppose that $\bar{a}$ were 1.2, but as a result of bias from epistasis and linkage the expected value of the Experiment III estimate were 1.2. Then assuming $c = .25$ and $r = 2$, the probability of the estimate being significantly above 1.0 would be .50 if the data furnished 168 degrees of freedom (Table 30.9), the same number required if $\bar{a}$ were 1.0 and the estimate unbiased. Thus, we see that the probability of an estimate significantly greater than one is a function of the expected value of the estimate rather than of $\bar{a}$ when the two are not equal. The corollary, that an estimate (obtained as described) significantly greater than one is not final proof of overdominance at the locus level, has been indicated in preceding sections.

CONCLUDING REMARKS

To attempt a general discussion of what has been presented appears unwise. It would almost certainly lead to some unnecessary repetition and could do more to confuse than to clarify. However, certain comments seem in order.

With regard to the experiments themselves, III appears definitely the most useful (1) because it is the most powerful, and (2) because it can be employed to learn something about the effect of linkage on the estimate of $\bar{a}$.

It should not be necessary to comment on the role of statistics in the devising and evaluation of schemes for investigating the inheritance of quantitative characters. If the importance of statistics in this area of research has not been adequately demonstrated by the foregoing, general statements could hardly be expected to be convincing. The point to be emphasized is that *more* theoretical investigation of experimental technics in quantitative inheritance is badly needed. For example, insofar as the three experiments considered here are concerned, more information is needed on the biases resulting from various sorts of epistasis. It is possible that such biases are greatest in Experiment III and would detract from its apparent superiority. It is also possible that the biases from epistasis differ between the experiments and that the differences vary with type of epistasis. In that event, comparison of results from two or more of the experiments could conceivably contribute to our knowledge of epistasis.

Investigation of the power of a variety of technics used in quantitative genetic research also would be fruitful. The intent is not to imply that there are no such procedures for which the power is known within satisfactory limits, but only to point out that there are some for which this is not the case. For example, mention has been made of the use of parent, F_1, F_2, and backcross means for investigating epistasis, but to the authors' knowledge there is nothing in the literature concerning amount of data required to insure that the chances of erroneous conclusions from such a study would be small.

Equally important is continued search for useful technics and procedures. It is entirely possible that approaches may thereby be discovered which are more efficient than any presently known. As a case in point, at the time the work described by Robinson *et al.* (1949) was planned we had not thought of the procedure designated here as Experiment III which, so far as we know, has not been previously described as a technic for investigation of dominance. Judging from findings of the preceding section, the same amount of work using the latter procedure would have provided considerably more precise estimates.

While attention herein has been devoted to estimation of average level of dominance, the experiments described provide other information as well. The data collected can be used also for estimation of additive genetic variance, variance due to dominance deviations, and the genetic and phenotypic covariances and correlations of pairs of characters.

LITERATURE

No attempt has been made to cite all of the various publications that in one way or another were stimulatory to the above discussion, since a careful attempt to assign credit where due would have made the manuscript considerably longer. Most interested readers will be familiar with relevant literature, but examples will be given here of papers that might have been cited.

The utilization of genetic variance component estimates is illustrated by numerous publications, for example, Baker *et al.* (1943). The composition (in terms of additive genetic variance and variance due to dominance deviations) of the estimable genetic variance components in the sort of population on which Experiment I is based is known generally and is indicated by Lush *et al.* (1948).

An experiment very similar to II but not designed with as specific information about dominance as its objective has been reported by Hazel and Lamoreux (1947).

The general pattern for genetic interpretation of variance components arising from Mendelian segregation was set in such papers as those by Fisher (1918), Fisher *et al.* (1932), and Wright (1935).

Other procedures for estimation of dominance have been described by Fisher *et al.* (1932), Mather (1949), and Hull (in this volume).

Bibliography

ANDERSON, EDGAR, 1939a The hindrance to gene recombination imposed by linkage: an estimate of its total magnitude. Amer. Nat. **73**:185–188.

————, 1939b Recombination in species crosses. Genetics **24**:668–698.

————, 1944 Homologies of the ear and tassel in *Zea mays*. Ann. Missouri Bot. Gard. **31**:325–342.

————, 1946 Maize in Mexico: a preliminary survey. Ann. Missouri Bot. Gard. **33**:147–247.

————, 1949 Introgressive hybridization. 109 pp. John Wiley & Sons, Inc., New York.

————, and WILLIAM L. BROWN, 1950 The history of common maize varieties in the United States corn belt. Jour. New York Bot. Gard. **51**:242–267.

————, and HUGH C. CUTLER, 1942 Races of *Zea mays*. I. Their recognition and classification. Ann. Missouri Bot. Gard. **29**:69–88.

————, and RALPH O. ERICKSON, 1941 Antithetical dominance in North American maize. Proc. Nation. Acad. Sci. U.S.A. **27**:436–440.

ANONYMOUS, 1949 Informe de los Años 1944–1948, Centro Nacional de Agronomia. El Salvador.

ARISTOTLE, History of animals. Tr. by D'Arcy W. Thompson. 633 pp. Oxford Press, Oxford. 1910.

ASHBY, E., 1930 Studies in the inheritance of physiological characters. I. A physiological investigation of the nature of hybrid vigour in maize. Ann. Botany **44**:457–467.

————, 1932 Studies in the inheritance of physiological characters. II. Further experiments upon the basis of hybrid vigour and upon the inheritance of efficiency index and respiration rate in maize. Ann. Botany **46**:1007–1032.

————, 1936 Hybrid vigour in maize. Amer. Nat. **70**:179–181.

————, 1937 Studies in the inheritance of physiological characters. III. Hybrid vigour in the tomato. Pt. I. Manifestation of hybrid vigour from germination to the onset of flowering. Ann. Botany (New Series) **1**:11–41.

ASHTON, T., 1946 The use of heterosis in the production of agricultural and horticultural crops. Imper. Bur. Plant Breed. and Genetics, School of Agric., Cambridge, England. 30 pp.

⁹ BAKER, A. L., and J. R. QUESENBERRY, 1944 Comparison of growth of hereford and F_1 hereford-shorthorn heifers. Jour. Animal Sci. **3**:322–325.

BAKER, MARVEL L., L. N. HAZEL, and C. F. REINMILLER, 1943 The relative importance of heredity and environment in the growth of pigs at different ages. Jour. Animal Sci. **2**:3–13.

BARTHOLLET, S., 1827 Phénomènes de l'acte mysterieux de la fécondation. Memor. Soc. Linn. Paris. **1**:81–83.

BARTON, A. A., 1950 Some aspects of cell division in *Saccharomyces cerevisiae*. Jour. Gen. Microbiol. **4**:84–86.

BEADLE, G. W., 1935 Crossing over near the spindle attachment of the X chromosomes in attached-x triploids of *Drosophila melanogaster*. Genetics **20**:179–191.

————, 1945a Biochemical genetics. Chem. Rev. **37**:15–96.

————, 1945b Genetics and metabolism in Neurospora. Physiol. Rev. **25**:643–663.

BEADLE, G. W., 1948   Some recent developments in chemical genetics. Fortschr. Chemie organ. Naturst. **5**:300–330.

——, 1949   Genes and biological enigmas. Pages 184–245; 316–317. Science in Progress. 6th Series. Yale University Press: New Haven.

——, and V. L. COONRADT, 1944   Heterocaryosis in *Neurospora crassa*. Genetics **29**:291–308.

——, and E. L. TATUM, 1941   Genetic control of biochemical reactions in Neurospora. Proc. Nation. Acad. Sci. U.S.A. **27**:499–506.

BEAL, WILLIAM J., 1876, 1877, 1881, 1882   Repts. Michigan State Board Agric.

——, 1878   The improvements of grains, fruits, and vegetables. Rept. Michigan State Board Agric. **17**:445–457.

——, 1880   Indian corn. Rept. Michigan State Board Agric. **19**:279–289.

BEALE, G. H., 1941   Gene relations and synthetic processes. Jour. Genetics **42**:197–214.

BERNSTEIN, FELIX, 1924   Ergebnisse einer biostatistischen zusammenfassenden Betrachtung über die erblichen Blutstrukturen des Menschen. Klin. Wochenschr. 3, II:1495–1497.

BLAKESLEE, A. F., J. BELLING, M. E. FARNHAM, and A. D. BERGNER, 1922   A haploid mutant in the jimson weed, *Datura stramonium*. Science **55**:646–647.

——, and S. SATINA, 1944   New hybrids from incompatible crosses in Datura through culture of excised embryos on malt media. Science **99**:331–334.

BLUNN, C. T., and M. L. BAKER, 1949   Heritability estimates of sow productivity and litter performance. Jour. Animal Sci. **8**:89–97.

BOIVIN, A., 1947   Directed mutation in colon bacilli by an inducing principle of desoxyribonucleic nature: its meaning for the general biochemistry of heredity. Cold Spring Harbor Symposia Quant. Biol. **12**:7–17.

BOLSUNOW, I., 1944   Zur Untersuchung der Heterosis bei *Nicotiana rustica* L. V. Fortgesetzte Selbstbefruchtung und Ernteertrag. Zeitschr. Pflanzenzucht. **26**:223–244.

BONNER, JAMES, and HARRIET BONNER, 1948   The B vitamins as plant hormones. Vitamins and Hormones. Academic Press, Inc.: New York. Vol. **6**:225–275.

——, and S. G. WILDMAN, 1946   Enzymatic mechanisms in the respiration of spinach leaves. Arch. Biochem. **10**:497–518.

BOYD, W. C., 1939   Blood groups. Tabulae Biologicae **17**:113–240.

——, 1943   Fundamentals of immunology. 446 pp. Interscience Publishers, Inc.: New York.

——, 1945   Rh blood factors: An orientation review. Arch. Path. **40**:114–127.

BRIEGER, F. G., 1950   The genetic basis of heterosis in maize. Genetics **35**:420–445.

BRILES, W. E., W. H. McGIBBON, and M. R. IRWIN, 1950   On multiple alleles effecting cellular antigens in the chicken. Genetics **35**:633–652.

BRINK, R. A., 1929   Studies on the physiology of a gene. Quart. Rev. Biol. **4**:520–543.

——, and D. C. COOPER, 1940   Double fertilization and development of the seed in angiosperms. Bot. Gaz. **102**:1–25.

——, ——, 1944   The antipodals in relation to abnormal endosperm behavior in *Hordeum jubatum* × *Secale cereale* hybrid seeds. Genetics **29**:391–406.

——, ——, 1947   The endosperm in seed development. Bot. Rev. **13**:423–541.

BROQUIST, H. D., and E. E. SNELL, 1949   Studies of the mechanism of histidine synthesis in lactic acid bacteria. Jour. Biol. Chem. **180**:59–71.

BROWN, WILLIAM L., 1949   Numbers and distribution of chromosome knobs in U.S. maize. Genetics **34**:524–536.

——, and EDGAR ANDERSON, 1947   The northern flint corns. Ann. Missouri Bot. Gard. **34**:1–28.

——, ——, 1948   The southern dent corns. Ann. Missouri Bot. Gard. **35**:255–268.

Bruce, A. B., 1910 The Mendelian theory of heredity and the augmentation of vigor. Science 32:627–628.

Bruner, D. W., and P. R. Edwards, 1947 Changes in the nonspecific antigens of Salmonella. Jour. Bact. 53:359.

Burger, J., 1809 Naturgeschichte, Culture und Benutzung des Mais. Wein.

Burkholder, Paul R., and Ilda McVeigh, 1940 Growth and differentiation of maize in relation to nitrogen supply. Amer. Jour. Bot. 27:414–424.

Buzzati-Traverso, A., 1947a Genetica di popolazioni in Drosophila. V. Selezione naturale in popolazioni artificiali di Drosophila melanogaster. Memor. Ist. Ital. Idrobiol. 4:41–62.

———, 1947b Su alcuni casi di evoluzione in bottiglia. Memor. Ist. Ital. Idrobiol. 4:115–120.

———, 1950 Genetic structure of natural populations and interbreeding units in the human species. Cold Spring Harbor Symposia Quant. Biol. 15:13–23.

Carnahan, H. L., 1947 Combining ability in flax (Linum usitatissimum). M.S. Thesis. Univ. of Minnesota.

Carroll, W. E., and E. Roberts, 1942 Crossbreeding in swine. Illinois Agric. Expt. Sta. Bull. 489.

Carson, H. L., 1946 The selective elimination of inversion dicentric chromatids during meiosis in the eggs of Sciara impatiens. Genetics 31:95–113.

Caspari, E., 1948 Cytoplasmic inheritance. Advances in Genetics Vol II:1–66. Academic Press, Inc.: New York.

———, 1950 On the selective value of the alleles Rt and rt in Ephestia kuhniella. Amer. Nat. 84:367–380.

Castle, W. E., 1946 Genes which divide species or produce hybrid vigor. Proc. Nation. Acad. Sci. U.S.A. 32:145–149.

Catcheside, D. G., 1944. Polarized segregation in an Ascomycete. Ann. Botany (New Series) 8:119–130.

Cavalli, L. L., 1950 The analysis of selection curves. Biometrics 6:208–220.

Chase, S. S., 1949a Monoploid frequencies in a commercial double cross hybrid maize, and in its component single cross hybrids and inbred lines. Genetics 34:328–332.

———, 1949b Spontaneous doubling of the chromosome complement in monoploid sporophytes of maize. Proc. Iowa Acad. Sci. 56:113–115.

Chipman, R. H., and T. H. Goodspeed, 1927 Inheritance in Nicotiana tabacum. VIII. Cytological features of purpurea haploid. Univ. California Publ. Bot. 11:141–158.

Christensen, H. M., and R. Bamford, 1943 Haploids in twin seedlings of peppers, Capsicum annuum L. Jour. Heredity 34:99–104.

Clark, Frances J., 1940 Cytogenetic studies of divergent meiotic spindle formation in Zea mays. Amer. Jour. Bot. 27:547–559.

Collins, G. N., 1909 A new type of Indian corn from China. U.S. Dept. Agric. Bur. Plant Ind. Bull. 161. 30 pp.

———, 1921 Dominance and the vigor of first generation hybrids. Amer. Nat. 55:116–133.

Comstock, R. E., and H. F. Robinson, 1948 The components of genetic variance in populations of biparental progenies and their use in estimating the average degree of dominance. Biometrics 4:254–266.

———, ———, and P. H. Harvey, 1949 A breeding procedure designed to make maximum use of both general and specific combining ability. Agron. Jour. 41:360–367.

———, and L. M. Winters, 1944 A comparison of effects of inbreeding and selection on performance in swine. Jour. Animal Sci. 3:380–389.

Cooper, D. C., and R. A. Brink, 1940 Partial self-incompatibility and the collapse of fertile ovules as factors affecting seed formation in alfalfa. Jour. Agric. Res. 60:453–472.

COOPER, D. C., and R. A. BRINK, 1944 Collapse of the seed following the mating *Hordeum jubatum* × *Secale cereale.* Genetics **29**:370–390.

——, ——, 1949 The endosperm-embryo relationship in an autonomous apomict, *Taraxacum officinale.* Bot. Gaz. **111**:139–153.

COPELAND, F. C., 1940 Growth rates in inbred and hybrid corn embryos. Collecting Net **15**:169.

COWAN, J. R., 1943 The value of double cross hybrids involving inbreds of similar and diverse genetic origin. Sci. Agric. (Ottawa) **23**:287–296.

COWIE, D. B., E. T. BOLTON, and M. K. SANDS, 1950 Sulfur metabolism in *Escherichia coli.* Jour. Bact. **60**:233–248.

CRABB, A. RICHARD, 1947 The hybrid corn makers: prophets of plenty. xxv+331 pp. Rutgers University Press: New Brunswick, New Jersey.

CROW, JAMES F., 1948 Alternative hypotheses of hybrid vigor. Genetics **33**:477–487.

——, 1952 Dominance and overdominance in heterosis. Heterosis, Chapter 18. Iowa State College Press: Ames, Iowa.

CUMMINGS, J. N., L. M. WINTERS, and H. A. STEWART, 1947 Heritability of some factors affecting productivity of brood sows. Jour. Animal Sci. **6**:297–304.

CUNNINGHAM, J. C., 1948 Maize bibliography for the years 1888–1916. Contributions Iowa Corn Res. Inst. **3**:67–189.

DANFORTH, C. H., 1927 Hereditary adiposity in mice. Jour. Heredity **18**:153–162.

DARLINGTON, C. D., and L. LA COUR, 1941 The genetics of embryo sac development. Ann. Botany (New Series) **5**:547–562.

DARWIN, CHARLES, 1868 The variation of animals and plants under domestication. J. Murray: London.

——, 1877 The effects of cross and self fertilization in the vegetable kingdom. viii+482 pp. D. Appleton and Company: New York.

DAVENPORT, C. B., 1908 Degeneration, albinism and inbreeding. Science **28**:454–455.

DAVIS, B. D., 1948 Isolation of biochemically deficient mutants of bacteria by means of penicillin. Jour. Amer. Chem. Soc. **70**:4267.

——, 1949 The isolation of biochemically deficient mutants of bacteria by means of penicillin. Proc. Nation. Acad. Sci. U.S.A. **35**:1–10.

DETURK, E. E., J. R. HOLBERT, and B. W. HOWK, 1933 Chemical transformations of phosphorus in the growing corn plant, with results on two first generation crosses. Jour. Agric. Res. **46**:121–141.

DEVRIES, HUGO, 1907 Plant breeding: comments on the experiments of Nilsson and Burbank. xvi+360 pp. The Open Court Publishing Company: Chicago.

DICKERSON, G. E., 1947 Composition of hog carcasses as influenced by heritable differences in rate and economy of gain. Iowa Agric. Expt. Sta. Res. Bull. 354. 31 pp.

——, 1949 Importance of heterosis for total performance in animals. Proc. Eighth International Congress of Genetics: Abstr. 560. (Suppl. Vol. of Hereditas, Berlingska Boktryckeriet, Lund, Sweden.)

——, 1951 Effectiveness of selection for economic characters in swine. Jour. Animal Sci. **10**:12–18.

——, and J. W. GOWEN, 1947 Hereditary obesity and efficient food utilization in mice. Science **105**:496–498.

——, and J. C. GRIMES, 1947 Effectiveness of selection for efficiency of gain in Duroc swine. Jour. Animal Sci. **6**:256–287.

——, J. L. LUSH, M. L. BAKER, J. A. WHATLEY, JR., and L. M. WINTERS, 1947 Performance of inbred lines and line-crosses in swine. Jour. Animal Sci. **6**:477.

——, ——, and C. C. CULBERTSON, 1946 Hybrid vigor in single crosses between inbred lines of Poland China swine. Jour. Animal Sci. **5**:16–24.

DOBZHANSKY, TH., 1941 Genetics and the origin of species. Second Edition. 446 pp. Columbia Univ. Press: New York.

———, 1943 Genetics of natural populations. IX. Temporal changes in the composition of populations of *Drosophila pseudoobscura*. Genetics 28:162–186.

———, 1947a A directional change in the genetic constitution of a natural population of *Drosophila pseudoobscura*. Heredity 1:53–64.

———, 1947b Genetics of natural populations. XIV. A response of certain gene arrangements in the third chromosome of *Drosophila pseudoobscura* to natural selection. Genetics 32:142–160.

———, 1949 Observations and experiments on natural selection in Drosophila. Proc. Eighth International Congress of Genetics: 210–224. (Suppl. Vol. of Hereditas, Berlingska Boktryckeriet, Lund, Sweden.)

———, 1950 Genetics of natural populations. XIX. Origin of heterosis through natural selection in populations of *Drosophila pseudoobscura*. Genetics 35:288–302.

———, A. M. HOLZ, and B. SPASSKY, 1942 Genetics of natural populations. VIII. Concealed variability in the second and fourth chromosomes of *Drosophila pseudoobscura*. Genetics 27:463–490.

DODGE, B. O., 1942 Heterocaryotic vigor in Neurospora. Bull. Torrey Bot. Club 69:75–91.

———, MARY B. SCHMITT, and ANITA APPEL, 1945 Inheritance of factors involved in one type of heterocaryotic vigor. Proc. Amer. Phil. Soc. 89:575–589.

DOERMANN, A. H., 1944 A lysineless mutant of Neurospora and its inhibition by arginine. Arch. Biochem. 5:373–384.

DUNN, L. C., and E. CASPARI, 1945 A case of neighboring loci with similar effects. Genetics 30:543–568.

EAST, EDWARD M., 1907 The relation of certain biological principles to plant breeding. Connecticut Expt. Sta. Bull. 158. 93 pp.

———, 1908 Inbreeding in corn. Rept. Connecticut Agric. Expt. Sta. for 1907. Pp. 419–428.

———, 1909 The distinction between development and heredity in inbreeding. Amer. Nat. 43:173–181.

———, 1921 A study of partial sterility in certain hybrids. Genetics 6:311–365.

———, 1936 Heterosis. Genetics 21:375–397.

———, and H. K. HAYES, 1912 Heterozygosis in evolution and in plant breeding. U.S. Dept. Agric. Bur. Plant Indust. Bull. 243. 58 pp.

———, and D. F. JONES, 1919 Inbreeding and outbreeding: their genetic and sociological significance. 285 pp. J. B. Lippincott Co.: Philadelphia and London.

———, ———, 1920 Genetic studies on the protein content of maize. Genetics 5:543–610.

EDWARDS, P. R., and D. W. BRUNER, 1942 Serological identification of Salmonella cultures. Kentucky Agric. Expt. Sta. Circ. 54. 35 pp.

EINSET, J., 1943 Chromosome length in relation to transmission frequency of maize trisomes. Genetics 28:349–364.

EMERSON, R. A., and G. W. BEADLE, 1932 Studies of Euchlaena and its hybrids with Zea. II. Crossing-over between the chromosomes of Euchlaena and those of Zea. Zeitschr. indukt. Abstamm.- u. Vererbungsl. 62:305–315.

———, and H. H. SMITH, 1950 Inheritance of number of kernel rows in maize. Cornell University Agric. Expt. Sta. Mem. 296. 30 pp.

EMERSON, S., 1947 Growth responses of a sulfonamide-requiring mutant strain of Neurospora. Jour. Bact. 54:195–207.

———, 1948 A physiological basis for some suppressor mutations and possibly for one gene heterosis. Proc. Nation. Acad. Sci. U.S.A. 34:72–74.

———, 1949 Competitive reactions and antagonisms in the biosynthesis of amino acids by Neurospora. Cold Spring Harbor Symposia Quant. Biol. 14:40–47.

EMIK, L. O., and C. E. TERRILL, 1949 Systematic procedures for calculating inbreeding coefficients. Jour. Heredity **40**:51–55.

EPHRUSSI, BORIS, 1942a Analysis of eye color differentiation in Drosophila. Cold Spring Harbor Symposia Quant. Biol. **10**:40–48.

———, 1942b Chemistry of "eye color hormones" of Drosophila. Quart. Rev. Biol. **17**: 327–338.

EVERETT, H. L., 1949 A genic series controlling chloroplast pigment production in diploid *Zea mays*. Proc. Nation. Acad. Sci. U.S.A. **35**:628–634.

FAIRFIELD SMITH, H., 1936 A discriminant function for plant selection. Ann. Eugenics **7**:240–250.

FERGUSON, L. C., 1941 Heritable antigens in the erythrocytes of cattle. Jour. Immunol. **40**:213–242.

———, CLYDE STORMONT, and M. R. IRWIN, 1942 On additional antigens in the erythrocytes of cattle. Jour. Immunol. **44**:147–164.

FISHER, R. A., 1918 The correlation between relatives on the supposition of Mendelian inheritance. Trans. Roy. Soc. Edinburgh **52**: Pt. 2, 399–433.

———, 1931 The evolution of dominance. Biol. Rev. Cambridge Phil. Soc. **6**:345–368.

———, 1949 The theory of inbreeding. 120 pp. Oliver and Boyd: Edinburgh.

———, F. R. IMMER, and OLOF TEDIN, 1932 The genetical interpretation of statistics of the third degree in the study of quantitative inheritance. Genetics **17**:107–124.

FLOR, H. H., 1947 Inheritance of reaction to rust in flax. Jour. Agric. Res. **74**:241–262.

FOCKE, W. O., 1881 Die Pflanzen-Mischlinge. 569 pp. G. Borntraeger: Berlin.

GAINES, E. F., and H. C. AASE, 1926 A haploid wheat plant. Amer. Jour. Bot. **13**:373–385.

GALLESIO, G., 1813 Teoria della riproduzione vegetal. 136 pp. Vienna.

GARNER, W. W., 1946 The production of tobacco. 516 pp. Blakiston Co.: Philadelphia.

GARROD, A. E., 1923 Inborn errors of metabolism. 2nd Edition. 216 pp. Oxford Univ. Press: London.

GÄRTNER, C. F., 1827 Correspondenz in der Flora. Bot. Zeitschr. **10**:74.

———, 1849 Versuche und Beobachtungen über die Bastarderzeugung im Pflanzenreich. 791 pp. Stuttgart.

GATES, R. R., 1929 A haploid Oenothera. Nature (London) **124**:948.

GOLDSCHMIDT, RICHARD, 1938 Physiological genetics. 375 pp. McGraw-Hill Book Company, Inc.: New York and London.

GOODALE, H. D., 1938 A study of inheritance of body weight in the albino mouse by selection. Jour. Heredity **29**:101–112.

GOWEN, J. W., 1945 Genetic aspects of virulence in bacteria and viruses. Ann. Missouri Bot. Gard. **32**:187–211.

———, and LESLIE JOHNSON, 1946 On the mechanism of heterosis—metabolic capacity of different races of *Drosophila melanogaster* for egg production. Amer. Nat. **80**:149–179.

———, J. STADLER, and L. E. JOHNSON, 1946 On the mechanism of heterosis—the chromosomal or cytoplasmic basis for heterosis in *Drosophila melanogaster*. Amer. Nat. **80**:506–531.

GRAY, ASA, 1858 Action of foreign pollen upon the fruits. Amer. Jour. Sci. and Arts (Series 2) **25**:122–123.

GREEN, J. M., 1948 Inheritance of combining ability in maize hybrids. Jour. Amer. Soc. Agron. **40**:58–63.

GREGORY, F. G., and F. CROWTHER, 1928. A physiological study of varietal differences in plants. I. A study of the comparative yields of barley varieties with different manuring. Ann. Botany **42**:757–770.

———, ———, 1931 A physiological study of varietal differences in plants. II. Further evidence for the differential response in yield of barley varieties to manurial deficiencies. Ann. Botany **45**:579–592.

GROSS, OSCAR, 1914 Über den Einfluss des Blutserums des Normalen und des Alkaptonuri-kers auf homogentisinsäure. Biochem. Zeitschr. 61:165–170.

GUSTAFSSON, Åke, 1938 Studies on the genetic basis of chlorophyll formation and the mechanism of induced mutating. Hereditas 24:33–93.

———, 1946 The effect of heterozygosity on variability and vigour. Hereditas 32:263–286.

———, 1947 The advantageous effect of deleterious mutations. Hereditas 33:573–575.

GUTHRIE, R., 1949 Studies of a purine-requiring mutant strain of *Escherichia coli.* Jour. Bact. 57:39–46.

HALDANE, J. B. S., 1937 The effect of variation on fitness. Amer. Nat. 71:337–349.

———, 1938 Essay "The Biochemistry of the Individual," in "Perspectives in Biochem-istry." Cambridge Univ. Press: London.

———, 1942 New paths in genetics. 206 pp. Harper and Brothers: New York.

———, 1950 Equilibrium under natural selection (abstr.). Heredity 4:138–139.

HARLAND, S. C., 1920 A note on a peculiar type of "rogue" in Sea Island cotton. Agric. News Barbados 19:29.

HARRINGTON, J. B., 1944 Intra-varietal crossing in wheat. Jour. Amer. Soc. Agron. 36:990–991.

HARVEY, PAUL H., 1939 Hereditary variation in plant nutrition. Genetics 24:437–461.

HATCHER, E. S. J., 1939 Hybrid vigour in the tomato. Nature (London) 143:523.

———, 1940 Studies in the inheritance of physiological characters. V. Hybrid vigour in the tomato. Pt. III. A critical examination of the relation of embryo development to the manifestation of hybrid vigour. Ann. Botany (New Series) 4:735–764.

HAYES, H. K., 1912 Correlation and inheritance in *Nicotiana tabacum.* Connecticut Agric. Expt. Sta. Bull. 171. 45 pp.

———, E. M. EAST, and E. G. BEINHART, 1913 Tobacco breeding in Connecticut. Con-necticut Agric. Expt. Sta. Bull. 176. 68 pp.

———, and R. J. GARBER, 1919 Synthetic production of high protein corn in relation to breeding. Jour. Amer. Soc. Agron. 11:309–319.

———, and F. R. IMMER, 1942 Methods of plant breeding. 432 pp. McGraw-Hill Book Company, Inc.: New York and London.

———, and I. J. JOHNSON, 1939 The breeding of improved selfed lines of corn. Jour. Amer. Soc. Agron. 31:710–724.

———, E. H. RINKE, and Y. S. TSIANG, 1946 Experimental study of convergent improve-ment and backcrossing in corn. Minnesota Agric. Expt. Sta. Tech. Bull. 172. 40 pp.

HAZEL, L. N., 1943 Genetic basis for constructing selection indexes. Genetics 28:476–490.

———, and W. F. LAMOREUX, 1947 Heritability, maternal effects and nicking in relation to sexual maturity and body weight in White Leghorns. Poultry Sci. 26:508–514.

———, A. L. MUSSON, and J. L. LUSH, 1948 Comparisons of inbred Poland China, Land-race and purebred boars on Iowa farms. Jour. Animal Sci. 7:512–513.

HEIDELBERGER, M., and O. T. AVERY, 1923 The soluble specific substance of pneumococ-cus. Jour. Exptl. Med. 38:73–79.

———, ———, 1924 The soluble specific substance of pneumococcus. Second Paper. Jour. Exptl. Med. 40:301–316.

———, E. A. KABAT, and M. MAYER, 1942 A further study of the cross reaction between the specific polysaccharides of type III and VIII penumococci in horse antisera. Jour. Exptl. Med. 75:35–47.

HEIMSCH, CHARLES, GLENN S. RABIDEAU, and W. GORDON WHALEY, 1950 Vascular de-velopment and differentiation in two maize inbreds and their hybrid. Amer. Jour. Bot. 37:84–93.

HENDERSON, C. R., 1948 Estimation of general, specific, and maternal combining abilities in crosses among inbred lines of swine. Unpublished Ph.D. thesis. Iowa State College Library, Ames, Iowa. 199 pp.

————, 1949 Estimation of general, specific, and maternal combining abilities in crosses among inbred lines of swine. Jour. Animal Sci. **8**:606.

————, 1950 Estimation of genetic parameters (abstr.). Ann. Math. Statistics **21**:309.

HERBERT, W., 1837 Amaryllidaceae. 428 pp. London.

HESTRIN, S., and CARL C. LINDEGREN, 1950 Carbohydrases in Saccharomyces haploid stocks of defined genotype. I. Fermentation and hydrolysis of alphaglucosides by yeast 6233. Arch. Biochem. **29**:315–333.

HETZER, H. O., W. V. LAMBERT, and J. H. ZELLER, 1940 Influence of inbreeding and other factors on litter size in Chester White swine. U.S. Dept. Agric. Circ. 570. 10 pp.

HILDEBRAND, F., 1868 Einige Experimente und Beobachtungen, etc. Bot. Zeitschr. **26**: 321–328.

HINSHELWOOD, C. N., 1946 The chemical kinetics of the bacterial cell. 284 pp. Oxford Univ. Press: London.

HIORTH, G., 1940 Eine Serie multipler allele für Blütenzeichnungen bei *Godetia amoena*. Hereditas **26**:441–453.

HODGSON, R. E., 1935 An eight generation experiment in inbreeding swine. Jour. Heredity **26**:209–217.

HOFFER, G. N., 1926 Some differences in the functioning of selfed lines of corn under varying nutritional conditions. Jour. Amer. Soc. Agron. **18**:322–334.

HOLDEN, P. G., 1948 Corn breeding at the University of Illinois 1895 to 1900. ii+10 pp. Privately published by the author: Charlevoix, Michigan.

HOLLAENDER, A., 1948 Mechanism of radiation effects and the use of radiation for production of mutations with improved fermentation. Ann. Missouri Bot. Gard. **32**:165–178.

HOROWITZ, N. H., 1950 Biochemical genetics of Neurospora. Advances in Genetics. Vol. III:33–71. Academic Press, Inc.: New York.

HOULAHAN, MARY B., and H. K. MITCHELL, 1948 Evidence for an interrelation in the metabolism of lysine, arginine, and pyrimidines in Neurospora. Proc. Nation. Acad. Sci. U.S.A. **34**:465–470.

HOUSER, T., 1911 Comparison of yields of first generation tobacco hybrids with those of parent plants. Amer. Breeders Rept. **7**:155–167.

HSU, K. J., 1950 Comparative studies in corn of the development of normal and dwarf plants. Ph.D. thesis. University of Minnesota.

HULL, FRED H., 1945a Recurrent selection for specific combining ability in corn. Jour. Amer. Soc. Agron. **37**:134–145.

————, 1945b Maize genetics cooperation, News Letter **19**:21–27. Dept. Plant Breeding, Cornell Univ., Ithaca, New York.

————, 1946a Regression analyses of corn yield data. (abstr.) Genetics **31**:219.

————, 1946b Overdominance and corn breeding where hybrid seed is not feasible. Jour. Amer. Soc. Agron. **38**:1100–1103.

————, 1952 Overdominance and recurrent selection. Heterosis, Chapter 28. Iowa State College Press: Ames, Iowa.

IMMER, F. R., 1941 Relation between yielding ability and homozygosis in barley crosses. Jour. Amer. Soc. Agron. **33**:200–206

IRWIN, M. R., 1939 A genetic analysis of species differences in Columbidae. Genetics **24**: 709–721.

————, 1947 Immunogenetics. Advances in Genetics Vol. I:133–160. Academic Press, Inc.: New York.

————, and L. J. COLE, 1936 Immunogenetic studies of species and of species hybrids from the cross of *Columba livia* and *Streptopelia risoria*. Jour. Exptl. Zool. **73**:309–318.

——, and R. W. CUMLEY, 1945 Suggestive evidence for duplicate genes in a species hybrid in doves. Genetics **30**:363–375.

JENKINS, M. T., 1929 Correlation studies with inbred and crossbred strains of maize. Jour. Agric. Res. **39**:677–721.

——, 1935 The effect of inbreeding and of selection within inbred lines of maize upon the hybrids made after successive generations of selfing. Iowa State College Jour. Sci. **9**:429–450.

——, 1940 The segregation of genes affecting yield of grain in maize. Jour. Amer. Soc. Agron. **32**:55–63.

JOHNSON, I. J., and H. K. HAYES, 1940 The value in hybrid combinations of inbred lines of corn selected from single crosses by the pedigree method of breeding. Jour. Amer. Soc. Agron. **32**:479–485.

JOHNSON, R. T., 1950 Combining ability in *Zea mays* as related to generations of testing, selection of testers and characters of the inbred lines. Ph.D. thesis. University of Minnesota.

JOHNSON, S. W., 1891 How crops grow. Orange Judd & Co.: New York.

JOLLOS, VICTOR, 1934 Dauermodifikationen und Mutationen bei Protozoen. Arch. f. Protistenk. **83**:197–219.

JONES, D. F., 1917 Dominance of linked factors as a means of accounting for heterosis. Genetics **2**:466–479.

——, 1918 The effects of inbreeding and crossbreeding upon development. Connecticut Agric. Expt. Sta. Bull. 207. 100 pp.

——, 1921 The indeterminate growth factor in tobacco and its effect upon development. Genetics **6**:433–444.

——, 1944 Equilibrium in genic materials. Proc. Nation. Acad. Sci. U.S.A. **30**:82–87.

——, 1945 Heterosis resulting from degenerative changes. Genetics **30**:527–542.

——, 1950 The interrelation of plasmagenes and chromogenes in pollen production in maize. Genetics **35**:507–512.

——, 1952 Plasmagenes and chromogenes in relation to heterosis. Heterosis, Chapter 14. Iowa State College Press: Ames, Iowa.

——, and P. C. MANGELSDORF, 1925 The improvement of naturally cross-pollinated plants by selection in self-fertilized lines. Connecticut Agric. Expt. Sta. Bull. 266. 69 pp.

KABAT, E. A., 1949 Immunochemical studies on blood group substances. Bact. Rev. **13**: 189–202.

KALMUS, H., 1945 Adaptive and selective responses of a population of *Drosophila melanogaster* containing *e* and *e⁺* to differences in temperature, humidity and to selection for developmental speed. Jour. Genetics **47**:58–63.

KARPER, R. E., 1930 The effect of a single gene upon development in the heterozygote in Sorghum. Jour. Heredity **21**:187–192.

KAUFFMANN, F., 1944 Die Bacteriologie der Salmonella Gruppe. 393 pp. Edwards: Ann Arbor, Michigan.

KEEBLE, F., and C. PELLEW, 1910 The mode of inheritance of stature and of time of flowering in peas (*Pisum sativum*). Jour. Genetics **1**:47–56.

KEMPTON, J. H., and J. W. MCLANE, 1942 Hybrid vigor and weight of germs in the seeds of maize. Jour. Agric. Res. **64**:65–80.

KIDDER, G. W., and V. C. DEWEY, 1948 Studies on the biochemistry of Tetrahymena. XIV. The activity of natural purines and pyrimidines. Proc. Nation. Acad. Sci. U.S.A. **34**:566–574.

KIESSELBACH, T. A., 1922 Corn investigations. Nebraska Agric. Expt. Sta. Res. Bull. 20. 151 pp.

KIESSELBACH, T. A., 1926   The comparative water economy of selfed lines of corn and their hybrids. Jour. Amer. Soc. Agron. 18:335–344.

———, 1930   The use of advanced generation hybrids as parents of double-cross seed corn. Jour. Amer. Soc. Agron. 22:614–626.

———, 1933   The possibilities of modern corn breeding. Proc. World's Grain Exhibition and Conference 2:92–112.

KIKKAWA, H., 1941   Mechanism of pigment formation in Bombyx and Drosophila. Genetics 26:587–607.

KINMAN, MURRAY L., and G. F. SPRAGUE, 1945   Relation between number of parental lines and theoretical performance of synthetic varieties of corn. Jour. Amer. Soc. Agron. 37:341–351.

KNIGHT, THOMAS ANDREW, 1799   An account of some experiments on the fecondation of vegetables. Phil. Trans. Roy. Soc. London. Pp. 195–204.

KOELREUTER, J. G., 1766   Vorläufigen Nachricht von einigen das Geschlecht der Pflanzen betreffenden Versuchen und Beobachtungen. 266 pp. Leipzig.

KOFT, B. W., E. Steers, and M. G. SEVAG, 1950   Replacement by D-lysine of p-aminobenzoic acid as a growth factor for Lactobacillus arabinosus 17-5. Arch. Biochem. 28:144–145.

KÖRNICKE, FR., 1876   Über einige Erscheinungen in Ökonomisch-botanischen Garten. Bonn, Niederrhein. Gesell. Sitzgsb. Pp. 47–48.

KOSMODEMJJANSKI, V. N., 1941   (Transgression in different generations of hybrids of Nicotiana tabacum.) All Union Mikojan Research Institute of the Tobacco and Makhorka Industry. Krasnodar 143:3–28. (In Russian.)

KOSTOFF, D., 1941   The problem of haploidy (Cytogenetic studies in Nicotiana haploids and their bearing to some other cytogenetic problems). Bibliogr. Genetica 13:1–148.

KRIDER, J. L., B. W. FAIRBANKS, W. E. CARROLL, and E. ROBERTS, 1946   Effectiveness of selecting for rapid and for slow growth rate in Hampshire swine. Jour. Animal Sci. 5:3–15.

LAMPEN, J. O., R. R. ROEPKE, and M. J. JONES, 1947   Studies on the sulfur metabolism in Escherichia coli. III. Mutant strains of E. coli unable to utilize sulfate for their complete sulfur requirements. Arch. Biochem. 13:55–66.

LANDSTEINER, K., 1900   Zur Kenntnis der antifermentativen, lytischen und agglutinierenden Wirkungen des Blutserums und der Lymphe. Zentralbl. Bakt. 27:357–362.

———, 1901   Ueber Agglutinationserscheinungen normalen menschlichen Blutes. Wien. Klin. Wochenschr. 14:1132–1134.

———, 1945   The specificity of serological reactions. Second Edition. 310 pp. Harvard University Press: Cambridge.

———, and P. LEVINE, 1927   Further observations on individual differences of human blood. Proc. Soc. Exptl. Biol. New York 24:941–942.

———, and A. S. WIENER, 1940   An agglutinable factor in human blood recognized by immune sera for Rhesus blood. Proc. Soc. Exptl. Biol. New York 43:223.

LARSON, R. E., and T. M. CURRENCE, 1944   The extent of hybrid vigor in F_1 and F_2 generations of tomato crosses. Minnesota Agric. Expt. Sta. Tech. Bull. 164. 32 pp.

LAWRENCE, W. J. C., and J. R. PRICE, 1940   The genetics and chemistry of flower colour variation. Biol. Rev. 15:35–58.

LECOQ, H., 1845   De la fécondation naturelle et artificielle de végétaux et de l'hybridation. 287 pp. Paris.

LEDERBERG, J., 1947   Gene recombination and linked segregations in Escherichia coli. Genetics 32:505–525.

———, 1949   Segregation in Escherichia coli. Records Genetics Soc. Amer. 18:99–100.

———, and N. ZINDER, 1948   Concentration of biochemical mutants of bacteria with penicillin. Jour. Amer. Chem. Soc. 70:4267–4268.

LEIBOWITZ, J., and S. HESTRIN, 1945 Alcoholic fermentation of the oligosaccharides. Advances Enzymol. 5:87–127.

LENG, E. R., C. M. WOODWORTH, and R. J. METZGER, 1949 Estimates of heritability and degree of dominance in certain quantitative characters of corn and soybeans. Records Genetics Soc. Amer. 18:101.

LEVINE, P., and E. M. KATZIN, 1940 Isoimmunization in pregnancy and the varieties of isoagglutinins observed. Proc. Soc. Exptl. Biol. New York 45:343–346.

————, and R. E. STETSON, 1939 An unusual case of intragroup agglutination. Jour. Amer. Med. Assoc. 113:126–127.

LEWIS, E. B., 1950 The phenomenon of position effect. Advances in Genetics Vol. III: 73–115. Academic Press, Inc.: New York.

L'HERITIER, PH., and G. TEISSIER, 1933 Elimination des formes mutantes dans les populations de Drosophiles. Cas des Drosophiles "ebony." Compt. Rend. Soc. Biol. 124: 882–885.

LINDEGREN, CARL C., 1949 The yeast cell, its genetics and cytology. 384 pp. Educational Publishers, Inc.: St. Louis, Missouri.

————, 1951 The mechanics of budding and copulation in Saccharomyces. Exptl. Cell Res. 2:305–311.

————, and GERTRUDE LINDEGREN, 1947 Depletion mutation in Saccharomyces. Proc. Nation. Acad. Sci. U.S.A. 33:314–318.

————, ————, 1951 Tetraploid Saccharomyces. Jour. Gen. Microbiol. 5:885–893.

————, and MARGARET RAFALKO, 1950 The structure of the nucleus of *Saccharomyces bayanus*. Exptl. Cell Res. 1:169–187.

LINDSTROM, E. W., 1929 A haploid mutant in the tomato. Jour. Heredity 20:23–30.

LOH, S. Y., 1949 Early testing as a means of evaluating F₁ heterosis between inbred lines of *Drosophila melanogaster*. Ph.D. Thesis. Iowa State College Library, Ames, Iowa.

LOHMANN, K., and P. SCHUSTER, 1937 Über die co-carboxylase. Naturwiss. 25:26–27.

LONGLEY, A. E., 1938 Chromosomes of maize from North American Indians. Jour. Agric. Res. 56:177–195.

————, 1941 Knob positions on teosinte chromosomes. Jour. Agric. Res. 62:401–413.

————, 1945 Abnormal segregation during megasporogenesis in maize. Genetics 30:100–113.

LONNQUIST, JOHN, 1950 The effect of selection for combining ability within segregating lines of corn. Agron. Jour. 42:503–508.

LORAIN, JOHN, 1825 Nature and reason harmonized in the practice of husbandry. 563 pp. Carey and Lea: Philadelphia.

LUCKWILL, L. C., 1937 Studies in the inheritance of physiological characters. IV. Hybrid vigour in the tomato. Pt. 2. Manifestations of hybrid vigour during the flowering period. Ann. Botany (New Series) 1:379–408.

————, 1939 Observations on heterosis in Lycopersicum. Jour. Genetics 37:421–440.

LUSH, J. L., 1945 Animal breeding plans. Third Edition. 443 pp. The Collegiate Press, Inc.: Ames, Iowa.

————, 1948 The genetics of populations. Unpublished manuscript. Ames, Iowa.

————, W. F. LAMOREUX, and L. N. HAZEL, 1948 The heritability of resistance to death in the fowl. Poultry Sci. 27:375–388.

————, and A. E. MOLLN, 1942 Litter size and weight as permanent characteristics of sows. U.S. Dept. Agric. Tech. Bull. 836. 40 pp.

————, P. S. SHEARER, and C. C. CULBERTSON, 1939 Crossbreeding hogs for pork production. Iowa Agric. Expt. Sta. Bull. 380. Pp. 83–116.

LWOFF, A., 1943 L'evolution physiologique, etude des pertes de fonctions chez les microorganismes. 308 pp. Hermann et cie.: Paris.

528   BIBLIOGRAPHY

Lyness, A. S., 1936   Varietal differences in the phosphorus feeding capacity of plants. Plant Physiol. 11:665–688.

MacArthur, John W., 1949   Selection for small and large body size in the house mouse. Genetics 34:194–209.

McCarty, M., 1946   Chemical nature and biological specificity of the substance inducing transformation of pneumococcal types. Bact. Rev. 10:63–71.

McClintock, Barbara, 1931   Cytological observations of deficiencies involving known genes, translocations and an inversion in Zea mays. Missouri Agric. Expt. Sta. Res. Bull. 163. 30 pp.

———, 1938   The fusion of broken ends of sister half-chromatids following chromatid breakage at meiotic anaphases. Missouri Agric. Expt. Sta. Res. Bull. 290. 48 pp.

McCluer, G. W., 1892   Corn crossing. Illinois Agric. Expt. Sta. Bull. 2. Pp. 82–101.

Malinowski, E., 1928   A peculiar case of heterosis in Phaseolus vulgaris. Zeitschr. indukt. Abstamm.- u. Vererbungsl., Supplementband II:1090–1093.

Mangelsdorf, P. C., 1939   Use of multiple top-crosses in southern corn improvement. Mimeo. Rept. First Southern Corn Improvement Conf. 1:33–35.

———, and James W. Cameron, 1942   Western Guatemala, a secondary center of origin of cultivated maize varieties. Bot. Mus. Leafl., Harvard Univ. 10:217–252.

———, and G. S. Fraps, 1931   A direct quantitative relationship between vitamin A in corn and the number of genes for yellow pigmentation. Science 73:241–242.

———, and R. G. Reeves, 1939   The origin of Indian corn and its relatives. Texas Agric. Expt. Sta. Bull. 574. 315 pp.

———, ———, 1945   The origin of maize, present status of the problem. Amer. Anthropologist 47:235–243.

———, and C. E. Smith, Jr., 1949   New archaeological evidence on evolution in maize. Bot. Mus. Leafl., Harvard Univ. 13:213–247.

Marshak, A. G., 1936   Growth differences in reciprocal hybrids and cytoplasmic influence on growth in mice. Jour. Exptl. Zool. 72:497–510.

Masing, R. A., 1938   Increased viability of heterozygotes for a lethal in Drosophila melanogaster. Compt. Rend. (Doklady) Acad. Sci. URSS 20:173–176.

———, 1939a   Different viability among flies of Drosophila melanogaster heterozygous for lethals. Compt. Rend. (Doklady) Acad. Sci. URSS 23:835–838.

———, 1939b   Analysis of vitality of flies of Drosophila melanogaster heterozygous for lethals arisen in nature. Compt. Rend. (Doklady) Acad. Sci. URSS 25:64–67.

Mather, K., 1942   The balance of polygenic combinations. Jour. Genetics 43:309–336.

———, 1943   Polygenic inheritance and natural selection. Biol. Rev. 18:32–64.

———, 1949a   The genetical theory of continuous variation. Proc. Eighth International Congress of Genetics 376–401. Suppl. Vol. of Hereditas, Berlingska Boktryckeriet, Lund, Sweden.

———, 1949b   Biometrical genetics. 158 pp. Dover Publications: New York.

Mendel, Gregor, 1865   Versuche über Pflanzen-Hybriden. Naturf. Ver. in Brünn Verh. IV:3–47.

Metz, C. W., 1938   Chromosome behavior, inheritance, and sex determination in Sciara. Amer. Nat. 72:485–520.

Michaelis, P., 1939   Über den Einfluss des Plasmons auf die Manifestation der Gene. Zeitschr. indukt. Abstamm.- u. Vererbungsl. 77:548–567.

———, 1940   Über reziprok verschiedene Sippen-Bastarde bei Epilobium hirsutum 78:187–237.

Moore, J. F., and T. M. Currence, 1950   Combining ability in tomatoes. Minnesota Agric. Expt. Sta. Tech. Bull. 188. 22 pp.

Morgan, D. T., Jr., 1950   A cytogenetic study of inversions in Zea mays. Genetics 35:153–174.

MORGAN, T. H., C. B. BRIDGES, and A. H. STURTEVANT, 1925 The genetics of Drosophila. Bibliogr. Genetica 2:1–262.

MORROW, G. E., and F. D. GARDNER, 1893 Field experiments with corn. Illinois Agric. Expt. Sta. Bull. 2. Pp. 173–203.

——, ——, 1893 Field experiments with corn. Illinois Agric. Expt. Sta. Bull. 2. Pp. 333–359.

MULLER, H. J., 1950 Radiation damage to genetic material. Amer. Sci. 38:33–59.

MUNDKUR, B. D., 1949 Evidence excluding mutations, polysomy, and polyploidy as possible causes of non-Mendelian segregations in Saccharomyces. Ann. Missouri Bot. Gard. 36:259–280.

——, 1950 Irregular segregations in yeast hybrids. Current Sci. 19:84–85.

——, and CARL C. LINDEGREN, 1949 An analysis of the phenomenon of long-term adaptation to galactose by Saccharomyces. Amer. Jour. Bot. 36:722–727.

MÜNTZING, A., 1930 Outlines to a genetic monograph of the genus Galeopsis with special reference to the nature and inheritance of partial sterility. Hereditas 13:185–341.

MURDOCH, H. A., 1940 Hybrid vigor in maize embryos. Jour. Heredity 31:361–363.

NABOURS, R. K., and L. L. KINGSLEY, 1934 The operation of a lethal factor in *Apotettix eurycephalus* (Grouse locusts). Genetics 19:323–328.

NAUDIN, C., 1865 Nouvelles recherches sur l'hybridité dans les végétaux. Nouv. Arch. Mus. Hist. Nat. Paris 1:25–174.

NAWASCHIN, S., 1899 Neuen beobachtungen über befruchtung bei *Fritallaria tenella* und *Lilium Martagon*. Bot. Zentralbl. 77:62.

NEAL, N. P., 1935 The decrease in yielding capacity in advanced generations of hybrid corn. Jour. Amer. Soc. Agron. 27:666–670.

ODLAND, M. L., and C. J. NOLL, 1948 Hybrid vigor and combining ability in eggplants. Proc. Amer. Soc. Hort. Sci. 51:417–427.

ÖSTERGREN, G., and R. PRAKKEN, 1946 Behavior on the spindle of the actively mobile chromosome ends of rye. Hereditas 32:473–494.

OVID (tr. by BROOKES MORE), 1922 Metamorphoses. 38 pp. Cornhill Publishing Co.: Boston.

PATEL, M. S., P. H. HARVEY, and W. C. GREGORY, 1949 Hybrid tobacco?—Why not? Res. and Farming, Spec. Tob. Issue, North Carolina Agric. Expt. Sta.: page 15.

PAULING, LINUS, HARVEY A. ITANO, S. J. SINGER, and IBERT C. WELLS, 1949 Sickle cell anemia, a molecular disease. Science 110:543–548.

PAYNE, K. T., and H. K. HAYES, 1949 A comparison of combining ability in F_2 and F_3 lines of corn. Agron. Jour. 41:383–388.

PHILLIPS, R. W., W. H. BLACK, BRADFORD KNAPP, JR., and R. T. CLARK, 1942 Crossbreeding for beef production. Jour. Animal Sci. 1:213–220.

PLOUGH, H. H., H. Y. MILLER, and M. E. BERRY, 1951 Alternative amino acid requirements in auxotrophic mutants of *S. typhimurium*. Proc. Nation. Acad. Sci. U.S.A. 37:640–644.

——, H. N. YOUNG, and M. GRIMM, 1950 Penicillin screened auxotrophic mutations in *Salmonella typhimurium* and their relation to X-ray dosage. Jour. Bact. 60:145–157.

POWERS, LEROY, 1936 The nature of the interaction of genes affecting four quantitative characters in a cross between *Hordeum deficiens* and *vulgare*. Genetics 21:398–420.

——, 1941 Inheritance of quantitative characters in crosses involving two species of Lycopersicon. Jour. Agric. Res. 63:149–174.

——, 1944 An expansion of Jones's theory for the explanation of heterosis. Amer. Nat. 78:275–280.

——, 1945 Relative yields of inbred lines and F_1 hybrids of tomato. Bot. Gaz. 106:247–268.

530 BIBLIOGRAPHY

Powers, LeRoy, 1950a Determining scales and the use of transformations in studies on weight per locule of tomato fruit. Biometrics 6:145–163.

———, 1950b Gene analysis of weight per locule in tomato hybrids. Bot. Gaz. 112:163–174.

———, L. F. Locke, and J. C. Garrett, 1950 Partitioning method of genetic analysis applied to quantitative characters of tomato crosses. U.S. Dept. Agric. Tech. Bull. 998. 56 pp.

———, and Channing B. Lyon, 1941 Inheritance studies on duration of developmental stages in crosses within the genus Lycopersicon. Jour. Agric. Res. 63:129–148.

Prakken, R., and A. Müntzing, 1942 A meiotic peculiarity in rye, simulating a terminal centromere. Hereditas 28:441–482.

Quinby, J. R., and R. E. Karper, 1946 Heterosis in Sorghum resulting from the heterozygous condition of a single gene that affects duration of growth. Amer. Jour. Bot. 33:716–721.

Rabideau, Glenn S., W. Gordon Whaley, and Charles Heimsch, 1950 The absorption and distribution of radioactive phosphorus in two maize inbreds and their hybrid. Amer. Jour. Bot. 37:93–99.

Rafalko, Margaret, and Carl C. Lindegren, in press Cytological observations of copulation and sporulation in Saccharomyces.

Ramiah, K., N. Parthasarathi, and S. Ramanujam, 1933 Haploid plant in rice (Oryza sativa). Current Sci. 1:277–278.

Randolph, L. F., 1932a The chromosomes of haploid maize with special reference to the double nature of the univalent chromosomes in the early meiotic prophase. Science 75:566–567.

———, 1932b Some effects of high temperature on polyploidy and other variations in maize. Proc. Nation. Acad. Sci. U.S.A. 18:222–229.

———, and H. E. Fischer, 1939 The occurrence of parthenogenetic diploids in tetraploid maize. Proc. Nation. Acad. Sci. U.S.A. 25:161–164.

Rasmusson, J., 1927 Genetically changed linkage values in Pisum. Hereditas 10:1–150.

Raut, Caroline, 1950 Effect of concentration of pantothenate on selection of a mutant for pantothenate synthesis in Saccharomyces cerevisiae. Genetics 35:381–395.

Reed, Ollie E., 1946 Is the crossbred dairy cow on the way? Country Gentlemen, June, 116:15, 61–64.

Reeves, R. E., and W. F. Goebel, 1941 Chemoimmunological studies on the soluble specific substance of pneumococcus. V. The structure of type III polysaccharide. Jour. Biol. Chem. 139:511–519.

Reeves, R. G., 1944 Chromosome knobs in relation to the origin of maize. Genetics 29:141–147.

———, 1950 The use of teosinte in the improvement of corn inbreds. Agron. Jour. 42:248–251.

Rhoades, M. M., 1942 Preferential segregation in maize. Genetics 27:395–407.

———, 1950 Meiosis in maize. Jour. Heredity. 41:59–67.

———, and Hilda Vilkomerson, 1942 On the anaphase movement of chromosomes. Proc. Nation. Acad. Sci. U.S.A. 28:433–436.

Richey, F. D., 1945a Bruce's explanation of hybrid vigor. Jour. Heredity 36:243–244.

———, 1945b Isolating better foundation inbreds for use in corn hybrids. Genetics 30:455–471.

———, 1946 Hybrid vigor and corn breeding. Jour. Amer. Soc. Agron. 38:833–841.

———, 1947 Corn breeding: gamete selection, the Oenothera method, and related miscellany. Jour. Amer. Soc. Agron. 39:403–412.

———, and G. F. Sprague, 1931 Experiments on hybrid vigor and convergent improvement in corn. U.S. Dept. Agric. Tech. Bull. 267. 22 pp.

ROBBINS, WILLIAM J., 1940 Growth substances in a hybrid corn and its parents. Bull. Torrey Bot. Club 67:565–574.

———, 1941a Factor Z in hybrid maize. Bull. Torrey Bot. Club 68:222–228.

———, 1941b Growth of excised roots and heterosis in tomato. Amer. Jour. Bot. 28:216–225.

———, and ROBERTA MA, 1942 Vitamin deficiencies of Ceratostomella and related fungi. Amer. Jour. Bot. 29:835–843.

———, 1946 A report on the growth of excised tomato roots. Jour. Arnold Arboretum 27:480–485.

———, 1952 Hybrid nutritional requirements. Heterosis, Chapter 7. Iowa State College Press: Ames.

ROBERTS, H. F., 1929 Plant hybridization before Mendel. vii+374 pp. Princeton University Press: Princeton.

ROBERTSON, D. W., 1932 The effect of a lethal in the heterozygous condition on barley development. Colorado Agric. Expt. Sta. Tech. Bull. 1. 12 pp.

———, and W. W. AUSTIN, 1935 The effect of one and of two seedling lethals in the heterozygous condition on barley development. Jour. Agric. Res. 51:435–440.

ROBINSON, H. F., R. E. COMSTOCK, and P. H. HARVEY, 1949 Estimates of heritability and the degree of dominance in corn. Agron. Jour. 41:353–359.

ROGERS, J. S., 1950 The inheritance of inflorescence characters in maize-teosinte hybrids. Genetics 35:541–558.

ROMAN, H., D. C. HAWTHORNE, and H. C. DOUGLAS, 1951 Polyploidy in yeast and its bearing on the occurrence of irregular genetic ratios. Proc. Nation. Acad. Sci. U.S.A. 37:79–84.

RYAN, F. J., G. W. BEADLE, and E. L. TATUM, 1943 The tube method of measuring the growth rate of Neurospora. Amer. Jour. Bot. 30:784–799.

———, and J. LEDERBERG, 1946 Reverse mutation and adaptation in leucineless Neurospora. Proc. Nation. Acad. Sci. U.S.A. 32:163–173.

SAGARET, A., 1826 Considerations sur la production des hybrides. Ann. d. Sci. Nat. 8:294–314.

SANBORN, J. W., 1890 Indian corn. Rept. Maine Dept. Agric. 33:54–121.

SATTERTHWAITE, F. E., 1946 An approximate distribution of estimates of variance components. Biometrics Bull. 2:110–114.

SCHRADER, F., 1931 The chromosome cycle of Protortonia primitiva (Coccidae) and a consideration of the meiotic division apparatus in the male. Zeitschr. Wiss. Zool. 138:386–408.

SHAMEL, A. D., 1905 The effect of inbreeding in plants. U.S. Dept. Agric. Yearbook for 1905. Pp. 377–392.

SHEN, SAN-CHIUN, 1950 The genetics and biochemistry of the cysteine-tyrosine relationship in Neurospora. Ph.D. Thesis California Inst. of Tech., Pasadena.

SHIFRISS, O., 1947 Developmental reversal of dominance in Cucurbita pepo. Proc. Amer. Soc. Hort. Sci. 50:330–346.

SHULL, A. F., 1912 The influence of inbreeding on vigor in Hydatina senta. Biol. Bull. 24:1–13.

SHULL, G. H., 1908 The composition of a field of maize. Rept. Amer. Breeders' Assoc. 4:296–301.

———, 1909 A pure-line method in corn breeding. Rept. Amer. Breeders' Assoc. 5:51–59.

———, 1910 Hybridization methods in corn breeding. Amer. Breeders' Mag. 1:98–107.

———, 1911a Experiments with maize. Bot. Gaz. 52:480–485.

———, 1911b The genotypes of maize. Amer. Nat. 45:234–252.

———, 1914 Duplicate genes for capsule form in Bursa bursa-pastoris. Zeitschr. indukt. Abstamm.- u. Vererbungsl. 12:97–149.

SHULL, G. H., 1921 Estimating the number of genetic factors concerned in blending inheritance. With rejoinder by W. E. Castle. Amer. Nat. 55:556–571.

———, 1922 Über die Heterozygotie mit Rücksicht auf den praktischen Züchtungserfolg. Beitrage z. Pflanzenzucht 5:134–158.

———, 1946 Hybrid seed corn. Science 103:547–550.

———, 1948 What is "heterosis"? Genetics 33:439–446.

SIERK, C. F., 1948 A study of heterosis in swine. (abstr.) Jour. Animal Sci. 7:515.

———, 1948 A study of heterosis in swine. Ph.D. Thesis, Univ. of Minnesota Library, Minneapolis.

SIMPSON, Q. I., 1907 Rejuvenation by hybridization. Rept. Amer. Breeders' Assoc. 3: 76–81.

SINGLETON, W. RALPH, 1935 Early research in maize genetics. Jour. Heredity 26:49–59; 121–126.

———, 1941 Hybrid vigor and its utilization in sweet corn breeding. Amer. Nat. 75: 48–60.

———, 1943 Breeding behavior of C_{30}, a diminutive P_{39} mutant whose hybrids show increased vigor. (Abstract) Genetics 28:89.

———, and O. E. NELSON, JR., 1945 The improvement of naturally cross-pollinated plants by selection in self-fertilized lines. IV. Combining ability of successive generations of inbred sweet corn. Connecticut Agric. Expt. Sta. Bull. 490. Pp. 458–498.

SMITH, H. H., and C. W. BACON, 1941 Increased size and nicotine production in selections from intraspecific hybrids of Nicotiana rustica. Jour. Agric. Res. 63:457–467.

SMITH, S. N., 1934 Response of inbred lines and crosses in maize to variations of nitrogen and phosphorus supplied as nutrients. Jour. Amer. Soc. Agron. 26:785–804.

SPRAGUE, G. F., 1936 Hybrid vigor and growth rates in a maize cross and its reciprocal. Jour. Agric. Res. 53:819–830.

———, 1946a Early testing of inbred lines of corn. Jour. Amer. Soc. Agron. 38:108–117.

———, 1946b The experimental basis for hybrid maize. Biol. Rev. Cambridge Phil. Soc. 21:101–120.

———, 1942–1949 Annual reports of corn breeding investigations conducted by the Division of Cereal Crops and Diseases. Bur. Plant Indust. S.A.E. and the Iowa Agric. Expt. Sta.

———, and B. BRIMHALL, 1950 Relative effectiveness of two systems of selection for oil content of the corn kernel. Agron. Jour. 42:83–88.

———, and M. T. JENKINS, 1943 A comparison of synthetic varieties, multiple crosses, and double crosses in corn. Jour. Amer. Soc. Agron. 35:137–147.

———, and L. A. TATUM, 1942 General vs. specific combining ability in single crosses of corn. Jour. Amer. Soc. Agron. 34:923–932.

SPRENGEL, C. K., 1793 Das entdeckte Geheimniss der Natur im Bau und in der Befruchtung der Blumen. 433 pp. Berlin.

SRB, A. M., and N. H. HOROWITZ, 1944 The ornithine cycle in Neurospora and its genetic control. Jour. Biol. Chem. 154:129–139.

STADLER, L. J., 1933 On the genetic nature of induced mutations in plants. Missouri Agric. Expt. Sta. Res. Bull. 204. 29 pp.

———, 1939 Some observations on gene variability and spontaneous mutation. Spragg Memorial Lectures, Michigan State College. Pp. 1–15.

———, 1944 Gamete selection in corn breeding. (abstr.) Jour. Amer. Soc. Agron. 36: 988–989.

———, 1945 Gamete selection in corn breeding. Maize Genetics Cooperation News Letter. 19:33–40.

STANDLEY, PAUL C., 1950 Teosinte in Honduras. Ceiba 1:58–61.

STEPHENS, S. G., 1950a Factors affecting the genetic complexity of a partially outcrossed population. Proc. Second Cotton Improvement Conference, Biloxi, Mississippi.

————, 1950b The internal mechanism of speciation in Gossypium. Bot. Rev. 16:115–149.

STERN, C., 1948 Negative heterosis and decreased effectiveness of alleles in heterozygotes. Genetics 33:215–219.

————, and EDWARD NOVITSKI, 1948 The viability of individuals heterozygous for recessive lethals. Science 108:538–539.

STEWART, H. A., 1945 An appraisal of factors affecting prolificacy in swine. Jour. Animal Sci. 4:250–260.

STORMONT, CLYDE, 1950 Additional gene controlled antigenic factors in the bovine erythrocyte. Genetics 35:76–94.

————, R. D. OWEN, and M. R. IRWIN, 1948 Gene action on cellular characters in cattle (abstr.) Genetics 33:126.

————, ————, ————, 1951 The B and C systems of bovine blood groups. Genetics 36:134–161.

STRANDSKOV, H. H., 1948 Blood group nomenclature. Jour. Heredity 39:108–112.

————, 1949 Recent views on the genetics of the Rh-Hr blood factors. Bull. New York Acad. Med. 25:249–255.

STRAUS, F. S., 1942 The genetic mechanism of heterosis as demonstrated by egg production in Drosophila melanogaster. Ph.D. Thesis, Iowa State College Library, Ames, Iowa.

————, and J. W. GOWEN, 1943 Heterosis: its mechanism in terms of chromosome units in egg production of Drosophila melanogaster. (abstr.) Genetics 28:93.

STRAUSS, B. S., 1950 Studies on vitamin B_6 requiring mutants of Neurospora crassa. Thesis, California Inst. of Tech., Pasadena.

STREHLER, B. L., 1950 The replacement of para-aminobenzoic acid by methionine in the growth of a Neurospora mutant. Jour. Bact. 59:105–111.

STRINGFIELD, G. H., 1950 Heterozygosis and hybrid vigor in maize. Agron. Jour. 42:145–152.

STUBBE, H., and K. PIRSCHLE, 1940 Über einen monogen bedingten Fall von Heterosis bei Antirrhinum majus. Ber. Deut. Bot. Ges. 58:546–558.

STURTEVANT, A. H., 1936 Preferential segregation in triplo-IV females of Drosophila melanogaster. Genetics 21:444–466.

————, and G. W. BEADLE, 1936 The relations of inversions in the X chromosome of Drosophila melanogaster to crossing over and disjunction. Genetics 21:554–604.

TABERNAEMONTANUS (JAKOB DIETRICH [THEODORUS] OF BERGZABERN), 1588. Neuw Kreuterbuch, etc., Franckfurt am Mayn.

TAN, C. C., 1946 Mosaic dominance in the inheritance of color patterns in the lady-bird beetle, Harmonia axyridis. Genetics 31:195–210.

TATUM, E. L., 1946 Induced biochemical mutations in bacteria. Cold Spring Harbor Symposia Quant. Biol. 11:278–283.

————, and J. LEDERBERG, 1947 Gene recombination in the bacterium E. coli. Jour. Bact. 53:673–684.

TEAS, H. J., 1950 Mutants of Bacillus subtilis that require threonine or threonine plus methionine. Jour. Bact. 59:93–104.

————, N. H. HOROWITZ, and M. FLING, 1948 Homoserine as a precursor of threonine and methionine in Neurospora. Jour. Biol. Chem. 172:651–658.

TEISSIER, G., 1942a Persistance d'un gène léthal dans une population de Drosophiles. Compt. Rend. Acad. Sci. (Paris). 214:327–330.

————, 1942b Vitalité et fecondité relatives de diverses combinations génétiques comportant un gène léthal chez la Drosophile. Compt. Rend. Acad. Sci. (Paris) 214:241–244.

————, 1944 Équilibre des gènes léthaux dans les populations stationnaires panmictiques. Rev. Scient. 82:145–159.

————, 1947a Variation de la fréquence du gène sepia dans une population stationnaire de Drosophiles. Compt. Rend. Acad. Sci. (Paris) 224:676–677.

TEISSIER, G., 1947b   Variation de la fréquence du gène ebony dans une population stationnaire de Drosophiles. Compt. Rend. Acad. Sci. (Paris) 224:1788–1789.

THOM, C., and R. A. STEINBERG, 1939   The chemical induction of genetic changes in fungi. Proc. Nation. Acad. Sci. U.S.A. 25:329–335.

THOMSEN, O., 1936   Untersuchungen über erbliche Blutgruppenantigene bei Hühnern, II. Hereditas 22:129–144.

TIMOFÉEFF-RESSOVSKY, N. W., 1940   Allgemeine Erscheinungen der Gen-Manifestierung. Handbuch d. Erbbiologie des Menschen, Berlin.

TORSSELL, ROBERT, 1948   Different methods in the breeding of lucerne. In Svalöf 1886–1946. Pp. 237–248. Carl Bloms Boktryckeri, Lund, Sweden.

TYLOR, E. B., 1865   Researches into the early history of mankind and development of civilization. 388 pp. London.

TYSDAL, H. M., and B. H. CRANDALL, 1948   The polycross progeny performance as an index of the combining ability of alfalfa clones. Jour. Amer. Soc. Agron. 40:293–306.

———, T. A. KIESSELBACH, and H. L. WESTOVER, 1942   Alfalfa breeding. Nebraska Agric. Expt. Sta. Res. Bull. 124. 46 pp.

U.S. COMMISSIONER OF PATENTS, 1851   Report for the year 1850, Part II, Agriculture, Washington.

VAN OVERBEEK, J., M. E. CONKLIN, and A. F. BLAKESLEE, 1942   Cultivation in vitro of small Datura embryos. Amer. Jour. Bot. 29:472–477.

VEATCH, C., 1930   Vigor in soybeans as affected by hybridity. Jour. Amer. Soc. Agron. 22:289–310.

VENNESLAND, B., and R. Z. FELSHER, 1946   Oxalacetic and pyruvic carboxylases in some dicotyledonous plants. Arch. Biochem. 11:279–306.

VILMORIN, H., 1867   Sur la fécondation du Mais. Bull. Soc. Bot. France 14:246–249.

WARREN, D. C., 1924   Inheritance of egg size in Drosophila melanogaster. Genetics 9:41–69.

WEAVER, HARRY LLOYD, 1946   A developmental study of maize with particular reference to hybrid vigor. Amer. Jour. Bot. 33:615–624.

WEATHERWAX, PAUL, 1950   The history of corn. Sci. Month. 71:50–60.

WEBBER, H. J., 1900   Xenia or the immediate effect of pollen in maize. U.S. Dept. Agric. Div. Veg. Phys. Bull. 22.

———, 1901   Loss of vigor in corn from inbreeding. (abstr.) Science 13:257–258.

WEIDENHAGEN, R., 1940   Handbuch der Enzymologie. Leipzig.

WEISS, M. G., C. R. WEBER, and R. R. KALTON, 1947   Early generation testing in soybeans. Jour. Amer. Soc. Agron. 39:791–811.

WELLHAUSEN, E. J., 1947   Comparación de variedades del maíz obtenidas en el Bajío, Jalisco y en la Mesa Central. Folleto Técnico No. 1, Oficina de Estudios Especiales, S.A.G., México, D.F.

———, and L. M. ROBERTS, 1948   Rocamex V-7, una variedad sobresaliente de maíz para sembrarse de riego en la Mesa Central. Folleto de Divulgación No. 3, Oficina de Estudios Especiales, S.A.G., México, D.F.

———, ———, 1949   Methods used and results obtained in corn improvement in Mexico. Iowa Agric. Expt. Sta. Res. Bull. 371:525–537.

———, ———, E. HERNÁNDEZ X., en colaboración con P. C. MANGELSDORF, 1951   Razas de Maíz en México, su origen, características y distribución. Folleto Técnico No. 5, Oficina de Estudios Especiales, S.A.G., México, D.F.

WHALEY, W. GORDON, 1944   Heterosis. Bot. Rev. 10:461–498.

———, 1950   The growth of inbred and hybrid maize. Growth 14:123–155.

———, CHARLES HEIMSCH, and GLENN S. RABIDEAU, 1950   The growth and morphology of two maize inbreds and their hybrid. Amer. Jour. Bot. 37:77–84.

———, and ALICE L. LONG, 1944   The behavior of excised roots of heterotic hybrids and their inbred parents in culture. Bull. Torrey Bot. Club. 71:267–275.

WHATLEY, J. A., JR., 1942 Influence of heredity and other factors on 180-day weight in Poland China swine. Jour. Agric. Res. **65**:249–264.

WHELDALE, M., 1910 On the formation of anthocyanin. Jour. Genetics **1**:133–158.

WHITAKER, T. W., and G. W. BOHN, 1950 The taxonomy, genetics, production and uses of the cultivated species of Cucurbita. Econ. Bot. **4**:52–81.

WHITE, P. B., 1929 The Salmonella group. In a system of bacteriology. Med. Res. Council (Great Brit.) **4**:86–158.

WIEGMANN, A. F., 1828 Über die Bastarderzeugung im Pflanzenreiche. Braunschweig. 40 pp.

WIENER, A. S., 1943 Blood groups and transfusion. Third Ed. 438 pp. Charles C. Thomas: Springfield.

——, and H. R. PETERS, 1940 Hemolytic reactions following transfusions of blood of the homologous group, with three cases in which the same agglutinogen was responsible. Ann. Internal Med. **13**:2306–2322.

WIGAN, L. G., 1944 Balance and potence in natural populations. Jour. Genetics **46**:150–160.

WINGE, Ö., 1935 On haplophase and diplophase in some Saccharomycetes. Compt. Rend. d. Lab. Carlsberg Ser. Physiol. **21**:77–112.

——, and C. ROBERTS, 1948 Inheritance of enzymatic characters in yeasts and the phenomenon of long-term adaptation. Compt. Rend. d. Lab. Carlsberg Ser. Physiol. **24**:263–315.

WINKLER, H., 1930 Die Konversion der Gene. 186 pp. Jena.

WINTERS, L. M., D. L. DAILEY, P. S. JORDAN, O. M. KISER, R. E. HODGSON, J. N. CUMMINGS, and C. F. SIERK, 1948 Experiments with inbreeding swine. Minnesota Agric. Expt. Sta. Bull. 400. 28 pp.

——, P. S. JORDAN, and R. E. HODGSON, 1944 Preliminary report on crossing of inbred lines of swine. Jour. Animal Sci. **3**:371.

——, O. M. KISER, P. S. JORDAN, and W. H. PETERS, 1935 A six years' study of crossbreeding swine. Minnesota Agric. Expt. Sta. Bull. 320. 18 pp.

——, ——, ——, ——, 1936 Crossbred swine for greater profits. Minnesota Ext. Div. Spec. Bull. 180. 12 pp.

WRIGHT, SEWALL, 1922a Coefficients of inbreeding and relationship. Amer. Nat. **56**:330–338.

——, 1922b The effects of inbreeding and crossbreeding on guinea pigs. I. Decline in vigor. II. Differentiation among inbred families. U.S. Dept. Agric. Tech. Bull. 1090.

——, 1922c The effects of inbreeding and crossbreeding on guinea pigs. III. Crosses between highly inbred families. U.S. Dept. Agric. Tech. Bull. 1121. 60 pp.

——, 1931a Inbreeding and recombination. Proc. Nation. Acad. Sci. U.S.A. **19**:420–433.

——, 1931b Evolution in Mendelian populations. Genetics **16**:97–159.

——, 1935 The analysis of variance and the correlations between relatives with respect to deviations from an optimum. Jour. Genetics **30**:243–256.

ZALOKAR, MARKO, 1948 The p-aminobenzoic acid requirement of the "sulfonamide-requiring" mutant strain of Neurospora. Proc. Nation. Acad. Sci. U.S.A. **34**:32–36.

——, 1950 The sulfonamide-requiring mutant of Neurospora: Threonine-methionine antagonism. Jour. Bact. **60**:191–203.

ZELLE, M. R., 1942 Genetic constitutions of host and pathogen in mouse typhoid. Jour. Infect. Dis. **71**:131–152.

ZIMMERMAN, P. W., and A. E. HITCHCOCK, 1949 Formative effects of several substituted phenoxy acids applied to Kalanchoe. Contrib. Boyce Thompson Inst. **15**:421–427.

ZIRKLE, CONWAY, 1935 The beginnings of plant hybridization. 231 pp. University of Pennsylvania Press: Philadelphia.

Index

PRINTED
IN U·S·A·